T. J. HOUSER

HANDBOOK OF NONPARAMETRIC STATISTICS

Investigation of Randomness, Moments, Percentiles, and Distributions

by

JOHN E. WALSH

System Development Corporation

D. VAN NOSTRAND COMPANY, INC.
PRINCETON, NEW JERSEY

TORONTO LONDON

NEW YORK

D. VAN NOSTRAND COMPANY, INC.
120 Alexander St., Princeton, New Jersey (*Principal office*)
24 West 40 Street, New York 18, New York

D. Van Nostrand Company, Ltd.
358, Kensington High Street, London, W.14, England

D. Van Nostrand Company (Canada), Ltd.
25 Hollinger Road, Toronto 16, Canada

Published simultaneously in Canada by
D. Van Nostrand Company (Canada), Ltd.

This book was written in connection with a research project sponsored in the public interest by System Development Corporation, Santa Monica, California.

PRINTED IN THE UNITED STATES OF AMERICA

To my mother,

Mrs. Lulu M. Walsh

PREFACE

The writing of this book is an outgrowth of the author's opinion that a thorough coverage of the nonparametric field, with orientation toward applications, should be valuable in many practical areas. This effort was begun in May 1956 on a personal basis and has been supported by the System Development Corporation since March 1959. The present book represents the first of a planned two-part work.

For practical reasons, only material developed prior to 1958 is considered in the handbook. However, this does not represent a severe restriction, since the procedures considered are numerous and important. Also, as a developmental research project, a number of the conceptually small but practically important gaps that occurred in the publications on this subject (to 1958) have been filled in by the author of the handbook.

This book is entirely the work of the author, and the responsibility for the material presented is exclusively his. Although great care was exercised to assure that the material presented is accurate, a work of this scope and magnitude undoubtedly contains a number of errors. The author would appreciate being informed of any errors that are discovered.

May 1962 JOHN E. WALSH

ACKNOWLEDGMENTS

In an attempt to correct errors and to assure that a truly thorough coverage is obtained, copies of the first draft of this book were sent to more than 80 statisticians for critical appraisal. The author is very grateful for the many comments that were received from these reviewers. The comments of H. S. Konijn, H. R. van der Vaart, and W. Hoeffding were especially useful.

Nearly all of the typing, much of the proofreading, and some of the editorial work were accurately and efficiently performed by Mrs. Rosella Schwanke. Her conscientious assistance has contributed greatly to the writing of this book. Proofreading and editorial help were received from Mrs. Ruth Keane. Assistance was also received from the SDC Library (Mrs. Lee Dorfman, Mr. Paul Simmons, and Mr. Halbert Watson) and from Mr. Lorimer F. McConnell, who handled the marketing and copyright problems involved.

The author of the handbook is indebted to the following authors for the use of their tables and graphs that appeared in journals (or reports): T. W. Anderson (Table 10.4), D. E. Barton (Table 10.6), Z. W. Birnbaum (Figure 9.2 and Table 10.2), Frieda Swed Cohn (Table 5.1), D. R. Cox (Table 7.6), D. A. Darling (Table 10.4), F. N. David (Tables 10.6, 11.1, 11.2, 11.4, 11.5), C. Eisenhart (Table 5.1), B. Epstein (Table 9.1), J. Kiefer (Tables 10.4, 11.3), M. Merrington (Table 4), L. H. Miller (Table 10.1), G. H. Moore (Table 5.3), F. Mosteller (Table 5.2), R. B. Murphy (Figure 9.1), P. S. Olmstead (Table 5.4), A. Rényi (Table 10.3), B. Sherman (Table 10.5), C. M. Thompson (Tables 2, 4), J. W. Tukey (Tables 7.2, 7.3, 7.9), W. A. Wallis (Table 5.3), Y. Watanabe (Table 11.3), F. Wilcoxon (Table 7.2), and H. S. Zuckerman (Figure 9.2). Also the cooperation of the Editors of journals in which these tables and figures appeared is appreciated.

Also the author is indebted to Sir Ronald A. Fisher, F. R. S., Cambridge, and to Dr. Frank Yates, F. R. S., Rothamsted, also to Messrs. Oliver and Boyd Ltd., Edinburgh, for permission to use material from tables in their books *Statistical Methods for Research Workers* (by Dr. Fisher) and *Statistical Tables for Biological, Agricultural, and Medical Research.* This material is used in Tables 7.1, 2, and 3.

Finally, the author would like to thank his wife, Mrs. P. Walsh, for the suggestion that he write a Handbook of Nonparametric Statistics and for valuable editorial advice and assistance.

TABLE OF CONTENTS

* The titles of presentations of results are stated in italics in the Table of Contents.

TABLE AND FIGURE LOCATIONS

FIGURE

Chapter 1

OUTLINE AND SCOPE OF HANDBOOK

INTRODUCTION

This is the first of two volumes of a handbook covering the nonparametric statistics field up to 1958. This handbook contains an organized presentation of a large number of nonparametric probability information procedures that are believed to be of practical importance. Only results dealing with the probability aspects of statistical data are considered. Supplementary discussions are included to help clarify the nonparametric procedures and their conceptual basis, and also to indicate their major areas of usefulness.

The reader is assumed to have a basic understanding of the field of mathematical statistics, but the technical level of the material presented is not overly high. However, some specially devised symbolism is used in stating procedures. This notation, which is not extensive, must be mastered before the handbook can be used efficiently. Use of this special symbolism, combined with a concise presentation format, allows a large number of procedures to be stated within an acceptable amount of space.

DESIRABILITY OF NONPARAMETRIC METHODS

Virtually all statistical information procedures are based on assumptions concerning probability properties of the observational data used in their application. The accuracy of the probability information obtained from a statistical procedure depends on how closely the assumed and actual properties agree. Thus statistical procedures whose approximate validity is not difficult to verify seem desirable. Nonparametric procedures fall in this category and have the additional advantage that they often do not require much effort for their application. The assumptions used for nonparametric methods are of a general nature; that is, they are approximately satisfied for a large class of the situations of interest. Also, these assumptions are almost always of a type for which acceptance (or rejection) can be established on the basis of elementary considerations.

Some of the nonparametric procedures are sometimes referred to as distribution-free procedures, also, in a few cases, as parameter-free procedures. In this handbook the term "nonparametric" is ordinarily used for results of this type.

INTERPRETATION OF "NONPARAMETRIC"

A precise and universally acceptable definition of the term "nonparametric" is not presently available. The viewpoint adopted in this handbook is that a statistical procedure is of a nonparametric type if it has properties which are satisfied to a reasonable approximation when some assumptions that are at least of a moderately general nature hold. That is, generality of application is the criterion for deciding on the nonparametric character of a statistical procedure. As an example, the binomial distribution is considered to be of nonparametric interest even though it is of an elementary parametric form. As another example, results based on the first few terms of the Gram-Charlier or of the Edgeworth series expansion for a probability distribution are considered to be nonparametric in some cases.

AVAILABILITY OF NONPARAMETRIC PROCEDURES

Due to the general nature of the assumptions used, no comprehensive theory has yet been developed for the nonparametric field, although steps have been taken in this direction. Instead, separate solutions to a wide variety of problems are spread through the statistical literature, and no one publication contains more than a modest percentage of them. Although a very large number of results have been published, their availability is limited by the isolated publication of many of them in diverse places that are not readily accessible and by the manner in which they are spread about in the more accessible statistical literature.

PURPOSE OF HANDBOOK

The desirable nature but limited availability of nonparametric methods indicates that a compilation of the more important results should be worthwhile. A handbook style of presentation seems most appropriate for stating a large number of procedures within an acceptable amount of space. The goal of the resulting handbook is to present statements of the more important nonparametric procedures in a concise but understandable form.

PRESENTATION OUTLINE FOR FIRST VOLUME

To obtain conciseness of presentation, a special mathematical symbolism is devised for representing distributions, deviates of standard distributions, observations, functions of observations, and population properties. This standardized notation is given in the second chapter. A detailed description of the presentation format is given in the third chapter. There the purpose and use of each part of the format is discussed. The fourth chapter contains a statement of some statistical concepts and terminology that are used in many of the procedure presentations. This material is either of a type that is not ordinarily encountered in mathematical statistics textbooks, or is specifically adapted for use in this handbook.

The fifth and following chapters contain statements of the nonparametric procedures selected for presentation. Procedures which deal with problems of a similar nature are grouped into the same chapter. Each chapter contains introductory material which includes a discussion of the types of problems considered and a statement of some of the characteristics of the procedures presented.

The fifth chapter contains tests of the random sample hypothesis for univariate observations. The sixth chapter is mainly concerned with Tchebycheff-type inequalities that involve population moments. The seventh and eighth chapters contain estimates and tests for expected values and population percentiles, respectively. The ninth chapter is concerned with distribution-free tolerance regions. The tenth chapter contains tests and estimates for probability distributions that are obtained on the basis of ungrouped data. The eleventh and final chapter of the first volume presents sequential, statistical decision theory, and general categorical data results for distributions.

The other volume of the handbook will contain the remainder of the procedures for the nonparametric field up to 1958. This second volume is expected to contain material that is concerned with the two-sample problem, the several-sample problem, analysis of variance, regression and discrimination, multivariate analysis, matching and comparison problems, and tests of symmetry and extreme observations.

PRACTICAL NATURE OF METHODS

The nonparametric procedures presented are exclusively of the type that have some application to practical problems. That is, all results given are designed to use data from actual statistical experiments. This handbook is intended to furnish the experimental statistician with a glossary of the nonparametric procedures that have some importance from a practical point of view. No nonparametric results of a purely theoretical or philosophical nature are presented.

SCOPE OF HANDBOOK

Highly specialized results which have been adequately covered elsewhere, such as population statistics (e.g., census) and acceptance sampling procedures, are not ordinarily considered in the handbook even when they are of a nonparametric nature. Also, results dealing with complicated stochastic processes (e.g., nonstationary) are not presented unless they are both of practical importance to the experimental statistician and easily stated. That is, the procedures presented are oriented toward the experimental statistician rather than toward the physicist or the electronics engineer.

The collection of nonparametric procedures presented in this handbook of two volumes is intended to include the more important results published prior to 1958, especially those available in an English language form. However, due to space limitations, several restrictions have been imposed on the nature and the extent of the material included. Some nonparametric procedures have already received extensive coverage in books dealing with mathematical statistics. Results for such cases are sometimes given in an abbreviated form, and the reader is referred to the books for more detailed descriptions. Also, in some cases, procedures which cannot be adequately presented in a reasonable amount of space and/or are difficult to apply have either been completely omitted or only referenced. Corrections and tables which were published in 1958 or later are sometimes included if they apply to results that were published prior to 1958.

Most of the material presented is for the case of continuous univariate populations. The multivariate and discrete cases receive less emphasis because fewer important results have been developed for these situations.

REFERENCE MATERIAL INCLUDED

For each procedure, the final part of its statement consists of a short bibliography of publications in which this procedure was considered. Most of these references are research papers, but books are also included if they contain material that is supplementary to that presented in the handbook. Ordinarily, a reference is not included unless its contents are of more than historical interest. To save space, the references are numbered and stated at the end of the handbook. Thus a bibliography consists of a set of numbers pertaining to the references at the end of the book.

EXTENSIONS BY AUTHOR OF HANDBOOK

The material presented consists of more than summaries of nonparametric results that were developed prior to 1958. From an applications viewpoint, there are many conceptually small but practically important gaps in the published nonparametric results. To increase the practical value of the nonparametric procedures, many of these gaps have been at least partially filled in by the author of the handbook, usually on a judgment basis. This additional material, which is the responsibility of the handbook's author, is of three principal types. First, some of the introductory material for the various chapters occurs for the purpose of filling in gaps. Second, for approximate procedures, the stated conditions under which these procedures are considered to be applicable are nearly always the responsibility of the author of the handbook. Finally for each procedure, statements are made about its application difficulty, about the alternative hypotheses to which it should be sensitive (for tests), about its sensitivity to its assumptions, and about the difficulty of verifying these assumptions. These statements often represent developments of the author of the handbook and are not directly stated in any of the references pertaining to the procedure considered.

RELATIVE WORTH OF PROCEDURES PRESENTED

The author of this handbook has made no attempt to explicitly specify the relative importance of procedures that are competitive for use. Ordinarily, the relative importance of two competitive statistical methods depends on many considerations. In fact, there usually exist situations where a given procedure is preferable to any competitive procedure that is considered in this handbook. The nonparametric field contains many specialized solutions to special problems. Although some of these special problems may be encountered less frequently than others, knowledge of the specialized solutions for all of these problems seems worthwhile.

The material presented for a procedure is often sufficient to allow a comparison to be made between this procedure and the competitive procedures that are given in the handbook. Concerning misuse when several procedures are available for handling the same situation, the technical level required to use the material of this handbook is about the same as that to make a satisfactory choice among competitive procedures that are presented in this handbook.

Chapter 2

STANDARDIZED NOTATION

INTRODUCTION

This chapter, in combination with Chapter 3, furnishes the basis for the statements of the nonparametric procedures. The presentation method and style of punctuation adopted are motivated by the desire to state each procedure adequately but as concisely as possible. For this purpose, a specially devised notation is introduced which is sufficiently flexible to handle many of the recurring types of situations, but is not overly cumbersome. Since this standardized notation has the same meaning for all presentations and only needs to be defined once, ambiguity should be reduced and space saved by its use. This notation was developed specifically for the purposes of this handbook and is not advocated for general use.

With respect to probability distributions, notation is introduced for a general distribution function, a general frequency function, the standardized univariate normal distribution and its derivatives, and for deviates of some of the standard distributions. With respect to observations, standardized notation is introduced for general nature univariate observations, general nature multivariate observations, order statistics, ranks, and for some of the more common functions of observations. With respect to population properties, standardized notation is given for population percentage points, population moments, and for some of the more common functions of population moments.

The standardized notation introduced in this chapter is summarized on the inside of the front cover of this book.

PROBABILITY DISTRIBUTION NOTATION

General Distribution and Frequency Functions

Unless the contrary is stated, the symbol $F(x)=P(X\leqslant x)$ is used for the distribution function (cumulative distribution function) of a univariate random variable X. Likewise, $F(x_1,\ldots,x_k)=P(X_1\leqslant x_1,\ldots,X_k\leqslant x_k)$

represents the joint distribution function (joint cumulative distribution function) for a k-variate random variable $(X_1, \ldots, X_k)$.

For the discrete and continuous cases, $f(x)$ is the frequency function for a univariate random variable and $f(x_1, \ldots, x_k)$ is the joint frequency function for a k-variate random variable (unless the contrary is stated). That is, for the absolutely continuous case, the frequency function (probability density function) satisfies

$$f(x)=dF(x)/dx, \qquad f(x_1, \ldots, x_k)=\partial^k F(x_1, \ldots, x_k)/\partial x_1 \ldots \partial x_k.$$

For the discrete case, the frequency function (discrete probability density function) is a probability value; i.e., $f(x)$ is the probability that the univariate random variable equals x and $f(x_1, \ldots, x_k)$ is the probability that the k-variate random variable equals $x_1, \ldots, x_k$.

Normal Distribution and its Derivatives

The symbol $\Phi(x)$ is used for the standardized normal (Gaussian) univariate distribution function; i.e.,

$$\Phi(x)=\frac{1}{\sqrt{2\pi}}\int_{-\infty}^{x} e^{-z^2/2}dz. \qquad (-\infty < x < \infty)$$

The derivatives of $\Phi(x)$ are denoted by

$$\Phi^{(k)}(x)=d^k\Phi(x)/dx^k. \qquad (k=1, 2, \ldots)$$

The frequency function for the univariate random variable that has a normal distribution with zero mean and unit variance is represented by $\varphi(x)$. Thus

$$\varphi(x)=\Phi^{(1)}(x)=\frac{1}{\sqrt{2\pi}}\, e^{-x^2/2}.$$

The derivatives of $\varphi(x)$ are denoted by

$$\varphi^{(k)}(x)=d^k\varphi(x)/dx^k. \qquad (k=1, 2, \ldots)$$

Deviates of Standard Distributions

The normal, chi-square, t, and F distributions occur (usually as approximations to actual distributions) in the presentation of nonparametric procedures. Consequently, notation is needed for the deviates of these distributions.

The symbols K_α and $K(\alpha)$ are used for the standardized normal deviate that is exceeded with probability α. Table 1 at the back of the handbook contains values of this deviate for $\alpha \leqslant \frac{1}{2}$. For $\alpha > \frac{1}{2}$, values are obtained from the relation $K_{1-\alpha}=K(1-\alpha)=-K(\alpha)=-K_\alpha$.

The symbol $\chi_\alpha{}^2(k)$ is used to denote the deviate of the chi-square distribution with k degrees of freedom that is exceeded with probability α. Table 2 at the back of the handbook contains values of $\chi_\alpha{}^2(k)$ for $k=1(1)30$ and for some values of α such that $.005 \leqslant \alpha \leqslant .995$. An approximation can be used to evaluate $\chi_\alpha{}^2(k)$ for $k > 30$.

The symbol $t_\alpha(k)$ denotes the deviate of the Student t distribution with k degrees of freedom that is exceeded with probability α. Table 3 at the back of the handbook contains values of $t_\alpha(k)$ for $k=1(1)30$, 40, 60, 120, ∞ and various values of $\alpha \leqslant \frac{1}{2}$. For $\alpha > \frac{1}{2}$, values are obtained from the relation $t_{1-\alpha}(k) = -t_\alpha(k)$. An approximation is given for evaluating $t_\alpha(k)$ for $k > 30$.

Finally, the symbol $F_\alpha(k_1, k_2)$ is used to represent the deviate of the F distribution with k_1, k_2 degrees of freedom that is exceeded with probability α. Table 4 at the back of the handbook contains values of $F_\alpha(k_1, k_2)$ for $\alpha = .005$, .01, .025, .05, .10, and $1 \leqslant k_1, k_2 \leqslant 30$, 40, 60, 120, ∞. Corresponding values for $\alpha = .995$, .99, .975, .95, and .90 can be obtained from the relation $F_{1-\alpha}(k_1, k_2) = 1/F_\alpha(k_2, k_1)$.

NOTATION ASSOCIATED WITH OBSERVATIONS

Introductory Remarks

In this handbook no notational distinction is made between random variables and observations. Ordinarily an observation is considered to be a random variable. When this is not the case, the manner in which the observation fails to be a random variable, of the population from which it was obtained, is explicitly stated.

General Notation for Observations

A large part of the notation introduced is for the purpose of representing the values of observations. This symbolism is needed for stating how the observation values are used in the application of the nonparametric procedures. The notational problem consists of assigning a convenient identification symbol to each observation. A desirable symbol might be expected to specify the method used to represent the data and to be reasonably concise. The notation developed was motivated by the desire to obtain a convenient observation symbolism of this type.

First, let us consider univariate observations. In all cases, these observations are divided into m groups and there are n_j observations in the jth group $(j = 1, \ldots, m)$. Within each group there is a specified assignment of the symbols of the observations. The notation used for representing the values of the observations is

$X(i)_j$ = value of the ith observation in the jth group $(i = 1, \ldots, n_j; j = 1, \ldots, m)$, where the values of $m, n_1, \ldots, n_m$ are given. For the special case where $m=1$, the notation is simplified by letting $X(i)_1 = X(i)$ and $n_1 = n$. Use of the symbol $X(i)_j$ implies that univariate observations are considered which are divided into m groups of sizes $n_1, \ldots, n_m$, respectively. This notation also implies that within groups the symbols can be assigned to the observations in any desired manner. That is, any specified assignment which preserves the grouping is permissible. If the symbol assignment used places the observations in a positional order for each group (e.g., chronological order), the value of i denotes the position of $X(i)_j$ in the sequence for the jth group.

The case of multivariate observations is handled in a fashion similar to that for the univariate case. The principal differences are that each group of univariate observations is considered to be a multivariate observation and that the assignment of symbols for the components of this multivariate observation is not arbitrary. In the general case, there are m multivariate observations and the jth observation is n_j-variate $(j=1, \ldots, m)$. The notation used for the multivariate case is

$$X(i)_j = \text{value of the } i\text{th entry in the } j\text{th multivariate observation } (i=1, \ldots, n_j;\ j=1, \ldots, m)$$

$$\{X(i)_j\}_m = \text{value of the } j\text{th multivariate observation } (j=1, \ldots, m) = \{X(1)_j, X(2)_j, \ldots, X(n_j)_j\}$$

where the values of $m, n_1, \ldots, n_m$ are given. When $m=1$, the simplified notation $n_1 = n$ and

$$\{X(i)_1\}_1 = \{X(i)\}_1 = \{X(1), \ldots, X(n)\}$$

is used. Besides identifying the multivariate observations, use of the symbol $\{X(i)_j\}_m$ implies that m multivariate observations are considered and that the jth observation is n_j-variate $(j=1, \ldots, m)$. Thus the basic information concerning the representation of the observational data is furnished by using this notation and specifying the values of $m, n_1, \ldots, n_m$.

The symbols $X(i)_j$ and $\{X(i)_j\}_m$ represent the general notation for assigning symbols to the observations. For the multivariate case, no other type of notation is introduced. However, two special methods of assigning symbols to the observations within groups are given for the univariate case. These special types of assignment are stated further on and special notation is introduced for each of them. If a specialized type of assignment is used but no special symbolism has been introduced for its identification, the general notation is utilized and the assignment method is stated separately.

Order Statistic Notation

Another method of assigning symbols within a group is on the basis of order statistics of their values. The notation used for order statistics within groups is

$$X[i]_j = i\text{th order statistic for the } j\text{th group } (i=1, \ldots, n_j; j=1, \ldots, m), \text{ where } X[1]_j \leqslant \ldots \leqslant X[n_j]_j$$

and $m, n_1, \ldots, n_m$ are given. The abbreviated notation $X[i]_1 = X[i]$ and $n_1 = n$ is used when $m=1$. Also the convention that $X[0]_j = -\infty$ and $X[n_j+1]_j = \infty$ is adopted. Sometimes, when $n_1 = \ldots = n_m = 1$, the notation $X[1]_1 \leqslant X[1]_2 \leqslant \ldots \leqslant X[1]_j \leqslant \ldots \leqslant X[1]_m$ is used for the order statistics of a set of m observations.

The use of $X[i]_j$ implies that univariate observations are considered which are divided into m groups of sizes $n_1, \ldots, n_m$, respectively. Also that the symbol assignment is such that the ith order statistic in the jth group is assigned the symbol $X[i]_j$.

Some of the nonparametric procedures use the median of a group of unequal observations (or the medians of groups of observations). The median of a group of observations which contains no ties is easily defined in terms of order statistics. Explicitly, the median of the jth group is given by

$$X[(n_j+1)/2]_j = \begin{cases} X[i]_j \text{ for } i = \frac{1}{2}(n_j+1), \text{ when } n_j \text{ is odd} \\ \frac{1}{2}X[i]_j + \frac{1}{2}X[i+1]_j \text{ for } i = \frac{1}{2}n_j, \text{ when } n_j \text{ is even.} \end{cases}$$

For $m=1$, the median of the group of observations is denoted by $X[(n+1)/2]$.

A censored set of univariate observations (e.g., a censored sample) is defined in terms of the order statistics of the entire set of observations that was censored. Explicitly, let the order statistics of the set of observations considered be $X[1]_j, \ldots, X[n_j]_j$. Then, if the r smallest observations and the s largest observations are censored, the resulting censored set of observations consists of $X[r+1]_j, \ldots, X[n_j - s]_j$. If $r=0$ or $s=0$, one-sided censoring occurs.

Notation When Ranks Used

Some nonparametric procedures are based on the ranks of the observations within the groups rather than on the values of these observations. There are many reasonable ways of choosing the values for the ranks, including choice on a random basis (see Chapter 4), and several of these ways occur in the statements of nonparametric procedures given in this handbook. However, a special rank notation is introduced only for the case where, for observations with different values, the integers from 1 to the number of observations are the ranking values used. That is, for the jth group the rankings used are $1, \ldots, n_j$ in case there are no ties; here the smallest observation is given rank 1 and the largest receives the rank n_j. The assignment of ranks to sets of tied observations can be accomplished in many ways. In this handbook, either the random assignment or the midrank method is ordinarily used.

The symbolism used for assigning ranks to the observations in the jth group is

$$X\langle i\rangle_j = \text{group rank of the } i\text{th observation in the } j\text{th group } (i=1, \ldots, n_j;\ j=1, \ldots, m),$$

where $m, n_1, \ldots, n_m$ are specified. The notation $X\langle i\rangle_1 = X\langle i\rangle$ and $n_1 = n$ is used when $m=1$.

The notation $X\langle i\rangle_j$ implies that univariate observations are considered which are divided into m groups of sizes $n_1, \ldots, n_m$, respectively. Also that $X\langle i\rangle_j$ is the rank of the ith observation in the jth group.

Remarks on Notation for Observations

The values for $m, n_1, \ldots, n_m$, as well as the particular groupings used for the case of univariate observations, are often at least partially at the disposal of the experimenter. This freedom of choice can frequently be used to obtain a more desirable type of data.

The general mathematical usage of ( ), [ ], { } has not been made ambiguous by their uses in representing the values of observations. Inclusion of the symbol X identifies the fact these symbols are used to represent observations.

Empirical Distribution Function Symbolism

For the univariate case and a sample of size n, the symbol for the empirical distribution function of the sample is $F_n(x)$, unless the contrary is stated. That is, $F_n(x)$ is equal to the proportion of the sample observations that have values at most equal to x.

For the k-variate case and a sample of size m, $F_m(x_1, \ldots, x_k)$ is the symbol for the joint empirical distribution function (unless the contrary is stated). That is, $F_m(x_1, \ldots, x_k)$ is the proportion of the sample of k-variate observations that have values which are less than or equal to $(x_1, \ldots, x_k)$ in every coordinate.

NOTATION ASSOCIATED WITH OBSERVATION MOMENTS

The observed moments for a set of data are constructed from the values of the observations of this set. These observed moments are especially useful when the set of observations is known to be a random sample.

To avoid a large number of special cases, the notation used is a combination of an operator type and a functional type. The operator type notation is used where only univariate moments are involved while the functional type of notation is used when joint moments are involved.

The "operator" M is used to represent the operation of forming the arithmetic average of the group of observations considered. For the standardized observation notation, the X can be deleted as a notational simplification. As examples,

$$MX(i)_j = M(i)_j = \sum_{i=1}^{n_j} X(i)_j/n_j$$

$$MX\langle i\rangle_j = M\langle i\rangle_j = \sum_{i=1}^{n_j} X\langle i\rangle_j/n_j.$$

Here $M(i)_1 = M(i)$, $M[i]_1 = M[i]$, and $M\langle i\rangle_1 = M\langle i\rangle$ when $m=1$. The "operator" S represents the operation of forming the standard deviation of the group of observations considered while S^2 denotes formation of the square of the standard deviation (variance), etc. That is,

$$SX[i]_j = S[i]_j = \left\{ \sum_{i=1}^{n_j} (X[i]_j - M[u]_j)^2/(n_j-1) \right\}^{1/2}$$

$$S^3(i)_j = [S(i)_j]^3, \quad S^4\langle i\rangle_j = [S^2\langle i\rangle_j]^2 = [S\langle i\rangle_j]^4,$$

etc. Here the subscript j is omitted when $m=1$.

In general, for the univariate case, M'_t denotes the operation of taking the tth moment about the origin for the group of observations considered. That is,

$$M'_tX[i]_j = M'_t[i]_j = \sum_{i=1}^{n_j} X[i]_j{}^t/n_j, \qquad (t=1, 2, \ldots)$$

etc. Likewise, M_t represents the operation of taking the tth moment about the observation mean for the group considered. That is,

$$M_tX(i)_j = M_t(i)_j = \sum_{i=1}^{n_j} [X(i)_j - M(u)_j]^t/n_j, \qquad (t=2, 3, \ldots)$$

etc. The subscript j is omitted when $m=1$.

This "operator" notation covers the univariate cases of principal interest. When situations involving univariate moments arise that are not covered by this standardized notation, appropriate symbolism is introduced in the chapters where these situations occur.

A functional type of notation is introduced for covariances and correlation coefficients, which are the only cases involving joint moments for which a standardized symbolism is introduced in this chapter. The symbol $C(X_u, Y_u)$ is used to denote the empirical covariance between the X and Y components of the bivariate observations (X_u, Y_u), $u=1,\ldots,n$. Explicitly,

$$C(X_u, Y_u)=\sum_{u=1}^{n}(X_u-MX_v)(Y_u-MY_v)/n.$$

When the bivariate observations are $[X(i)_1, X(i)_2]$, $i=1,\ldots,n$,

$$C[X(i)_1, X(i)_2]=\sum_{i=1}^{n}[X(i)_1-M(u)_1][X(i)_2-M(u)_2]/n.$$

When the bivariate observations are $\{X[i], X\langle i\rangle\}$

$$C\{X[i], X\langle i\rangle\}=\sum_{i=1}^{n}\{X[i]-M[u]\}\{X\langle i\rangle-M\langle u\rangle\}/n,$$

etc.

The symbol $R(X_u, Y_u)$ denotes the empirical correlation coefficient between the X and Y components of the n bivariate observations (X_u, Y_u). This symbol is defined by

$$R(X_u, Y_u)=C(X_u, Y_u)/(SX_u)(SY_u).$$

For example,

$$R\{X(i), X[i]\}=C\{X(i), X[i]\}/S(i)S[i],$$

etc.

NOTATION FOR POPULATION PROPERTIES

Here too it is convenient to introduce an operator-type notation for the univariate situations and for some of the multivariate situations. A type of functional notation is used for covariances and correlation coefficients, the only properties nontrivially involving joint population moments for which standardized symbolism is presented in this chapter. The items for which notation is given are percentage points, expected values, moments, and functions of moments.

The symbol θ_p is used to represent the operation of forming the $100p$-percent point for the distribution of the random univariate variable considered. When no ambiguity exists, θ_p can be used alone as the symbol for the $100p$-percent point. Otherwise θ_p is associated with the random observation to which it applies; for cases involving the standardized symbolism for an observation, the X is deleted as a notational simplification. As examples

$\theta_p[X(i)_j]=\theta_p(i)_j=100p$-percent point of distribution for $X(i)_j$

$\theta_p\{X[i]_j\}=\theta_p[i]_j=100p$-percent point of distribution for $X[i]_j$,

etc. The subscript j is omitted when $m=1$.

The operator E denotes the operation of forming the expected value of the random observation considered. As examples,

$$EX(i)_j = \text{expected value of } X(i)_j$$

$$EX\langle i\rangle_j = \text{expected value of } X\langle i\rangle_j$$

$$EX(i)_j^t = \text{expected value of } X(i)_j^t$$

$$EX[i]_j^t = \text{expected value of } X[i]^t$$

$$E\{X(i)_j\}_m = \text{expected value of } \{X(i)_j\}_m = \{EX(1)_j, \ldots, EX(n_j)_j\},$$

etc. Population moments are particular cases of expected values. In fact, EY is used to denote the population mean for a random observation Y and EY^t is used to denote the tth population moment about the origin for Y.

A special operator-type notation is introduced for representing some of the population moments and functions of population moments. This symbolism can be defined in terms of the operator E and is given by

$$\sigma Y = [E(Y - EY)^2]^{1/2}$$

$$\sigma^4 Y = (\sigma Y)(\sigma^3 Y) = (\sigma^2 Y)^2 = (\sigma Y)^4$$

$$\mu_t Y = E(Y - EY)^t, \qquad (t = 2, 3, \ldots)$$

$$\alpha_t Y = (\mu_t Y)/\sigma^t Y, \qquad (t = 3, 4, \ldots)$$

for any random variable Y for which the prescribed expected values exist. For cases involving the standardized notation for an observation, the X is deleted for purposes of simplicity. As examples,

$$\sigma X(i)_j = \sigma(i)_j, \quad \mu_t X\langle i\rangle_j = \mu_t\langle i\rangle_j$$

etc. The subscript j is omitted when $m = 1$.

The functional form of notation used for the covariance between two random variables X and Y, for which the covariance exists, is

$$\text{cov}(X, Y) = E[(X - EX)(Y - EY)].$$

As examples

$$\text{cov}[X(i)_j, X(i)_k] = E\{[X(i)_j - EX(i)_j][X(i)_k - EX(i)_k]\}$$

$$\text{cov}\{X[u]_j, X\langle v\rangle_k\} = E\{(X[u]_j - EX[u]_j)(X\langle v\rangle_k - EX\langle v\rangle_k)\},$$

etc. The notation used for correlation coefficients is

$$\rho(X, Y) = \text{cov}(X, Y)/(\sigma X)(\sigma Y).$$

For example,

$$\rho\{X(u)_j, X[v]_k\} = \text{cov}\{X(u)_j, X[v]_k\}/\sigma(u)_j\sigma[v]_k,$$

etc.

CONCLUDING REMARKS

A substantial amount of space is saved by not displaying equations and other expressions that occur in the presentation of a statistical procedure. Due to the condensed nature of the presentation format, no difficulties seem to be introduced by eliminating displayed material there. However, in some cases, additional space is introduced to separate equations and other expressions when they are of a lengthy and/or a complicated nature.

Extensive use is made of the slash line / for representing division. Throughout, this is done in a precise fashion. As an example, the relation

$$1/5n \leqslant \alpha \leqslant 1 - 1/5n$$

is the same as the relation

$$\frac{1}{5n} \leqslant \alpha \leqslant 1 - \frac{1}{5n}$$

and is not to be confused with

$$(\tfrac{1}{5})n \leqslant \alpha \leqslant 1 - (\tfrac{1}{5})n.$$

Also .025 is used instead of 0.025, etc. The notation $\doteq$ is used to represent approximate equality.

Chapter 3

DESCRIPTION AND USE OF FORMAT

INTRODUCTION

Although many nonparametric procedures are worthy of being included in this handbook, the amount of available space is limited. Thus a method is needed for presenting the pertinent features of a procedure in a small amount of space. This presentation problem is handled by developing a standard format which is of an abbreviated nature. The combination of this format and the notation already presented allows each nonparametric procedure to be stated in a concise fashion. This chapter contains a detailed description of the format adopted and its use. *A condensed version of this format is printed inside the back cover of this book.* An understanding of Chapter 3 is required for efficient use of the material presented in the following chapters.

OUTLINE OF FORMAT

First, let us consider a short statement of the headings and corresponding material for the format adopted. The following outline indicates the major features of this format:

Name (of procedure considered)

Data

1. Type of observations used
2. Special features of data and/or preliminary operations performed
3. Notational statement of observations used
4. Restrictions imposed on $m, n_1, \ldots, n_m$

Description

1. Type of procedure used or situation considered
2. Population properties investigated

Assumptions

1. Independence and/or random sample assumptions
2. Other qualitative-type population property restrictions
3. Quantitative-type restrictions on population properties

Results

1. Supplementary operations on the data and special notation for stating results
2. Statement of the nonparametric procedure
3. Tables, graphs, and relations for use in applying this procedure
4. Discussion and supplementary information

Characteristics

1. Level of computational effort required
2. Efficiency and consistency properties of procedure
3. Extent of symmetrical use of the observations
4. Sensitivity of the procedure to the assumptions
5. Difficulty of verifying the assumptions
6. Additional remarks, if any

Bibliography

More detailed descriptions of the types of material included under these seven headings are given next.

NAME OF NONPARAMETRIC PROCEDURE

The information listed for the first heading of the format is used for identifying the nonparametric procedure considered. The established name is used for the case of a well-known procedure. Short identification titles have been devised for the other cases. If the procedure considered is associated with one or more originators, the name of this person (persons) is given in parentheses at the end of the name of the procedure.

DATA USED IN APPLICATION

The material of the second format heading, Data, contains a specification of the observational data required for application of the procedure. The nature of the observations is considered first and stated after the numeral 1. In most cases, the observations are of one of four types, namely, continuous or discrete and univariate or multivariate. However, this information can be more specialized, such as stating that 0 and 1 are the only possible values (binomial case). In some cases, the fact that the observations are unequal (no ties) is the only information that is needed.

Usually the observations for a procedure are exclusively of one type. Most of the procedures given in this handbook are based on continuous univariate observations.

For some procedures the observations must have special features that are not found in the usual kind of data. As an example, some procedures are developed expressly for life-testing situations. Then the data are such that a specified number of the smallest order statistics can be determined without the necessity of evaluating the remaining observations of the set. Also, for some procedures, preliminary operations must be, or should be, performed before the actual experimentation is started. Usually the purpose of the preliminary operations is to assure that the observations have specified general-type probability properties. For example, many experiments involve a time and/or location assignment of the items considered. Convenient nonparametric probability properties frequently can be obtained if the assignment is made on a suitable random basis. The special features of the data and/or the preliminary operations are stated after the numeral 2. The word "none" is stated if no special features or preliminary operations are required.

Numeral 3 under the data heading contains a notational statement of the observations used by the procedure. That is, the symbols used to represent the observation values and any necessary explanation of this symbolism are given here. This statement can be very brief for univariate situations based on either order statistics or ranks. For these cases, listing of the appropriate symbol, $X[i]_j$, $X[1]_j$, or $X\langle i\rangle_j$, is usually sufficient, where the subscript is deleted when $m=1$ for all observations considered. In the more general cases, statement of only $X(i)_j$ or $\{X(i)_j\}_m$ is often satisfactory, but additional explanation may be required in some cases; here too, the j subscript is deleted if $m=1$ for all the observations considered.

In all cases, one or more of $X(i)_j$, $X[i]_j$, $X[1]_j$, $X\langle i\rangle_j$, or $\{X(i)_j\}_m$, perhaps with the j subscript deleted, is used in the notational statement for the observations. Then the groupings and numbers of observations are based on the values of $m, n_1, \ldots, n_m$. In many cases limitations are placed on the values of these integers. For example, both the value of m and lower bounds for $n_1, \ldots, n_m$ are frequently specified. However, the lower bound relations are sometimes stated under the Results heading, rather than after the numeral 4 for this heading. If no restrictions are imposed (other than $m \geqslant 1$, $n_1 \geqslant 1, \ldots, n_m \geqslant 1$), the word "none" is stated after the numeral 4.

DESCRIPTION OF PROCEDURE

The material following the third format heading, Description, is used for specifying the nature of the procedure presented. The procedure type and the population properties investigated are considered under this heading. The procedure type is stated after the numeral 1 and identifies this procedure as furnishing point estimates, confidence regions (intervals), significance tests, tolerance regions, bounds for a probability expression, useful probability relations, etc. When a probability procedure can be identified as one-sided or two-sided, this information is given. The precision level of the probability procedure (see Chapter 4) is also stated after the numeral 1. The population properties investigated are stated after the numeral 2 and can be of many kinds. An effort is made to state these properties in a concise manner. Ordinarily, qualitative properties are expressed in words while quantitative properties are stated in terms of symbols. Any symbolism appearing here is consistent with the other notation used in stating the procedure.

PROCEDURE ASSUMPTIONS

The material following the fourth format heading, Assumptions, contains a statement of the supplementary probability knowledge which is assumed for the procedure presented. All the procedures stated in this handbook are based on one or more assumptions about the probability properties of the observations used, although for significance tests the assumptions are sometimes contained exclusively in the null hypothesis (e.g., for randomness tests). These procedure assumptions fall into two general categories, qualitative and quantitative. However, the qualitative properties of statistical independence and random sampling are considered separately due to their use for nearly all of the procedures considered. The statistical independence and/or random sample situation assumed is stated after the numeral 1 of the Assumptions heading. If no assumptions of this nature are made, the word "none" is stated following the numeral 1.

The other qualitative properties assumed for the procedure considered are stated after the numeral 2. These properties include population symmetry, unimodal populations, existence of specified moments, etc. If no qualitative properties are assumed, other than those stated after numeral 1, the word "none" is stated after the numeral 2.

The quantitative properties consist of quantitative relations involving population constants and distributions. These relations are usually stated in terms of symbols. Nearly all of the population constants considered are either percentage points or moments. An explanation is given for the symbolism in cases where this notation has not already been defined. The quantitative properties assumed for the procedure are stated after the numeral 3. The word "none" is stated here if no quantitative properties are assumed.

In some cases, e.g. when bounded probability procedures are involved, two or more different sets of assumptions may be stated. Then the assumptions belonging to the first set are referred to as Case (I), those belonging to the second set as Case (II), etc.

STATEMENT OF PROCEDURE RESULTS

The fifth heading of the format is titled Results. Here the procedure is stated in a form that is concise but sufficiently detailed for most purposes. Unless the procedure is of a simple nature, special notation may be used for its statement. Also, in some cases, the observation values are converted into a special form before the procedure is stated. This might involve a transformation of variable, determination of runs, etc. The supplementary operations and notation used in this data conversion are stated after the numeral 1. The special notation introduced for a given procedure is not necessarily consistent with the special notation introduced for other procedures. When no supplementary data operations or special symbols are used, the word "none" is stated after the numeral 1.

Given the observational data expressed in the desired form, the nonparametric procedure is stated following the numeral 2. The statement is always such that the confidence coefficient properties (value, approximate value, bounds, etc.) which correspond to a confidence region are explicitly specified. Similarly for significance tests and their significance levels; here, unless the contrary is stated, each test has significance level α (either exactly or approximately). The stated procedure may involve several different types of confidence regions or several different types of tests (one-sided, two-sided, etc.). For bounded probability procedures, the confidence region and significance test expressions usually remain unchanged, but the bounds for the confidence coefficients and significance levels vary with the assumptions used; i.e., Case (I), Case (II), etc.

Some of the procedures utilize quantities whose values are tabulated, graphed, or stated as explicit relations. If a table or graph applies to only one procedure, it is presented with that procedure. When a table or graph is only used for two or more procedures that appear in the same chapter, it is located at the first place where it is used. In all cases, a listing of the tables and graphs used for a procedure, and their locations, are given following the numeral 3, along with the relations for this procedure. Sometimes the stated relations are only applicable if specified conditions hold, which often involve the number of observations. In virtually all cases, these conditions are based on judgment and were specifically developed for use in this handbook (by its author). When no tables, graphs, or relations are used, the word "none" is stated after the numeral 3.

Sometimes additional remarks about the applications, extensions, properties, etc. of the procedure are desirable. For the case of significance tests, this might be concerned with the use of alternative critical regions. If the procedure merely furnished values of some specified moments, some methods of obtaining approximate probability values on the basis of these moments might be suggested. Any supplementary information or discussion concerning the procedure or its use is given following the numeral 4. If no additional discussion seems necessary, the word "none" is stated after the numeral 4.

CHARACTERISTICS OF PROCEDURE

The material of the sixth format heading, Characteristics, is concerned with the desirability of the procedure from a practical viewpoint. If a procedure is of only moderate practical value, is difficult to apply, and/or has a low efficiency, its worth may be questionable for many types of practical problems. A rough indication of the amount of computational effort needed is given after the numeral 1. The levels listed for the computational effort are high, medium, and low. A high level implies that a very large amount of computation is required. For the medium level, a substantial but not overly large amount of computation must be performed. A low level of effort implies that not very much computation is needed. In some cases the level of the computational effort may be dependent on the numbers of observations in the groups and other considerations. Then the computational level is stated as a function of the additional considerations and may involve two or more levels. Usually, the statement of the level of computation required is based on the judgment of the author of the handbook and does not represent a precise evaluation.

The known efficiency and consistency properties of the procedure are stated after the numeral 2. When the procedure is a test, this includes designation of the alternative hypotheses that the test guards against. Efficiencies are often based on the assumption of specialized situations for which corresponding "best" procedures exist (see Chapter 4 for discussion). Then the situations assumed are stated and identified with the efficiency values. If an efficiency summary is given for the procedures of a chapter, reference to this summary may be the major statement made concerning efficiency. Sometimes the alternatives to which a test should be sensitive can be identified on a judgment basis. The author of the handbook has performed this identification at nearly all places where power properties are not stated for these alternatives. Some of the nonparametric procedures given have not yet been investigated from an efficiency or consistency viewpoint, and the situations to which they are sensitive are not apparent. For these procedures the word "unknown" is stated after the numeral 2.

The random sample concept is very important for many of the nonparametric procedures. Thus the ability to test this assumption without affecting the procedure probability properties is very desirable. Independent testing can often be accomplished on the basis of an appropriate ordering of the observations in sequence positions if the procedure uses the observations within each group in a symmetrical fashion (see Chapter 4). In terms of the general notation, the observations of the jth group are used symmetrically if the procedure statistics have fixed values for all possible assignments of the symbols $X(i)_j$ to the observations. The extent to which the observations are used symmetrically in the procedure is stated following the numeral 3.

The sensitivity of a procedure to deviations from the assumptions used in its derivation is of considerable practical interest. Ordinarily, procedure assumptions are not verifiable in even a moderately precise fashion. Consequently, a procedure is of doubtful practical worth if small changes in its assumptions can cause large changes in its properties. A qualitative assessment of the sensitivity of the procedure to assumption variations is given after the numeral 4. This assessment is usually based on the judgment of the author of the handbook. If no assumption sensitivity information is available for this procedure, the word "unknown" is stated following the numeral 4.

Even if a procedure is not overly sensitive to its assumptions, substantial violation of these assumptions can destroy the usefulness of the procedure. Thus, at least rough verification should be obtained for its assumptions before a procedure is chosen for application. In some cases, even approximate verification can be very difficult. The practical worth of the procedure is questionable for these cases. In other cases, approximate verification of the procedure assumptions may be easily accomplished. The numeral 5 is followed by a qualitative statement of the difficulty level ordinarily encountered in approximately verifying the assumptions for the procedure considered. This evaluation of the difficulty level is usually based on the judgment of the author of the handbook. The level of difficulty may vary with changes in the numbers of observations, and is expressed as a function of the numbers of observations when this is the case. If the separate assumptions of a set involve different levels of difficulty, the highest of the resulting levels is stated as the difficulty level for the procedure. For bounded probability procedures involving more than one set of assumptions, the level of difficulty for approximate verification is stated separately for each set [Case (I), Case (II) etc.].

In some cases, a procedure has important characteristics not covered under numerals 1–5. These additional characteristics are discussed following numeral 6. In particular, the practical value of a procedure can be indicated here. The word "none" is inserted after the numeral 6 when there seem to be no additional characteristics of importance.

BIBLIOGRAPHY FOR PROCEDURE

The seventh and final format heading, Bibliography, contains a listing, by number, of most of the more important publications dealing with the procedure considered. The numbers given represent references that are listed at the end of the handbook. In this list of references, the information given for each article, stated in the order of presentation, consists of its author(s), title, place published, date published, and usually page numbers. In the case of a book, the name of the book is stated in place of the article title. Initials of authors are used in place of their given names. In some cases, the title of the article has been translated into English form; then the language in which the article is written is usually stated, in parentheses, at the end of the reference.

To help reduce the space required for presentation, short abbreviations are often adopted for the names of journals and other places of publication. A list of these short abbreviations is given at the end of the book. Virtually all the material considered was published after 1870. Consequently, space is saved by giving only the last two digits of the year of publication for publication dates of 1871 and later. For the case of a journal, the volume number immediately follows the abbreviation for the journal name (if the volume number is stated). Confusion between the volume number of a journal and its year of publication is avoided by setting the publication date off with commas and using an apostrophe at the front of the two-digit number ('50 for 1950, etc.).

Deviations from this format for presenting references do occur in a few cases (e.g., with respect to company reports). For these situations enough additional detail is given for unambiguous identification of the article or report considered.

To illustrate how references to publications are listed (at the back of the handbook), except for use of abbreviations for the place of publication, consider

237 Hemelrijk, J., A family of parameter-free tests for symmetry with respect to a given point I, II, *Proceedings Koninklijke Nederlandse Akademie van Wetenschappen* 53, '50, 945–55 and 1186–98

224 Hald, A., *Statistical theory with engineering applications*, John Wiley and Sons, '52

The first publication is a paper titled "A family of parameter-free tests for symmetry with respect to a given point I, II" by J. Hemelrijk. This article was published in *Proceedings Koninklijke Nederlandse Akademie van Wetenschappen*, Volume 53, 1950, pages 945–955 and pages 1186–98. The second publication is a book titled *Statistical theory with engineering applications* by A. Hald. This book was published by John Wiley and Sons in 1952.

The references are presented alphabetically with respect to author's name. In the case of multiple authors, a reference is listed with respect to the name of the author who is stated first (the "senior" author). In case of several articles by the same author, or a group of multiple authors, chronological ordering is used. Thus the list furnishes both an author index for references and a list for use in bibliographies.

EXAMPLE OF FORMAT USE

The material for a procedure presentation is given in a consecutive fashion. That is, each heading does not necessarily begin a new line. In order to emphasize the presentation subdivisions, the format headings and the numerals for subheadings are listed in bold-face type. Also, spaces are inserted so that important statements and complicated expressions are partially displayed.

To illustrate use of the format, consider the following procedure presentation (see page 64).

Test Based on Total Number of Runs

Data 1 Unequal univariate observations **2** Order of symbol assignment to observations appropriate for testing randomness properties **3** $X(i)$ **4** $m=1$ **Description 1** Exact sig. test **2** Random sample null hyp. Altern. hyp. are a shift and/or a trend **Assumptions 1** None **2** None **3** None **Results 1** Observation denoted by a if it exceeds observation median and by b otherwise. Median observation discarded if n odd. $N =$ no. a's $=$ no. b's. $X =$ total no. runs of a's and of b's **2** *Tests*: Accept existence of shift and/or trend if $X < X_\alpha$, where α is sig. level **3** Table 5.1 gives X_α for $N \leqslant 20$ and α near .01, .05, .10, .20, .30. For $N \geqslant 20$ and $1/4N \leqslant \alpha \leqslant 1-1/4N$, $X_\alpha \doteq 3/2 + N - K_\alpha[(N^2-N)/(2N-1)]^{1/2}$, for α such that this quantity integral **4** None **Characteristics 1** Low **2** See pages 77–80. Not very powerful unless $N \geqslant 10$. Consistent against most altern. hyp. of interest. Some power fct. results given in ref. 39, 134, and 354 **3** Independent of procedures using same observations symmetrically **4** None **5** None **6** In more recent stat. books **Bibliography** Ref. 37, 39, 42, 134, 151, 211, 224, 295, 298, 316, 351, 354, 398, 486, 495, 501, 505, 507, 544, 590 (pages 200–17), 595.

Thus the procedure is presented in a moderately small amount of space. Examination of the format outline and the above example should make the presentation method reasonably clear. However, a couple of points may be worth mentioning. First, on the basis of the specialized notation adopted, the total number of observations is $n = n_1$ for the case considered. Second, not all notation used has a standardized meaning. Notation in addition to the standardized notation is often introduced for the presentation of a given procedure.

NOTATION CONSISTENCY

The major subheadings of a chapter are called sections. There are also subheadings within sections. For the presentations, the standardized notation presented in Chapter 2, and summarized inside the front cover, is used consistently throughout the handbook. However, not all of the notation used in presenting a statistical procedure is consistent with that given in other presentations. However, the notation ordinarily is consistent among all presentations that are contained in the same section. That is, in all important situations, the notation has a fixed meaning within a section but can have different meanings in different sections.

NONREPETITION OF MATERIAL

Some parts of the presentations may be the same for all procedures within a section. To save space, material which is the same for all the procedures of a section is stated at the beginning of the presentations and deleted from the procedure presentations of that section. Thus, to obtain the complete statement of a procedure, the fixed presentation material for the section containing the procedure should be examined. For convenience of reference, the number of the page containing the fixed material for the section is stated at the top of each page containing part or all of a procedure presentation. This reference page number is distinguished from the actual number of the page on which it appears by using the prefix FMS. Thus FMS 123 implies that the fixed material for that section begins on page 123 of the handbook.

CONFIDENCE REGION PREFERENCE OVER TESTS

As described in Chapter 4, a standard method of obtaining significance tests is on the basis of confidence regions. That is, given confidence regions, the corresponding significance tests can be determined in a straightforward manner. Consequently, significance test procedures are presented only for cases where these tests are not obtained directly from confidence regions. In all other cases, only the confidence region procedures are stated.

Often a confidence region and the properties of its confidence coefficient are furnished by stating the properties of a specified probability expression. Here the confidence region is defined by the relation considered in the probability expression and the confidence coefficient is the value of this probability.

DISCUSSION WITHOUT PROCEDURE PRESENTATIONS

In some cases, classes of procedures are encountered that seem to be worthy of mention but for which presentation does not seem to be appropriate. For such cases, a discussion of this type of procedure is sometimes given and its special features outlined. However, the material presented is limited to at most a bibliography of the results that have been obtained for this type of situation.

Chapter 4

DISCUSSION OF CONCEPTS AND SPECIAL TERMINOLOGY

INTRODUCTION

Most of the concepts and terminology encountered in this handbook are well known in the field of mathematical statistics. However, some of the concepts and terminology used, although known to specialists in the field, are not so well established. Also, for the special purposes of the handbook, some of the concepts have been modified (generalized), and some additional terminology has been introduced. This chapter contains a discussion of the concepts and terminology which are either not well known or were developed specifically for the presentations of this handbook.

The purpose, the types, and the efficiency measurement of statistical procedures are discussed first. Then some special terminology is introduced for identifying the precision levels of statistical procedures. Following this is a statement of the types of point estimation considered, a definition of permutation tests, and an outline of a method for constructing confidence intervals from significance tests. Definitions for independence, random sample, and population symmetry are given next. Following this, a generalization of the interpretation for order of magnitude notation is given, the problem of verifying the assumptions of distribution continuity and differentiability is discussed, and a method of converting data to a continuous form is outlined. Next, several families of probability distributions that can be used to approximate a distribution on the basis of its first few moments are defined and discussed. Finally, some remarks are made concerning an advantage of procedures which use the observations in a symmetrical fashion and U statistics are defined; also life-testing, censored data situations, and considerations in the choice of hypotheses are discussed.

PURPOSE OF STATISTICAL PROCEDURES

Conceptually, any probability process yielding observations can be represented by a joint distribution function. If this distribution function were completely known, there would be no point in considering the observations from the process. From the viewpoint of mathematical statistics, all the information that is obtainable would be known. That is, determination of the underlying distribution represents the maximum amount of information that can be obtained on the basis of observational data.

For situations involving experimentation, the distribution function for a probability process is seldom ever known, even to a reasonable approximation, except on the basis of data. Moreover, the observational data available are almost always insufficient to determine the distribution function to a reasonable approximation. Consequently, the quantity investigated is often some special property of this distribution function rather than the entire distribution function.

The properties investigated by statistical procedures usually involve population constants (also referred to as probability constants). For the univariate observation case, population percentage points and functions of population moments have received the principal emphasis in the field of nonparametric statistics. For the multivariate case, functions of moments have received the major attention. Also nonnumerical properties such as existence of a random sample and population symmetry have been considered.

Population constants such as moments and percentage points are frequently referred to as population parameters. This terminology is not used in this handbook because it might lead to confusion between the parametric and the nonparametric cases of mathematical statistics.

TYPES OF STATISTICAL PROCEDURES

The three types of procedures that are nearly always used for obtaining probability information about a specified probability constant are point estimates, confidence regions, and significance tests. Tolerance regions and statistical decision procedures also occur, but these can be considered to be a generalization of confidence regions and significance tests, respectively. In this handbook, no distinction is made between an estimate and an estimator in point estimation.

When confidence regions exist for a population constant, these regions can be converted into significance tests of the null hypothesis that this probability constant has a specified value. Explicitly, the significance test formed from a given confidence region is:

Reject the null hypothesis that the probability constant considered equals the specified value if this specified value is not contained in the given confidence region.

The significance level for this test equals unity minus the value of the confidence coefficient for the given region. A corresponding procedure can be used for testing a probability distribution on the basis of a confidence band for that distribution (see Chapter 10).

When the population property investigated is not of a numerical nature, only the significance test procedure is ordinarily available for use. Then the null hypothesis for the test used asserts that the qualitative property being investigated is satisfied.

INTERPRETATION OF "NONPARAMETRIC" FOR HYPOTHESES ABOUT DISTRIBUTIONS

For tests and statistical decision theory results that investigate probability distributions, "nonparametric" has a somewhat broader interpretation than for other situations. For tests of distributions, a well-established nonparametric null hypothesis is that the distribution for the population sampled equals a distribution which is completely specified. Evidently, the null hypothesis is generalized if all that is asserted is that the distribution is of a specified parametric form that includes the completely specified distribution as a special case. Thus, for the situation of distributions, the nonparametric tests have null hypotheses of the type that is ordinarily associated with the parametric case. As an example, this occurs when the chi-square goodness of fit test is used for nonparametric testing of simple or composite null hypotheses. It also occurs in the application of some of the results that have been developed in statistical decision theory.

Nonparametric tests and decision procedures for distributions are identified by their generality of application. That is, although the possible decisions are stated in a parametric form, the over-all class of decisions that can be handled by the test or decision procedure is of a nonparametric nature.

USE OF STATISTICAL DECISION THEORY

Except for a few isolated cases, the only nonparametric material that uses statistical decision theory is that presented in Chapter 11 for probability distributions. On the basis of a specified loss function and perhaps some supplementary information, the usual problem is to select one, of several possible distributions, as that which yielded the sample values. The distribution selected is that which minimizes the risk, where the risk depends on the loss function, the supplementary information, and the sample values. Ref. 67 contains a description of statistical decision theory.

For the problem outlined, statistical decision theory has the advantage of being able to use supplementary information and of allowing for the losses incurred by wrong decisions. Its principal disadvantage is that its probability properties are usually of a subjective nature and difficult to interpret in the sense of the frequency representation of probability.

CONSISTENCY OF A PROCEDURE

Discussion

As the number of observations increases, any reasonable statistical procedure should furnish increasingly precise information about the population property being investigated. In fact, for an unlimited number of observations, the information about the population property should be exact, in a specified sense, with probability one. This section contains descriptions of what consistency implies for point estimates, confidence regions, and significance tests. More precise definitions of consistency are given in ref. 186 (pages 108 and 143) and in ref. 544 for some of these cases.

Consistent Estimates

As the number of observations increases, any reasonable type of point estimate should tend to take on values which approach the value of the probability constant estimated. This limiting requirement for a reasonable type of estimate is referred to as estimate consistency. An estimate is consistent if it converges in a probability sense to the value of the constant estimated as the number of observations increases indefinitely. That is, the limiting probability that a value exceeds any fixed deviation from the value of the constant approaches zero even though the fixed deviation may be as small as desired. In the multidimensional case, a deviation refers to the distance, in some sense, between the constant point and the estimate point.

Confidence Region Consistency

As the number of observations increases, any reasonable type of confidence region with fixed confidence coefficient should converge, in some sense, to the value of the probability constant being investigated. That is, the region boundaries that are not fixed should converge to the value of this constant. These limiting requirements for a reasonable type of confidence region are analogous to estimate consistency and might be referred to as confidence region consistency.

Significance Test Consistency

A significance test is a function of the number of observations on which it is based. Suppose that this number of observations becomes indefinitely large. Then, in the limit, any reasonable type of test with fixed significance level should be certain to reject the null hypothesis when any of the alternative hypotheses being investigated is satisfied. That is, any fixed deviation from the null hypothesis that is due to one of these alternative hypotheses should be detected with probability one. This limiting requirement for a reasonable type of test is called significance test consistency and is analogous to estimate and confidence region consistency.

EFFICIENCY OF A PROCEDURE

General Remarks

The efficiency of a procedure furnishes a measure of how much of the total available information obtainable on the basis of the observations is yielded by this procedure. Suppose that a specified class of procedures is considered for investigating a stated population property and, for the situations of interest, one of these procedures always furnishes at least as much "information" about this property as any of the others. This "best" procedure evidently can be considered to have a 100 percent efficiency. For the case of a random sample, the efficiencies of the other procedures of the class can be evaluated by increasing their sample sizes until the information furnished is equivalent to that given by the best procedure. Here, fractional sample sizes are allowed, whose information content is determined by interpolation from that for integral sample sizes. Then the efficiency of a procedure is taken to be the actual number of sample values divided by the number of sample values for which the given procedure is information equivalent to the best procedure. Thus an efficiency of 100γ percent implies that the given procedure based on $1/\gamma$ as many sample values has an information content equivalent to that of the best test based on the actual sample size. Ref. 391 contains a discussion of the determination of efficiencies of nonparametric procedures. In this handbook, procedure efficiencies are only considered for the case of random samples.

Nonparametric procedures are of a general nature and do not require much knowledge about the population which produced the sample values. Consequently, obtaining a best procedure which holds for a wide class of situations of interest, including the many possible types of populations, is sometimes not feasible or even possible. A method of avoiding this difficulty and still obtaining at least a rough idea of the procedure efficiency consists in restricting the population sampled, for efficiency analysis considerations, to be of a type that is of practical interest and for which a best procedure exists. The well-known normal population is often used for this purpose.

Point Estimate Efficiency

The interpretation of information equivalence for two procedures depends on the type of procedure considered. In the case of point estimation of a univariate probability constant, a comparison of the expected variation of the estimates about the constant (measured by the mean square error) is often satisfactory for determining information equivalence.

When the probability constant estimated is multidimensional, a comparison is more difficult since the relative worth of each component of the constant should be taken into consideration. However, a best unbiased estimate can sometimes be obtained in the sense that among all estimates of the specified probability constant which are unbiased for all populations of the class considered this estimate has minimum concentration ellipsoid (see, e.g., ref. 186, page 51). That is, let $(X_1, \ldots, X_k)$ be a random variable with $\sigma_{ij} = \text{cov}(X_i, X_j)$ and $\|\sigma^{ij}\| = \|\sigma_{ij}\|^{-1}$. The ellipsoid of concentration for $(X_1, \ldots, X_k)$ is defined by

$$\sum_{i,j=1}^{k} \sigma^{ij}(X_i - EX_i)(X_j - EX_j) = k + 2,$$

where EX_i is the expected value of X_i. An unbiased multivariate estimate is said to have minimum concentration ellipsoid if its ellipsoid is contained in (equality allowed) the ellipsoid of concentration for every other estimate which is unbiased for the class of populations considered.

For both the univariate and multivariate cases, estimates can be obtained which are optimum in the sense that their use tends to minimize the maximum risk from estimation errors. Estimates with this property are called minimax estimates and are described on page 39.

The problem of point estimation of a probability distribution can be complicated with respect to efficiency evaluation. If the estimation is for the value of the distribution at an identified point, the distribution value represents a probability constant and the methods for determining the efficiency of an estimate for a probability constant can be used. If the distribution is estimated over a region, however, the efficiency of the estimate can be measured in many ways. Some of these efficiency evaluation methods depend on expected variation considerations; others depend on minimax considerations, etc. Chapter 10 contains descriptions for some of these methods.

Confidence Region Efficiency

A method of determining information equivalence that appears to be satisfactory for confidence regions consists in first converting each confidence region of the class considered into the corresponding significance test. Then two confidence regions are taken to be information equivalent if the significance tests they yield are information equivalent.

Significance Test Efficiency

Finally, let us specify when two significance tests are to be adjudged information equivalent. First, the tests are required to have the same significance level. Second, they have equivalent power functions for the alternative hypotheses of importance. This definition reduces the problem to that of deciding when two tests have equivalent power functions for a specified class of alternatives.

One possible definition of power function equivalence over a set of alternative hypotheses is to require that the over-all difference between the power function values is zero. Here all alternative hypotheses considered might receive equal emphasis in determining the over-all difference between the two power functions. Another procedure consists in restricting the set of alternatives to a single hypothesis which is of predominant interest or representative of the alternatives of major interest. Then power function equivalence implies equal power function values for this alternative hypothesis.

The asymptotic case, namely where the sample sizes for the tests are very large, is usually much easier to handle than cases with at most moderate sample sizes. For this case, asymptotic power function equality, for entire classes of alternative hypotheses, can often be obtained for two tests by increasing the sample size for one of the tests by a fixed ratio. However, an asymptotic analysis does not necessarily furnish a good indication of the situation that exists for medium and small sized samples.

Most Stringent Tests

The concept of a most stringent test can be used for situations where a most powerful test does not exist. Although not so helpful in evaluating efficiencies, this concept is useful in determining tests that are optimum in the sense of being most stringent. For a specified family of tests and a specified class of alternative hypotheses, a most stringent test always exists.

Now let us consider the definition of a most stringent test (see, e.g., ref. 307). For each test, compute its power function values for the alternative hypotheses of the specified class. Consider the envelope of the power function values for the various tests (i.e., the maximum power over all tests for each of the alternative hypotheses). For each test, determine the maximum difference (over all alternative hypotheses) between the power function for this test and the corresponding value for the envelope of power function values. A test is said to be most stringent (for the family of tests and class of alternative hypotheses considered) if the value of its maximum difference is minimum for all of the tests considered.

Remark About Asymptotic Efficiencies

The fact that a procedure has an asymptotic efficiency of zero does not necessarily imply that this procedure is useless for large sample sizes. The variance of an estimate with zero asymptotic efficiency can tend to zero as the sample size increases. Also the power function of a test with zero asymptotic efficiency can tend to unity at all alternative hypotheses that are considered. An asymptotic efficiency is a relative rather than an absolute measure of the usefulness of a statistical procedure.

DETERMINATION OF ADEQUATE SAMPLE SIZES

A problem somewhat related to the evaluation of efficiencies is that of determining when the sample size for a nonsequential procedure is sufficiently large to yield an adequate amount of information about the population property investigated. This involves specifying the manner in which information is measured and also deciding on what is considered to be an adequate amount of information. The methods of measuring information for the efficiency case are applicable to the determination of adequate sample sizes. Additional measures of information are also available. The decision as to what constitutes an adequate amount of information is ordinarily a judgment of the experimenter which, to avoid bias, should be made without knowledge about the outcome of the experiment. Given the method for measuring information and a specification of the minimum amount that is adequate, any sample size at least equal to smallest size which yields the specified amount of information is considered to be satisfactory. For brevity, the smallest of the satisfactory sample sizes for a procedure is referred to as the adequate sample size for that procedure.

In many cases, the amount of information yielded by a procedure for given sample sizes is only approximately evaluated. Sometimes, the approximate evaluation is of an estimation nature. That is, the situation is such that the total sample can be obtained in two stages and the information furnished for given total sample sizes can be estimated from the first-stage sample. The number of additional sample values for the second stage equals the adequate sample size determined from the estimate of information less the sample size for the first stage. This two-stage approach is of a rough nature and, in some cases, can have noticeable conditional effects on the probability properties of the statistical procedure. However, it is the best available for many situations; also, the conditional effects are usually unimportant when the size of the second-stage sample is not small compared to the size of the first-stage sample.

To minimize conditional effects from the estimation of the criterion by two-stage sampling, the first-stage sample should be no larger than that which is necessary to obtain reasonably accurate estimation. To at least roughly accomplish this, the first-stage sample can itself be taken in two stages (so that three-stage sampling is used). The first of these substages is definitely smaller than needed for reasonably accurate estimation of the criterion. On the basis of this substage sample, an estimate is obtained for the variation of the estimate of the criterion that will be obtained from the entire first-stage sample. This estimate of the variation, which is a function of the total sample size for the first-stage, is used to determine the sample size for the first-stage. That is, the first-stage sample size should be such that the estimate for the criterion obtained from the first-stage sample is reasonably accurate but not overly so. A method of accomplishing this consists in specifying a maximum value for the estimate of the variation of the estimate of the criterion value. The first-stage sample size is the smallest value yielding an estimated variation less than this specified maximum. Here mean square error, coefficient of variation, etc. might be used to represent the variation of the estimate of the criterion.

For point estimation of a univariate probability constant, mean square error furnishes one measure of information. When the estimate is determined on the basis of a loss function (e.g., minimax estimation), the risk associated with an estimate represents a measure of information. Also, the coefficient of variation, or unity minus the coefficient of variation, can be used to measure the information furnished by an estimate. In this handbook, the coefficient of variation is expressed in terms of the mean square error. That is, the coefficient of variation equals the reciprocal of the value of the probability constant estimated times the square root the expected value of the square of the difference between the values of the estimate and the probability constant. In some cases, modified forms of the coefficient of variation are useful (see page 298). For point estimation situations, the sample size is deemed adequate when the value of the criterion (mean square error, risk, coefficient of variation, etc.) is at most equal to a specified value which is considered to be sufficiently small.

In the case of confidence regions, the general approach of conversion to significance tests and determining adequate sample sizes for these tests can often be utilized. For confidence intervals, a method that is sometimes useful consists in considering each variable endpoint to be an estimate. Adequate sample sizes are determined for each such estimate (there may be only one) and the maximum of these sample sizes is considered to be adequate for the confidence interval. Another method consists in using a first-stage sample to estimate the difference, as a function of the total sample size, between each variable endpoint and the true value of the population constant to which the confidence interval applies. Then the total sample size is considered to be adequate when these estimated differences (there may be only one) are sufficiently small. Some special methods are used in determining adequate sample sizes for confidence bands for distributions (see pages 315 and 350).

For tests, the principal methods of measuring information are those mentioned for determination of efficiencies. That is, power function considerations furnish the major basis for determining adequate sample sizes. A method that is often applicable consists in specifying a simple alternative hypothesis that is representative of the alternatives of principal interest and requiring that the power at this alternative have at least a stated value. Then the smallest sample size such that at least this stated power occurs for this alternative is considered to be adequate.

In some senses, required sample sizes are adequate sample sizes for tolerance regions. That is, specification of the type of tolerance region (number of statistical blocks, etc.) and its properties (value for the expected coverage, a given probability of a stated coverage, etc.) determine the required sample size for this tolerance region. However, at least for point estimation, the mean square error and/or the coefficient of variation for the amount of population coverage may also be of interest. To obtain a tolerance region which has stated properties and a specified value for the mean square error or the coefficient of variation of its coverage, the type of region is changed.

For decision theory results, the value of the expected loss (risk) furnishes the basis for determination of adequate sample sizes. That is, a maximum allowable value for the risk is specified. The smallest sample size for which the risk has at most this value is considered to be adequate.

PRECISION LEVELS OF NONPARAMETRIC PROCEDURES

Discussion

Nonparametric procedures can have several different levels of probability precision. For the special purposes of this handbook, the precision levels are divided into the three categories: exact, theoretical-approximate, and judgment-empirical. Here an exact procedure is one that has precisely determined properties. The probability properties of a theoretical-approximate procedure are not exact but do have some theoretical basis. Judgment-empirical procedures are usually obtained from judgment-type interpolations and/or extrapolations based on the results for special cases. Following are more detailed descriptions of these three categories for precision levels of nonparametric procedures.

Exact Procedures

The most desirable type of information procedure is that with precise probability properties. For point estimates, this implies that the representative property required of the estimate is exactly satisfied. As an example, the sample mean is a precise expected value estimate of the mean of the population sampled; i.e., the expected value of the sample mean exactly equals the population mean. When the procedure is a confidence region, exactness implies that the confidence coefficient value is precisely determined on the basis of the procedure assumptions. Similarly, for significance tests, the concept of exact probability properties refers to precise determination of the significance level value. In some cases, exact procedures (e.g., tests) are obtained through use of an independent random process. Then the procedures are said to be randomized-exact. For brevity, procedures that are randomized-exact are sometimes referred to as randomized procedures.

Theoretical-Approximate Procedures

Significance tests and confidence regions with unknown but bounded probability levels represent theoretical-approximate procedures of one type. That is, the procedure assumptions are not sufficient to precisely determine the probability value (significance level or confidence coefficient) for the procedure considered. However, this value is known to lie between two bounds that are determined by the procedure assumptions. If these bounds are not too far apart, the test or confidence region can still be useful even though its probability level is not precisely known. For some general types of situations, procedures with imprecise probability properties of this kind are about the best that can be obtained. One method of deriving bounded probability results is on the basis of Tchebycheff-type inequalities. Chapter 6 is devoted to inequalities of this nature.

Procedures of another kind can be obtained by expanding exact probability expressions (perhaps for probability constants) and neglecting terms which are believed to be unimportant. Expressions with neglected terms are used for expected value determinations as well as in deriving approximate tests and confidence intervals. If the omitted terms are of a small order of magnitude, the approximate procedure should be acceptable for nearly all practical situations.

Use of the first few terms of the Gram-Charlier A or of the Edgeworth series expansion for a distribution function (or frequency function) represents an example of the use of expansions. Many approximate procedures are based on the assumption that the univariate distribution encountered can be adequately represented by the first four or the first seven terms of its standardized Edgeworth series. Nonparametric generalizations of the first seven terms of its Edgeworth expansion are sometimes considered for approximating a distribution. The Pearson system of distributions, based on the first four population moments, is also sometimes used for approximating probability distributions, etc.

Although the expansions are not necessarily made on the basis of the number of observations, this is often the case. Asymptotic results are usually derived from the first terms of expansions based on numbers of observations. Thus asymptotic procedures represent special cases of expansions with neglected terms. By retaining additional terms, results can be obtained which are reasonably accurate for much smaller numbers of observations than are required for the asymptotic case. Unfortunately, results based on extra terms are frequently much more complicated than the corresponding asymptotic results.

For expansions made on the basis of the numbers of observations, ordinarily the error involved is only stated as an order term. That is, if n is the number of observations, the error term is usually stated in the form $O(n^{-a})$ or $o(n^{-b})$, so that the order of magnitude of the error is specified but its explicit expression is not stated.

Specifying minimum numbers of observations for the applicability of a procedure based on an expansion in terms of number of observations is not easy for the nonparametric case. The method usually adopted for confidence intervals and tests consists in relating the allowable range of probability values to the number of observations and then specifying minimum numbers which are larger than those ordinarily needed for most situations of interest. The procedure of requiring a number of observations that is larger than the number needed for most situations of interest is also applied to point estimates. This conservative method of specifying lower bounds for numbers of observations eliminates some cases for which application is valid, but tends to assure that the statistical procedures are not used for cases where they are greatly in error.

Virtually all of the minimum numbers of observations stated for applicability of approximate procedures were developed by the author of the handbook on a judgment basis. That is, the expressions for minimum numbers of observations are not the responsibility of the authors of the articles on which the statistical procedures are based, although these expressions are based on the material of these and related articles. Determination of these expressions for minimum numbers of observations represents some of the developmental-type research that was performed by the author of the handbook to increase the practical value of the procedures.

Judgment-Empirical Procedures

Most of the judgment-empirical results are based on investigation of the sensitivity of a parametric procedure to moderate changes in the assumptions used in its derivation. A procedure which remains reasonably accurate for diverse sets of assumptions can be considered approximately nonparametric even though it was originally derived on a parametric basis.

The judgment-empirical procedures presented are ordinarily obtained from interpolations and/or extrapolations based on the results for a few or a moderate number of special cases. These special cases can be exact, theoretical–approximate, experimental (e.g., determined by a sampling scheme), etc. One method consists in computing the first few moments for the statistic of the procedure considered (for each of the special cases). Then, for each case, the distribution of this statistic is approximated on the basis of these moments (e.g., by the first few terms of the Edgeworth series expansion, etc.), and approximate properties of the procedure are derived on the basis of this distribution.

The established accuracy for a judgment–empirical procedure is usually definitely lower than that for a corresponding theoretical–approximate procedure. However, a procedure that has both a theoretical–approximate and a judgment–empirical basis ordinarily has a definitely stronger established accuracy level than a procedure which has only a theoretical–approximate basis.

TYPES OF POINT ESTIMATION CONSIDERED

The most commonly encountered estimation procedures for the nonparametric field are expected value estimation, median estimation, and minimax estimation. This section contains a short description for each of these three methods of estimation. As already mentioned, in this handbook no distinction is made between an estimate and an estimator, with estimate being the word used.

A statistic is an expected value (unbiased) estimate of a given population probability constant if the value of the probability constant is the mean of the probability distribution for this statistic. A statistic is a median estimate of a probability constant if the value of the constant is a median of the distribution for this statistic. Here an expected value estimate or a median estimate can be exact or approximate. A statistic is an approximate expected value estimate if its expected value approximately equals the probability constant, etc.

The concept of a risk function is introduced for the determination of a minimax estimate. Here a sample is drawn from a population whose probability distribution is known to belong to a family $\{g\}$ of probability distributions. The problem is to estimate a probability constant C_G of the population yielding the sample, where G is the probability distribution of this population. The loss that results from using an estimate h (a function of the sample values) is denoted by $L(h, C_G)$, and the risk function equals the expected value of the loss function subject to the condition that G is the distribution of the population sampled. The square of the difference between the estimate and the constant estimated, i.e. $(h-C_G)^2$, is often the expression used for $L(h, C_G)$. Given the risk function, the minimax choice for the estimate h is any function of the sample values that belongs to the class of allowable estimates and minimizes

$$\sup_{G\epsilon\{g\}}[E_G L(h, C_G)]$$

with respect to this class. This estimate is optimum in the sense that, on the average, it minimizes the maximum risk with respect to the family of possible distributions.

Expected value and minimax procedures also are used for estimating distribution functions and frequency functions over specified sets of points. A function of the sample values $h(x_1, \ldots, x_k)$, $k \geqslant 1$, is an expected value estimate of a probability distribution $G(x_1, \ldots, x_k)$ over a set of values for $(x_1, \ldots, x_k)$ if

$$Eh(x_1, \ldots, x_k) = G(x_1, \ldots, x_k)$$

(exactly or approximately) for all the points of this set. It is a minimax estimate if the supremum, with respect to the class of probability distributions considered, of a specified "average" of the values of

$$E_G L[h(x_1, \ldots, x_k), G(x_1, \ldots, x_k)]$$

over the set of points considered is minimum.

PERMUTATION TESTS

A type of significance test that has great generality of application and can often be constructed so that it has a high efficiency is the permutation test (see, e.g., ref. 244). Let $X(1), \ldots, X(n)$ be n univariate observations. These n values are considered to be fixed numbers, and probability enters only with regard to a specified class of permutations of these numbers or their signs. As an example, the class of permutations might consist of the 2^n ways of assigning + and − signs to the $|X(i)|$. As another example, the class of permutations might consist of the $n!$ ways of arranging the $X(i)$ in a line. From a probability viewpoint, all the permutations of the class considered are taken to be equally likely under the null hypothesis for the permutation test. A common method of assuring that all permutations are equally likely under the null hypothesis is to use an appropriate randomization operation on the data or on the sources for the data.

A permutation test is defined as follows: Let $t\{X(i)\}=t\{X(1),\ldots,X(n)\}$ be a specified function of the n observations while the number of permutations in the class considered is A. For each possible value of $\{X(i)\}=\{X(1),\ldots,X(n)\}$ let

$$t_1\{X(i)\} \leqslant t_2\{X(i)\} \leqslant \ldots \leqslant t_A\{X(i)\}$$

be the ordered values of $t\{X(i)\}$ for the A permutations of $X(1),\ldots,X(n)$. Given a significance level α, let K be the value of A minus the largest integer contained in $A\alpha$. Use $T^+\{X(i)\}$ to denote the number of the $t_u\{X(i)\}$ whose values exceed $t_K\{X(i)\}$ and $T^0\{X(i)\}$ to denote the number whose values equal $t_K\{X(i)\}$; also let

$$p\{X(i)\}=[A\alpha-T^+\{X(i)\}]/T^0\{X(i)\}$$

for $T^0\{X(i)\}>0$ and $p\{X(i)\}=0$ otherwise. Then the permutation test with null hypothesis H_0 and significance level α is given by

Reject H_0 if $t\{X(i)\}>t_K\{X(i)\}$ for the observed $\{X(i)\}$. Reject H_0 with probability $p\{X(i)\}$ if $t\{X(i)\}=t_K\{X(i)\}$. Otherwise do not reject H_0.

By suitable choice of the function $t\{X(i)\}$, one-sided or two-sided tests can be obtained.

CONFIDENCE INTERVALS FROM TESTS

The problem of determining significance tests from confidence regions has already been considered in this chapter. Sometimes the converse problem of determining confidence regions for a population probability constant on the basis of significance tests for the value of this constant also arises. If the tests were originally obtained from confidence regions, the solution to this converse problem is straightforward. In some cases, however, the tests were not obtained directly from confidence regions. This is usually the situation for permutation tests and for tests based on observation signs and/or ranks. Then obtaining confidence regions from significance tests is not such a straightforward operation. This section contains an outline of a method for obtaining confidence intervals from tests when the constant considered affects the location of a population distribution function but not its shape.

The tests considered are characterized by the following five requirements. First, the data are a set of univariate observations. Second, the hypothetical value of the probability constant (specified by the null hypothesis) is subtracted from the value for each observation. Third, the test statistic is based on the values of these differences, which are the only place where the value for the probability constant occurs in the test statistic. Fourth, the test statistic is a monotonic function of the hypothetical value for the constant. Fifth, two types of one-sided tests and one type of two-sided tests occur. For one kind of one-sided test, the null hypothesis is rejected if the test statistic exceeds a specified value; for the other type of one-sided test, the null hypothesis is rejected if this statistic is less than a specified value. For the two-sided tests, the null hypothesis is rejected if the test statistic either exceeds a specified value or is less than a specified value.

Let us consider determination of confidence intervals from a one-sided test which has significance level α and rejects the null hypothesis if the test statistic exceeds a specified critical value. First, the observed values are inserted into the test statistic; then the probability constant value for which the test statistic equals the specified critical value is determined. The interval of probability constant values such that the statistic exceeds the critical value is a one-sided confidence interval for the probability constant and has confidence coefficient α; thus, the complementary interval of probability constant values furnishes a one-sided confidence interval with coefficient $1-\alpha$.

A similar method is used for the case of a one-sided test which has significance level α and rejects if the test statistic is less than a specified critical value. First, the probability constant value such that the test statistic equals the specified critical value is determined. Then the interval of probability constant values for which the statistic is less than the critical value is a one-sided confidence interval with coefficient α, and the interval of values such that the statistic is at least equal to this critical value is a one-sided confidence interval with coefficient $1-\alpha$.

Finally, let us consider determination of the corresponding confidence interval for the case of a two-sided test with significance level $\alpha_1+\alpha_2$, where α_1 is the contribution of the upper tail of the test and α_2 is the contribution of the lower tail. Here two values are determined for the probability constant, namely, the value for which the test statistic equals the upper (larger) specified critical value and the value for which the test statistic equals the lower (smaller) specified critical value. The closed interval of values between these two values for the probability constant furnishes a two-sided confidence interval with coefficient $1-\alpha_1-\alpha_2$. Similar results can be obtained from two-sided tests where the critical region is such that the test statistic can equal one or both of the two specified critical values; then the resulting two-sided confidence interval is either half-open or open.

DEFINITIONS FOR INDEPENDENCE, SAMPLE, AND SYMMETRY

Although the concepts of independent observations, a random sample, and a symmetrical population are rather well-known, it seems worthwhile to define them again here. Let $X_1, \ldots, X_n$ be observations which are not necessarily univariate, or expressed in the same types of units, or even of the same dimensionality, and let $F(x_1, \ldots, x_n)$ be the joint distribution function of these observations while $G_i(x_i)$ is the distribution function of X_i $(i=1, \ldots, n)$. Then $X_1, \ldots, X_n$ are statistically independent if and only if

$$F(x_1, \ldots, x_n) = G_1(x_1) \ldots G_n(x_n)$$

for all values of $(x_1, \ldots, x_n)$. In addition, suppose that $X_1, \ldots, X_n$ have the same dimensionality and that corresponding coordinates of these observations have the same meaning and are expressed in the same type of unit. That is, all the first coordinates have the same meaning and are expressed in the same unit (time, feet, pounds, number of flower petals, etc.) and likewise for all the second coordinates (if the observations are not univariate), etc. Then $X_1, \ldots, X_n$ are a random sample, from the population $G(x)$ with x having the same dimensionality as the X's, if

$$F(x_1, \ldots, x_n) = G(x_1) \ldots G(x_n)$$

for all $(x_1, \ldots, x_n)$.

Finally, let us consider when a population is to be considered symmetrical. The univariate population with distribution function $F(x)$ and random variable X is said to be symmetrical about a point φ if

$$P(X \leqslant x) \equiv F(x) = 1 - F[(2\varphi - x) -] \equiv P(X \geqslant 2\varphi - x)$$

for all x.

GENERALIZATION FOR ORDER OF MAGNITUDE NOTATION

When terms of an expansion are neglected, their limiting order of magnitude can be expressed as a general-type function of the quantity with respect to which the expansion is made. The quantity used for expanding is nearly always considered to tend to either zero or infinity. Which limit applies is ordinarily evident from the type of situation considered. In cases of doubt, the limit used is stated explicitly. Suppose the expansion is with respect to a quantity z. Two order expressions that are often used to specify the order of a term, or sum of terms, are denoted by $O(z)$ and $o(z)$. Let L denote the limit of z. Then

$$O(z) \text{ implies that } \lim_{z \to L} \left[\frac{\text{(terms considered)}}{z} \right] = \text{constant}$$

$$o(z) \text{ implies that } \lim_{z \to L} \left[\frac{\text{(terms considered)}}{z} \right] = 0.$$

Usually $L=0$ for the cases considered in this handbook.

For the purposes of this handbook, the symbols $O(z)$ and $o(z)$ are generalized so as to also specify the order of magnitude of terms that have probability distributions. For a random element Y of the type for which this notation is used in the handbook, the relation $Y=O(z)$ is equivalent to the assertion that z equals $\max(z_1, z_2)$, where the expected value of Y is $O(z_1)$ and the standard deviation of Y is $O(z_2)$. Likewise, $Y=o(z)$ is equivalent to the assertion that z equals $\max(z'_1, z'_2)$, where the expected value of Y is $o(z'_1)$ and the standard deviation of Y is $o(z'_2)$. For example, let the expected value of Y be $5/n$ and the standard deviation of Y be $1/6n^{1/2}$, where n is the number of observations on which the statistic Y is based. Then Y is $O(n^{-1/2})$ for Y of the type for which this notation is used, since the expected value of Y is $O(n^{-1})$ and the standard deviation of Y is $O(n^{-1/2})$. The sense in which an order of magnitude symbol is used can virtually always be determined from the nature of the situation in which it occurs. A more general interpretation of order of magnitude notation is given in ref. 331.

VERIFICATION OF CONTINUITY AND DIFFERENTIABILITY

The question of population continuity can ordinarily be settled on the basis of the type of data considered. If the data are of a conceptually continuous nature (weight, time, length, area, etc.) and the measurements are not too coarse, the population involved can usually be considered to have a continuous distribution function. Strictly speaking, due to limitations in measurement accuracy, the assumption of a continuous population is an idealization which can only be approximated. However, results obtained on the basis of a reasonably close approximation to this idealization are nearly always reasonably accurate.

The measurement accuracy limitation implies that in practice very little generality is lost by assuming that a continuous population has an absolutely continuous distribution function; i.e., that a frequency function (probability density function) always exists for the continuous case. In addition, without much loss of generality for practical situations, this frequency function can be considered to have reasonably well-behaved derivatives of all orders. In practice there is always some limitation on the accuracy to which measurements can be made. Thus observations always come from discrete populations (which can be thought of as grouped continuous populations). This implies that a frequency function can only be specified up to a set of region restrictions that are determined by the measurement limitations; that is, integrations of the frequency function over these regions have fixed values. All frequency functions satisfying these region restrictions are equivalent as far as representing the actual statistical population is concerned. The most well-behaved of these frequency functions can be considered to be the one that occurs. Since region restrictions ordinarily do not have much effect on the ability of a curve to be of a smooth nature, not much generality would seem to be lost by assuming that the best behaved frequency function has reasonably well-behaved derivatives of all orders.

CONVERSION OF DATA TO CONTINUOUS FORM

In principle, data of any type can be converted to a continuous form where the joint distribution of the converted data differs very slightly from the joint distribution of the original data. Namely, for univariate observations, let an infinitesimally small random value from a continuous population be added to each observation value. For the multivariate case, an infinitesimally small random value from a continuous population is added to each coordinate of every multivariate observation.

In practice, obtaining a random value, infinitesimal or otherwise, from an exactly continuous distribution is impossible. However, many nonparametric procedures use the continuity property only to the extent of assuring that no ties occur among observations or among specified functions of observations. If the infinitesimal random values added to the observations are a random sample, which is a valid way to obtain these values, the randomization method of breaking ties is virtually always satisfactory for one class of situations. These are the situations where the only use made of continuity is to establish an ordering among the values within one or more sets of observations or functions of observations. Here, of course, the functions of the observations are such that they would have zero probability for ties if the data were truly continuous; also, any randomization process used has the property that all orderings of the tied values are equally likely.

The randomization method of converting data to a continuous form is used directly in Chapter 5. It is used indirectly in Chapter 7, in the sense that randomization is suggested as one method of breaking ties. The randomization method can also be used in one or two places in Chapter 8 and in many places in Chapter 9.

Of course, in some cases the slight difference between the distribution of the converted data and that of the original data can be important. Then the method outlined here for converting data to a continuous form should not be used. However, the conversion to a continuous form should nearly always be appropriate when the data are of a conceptually continuous nature but the measurements are coarse. Also, with suitable interpretation, this conversion can be useful for many cases where the data are of a fundamentally discontinuous nature (e.g., discrete with only a few possible values).

APPROXIMATION DISTRIBUTIONS

Introduction

One method for theoretical–approximate analysis consists in determining the first few moments for the statistic considered and approximating its distribution on the basis of these moments. Then approximate probability properties of the statistic are derived through the use of this distribution. This section contains descriptions for several families of distributions that can be used to approximate the distribution function (or frequency function) of a continuous population on the basis of its first few moments. Explicitly considered are the Gram-Charlier *A* series, the Edgeworth series, generalizations of the Edgeworth series, and the Pearson system of distributions. A bibliography for some other results of this nature is given at the end of the section. To aid in the use of the Gram-Charlier *A* and the Edgeworth series (including generalizations), values of $\varphi(x)$ are given in Table 1 at the end of the handbook.

Gram-Charlier A *Series*

The first five terms of the Gram-Charlier *A* series expansion for the distribution function of a univariate random variable X are given by (also see ref. 118, pages 222–27)

$$\begin{aligned} F(x) = {} & \Phi[(x-EX)/\sigma X] - (\alpha_3 X)\Phi^{(3)}[(x-EX)/\sigma X]/3! \\ & + (\alpha_4 X - 3)\Phi^{(4)}[(x-EX)/\sigma X]/4! \\ & + [10\alpha_3 X - \mu_5 X/(\sigma X)^5]\Phi^{(5)}[(x-EX)/\sigma X]/5! \\ & + [30 - 15\alpha_4 X + \mu_6 X/(\sigma X)^6]\Phi^{(6)}[(x-EX)/\sigma X]/6! \end{aligned}$$

The first few terms of its Gram-Charlier *A* series often furnish a reasonable approximation to the distribution function of a continuous population. However, if the moment values differ noticeably from the corresponding moments for the case of normality, the resulting approximation may not even satisfy the basic requirements for a distribution function (see ref. 38).

Edgeworth Series and Generalizations

For Edgeworth series, the distribution function of X is expanded in the form (also see ref. 118, pages 227–31).

$$\begin{aligned} F(x) = {} & \Phi[(x-EX)/\sigma X] - (\alpha_3 X)\Phi^{(3)}[(x-EX)/\sigma X]/3! \\ & + (\alpha_4 X - 3)\Phi^{(4)}[(x-EX)/\sigma X]/4! \\ & + 10(\alpha_3 X)^2\Phi^{(6)}[(x-EX)/\sigma X]/6! \end{aligned}$$

$$+[10\alpha_3 X-\mu_5 X/(\sigma X)^5]\Phi^{(5)}[(x-EX)/\sigma X]/5!$$
$$-35(\alpha_3 X)(\alpha_4 X-3)\Phi^{(7)}[(x-EX)/\sigma X]/7!$$
$$-280(\alpha_3 X)^3\Phi^{(9)}[(x-EX)/\sigma X]/9!+\dots.$$

As for the Gram-Charlier A series, if the moment values differ noticeably from those for normality, an approximation based on the first few terms of this Edgeworth series expansion may not be a distribution function (see ref. 38).

A generalized form of the first seven terms of the Edgeworth series is

$$F(x)=\Phi[(x-A)/B]+C\Phi^{(4)}[(x-A)/B] + D(\alpha_3 X)^2\Phi^{(6)}[(x-A)/B]+g[(x-A)/B],$$

where, subject to the conditions that $F(x)$ has the properties of a distribution function for the range of x values considered and that $g(z)$ is an odd function of z, the function g and the constants A, B, C, D are arbitrary.

Again requiring the function g to be odd and $F(x)$ to have the properties of a distribution function for the range of x values considered, a further generalization is furnished by

$$F(x)=\Phi[(x-A)/B]+C\Phi^{(4)}[(x-A)/B]+D\Phi^{(6)}[(x-A)/B]+g[(x-A)B]$$

where, subject to the imposed conditions, $g(z)$, A, B, C, D are arbitrary.

Cornish-Fisher Expansions

For statistics whose moments are functions of the number of observations n, such as the sample mean and sample percentiles, an inverse use of the Edgeworth series yields a function of the statistic and its moments that is approximately normally distributed. Also, approximate expressions can be obtained for percentage points of a statistic in terms of its moments and the corresponding percentage points of the standardized normal distribution.

Let X be the statistic and $EX=a$, $\sigma^2 X=b^2/n$, $\alpha_3 X=c/\sqrt{n}$, and $\alpha_4 X=d/n$. Then the distribution of the random variable

$$\frac{X-a}{b/\sqrt{n}}-\frac{c}{6\sqrt{n}}\left[\left(\frac{X-a}{b/\sqrt{n}}\right)^2-1\right]-\frac{d}{24n}\left[\left(\frac{X-a}{b/\sqrt{n}}\right)^3-3\left(\frac{X-a}{b/\sqrt{n}}\right)\right] + \frac{c^2}{36n}\left[4\left(\frac{X-a}{b/\sqrt{n}}\right)^3-7\left(\frac{X-a}{b/\sqrt{n}}\right)\right]$$

is standardized normal plus terms that are $O(n^{-3/2})$. Let θ_p be the $100p$ percentage point of X. Then

$$\frac{\theta_p-a}{b/\sqrt{n}}=-K_p+\frac{c}{6\sqrt{n}}(K_p{}^2-1)-\frac{d}{24n}(K_p{}^3-3K_p)+\frac{c^2}{36n}(2K_p{}^3-5K_p)$$

plus terms that are $O(n^{-3/2})$. For further information about expansions of these types, see ref. 108 and ref. 275 (pages 156–59).

Pearson System of Distributions

For the continuous univariate case, many of the parametric frequency functions $y=f(x)$ that have received attention satisfy a differential equation of the form

$$dy/dx=(x+a)y/(b_0+b_1x+b_2x^2),$$

where a and the b's are constants which can be expressed in terms of the first four moments of $f(x)$. Thus, through use of this differential equation, knowledge of the first four moments of a distribution uniquely determines a frequency function which can be used to approximate the frequency function yielding these moments. Experience indicates that the Pearson system frequency function determined in this manner often furnishes a reasonably close approximation to the actual distribution. Hence evaluation of the first four moments of a continuous random variable and determination of the corresponding Pearson system frequency function represents one way of approximately determining probability properties for this variable. A full account of the Pearson system and its application is given in ref. 160; also see ref. 114 and 275.

Bibliography for Additional Results

The reference material given here is concerned with approximation distributions of some other types and with properties and generalizations of the families of distributions that are explicitly considered in this section. In particular, approximation of $F(x)$ by an expression of the form $1-(1+x^c)^{-b}$ is examined in ref. 83 and 233, while use of the Gram-Charlier B series to approximate the distribution of a discrete random variable is considered in ref. 72. The abbreviated bibliography given is the following: Ref. 38, 72, 83, 117, 123, 166, 167, 233, 369, 379, 468, 519.

ADVANTAGE OF PROCEDURES USING OBSERVATIONS SYMMETRICALLY

Many of the procedures given in this handbook are based on the assumption of a random sample. As a preliminary step in the application of such a procedure, a separate significance test could be used to investigate the validity of the random sample hypothesis. For some situations, use of this extra test could have a strong conditional effect on the joint distribution of the observations; then the validity of the procedure (which re-uses the observations under the assumption that they are a random sample) becomes very questionable. For an important class of statistical procedures based on univariate observations, however, preliminary tests of the random sample hypothesis can be devised which have no effect on the probability properties of the procedure considered. These are the procedures which are based exclusively on statistics which are symmetrical with respect to use of the observation values.

Let the observation values be univariate and denoted by $X(1), \ldots, X(n)$. A statistic based on these observation values is said to be symmetrical with respect to their use if the value of this statistic is independent of which observation is called $X(1)$, which observation is called $X(2)$, etc. Examples of statistics that make symmetrical use of the observations $X(1), \ldots, X(n)$ are $M(i)$, $S(i)$, $M'_t(i)$, $M_t(i)$, and, for each value of i, $X[i]$.

When the procedure considered makes symmetrical use of the univariate observation values, this procedure is independent of a random sample test which is based entirely on the locations of the observations in a sequence such that the sequence positions do not depend on the observation values. One method of obtaining such a sequence consists in letting $X(1)$ be the first observation whose value is determined, $X(2)$ the second observation whose value is determined, etc.; i.e., the observations are placed in a time-ordered sequence. The randomness tests of Chapter 5 are based exclusively on the positions of univariate observations in an appropriate sequence.

U *STATISTICS*

Let $\mathbf{X}_1, \ldots, \mathbf{X}_n$ be n independent k-variate random variables (perhaps univariate), where $\mathbf{X}_u = (X_u^{(1)}, \ldots, X_u^{(k)})$, while $G(\mathbf{x}_1, \ldots, \mathbf{x}_r)$ is a function of $r(r \leqslant n)$ vectors $\mathbf{x}_v = (x_v^{(1)}, \ldots, x_v^{(k)})$. A U statistic is a function of the random variables $\mathbf{X}_1, \ldots, \mathbf{X}_n$ that is of the form

$$\sum{}' G(\mathbf{X}_{s(1)}, \ldots, \mathbf{X}_{s(r)})/n(n-1)\ldots(n-r+1),$$

where the summation extends over the $n(n-1)\ldots(n-r+1)$ ways of selecting values for $[s(1), \ldots, s(r)]$ by choosing r different integers from $1, \ldots, n$ and permuting them in every possible fashion.

If $\mathbf{X}_1, \ldots, \mathbf{X}_n$ are a random sample, the U statistics have some optimal properties as unbiased estimates. These optimal properties are considered in Chapter 7. For additional information about U statistics, see ref. 229, 243, and 186 (pages 137–39, 223–35).

LIFE-TESTING AND CENSORED DATA—DISCUSSION

For some experimental situations involving univariate observations, only the values of specified order statistics of a set of observations are available. In some cases, the fact that only specified order statistics are available is a deliberate part of the experiment. In many cases, however, the experiment was intended to evaluate the other order statistics but failed to do so. In all cases, the statistical procedures applied must be based exclusively on the order statistics whose values are available. Much of the material considered in this handbook is based on specified order statistics of sets of univariate observations and thus is applicable to situations of this nature.

Censoring of a set of univariate observations is a special case of the situation where only specified order statistics are available. Usually, the censoring is an accidental occurrence. For life-testing situations, however, deliberate censoring can often be used to advantage (see, e.g., Chapter 8). Here a group of items are life-tested until a specified number have failed. The observation values are the times to failure (or some increasing continuous monotonic function of time to failure) for these items. Thus the observations are the smallest order statistics of a specified set of observations. Often substantial time and/or cost can be saved, without loss of efficiency, by starting with a larger set of items, discontinuing the experiment when only a relatively small percentage of the items have failed, and using statistical procedures based on the available order statistics. Chapter 8 contains a more detailed discussion of this possibility for the case of investigating smaller population percentiles.

A random type of censoring occurs for some of the sequential life testing situations that are considered in Chapter 11. That is, only the smallest order statistics of a sample are used, but the largest order statistic that needs to be evaluated is a random determination. Random censoring can also occur when the allowable values for univariate observations are restricted to a specified set; e.g., this is the case if the possible values are truncated from above and/or below. Some procedures for investigating a distribution over specified restricted sets of points are given in Chapters 10 and 11; in particular, many of the nonsequential tests and some of the decision results given in Chapter 11 for categorical data are applicable to this situation.

CONSIDERATIONS IN CHOICE OF HYPOTHESES

Usually, a test is considered to have a null hypothesis and an alternative hypothesis (although, in one of the presentations of Chapter 11, there are two alternative hypotheses, so that one of three eligible hypotheses is selected on the basis of the test). Then the region of possible hypotheses is divided into three parts. One part is associated with the situation represented by the null hypothesis, another part is associated with the alternative hypothesis, and the third part consists of hypotheses that are not associated with either the null or the alternative hypothesis. That is, if the true hypothesis falls in the indifference region, not much loss occurs with respect to falsely considering that the null hypothesis is true or that the alternative hypothesis is true. However, a substantial loss occurs if the true hypothesis falls in the null hypothesis region but is considered to fall in the alternative hypothesis region, or vice versa.

The first step in selecting a null and an alternative hypothesis is to specify the class of hypotheses that is to be considered. Next, on the basis of the technical aspects of the experimentation to be performed, the region of possible hypotheses is divided into the null hypothesis associated region, the alternative hypothesis associated region, and the indifference region. Ideally, if general composite hypotheses were permissible, the null hypothesis would consist of the null hypothesis associated region and the alternative hypothesis would consist of the alternative hypothesis region. Unfortunately, the tests considered seldom allow for the use of such general hypotheses. Consequently, subject to the permissible degree of generality (which may require simple hypotheses), a null hypothesis is chosen which is considered to be representative of the null hypothesis associated region and an alternative hypothesis is chosen which is representative of the alternative hypothesis associated region. The test is then based on these null and alternative hypotheses.

Similar considerations apply to tests with three or more hypotheses and to statistical decision theory procedures. When three or more hypotheses are involved, however, indifference regions with several different levels of indifference can occur. In decision theory, this situation can be handled by using hypotheses to represent some or all of the indifference regions and by using a risk function that allows for the various levels of indifference.

USE OF RANDOM RANKS

As noted in Chapter 2, many different kinds of values can be used to represent the ranks of a set of univariate observations. The principal requirement is that the ranks have the same ordering, with respect to algebraic value, as the corresponding observations. That is, the smallest of the set of rank values is the rank of the smallest observation, etc. In particular, the values used for a set of ranks could be obtained as a random sample from some completely specified univariate population. Rank values obtained in this way are called random ranks. The probabilistic manner in which the rank values are obtained is taken into consideration in determining the properties of tests based on random ranks.

The use of random ranks to obtain significance tests, rather than ranks with fixed values, has both advantages and disadvantages. One advantage is that specified alternative hypotheses (of a parametric nature) can often be emphasized by suitable choice of the probability distribution that yields the random ranks.

Another advantage is that the development of approximate tests is relatively easy when random ranks are used; also, tests that have already been developed are applicable in some cases. For many situations where the use of random ranks is appropriate, the null hypothesis implies that replacement of each observation by its rank results in the ranks being a random sample from the population which yielded their values. That is, the properties of the experiment, in combination with the random method used to obtain the set of ranks, are such that this situation occurs. In particular, if the observations are ordered in some manner that does not depend on their values, so that the corresponding ordering is obtained for the ranks of these observations, this ordering has no conditional effect on the joint distribution of the ranks. This random sample property of the ranks allows an approximate null distribution for a test statistic to be determined without much difficulty when the number of observations is not too small. Namely, the first few moments of this statistic under the null hypothesis are determined and used as a basis for approximating the null distribution (by the first few terms of the Edgeworth series, of the Gram-Charlier series, by the Pearson curves, etc.).

The principal disadvantages of the use of random ranks are that additional variation is introduced into the data and that additional effort is required in determining the values of these ranks. Whether the advantages outweigh the disadvantages depends on the particular situation being considered.

Some situations occur where the values of the observations are treated as if they were ranks. That is, the tests are conditional in that the values of the observations, or a specified function of the observations, are considered to be fixed numbers. Situations of this nature are not to be confused with the use of random ranks, which are not considered to be fixed numbers in the tests where they are used.

None of the presentations given in the handbook involve the use of random ranks. However, in nearly all cases, parallel tests based on random ranks can be obtained from tests based on fixed ranks; that is, the fixed ranks (perhaps observation values) are replaced by random ranks in the test statistic. Of course, the null distribution of the test statistic usually must be redetermined when this replacement is made.

As mentioned above, in some cases direct use can be made of tests that have already been developed for sampling from completely specified populations. The uniform (rectangular) population $[0, 1]$, the standardized normal population, and the population with frequency function e^{-x} $(x \geqslant 0)$ are examples of populations for which a number of tests have been developed. Tests that have been developed for parametric situations (one or more unknown parameters) are also useful in some cases. Namely, when the type of test is appropriate and the completely specified population is a special case of the parametric population but corresponding tests have not been developed for this completely specified population.

Chapter 5

TESTS OF RANDOMNESS

INTRODUCTION

Discussion

Many nonparametric procedures are based on the assumption of a random sample of univariate observations. Also randomness of a set of univariate observations is sometimes itself the property investigated. Consequently, it is desirable to have procedures for testing whether a set of univariate observations constitutes a random sample. This chapter presents some nonparametric procedures of this type; that is, the null hypothesis tested is that a given set of observations is a random sample. These procedures are based on runs above and below the median, runs up and down, correlation coefficient type statistics, etc. All of the randomness tests presented are based on the placement of the observations in an appropriate type of sequence. This sequence has the property that the test is based on the positions of the observations and that these positions are suitable for investigating the alternative hypotheses of interest. A valuable property of these randomness tests is that their use does not result in any conditional probability effect on procedures which re-use the same observations in a symmetrical fashion.

A type of situation which falls under the heading of a random sample investigation is the testing of a set of digits for randomness (e.g., a "random" digit table). This situation is of a specialized nature and not of much interest to the experimental statistician. Consequently, no material that is specifically for handling this problem is presented.

For multidimensional cases, randomness itself is often the property of direct and major interest. For example, the contagious properties of a lattice arrangement of plants to a specified kind of disease might be examined. No procedures are presented for this multidimensional type of situation, but a discussion and a short bibliography are given.

No tests of the random sample null hypothesis are presented for the multivariate case. However, the randomness tests for the univariate case can be used to test the hypothesis that a set of multivariate observations (same dimensionality) are a sample from a multivariate population with this dimensionality. The procedure is to convert each multivariate observation to a univariate observation by use of the same suitable function of the observation coordinates. Then the univariate observations are a random sample if the multivariate observations are a random sample.

Determination of Sequence Order

The first step in applying a test of the random sample hypothesis consists of placing the n univariate observations considered in an appropriate sequence order. Conceptually, the univariate observations can be considered to correspond to bivariate observations with first entries equal to the positions $1, \ldots, n$ and second entries equal to the different univariate observation values. That is, each of the integers $1, \ldots, n$ is used as a first entry, and each of the univariate observations is used as a second entry for the n bivariate observations. Then the sequence order for the univariate observations is determined by placing the bivariate observations in a sequence according to the natural order $(1, \ldots, n)$ of their first entries. Thus, the first univariate observation in the sequence has 1 as first entry of the bivariate observation in which it is contained, etc.

The method of assigning the integers $1, \ldots, n$ to the n univariate observations, in order to form the bivariate observations, depends on the experimental situation considered. That is, this assignment should result in a sequence ordering for the univariate observations that can be used to test their randomness properties against the alternative hypotheses of interest. A common method of assignment is on the basis of the times at which the observations are produced. Then the first observation produced is assigned the integer 1, etc. Sometimes each observation is produced at a different location. Then the observations can be ordered on the basis of location. Also a combination of location and time can be used. In all cases a single set of univariate observations is considered and the value of i in the standard notation $X(i)$ furnishes the position of that observation in the sequence ordering used.

Handling of Ties

For the tests presented in this chapter, the observations can be considered to have continuous distributions. Conceptually, this is accomplished by independently adding an infinitesimally small random value from the same continuous population to each observation value. Practically, ties among observations, and among values of functions of the observations that would have no tied values for continuous data, are broken by the use of independent randomization processes. Here randomization implies that all possible orderings of the values are equally likely for a tied set. For the types of randomness properties investigated in this chapter, the null hypothesis is preserved by the use of this procedure for establishing value orderings for tied sets of values.

The preference for the randomization method of handling ties is due to the fact that it preserves the property that the randomness tests presented have no conditional effect on procedures which re-use the observations in a symmetrical manner (see ref. 454 for case of tests based on ranks). Also, this method is applicable for all the procedures presented. In many cases, only the concept of using randomization to break ties may be needed; that is, no actual application of randomization is made even though tied values occur. As an example, if no ties occur at the sample median, randomization is not needed for tests based on runs above and below the median. As another example, randomization usually is not needed when a test is based on a probability approximation, even though the validity of the approximation may conceptually depend on the use of randomization for breaking any ties that occur. Incidentally, the breaking of ties that occurs for tests of the random sample hypothesis is not carried over to other uses of the same observations. An independent procedure should be used in breaking ties for any re-use that is made of these observations.

Other methods can also be used for handling ties but many of these do not have the property that the resulting randomness tests have no conditional effect on procedures which re-use the observations symmetrically. However, in most cases the conditional effects imposed are probably not very strong. For example, the midrank method of handling ties could be used for the tests that are based on ranks and, unless the ties are extensive, probably does not have much conditional effect on the probability properties of statistical procedures re-using the observations symmetrically.

Basis for Randomness Tests

If the observations are truly a random sample, all possible positionings of their values in the sequence are equally likely, although the converse is not necessarily true (however, see ref. 307). This positioning probability property is the basis for the randomness tests presented. In constructing these tests, the observation values can be considered to be fixed quantities. The only probability properties taken into consideration are those based on the positions of the observations in the sequence. This limitation tends to decrease the efficiency of these tests as compared to tests in which the observation values are considered to be random variables. However, this disadvantage is often offset by the property that tests based entirely on positioning impose no conditional effects on procedures that re-use the same observations symmetrically. Also, in some cases, tests based entirely on sequence positions have high efficiencies with respect to alternative hypotheses that are of interest.

Alternative Hypotheses Considered

Four types of alternative hypotheses are considered for the tests presented for the random sample null hypothesis. These are:

1. The presence of shifts in average level
2. The presence of trends in average level
3. The presence of cyclic movements in average level
4. Specific parametric alternatives.

A more detailed description of these alternatives is given in the Relative Efficiency Summary section (pages 77–80).

Each test presented furnishes protection against one or more of these four types of alternative hypotheses. A brief summary of the available information about the efficiencies of the tests presented, with respect to alternative types 1–3, is given on pages 77–80. Only two tests are presented which have alternatives of type 4, and these tests are optimum for stated situations of a restricted nature.

Testing Dispersion and Other Population Properties

The types of randomness tests that are designed to protect against changes in average population level can also be used to test changes in population dispersion and changes in other population properties which can be represented by a function of a few sample values. The method used consists in first dividing the original sequence into sets of consecutive observations so that each set contains the same number of observations. If the total number of observations is not an integral multiple of the desired number of observations per set, a few observations are randomly deleted so that this condition is satisfied. Then the same function of the observations is evaluated for each of these sets. This function is selected so that the population property of interest is being investigated. For example, if dispersion is the property investigated, the function might be the observed variance of the values of a set.

Under the null hypothesis of a random sample, the values of the functions themselves form a random sample. The position of a function value in the sequence of function values is the same as the position of the set which was used for computing this function value in the sequence of the original observations. In the following randomness test presentations, the alternative hypotheses mentioned can apply to population dispersion or any other population property that can be investigated on the basis of a function of a few sample values.

Random Ranks—Discussion

As mentioned in Chapter 4, random ranks can be useful in obtaining significance tests for situations where the use of ranks is appropriate. In a sense, all of the randomness tests presented in this chapter are based on ranks of some type (the observation values are used as if they were ranks in most cases). The corresponding tests with the fixed rank values replaced by random ranks may be useful for some situations. Namely, special types of alternative hypotheses can be emphasized through choice of the completely specified population yielding the random ranks. Also, reasonably accurate determination of the null distribution of the test statistic is ordinarily not difficult, even for samples that are of only moderate size (see Chapter 4). Although the random ranks are not considered to be fixed values, the resulting tests have the property that they are independent of statistical procedures which re-use the observations in a symmetrical manner.

Tests Based on Chapter 7 Results

The observed values are furnished in a sequence order, can be considered to be from continuous populations, and, if they are a random sample, are independent and have the same probability distribution. Thus, if a pairing is done (without any knowledge about the values of the observations), the difference of the values of a pair of observations has a symmetrical distribution with zero median under the null hypothesis of a random sample. Let the number of observations be even (randomly delete one observation if n is odd). Then N pairs can be formed such that no observation occurs in more than one pair, where N is the largest integer contained in $n/2$. Under the null hypothesis of a random sample, the differences of these pairs are a random sample of size N from a symmetrical population with zero mean (median) which, on the basis of the randomization, can be considered continuous. Many of the symmetrical distribution results of Chapter 7 can be applied directly to test the null hypothesis that these observations have this property. In using this testing method, the values of the observations can be considered fixed with only their positions in the sequence being random; the continuity induced by use of randomization is only applied to assure that no ties occur.

The alternative hypothesis emphasized is determined by the method used to pair the observations. If upward trend is investigated, the differences

$$X(1)-X(2),\ X(3)-X(4), \ldots,\ X(2N-1)-X(2N)$$

could be used in conjunction with a one-sided test with the alternative that the population median is negative. If a shift of unknown direction, occurring somewhere near the middle of the sequence of observations, is investigated, the differences

$$X(1)-X(2N),\ X(2)-X(2N-1),\ldots,X(N)-X(N+1)$$

could be used in conjunction with a two-sided test of whether the population median is zero. If an upward trend followed by a downward trend, with the peak somewhere near the middle of the sequence, is investigated, the differences

$$X(1)-X(2),\ldots,X(N-1)-X(N),\quad X(N+2)-X(N+1),\ldots,X(2N)-X(2N-1)$$

could be used in conjunction with a one-sided test having the alternative that the population median is negative. If a repetitive cycle with five observations between peaks and starting at a peak is investigated, the differences could be

$$X(1)-X(2),\quad X(3)-X(4),\quad X(6)-X(5),\quad X(7)-X(8),\quad X(9)-X(10),\quad X(12)-X(11),\ldots,X(6r+1)-X(6r+2),\quad X(6r+3)-X(6r+4),\quad X(6r+6)-X(6r+5),\ldots$$

where $r=0, 1, \ldots,$ largest integer in $(2N-1)/6$, and the last pair consists of $X(2N-1)$, $X(2N)$. These differences could be used in conjunction with a one-sided test having the alternative that the population median is positive, etc.

Random Sample Testing for Multivariate Case

As already mentioned, randomness tests for the univariate case can be used to test the random sample hypothesis for multivariate cases. This can be accomplished by choosing a real function of the observation coordinates, independently of the values of the observations, and using this function to convert each multivariate observation to a univariate observation. The resulting univariate observations are a sample if the multivariate observations are a sample. In many cases, a suitable selection of the conversion function will establish a correspondence between alternative hypotheses that are of interest for the multivariate situation and alternative hypotheses that are considered for the univariate tests. Moreover, use of this method in conjunction with the material presented in Chapter 5 furnishes tests that are independent of any procedure that re-uses the multivariate observations in a symmetrical fashion. Some tests which directly deal with the multivariate random sample problem will be given in the multivariate analysis part of the second volume of this handbook.

Application to Transformed Observations

In some cases, a set of observations may be known not to be a random sample. However, it is believed that a random sample will be obtained if the observations are transformed in a specified manner (possibly different for each observation). Then the procedure is first to transform the observations and then test the random sample hypothesis. Here the transformations should be selected independently of the observation values and the observations could be univariate or multivariate.

As an example, a set of univariate observations might be known to be independent and from populations with the same shape but not the same location. Then, if the relative locations can be specified, subtraction of a suitable value from each observation yields a set of observations that is a random sample, etc.

Use for Two-Sample and Several-Sample Problems

The randomness tests presented in this chapter are directly applicable to the univariate two-sample problem. Let the two independent samples be of sizes N_1 and N_2, where $N_1+N_2=n$. Under the null hypothesis, the combined set of n observations is a random sample. The alternative hypotheses emphasized are determined by the sequence positions that are chosen (without knowledge of the observation values) for, say, the values of the first sample. As an example, the first sample might be placed in the first N_1 sequence positions; then randomness tests which emphasize population shifts would be appropriate. As another example, if $N_1=N_2/r$ with r an integer, an observation of the first sample might be placed in the positions $1, r+1, 2r+1, \ldots, (N_1-1)r+1$; then randomization tests which emphasize cycles in average population value would be appropriate. An advantage of using the material of Chapter 5 for the two-sample problem is that the resulting tests are independent of any procedure that re-uses the combined set of n observations in a symmetrical manner. That is, if the two-sample test supports the hypothesis of the same population, the two samples can be combined into a single sample and any procedure using the values of this combined sample symmetrically is independent of the two-sample test.

The same approach can be used for the univariate several-sample problem. Under the null hypothesis, the combined set consisting of the several samples is itself a random sample. A rather broad class of alternative hypotheses concerning average population level, for each of the populations yielding a sample, can be investigated by appropriate choice of the sequence positions for the observations of the combined set. For example, increasing shift and/or trend can be tested by placing the observations from the population whose average level is specified to be smallest (by the alternative) in the first positions, those from the population with the second to smallest average level in the next positions, . . . , and the observations from the population with the specified largest average value in the last positions. This placement of the observations, combined with the use of a randomness test that emphasizes increasing shift and/or trend, should yield a satisfactory test for this alternative, etc. Here too the use of a randomness test has the advantage of being independent of any procedure that re-uses the combined set of observations in a symmetrical fashion.

Tests for Independence of Coordinates of Multivariate Variables

The randomness tests of this chapter can be used to test the independence of the coordinates of a bivariate random variable on the basis of a random sample from the bivariate population. Here the values of one coordinate are used to place the values of the other coordinate in a sequence order that is meaningful with respect to the alternative hypotheses of interest. Then the values of this sequence are tested for randomness. That is, the only use made of the values of one coordinate is to determine the sequence order for the values of the other coordinate. Usually, the sequence position is with respect to increasing values of the coordinate that is used to determine the sequence order; ties in the value of this coördinate can be broken by the use of randomization. Then randomness tests which emphasize trend alternatives are appropriate. Alternatively, the values of the coordinate determining sequence position could be placed in an order where they vary in a cyclical fashion. Then tests which emphasize cyclical alternatives are appropriate.

This method can also be used to test whether two mutually exclusive groups of coordinates of a multivariate random variable are independent. Here these two groups are not necessarily all the coordinates of the multivariate variable considered. This is accomplished by converting each group of coordinates into a univariate value on the basis of a function that is chosen independently of the sample values. In this way a bivariate variable is obtained and independence of the two groups of coordinates is investigated by testing the independence of the coordinates of the resulting bivariate variable. In many cases, suitable selection of the conversion functions will establish a correspondence between alternative hypotheses that are of interest for the two groups of coordinates and the alternatives that are considered for tests of the independence of the coordinates of a bivariate random variable.

Use for Testing Population Symmetry

The Chapter 5 tests of the random sample hypothesis for univariate observations can be used to test whether a univariate population is symmetrical (on the basis of a sample from that population). The first step in the procedure is to divide the sample values into groups of size three or larger, where the groups are arranged in a sequence and each group contains the same number of observations. Unless the sample size is an integral multiple of the group size, a few of the observations will be discarded; an additional group, with fewer observations than the other groups, is included to contain the observations that are discarded. Once the division into groups is completed, this additional group is eliminated from further consideration. To avoid bias, the division into groups is made without any knowledge about the values of the observations or by the use of an independent randomization process (such that all possible divisions are equally likely).

For the next step, a function of the observations within a group is specified; the same function is used for all the groups that occur for the test. This function is such that, for each group of observations, it yields a statistic that is symmetrically distributed about zero when the population sampled is symmetrical. Using the given function, a statistic whose value is one-dimensional is obtained for each group, with the statistics being placed in the same sequence order as the groups. Let g be the number of statistics (one for each group) and let g' be the largest integer that is at most equal to $g/2$. Then, multiply g' of these statistics by -1, where the selection of the statistics to receive the -1 factor is based on the positions of the statistics in the sequence but not on their values. To avoid bias, the positions where -1 is used should be selected prior to the division of the sample values into groups. Using the same sequence positions, this modification yields another sequence of statistics. If the population sampled is symmetrical, this modified set of statistics is a random sample; moreover, these statistics are placed in a sequence order that is meaningful for the randomness test that is used. Thus, population symmetry can be investigated by testing whether these statistics constitute a random sample.

The selection of the positions for the factor -1 is done so that the types of alternatives emphasized by the randomness test occur when the population sampled is not symmetrical. If the randomness test is sensitive to a shift in average population value, the last g' positions of the sequence could receive the -1 factor. If the randomness test is sensitive to cyclical changes in average value, alternate positions (those with even numbers) could receive the factor -1, etc.

The function which is used in obtaining the statistic for a group should be chosen so that, in conjunction with the randomness test used, the alternative hypotheses of principal interest are emphasized. For groups of size three and four, a moderate amount of freedom is available with regard to the choice of this function. A very substantial amount of freedom is available for groups of size five and larger. The allowable forms for this function are described on pages 143–45, where the use of the results of Chapter 7 for obtaining tests of population symmetry is outlined. The function used can be such that the expected values of the resulting statistics do not exist.

By suitable selection of the randomness test used, of the positions that receive the -1 factor, and of the function used in determining the statistics, a test of symmetry that at least roughly emphasizes some of the alternatives of interest should be obtainable. Since the randomness tests emphasize changes in average population value, the tests of symmetry obtained by the method outlined here should be sensitive to alternatives where the medians of the statistics are not zero.

Remark on Joint Tests

Some nonparametric tests simultaneously investigate the random sample hypothesis and some other hypothesis that is based on the assumption of a random sample. For example, the null hypothesis could assert that the observations are a random sample from a univariate population with median value $\theta_{\frac{1}{2}}^{(0)}$. Then the test could be obtained as a combination of two tests, where one test is based on the number of values that are greater than $\theta_{\frac{1}{2}}^{(0)}$, and the other test is based on the number of runs above and below $\theta_{\frac{1}{2}}^{(0)}$. Combined tests of this nature are not considered in this chapter.

RUNS ABOVE AND BELOW MEDIAN

Discussion

Let an observation whose value exceeds the observation median $X[(n+1)/2]$ be denoted by an a while an observation whose value is less than $X[(n+1)/2]$ is denoted by b. For n odd, $X[(n+1)/2]$ is one of the observation values; this median observation is not considered to be either an a or a b and is deleted. (Results with slightly higher efficiencies can be obtained if the median observation is not deleted when n is odd. However, tradition and simplicity of presentation favor this deletion.) Thus a sequence of N a's and N b's is obtained, where N is the largest integer contained in $n/2$. Runs of these a's and b's are called runs above and below the median.

Only two randomness tests are presented for the case of runs above and below the median. One test is based on the total number of runs of both kinds of elements. The other is based on the length of the longest run of either kind of element. Tests based on the number of runs of a's, or on the longest run of a's, are sometimes of interest. Similarly for such tests based on the b's. Randomness tests of this nature are not given here but can be obtained from the material of ref. 351 and 590 (pages 200–17), also from the bibliography for the two tests that are presented.

Randomness can also be tested on the basis of runs of three kinds of elements, four kinds of elements, etc. Results for these more complicated types of situations are given in ref. 351 and 551.

Fixed Material for Section

The part of the presentations which remains the same for the procedures stated in this section, but not for the procedures in all other sections of this chapter, is:

Data 1 Unequal univariate observations **2** Order of symbol assignment to observations appropriate for testing randomness properties **3** $X(i)$ **4** $m=1$ **Description 1** Exact sig. test **2** Random sample null hyp.; implies that all possible arrangements of observation positions in the sequence considered are equally likely. Altern. hyp. are shift and/or trend **Assumptions 1** None **2** None **3** None **Results 1** Randomization used to break ties. Observation denoted by a if it exceeds observation median and by b otherwise. Median observation discarded if n odd. $N=$no. a's$=$no. b's **2** Each test has sig. level α **4** None **Characteristics 1** Low **2** See pages 77–80 **3** Not used symmetrically, but independent of any procedure re-using the observations symmetrically **4** None **5** None.

This material is stated for reference and not repeated in the procedure statements of this section.

Test Based on Total Number of Runs

Results 1 $X=$no. runs of a's and b's **2** *Test*: Accept shift and/or trend if $X<X_\alpha$ **3** Table 5.1 gives X_α for $N\leqslant 20$ and α near .01, .05, .10, .20, .30. For $N\geqslant 20$ and $1/4N\leqslant\alpha\leqslant 1-1/4N$, $X_\alpha \doteq \frac{3}{2}+N-K_\alpha[(N^2-N)/(2N-1)]^{\frac{1}{2}}$, for α such that this quantity integral **Characteristics 2** Consistent for most altern. hyp. of interest. Some power fct. results given in ref. 39, 134, and 354 **6** In more recent stat. books **Bibliography** Ref. 37, 39, 42, 134, 151, 211, 224, 295, 298, 316, 351, 354, 398, 486, 495, 501, 505, 507, 544, 590 (pages 200–17), 595.

Test Based on Longest Run

Results 1 $Y=$longest run of a's or b's **2** *Test*: Accept shift and/or trend if $Y>Y_\alpha$ **3** Table 5.2 gives Y_α for $5\leqslant N\leqslant 20$ and $.01\leqslant\alpha\leqslant .40$. For $N>20$ and $1/N\leqslant\alpha\leqslant 1-1/N$, $Y_\alpha \doteq -\log_{10}[-(1/N)\log_e(1-\alpha)]/\log_{10}2$, using Poisson approx., for α such that this quantity integral **Characteristics 2** Some power fct. results given in ref. 39 **6** Useful in qual. control chart

TABLE 5.1. VALUES OF X_α WHEN $N \leqslant 20$ FOR TOTAL RUNS ABOVE AND BELOW MEDIAN*

N \ α	Near .01	Near .05	Near .10	Near .20	Near .30
2					3(.33)
3			3(.10)		4(.30)
4	3(.028)		4(.11)		5(.37)
5	3(.008)	4(.040)		5(.17)	6(.36)
6	4(.013)	5(.067)		6(.18)	7(.39)
7	5(.025)		6(.078)	7(.21)	8(.38)
8	5(.009)	6(.031)	7(.10)	8(.21)	9(.40)
9	6(.012)	7(.044)	8(.11)	9(.24)	10(.40)
10	7(.019)	8(.051)	9(.13)	10(.24)	11(.41)
11	7(.007)	9(.063)	10(.13)		11(.26)
12	8(.009)	10(.070)	11(.15)		12(.26)
13	9(.013)	10(.034)	11(.081)	12(.16)	13(.28)
14	10(.015)	11(.041)	12(.087)	13(.17)	14(.28)
15	10(.007)	12(.046)	13(.097)	14(.17)	15(.29)
16	11(.009)	13(.053)	14(.10)	15(.19)	16(.29)
17	12(.011)	14(.057)	15(.11)	16(.19)	17(.30)
18	13(.013)	15(.064)	16(.12)	17(.20)	18(.30)
19	13(.006)	15(.034)	17(.13)	18(.20)	19(.31)
20	14(.007)	16(.038)	17(.075)	19(.21)	20(.31)

* The true value of α is stated in parentheses. Based on ref. 507: Tables for testing randomness of grouping in a sequence of alternatives, F. Swed and C. Eisenhart, *Annals of Mathematical Statistics*, Vol. 14, 1943, pages 66–87. Used with the kind permission of the authors, Frieda Swed Cohn and Churchill Eisenhart, and of the Editor of the *Annals of Mathematical Statistics*.

form **Bibliography** Ref. 37, 39, 151, 211, 224, 279, 295, 298, 316, 351, 365, 508, 590 (pages 200–17).

RUNS UP AND DOWN

Discussion

Consider the sequence of observation differences $X(2)-X(1)$, $X(3)-X(2), \ldots, X(n)-X(n-1)$. In this sequence, replace a difference by the symbol + if it is positive and by the symbol − if negative. Thus, since the observations are required to be unequal for the tests of this section, a sequence of $n-1$ plus and/or minus signs is obtained. Runs of the symbols of this sequence are referred to as runs up and down.

Randomness tests based on runs up and down are designed to protect against the alternative of a trend in average population value. Several

TABLE 5.2. VALUES OF α FOR GIVEN N AND LONGEST RUN Y_α ABOVE OR BELOW MEDIAN*

N \ Y_α	4	5	6	7	8	9	10
5	.23	.04					
6	.36	.10					
7		.16	.01				
8		.21	.05				
9		.26	.08	.01			
10		.29	.11	.03	.01		
11			.14	.05	.02		
12			.17	.07	.025		
13			.20	.09	.030		
14			.22	.10	.035	.01	
15			.25	.11	.040	.01	
16			.27	.12	.045	.015	
17			.29	.13	.050	.015	
18			.31	.14	.055	.020	
19			.33	.15	.060	.020	
20			.35	.16	.065	.025	.01

* Based on ref. 365: Note on application of runs to quality control charts, F. Mosteller, *Annals of Mathematical Statistics*, Vol. 12, 1941, pages 228–32. Used with the kind permission of the author, Frederick Mosteller, and of the Editor of the *Annals of Mathematical Statistics*.

types of tests are considered and some are of an asymptotic nature. The tests presented are based on the number of plus signs and on runs of various kinds. Some general results which apply only to a discrete population with a finite number of values are given in ref. 284.

Fixed Material for Section

Data 1 Unequal univariate observations **2** Order of symbol assignment to observations appropriate for testing randomness properties **3** $X(i)$ **4** $m=1$ **Description 2** Random sample null hyp.; implies that all possible arrangements of observation positions in the sequence considered are equally likely **Assumptions 1** None **2** None **3** None **Results 1** Randomization used to break ties. Sequence consists of signs of $X(2)-X(1), \quad \ldots, X(n)-X(n-1),$ in that order **2** Each test has sig. level α **4** None **Characteristics 3** Not used symmetrically, but independent of any procedure re-using the observations symmetrically **4** None **5** None.

Tests Based on Number of Plus Signs (Moore-Wallis)

Description 1 Three types of exact sig. tests **2** Altern. hyp. are upward trend, downward trend, trend (up or down) **Results 1** $X=$no. of $+$'s

2 *Tests*: Accept upward trend if $X > X_\alpha$. Accept downward trend if $X < X'_\alpha$. Accept trend (up or down) if $X > X_{\alpha/2}$ or $X < X'_{\alpha/2}$ **3** Table 5.3 gives X_α and X'_α for $n < 13$ and various α. For $n \geqslant 13$ and $1/3n \leqslant \alpha \leqslant 1 - 1/3n$, $X'_\alpha \doteq \frac{1}{2} + (n-1)/2 - K_\alpha[(n+1)/12]^{1/2}$, $X_\alpha \doteq -\frac{1}{2} + (n-1)/2 + K_\alpha[(n+1)/12]^{1/2}$, where, in each case, α such that quantity integral **Characteristics 1** Low **2** See efficiency summary (pages 77–80). Asymptotic power obtainable from methods of ref. 310 and 328. Some power function values are given in ref. 180 and 499 **6** In more recent stat. books **Bibliography** Ref. 180, 186, 200, 299, 310, 328, 353, 499, 501, 502, 551.

TABLE 5.3. VALUES OF α FOR GIVEN $x_\alpha(n)$ AND $n \leqslant 12$ SUCH THAT $X'_\alpha = n/2 - |x_\alpha(n) - (n-1)/2|$ AND $X_\alpha = (n-2)/2 + |x_\alpha(n) - (n-1)/2|$ FOR NUMBER OF +'s IN RUNS UP AND DOWN*

$x_\alpha(n)$ \ n	3	4	5	6	7	8	9	10	11	12
0	.167	.042	.008							
1			.225	.081	.024	.006				
2					.260	.113	.042	.013	.004	
3							.285	.139	.049	.022
4									.303	.161

* Here, $x_\alpha(n)$ is an auxiliary quantity used in determining X_α and X'_α. Table is based on ref. 353: Time series significance tests based on signs of differences, G. H. Moore and W. A. Wallis, *Journal of the American Statistical Association*, Vol. 38, 1943, pages 153–64. Used with the kind permission of the authors, G. H. Moore and W. A. Wallis, and of the Editor of the *Journal of the American Statistical Association*.

Tests Using Total Number of Runs

Description 1 Three types of exact sig. tests **2** Altern. hyp. are trend, cycles, trend or cycles **Results 1** Y = total no. runs of +'s and −'s **2** *Tests*: Accept trend if $Y < Y'_\alpha$. Accept cycles if $Y > Y_\alpha$. Accept trend or cycles if $Y < Y'_{\alpha/2}$ or $Y > Y_{\alpha/2}$ **3** For $n \geqslant 20$ and $1/3n \leqslant \alpha \leqslant 1 - 1/3n$, $Y'_\alpha \doteq \frac{1}{2} + (2n-1)/3 - K_\alpha[(16n-29)/90]^{1/2}$, $Y_\alpha \doteq -\frac{1}{2} + (2n-1)/3 + K_\alpha[(16n-29)/90]^{1/2}$, where, in each case, α such that quantity integral **Characteristics 1** Low **2** See pages 77–80. Asymptotic power obtainable using method of ref. 310 **6** In recent stat. books **Bibliography** Ref. 18, 180, 186, 200, 224, 310, 311, 501, 502, 551, 595, 597.

Tests Based on Longest Runs

Description 1 Three types of exact sig. tests **2** Altern. hyp. are upward trend, downward trend, trend (up or down) **Results 1** Z = longest run of

+'s. Z' = longest run of −'s **2** *Tests*: Accept upward trend if $Z > Z_\alpha$. Accept downward trend if $Z' > Z_\alpha$. Accept trend (up or down) if $Z > Z_{\alpha/2}$ or $Z' > Z_{\alpha/2}$ **3** Table 5.4 gives α versus $Z_{\alpha/2}$ for $n \leqslant 14$. Using Poisson approx., for $1/n \leqslant \alpha \leqslant 1 - 1/n$, Z_α is the integer z satisfying $[n(z+2) - (z^2+3z+1)]/(z+3)! = -\log_e(1-\alpha)$, provided $4 \leqslant z \leqslant n-2$ and $\alpha \leqslant .3$; here α values restricted to those where Z_α integral **Characteristics 1** Low to medium **2** Unknown, but asymptotic power obtainable using method of ref. 310 **6** In more recent stat. books **Bibliography** Ref. 200, 224, 279, 310, 311, 400, 595, 597.

TABLE 5.4. VALUES OF $\alpha = P(Z' > Z_{\alpha/2}$ OR $Z > Z_{\alpha/2})$, GIVEN RANDOMNESS, FOR LONGEST RUN UP OR DOWN*

n \ $Z_{\alpha/2}$	3	4	5
4	.083		
5	.150	.017	
6	.217	.031	
7	.275	.044	
8		.058	
9		.071	.010
10		.085	.012
11		.098	.015
12		.111	.017
13		.124	.019
14		.137	.022

* Based on ref. 400: Distribution of sample arrangements for runs up and down, P. S. Olmstead, *Annals of Mathematical Statistics*, Vol. 17, 1946, pages 24–33. Used with the kind permission of the author, Paul S. Olmstead, and of the Editor of the *Annals of Mathematical Statistics*.

Chi-Square Based on Expected and Observed Runs (Wallis-Moore)

Data 4 $n \geqslant 6$ **Description 1** Theoretical-approximate sig. test **2** Altern. hyp. is trend or cycles **Results 1** Exclude run at beginning and run at end of sequence. o_1 = no. runs of length 1, o_2 = no. runs of length 2, o_3 = no. runs of length > 2, $e_1 = 5(n-3)/12$, $e_2 = 11(n-4)/60$, $e_3 = (4n-21)/60$ **2** *Test*: Accept trend or cycles if $(o_1-e_1)^2/e_1 + (o_2-e_2)^2/e_2 + (o_3-e_3)^2/e_3 > \chi'^2_\alpha$ **3** For $n \geqslant 13$ and $1/n \leqslant \alpha \leqslant 1-1/n$, $\chi'^2_\alpha \doteq \frac{7}{6}\chi_\alpha^2(2)$ if $\sum(o_i-e_i)^2/e_i \leqslant 6.3$ and $\chi'^2_\alpha \doteq \chi_\alpha^2(\frac{5}{2})$ otherwise, with $\chi_\alpha^2(\frac{5}{2})$ obtained from interpolation **Characteristics 1** Low to medium **2** Not very sensitive to trends. Unknown efficiency **6** None **Bibliography** Ref. 200, 353, 549, 550, 595.

Some Chi-Square and F-Ratio Tests

Data 4 $n \geqslant 4$ **Description 1** Four types of theoretical-approximate sig. tests **2** Altern. hyp. is trend or cycles **Results 1** X = no. +'s, Y = total no.

runs, y_1 = no. runs of length 1, y_2 = no. runs of length 2, y_3 = no. runs of length > 2. $E_X = (n-1)/2$, $E_Y = (2n-1)/3$, $E_1 = (5n+1)/12$, $E_2 = (11n-14)/60$, $E_3 = (4n-11)/60$, $\sigma_X{}^2 = (n+1)/2$, $\sigma_Y{}^2 = .178n - .323$, $\sigma_{11} = .424n - .482$, $\sigma_{12} = \sigma_{21} = -.091n - .081$, $\sigma_{13} = \sigma_{31} = -.072n + .162$, $\sigma_{22} = 1.126n - 1.630$, $\sigma_{23} = \sigma_{32} = -.041n + .108$, $\sigma_{33} = .047n - .113$ **2** *Tests*: Accept trend or cycles if $(X-EX)^2/\sigma_X{}^2 + (Y-E_Y)^2/\sigma_Y{}^2 > \chi_\alpha{}^2(2)$. Accept trend or cycles if $(X-E_X)^2\sigma_Y{}^2/(Y-E_Y)^2\sigma_X{}^2 > F_{\alpha/2}(1, 1)$ or $< F_{1-\alpha/2}(1,1)$. Accept trend or cycles if $(X-EX)^2/\sigma_X{}^2 + \sum_{u,\,v=1}^{3} \sigma^{uv}(y_u - E_u)\,(y_v - E_v) > \chi_\alpha{}^2(4)$, where $\|\sigma^{uv}\| = \|\sigma_{uv}\|^{-1}$. Accept trend or cycles if $3(X-E_X)^2/\sigma_X{}^2\{\sum_{u,\,v=1}^{3} \sigma^{uv}(y_u - E_u)(y_v - E_v)\} > F_{\alpha/2}(1, 3)$ or $< F_{1-\alpha/2}(1, 3)$ **3** Tests valid for $n \geqslant 25$ and $1/n \leqslant \alpha \leqslant 1 - 1/n$ **Characteristics 1** Medium **2** Unknown, but asymptotic power obtainable using method of ref. 310 **6** None **Bibliography** Ref. 200, 310, 311, 597.

CORRELATION COEFFICIENT STATISTICS

Basis for Correlation Tests

Another method for testing whether a sequence of univariate observations constitutes a random sample is through the use of correlation coefficient type statistics. As already mentioned, the n observations can be thought of as bivariate. The second entry of each bivariate observation is one of the values of the sequence and the first entry is the position of this univariate observation in the sequence. Under the null hypothesis that the univariate observations are a random sample, these n bivariate observations are a bivariate random sample; moreover, the entries of this bivariate variable are statistically independent and, therefore, uncorrelated. Thus deviations from randomness can be investigated by applying correlation testing procedures to this set of bivariate observations. Rejection of the hypothesis of zero correlation automatically implies rejection of the random sample hypothesis.

Correlation Tests Considered

The type of bivariate variable used for correlation tests of randomness has different of the integers 1, . . ., n for the values of one entry and unequal univariate observations for the values of the other entry. Any tests that can be applied to this kind of data for investigating independence of the entries are eligible for use. However, only three types of tests are considered in this section. These are tests using a serial correlation coefficient type statistic, Kendall's rank correlation coefficient, and Spearman's rank correlation coefficient. Other tests for investigating correlation existence can be obtained by making appropriate use of the material given in the second volume of the handbook for testing independence between the components of a bivariate variable. The correlation type statistics used in this section are also considered in that part of the second volume, and the bulk of their bibliography is given there.

Types of Serial Correlation Statistics

Several serial correlation coefficient type statistics have appeared in the literature. These include

$$\frac{1}{n-1}\sum_{i=1}^{n-1}[X(i+1)-X(i)]^2, \qquad 1-\frac{1}{2nS^2(i)}\sum_{u=1}^{n-1}[X(u+1)-X(u)]^2,$$

$$\frac{1}{(n-h)S^2(i)}\sum_{u=1}^{n-h}[X(u)-M(i)][X(u+h)-M(i)], \qquad \sum_{i=1}^{n-h}X(i)X(i+h),$$

$$\frac{1}{nS^2(i)}\sum_{u=1}^{n}[X(u)-M(i)][X(u+h)-M(i)], \qquad \sum_{i=1}^{n}X(i)X(i+h),$$

where h can have the values $1, \ldots, n-1$ and $X(i+h)$ equals $X(i+h-n)$ if $i+h>n$. If n is not too small and h is prime to n, or if $n>2h$, use of any of these statistics is approximately equivalent to use of

$$\sum_{i=1}^{n}X(i)X(i+1).$$

Consequently, only procedures based on this statistic are considered. These procedures are also applicable if the univariate observation values are replaced by their ranks.

Fixed Material for Section

Data 1 Unequal univariate observations **2** Order of symbol assignment to observations appropriate for testing randomness properties **4** $m=1$ **Description 2** Random sample null hyp.; implies that all possible assignments of observation positions in the sequence considered are equally likely **Assumptions 1** None **2** None **3** None **Results 1** Randomization used to break ties, including ties among values of any fcts. of observations which would not have tied values if data continuous **2** Each test has sig. level α **Characteristics 2** See pages 77–80. Each test consistent against trend and/or shift altern. hyp. specified in its Description **3** Not used symmetrically, but independent of any procedure re-using the observations symmetrically **4** None **5** None.

Circular Serial Correlation Coefficient Test (Wald-Wolfowitz)

Data 3 $X(i)$ **Description 1** Theoretical-approximate sig. test **2** Altern. hyp. is trend or cycles **Results 1** $X=\sum_{i=1}^{n}X(i)\,X(i+1)$, where $X(n+1)=X(1)$. Under the null hyp., $EX=(A_1{}^2-A_2)/(n-1)$, $\sigma^2X=(A_2{}^2-A_4)/$

$(n-1)+(A_1^4-4A_1^2A_2+4A_1A_3+A_2^2-2A_4)/(n-1)(n-2)-(A_1^2-A_2)^2/(n-1)^2$, where $A_k=nM'_k(i)$ **2** *Test*: Accept trend or cycles if $|X-EX|>X_{\alpha/2}$ **3** For $n\geqslant 25$, $1/n\leqslant\alpha\leqslant 1-1/n$, and $\max_k[X(k)-M(i)]^2/nM_2(i)\leqslant 5/2n$, $X_{\alpha/2}\doteq K_{\alpha/2}\sigma X$ **4** Corresponding one-sided tests obtainable by use of relations $X-EX>X_\alpha$ and $X-EX<-X_\alpha$. Then approx. to X_α usable when $n\geqslant 30$ and $3/2n\leqslant\alpha\leqslant 1-3/2n$. Method of obtaining tests when statistic is $\sum_{i=1}^{n}X(i)X(i+h)$, where $X(i+h)=X(i+h-n)$ when $i+h>n$, furnished by ref. 388 and 546 **Characteristics 1** Low to medium **2** Most powerful permutation test if altern. hyp. is joint normal dist. with equal variances and positive circular serial correlation of lag 1 **6** None **Bibliography** Ref. 42, 180, 200, 307, 388, 419, 453, 501, 502, 546, 601.

Kendall's Rank Correlation Coefficient Test

Data 3 $X(i)$ **Description 1** Three types of exact sig. tests **2** Altern. hyp. are upward trend and/or shift, downward trend and/or shift, trend and/or shift (up or down) **Results 1** $H_{uv}=+1$ if $X(u)>X(v)$ and $=-1$ otherwise. $Y=\sum_{u>v=1}^{n}H_{uv}$ **2** *Tests*: Accept downward trend and/or shift if $Y<-Y_\alpha$. Accept upward trend and/or shift if $Y>Y_\alpha$. Accept trend and/or shift (up or down) if $|Y|>Y_{\alpha/2}$ **3** For $n\geqslant 10$ and $1/4n\leqslant\alpha\leqslant 1-1/4n$, $Y_\alpha\doteq -1+K_\alpha[n(n-1)(2n+5)/18]^{1/2}$, for α such that this quantity an odd integer when $n(n-1)/2$ odd and an even integer when $n(n-1)/2$ even. Ref. 276 furnishes Y_α for $n<10$ **4** Equivalent to T test of ref. 329 **Characteristics 1** Low to medium **2** Lower bound for power obtainable from material of ref. 276 for n not too small **6** Ref. 161 contains modification for testing randomness of subsets of observations **Bibliography** Ref. 121, 122, 125, 141, 143, 155, 161, 180, 186, 224, 228, 243, 271, 273, 276, 277, 329, 358, 388, 439, 453, 455, 464, 476, 486, 498, 501, 512, 551, 582.

Spearman's Rank Correlation Coefficient Test

Data 3 $X\langle i\rangle$ **Description 1** Three types of exact sig. tests **2** Altern. hyp. are upward trend and/or shift, downward trend and/or shift, trend and/or shift (up or down) **Results 1** $Z=(1/2)\sum_{i=1}^{n}[X\langle i\rangle-i]^2-(n^3-n)/12$ **2** *Tests*: Accept upward trend and/or shift if $Z<-Z_\alpha$. Accept downward trend and/or shift if $Z>Z_\alpha$. Accept trend and/or shift (up or down) if $|Z|>Z_{\alpha/2}$ **3** For $n\geqslant 10$ and $1/4n\leqslant\alpha\leqslant 1-1/4n$, $Z_\alpha\doteq -\frac{1}{2}+[(n^3-n)/12]t_\alpha(n-2)[n-2+t_\alpha(n-2)^2]^{-\frac{1}{2}}$. For $n\geqslant 25$ and $1/4n\leqslant\alpha\leqslant 1-1/4n$, $Z_\alpha\doteq -\frac{1}{2}+K_\alpha(n-1)^{\frac{1}{2}}n(n+1)/12$. In all cases, α such that Z_α an even multiple of $\pm\frac{1}{2}$ when $(n^3-n)/12$ integral and an odd multiple of $\pm\frac{1}{2}$ when $(n^3-n)/12$ not integral. Ref. 396 gives values of Z_α for $n\leqslant 10$ **4** $-12Z/(n^3-n)$ is Spearman's rank correlation coeff. for bivariate variable where first entry is sequence position and second entry is observation value **Characteristics 1** Low **2** Ref. 35 contains method for computing power fct. values in terms of a numerically expressed nonparametric type of alternative which indicates increasing lack of randomness **6** None **Bibliography** Ref. 35, 112, 121, 122, 141, 155, 180, 186, 243, 255, 276, 277, 319, 396, 397, 486, 489, 498, 501, 502, 551.

STATISTICS BASED ON SIGNS OF DIFFERENCES

Discussion

Randomness test statistics can be devised which are weighted summations depending on the number and location of signs for the differences of specified sequence observations or functions of these observations. In fact, several tests whose statistics can be expressed in this form have already been presented. These are the tests in the section on runs up and down, Kendall's rank correlation coefficient test, and Spearman's rank correlation coefficient test. Some additional tests of this nature appear to be worthwhile and are presented in this section.

Fixed Material for Section

Data 1 Unequal univariate observations **2** Order of symbol assignment to observations appropriate for testing randomness properties **4** $m=1$ **Description 2** Random sample null hyp.; implies that all possible arrangements of observation positions in the sequence considered are equally likely **Assumptions 1** None **2** None **3** None **Results 1** Randomization used to break ties **2** Each test has sig. level α **4** None **Characteristics 3** Not used symmetrically, but independent of any procedure re-using the observations symmetrically **4** None **5** None **6** None.

Mann's Trend Test

Data 3 $X(i)$ **Description 1** Two types of exact sig. tests **2** Altern. hyp. are upward trend, and downward trend **Results 1** K = smallest integer k which satisfies all the inequalities $X(1) > \max[X(k), X(k+1), \ldots, X(n)]$, $X(2) > \max[X(k+1), \ldots, X(n)]$, $\ldots$, $X(n-k-1) > \max[X(n-1), X(n)]$, $X(n-k) > X(n)$. K' = smallest integer k' which satisfies all the inequalities $-X(1) > \max[-X(k'), \ldots, -X(n)]$, $\ldots$, $-X(n-k') > -X(n)$ **2** *Tests*: Accept downward trend if $K < k_\alpha$. Accept upward trend if $K' < k_\alpha$ **3** For $n \geqslant 10$, $k_{.0098} = n-4$, $k_{.0284} = n-3$, $k_{.0792} = n-2$, $k_{.2083} = n-1$, $k_{.5} = n$ **Characteristics 1** Upper low to medium **2** If $P[X(u) > X(v)]$ increases rapidly with $v-u$, test based on K seems more powerful against trend than corresponding Kendall rank corr. coeff. test; likewise for test based on K' if this prob. decreases rapidly with $v-u$ **Bibliography** Ref. 143, 329.

All Observations Used—Optimal Weighting (*Cox-Stuart*)

Data 3 $X(i)$ **Description 1** Three types of exact sig. tests **2** Altern. hyp. are upward trend and/or shift, downward trend and/or shift, trend and/or shift (up or down) **Results 1** $h_{uv}=1$ if $X(u)>X(v)$ and $=0$ otherwise. $N=$ largest integer contained in $n/2$. $X=\sum_{w=1}^{N}(2N-2w+1)h_{w,\,2N-w+1}$ **2** *Tests*: Accept upward trend and/or shift if $X<X'_{\alpha}$. Accept downward trend and/or shift if $X>X_{\alpha}$. Accept trend and/or shift (up or down) if $X<X'_{\alpha/2}$ or $X>X_{\alpha/2}$ **3** For $N\geqslant 10$ and $1/2N\leqslant\alpha\leqslant 1-1/2N$, $X'_{\alpha}\doteq\frac{1}{2}+N^2/2-K_{\alpha}[N(4N^2-1)/12]^{1/2}$, $X_{\alpha}\doteq-\frac{1}{2}+N^2/2+K_{\alpha}[N(4N^2-1)/12]^{1/2}$, where, for each case, α such that quantity is integral **Characteristics 1** Low **2** See pages 77–80. Ref. 112 contains asymptotic efficiencies for tests of dispersion. Weighting optimum, among statistics of this type, for altern. hyp. of normal regression **Bibliography** Ref. 112, 453, 502.

All Observations Used—Equal Weighting (*Cox-Stuart*)

Data 3 $X(i)$ **Description 1** Three types of exact sig. tests **2** Altern. hyp. are upward trend and/or shift, downward trend and/or shift, trend and/or shift (up or down) **Results 1** $h_{uv}=1$ if $X(u)>X(v)$ and $=0$ otherwise. $N=$ largest integer contained in $n/2$. $Y=\sum_{w=1}^{N}h_{w,\,N+w}$ **2** *Tests*: Accept upward trend and/or shift if $Y<Y'_{\alpha}$. Accept downward trend and/or shift if $Y>Y_{\alpha}$. Accept trend and/or shift (up or down) if $Y<Y'_{\alpha/2}$ or $Y>Y_{\alpha/2}$ **3** For $N\geqslant 10$ and $1/2N\leqslant\alpha\leqslant 1-1/2N$, $Y'_{\alpha}\doteq\frac{1}{2}+N/2-\frac{1}{2}K_{\alpha}\sqrt{N}$, $Y_{\alpha}\doteq-\frac{1}{2}+N/2+\frac{1}{2}K_{\alpha}\sqrt{N}$, where, for each case, α such that quantity integral **Characteristics 1** Low **2** See pages 77–80 **Bibliography** Ref. 112, 453, 502.

Optimum Observation Subset—Equal Weighting (*Cox-Stuart*)

Data 3 $X(i)$ **Description 1** Three types of exact sig. tests **2** Altern. hyp. are upward trend and/or shift, downward trend and/or shift, trend and/or shift (up or down) **Results 1** $h_{uv}=1$ if $X(u)>X(v)$ and $=0$ otherwise. $N'=$ largest integer contained in $n/3$. $Z=\sum_{w=1}^{N'}h_{w,\,2N'+w}$ **2** *Tests*: Accept upward trend and/or shift if $Z<Z'_{\alpha}$. Accept downward trend and/or shift if $Z>Z_{\alpha}$. Accept trend and/or shift (up or down) if $Z<Z'_{\alpha/2}$ or $Z>Z_{\alpha/2}$ **3** For $N'\geqslant 10$ and $1/2N'\leqslant\alpha\leqslant 1-1/2N'$, $Z'_{\alpha}\doteq\frac{1}{2}+N'/2-\frac{1}{2}K_{\alpha}\sqrt{N'}$, $Z_{\alpha}\doteq-\frac{1}{2}+N'/2+\frac{1}{2}K_{\alpha}\sqrt{N'}$, where, for each case, α such that quantity integral **Characteristics 1** Low **2** See pages 77–80. Ref. 112 contains asymptotic efficiencies for tests of dispersion. Test represents optimum observation choice of type considered for normal regression altern. hyp. **Bibliography** Ref. 112, 453.

Comparison With Observation Median (*Brown-Mood*)

Data 3 $X(i)$ **Description 1** Three types of exact sig. tests **2** Altern. hyp. are upward trend and/or shift, downward trend and/or shift, trend and/or shift (up or down) **Results 1** N = largest integer contained in $n/2$. W = no. of the N differences $X(1)-X[(n+1)/2]$, ..., $X(N)-X[(n+1)/2]$ that are positive **2** *Tests*: Accept upward trend and/or shift if $W < W'_\alpha$. Accept downward trend and/or shift if $W > W_\alpha$. Accept trend and/or shift if $W < W'_{\alpha/2}$ or $W > W_{\alpha/2}$ **3** For $N \geqslant 10$ and $1/2N \leqslant \alpha \leqslant 1-1/2N$, $W'_\alpha \doteq \frac{1}{2} + N/2 - \frac{1}{2}K_\alpha N/\sqrt{2N-1}$, $W_\alpha \doteq -\frac{1}{2} + N/2 + \frac{1}{2}K_\alpha N/\sqrt{2N-1}$, where, for each case, α such that quantity integral **Characteristics 1** Low **2** See pages 77–80 **Bibliography** Ref. 78, 112, 502.

Curvilinear Ranking Test (*Moran*)

Data 3 $X\langle i\rangle$ **Description 1** Two types of exact sig. tests **2** First altern. hyp. consists of either monotonic trend, or increasing trend followed by decreasing trend. Second altern. hyp. is monotonic trend, or decreasing trend followed by increasing trend **Results 1** D = least no. position interchanges to change observed ranking to first altern. hyp. form. D' = least no. interchanges to change observed ranking to second altern. hyp. form **2** *Tests*: Accept first altern. hyp. if $D > D_\alpha$. Accept second altern. hyp. if $D' > D_\alpha$ **3** For $n \geqslant 10$ and $1/\sqrt{10n} \leqslant \alpha \leqslant 1-1/\sqrt{10n}$, $D_\alpha \doteq E_D - \frac{1}{2} + K_\alpha \sigma_D$ for α such that this quantity integral, where $E_D = \frac{1}{4}\{\sum_{i=3}^{n}(i-3) + (\frac{1}{3}+\frac{1}{5}+\ldots+1/I)\}$, $\sigma_D{}^2 = \{n(n+1)(2n+1)/6 - 4n + 3\}/48 + \frac{1}{8}[\frac{1}{2}(n-1)]^* - (1/3^2 + 1/5^2 + \ldots + 1/I^2)/16$; here $[\frac{1}{2}(n-1)]^*$ is the largest integer contained in $\frac{1}{2}(n-1)$ and I is the largest odd integer that does not exceed n. Exact values of D_α given in ref. 360 for $n = 2, \ldots, 14$ **Characteristics 1** Medium **2** Unknown, but similarity to Kendall rank corr. coeff. indicates high efficiency for normal regression **Bibliography** Ref. 360.

Breaking of Records Test (*Foster-Stuart*)

Data 3$X(i)$ **Description 1** Three types of exact sig. tests **2** Altern. hyp. are upward trend, downward trend, and trend (up or down) **Results 1** $h_i = 1$ if $X(i) > \max[X(1), \ldots, X(i-1)]$ $= -1$ if $X(i) < \min[X(1), \ldots, X(i-1)]$, and $=0$ otherwise. $h'_i = 1$ if $X(i) > \max[X(i+1), \ldots, X(n)]$, $= -1$ if $X(i) < \min[X(i+1), \ldots, X(n)]$, and $=0$ otherwise. $H = \sum_{i=2}^{n} h_i - \sum_{i=1}^{n-1} h'_i$ **2** *Tests*: Accept upward trend if $H > H_\alpha$. Accept downward trend if $H < -H_\alpha$. Accept trend (up or down) if $|H| > H_{\alpha/2}$ **3** For $8 \leqslant n \leqslant 130$ and $1/\sqrt{10n} \leqslant \alpha \leqslant 1-1/\sqrt{10n}$, $H_\alpha \doteq -\frac{1}{2} + (.48 + 2.78\sqrt{\log_{10} n})K_\alpha$, for α such that this quantity integral. For $n > 130$ and $1/\sqrt{10n} \leqslant \alpha \leqslant 1-1/\sqrt{10n}$, $H_\alpha \doteq \frac{1}{2} + (2\log_e n - .846)K_\alpha$, for α such that this quantity integral **Characteristics 1** Low **2** See pages 77–80. Power fct. values are stated in ref. 180 **Bibliography** Ref. 143, 180, 181, 453, 502, 503.

Runs of Consecutive Elements (Wolfowitz)

Data 3 $X\langle i\rangle$ **Description 1** Exact sig. test **2** Altern. hyp. is trend or cycles **Results 1** $G_u=0$ if $X\langle u\rangle > X\langle u+1\rangle+1$ or $X\langle u\rangle < X\langle u+1\rangle-1$, and $=1$ otherwise ($u=1,\ldots,n-1$). $G=\frac{1}{2}\sum_{u=1}^{n-1} G_u$ **2** *Test*: Accept trend or cycles if $G \geqslant G_\alpha$ **3** For $n \geqslant 10$ and $1/n \leqslant \alpha \leqslant 1-1/n$, G_α defined by $\sum_{g=G_\alpha}^{\infty} \{2^g/e^2 g!\}\{1-(g^2-3g)/2n\}=\alpha$, for α such that G_α integer **Characteristics 1** Low if G_α known **2** Unknown **Bibliography** Ref. 269, 453, 596.

MOST POWERFUL TESTS (SPECIFIC PARAMETRIC ALTERNATIVES)

Introduction

Two types of tests are presented which have the same form of alternative hypotheses. The type of alternative hypotheses considered requires that the observations are independently drawn from normal populations having a common variance and with means that are of a specified form and not all equal. Explicitly, the alternative hypothesis asserts that $X(1),\ldots,X(n)$ have a joint frequency function of the form

$$(2\pi\sigma^2)^{-(1/2)n} \exp\left\{-\frac{1}{2\sigma^2}\sum_{i=1}^{n}[X(i)-a_i\xi-\eta]^2\right\},$$

where $a_1,\ldots,a_n$ are specified numbers (not all equal) and ξ, η, σ are unknown parameters.

One type of test furnishes the most powerful one-sided and most stringent two-sided permutation tests for the alternative hypothesis considered (see page 40 for definition of permutation test). The other type of test furnishes the most powerful one-sided and most stringent two-sided rank order tests for the case of numerically small values of ξ/σ. Both types of tests are asymptotically most powerful against this alternative hypothesis for the special case where the null hypothesis specifies that the observations are a sample from a normal population.

The permutation tests are most powerful one-sided and most stringent two-sided for a broad class of alternatives which includes the normal alternatives considered above as a special case. Explicitly, this class of alternatives consists of all populations with joint frequency functions of the form

$$\prod_{i=1}^{n} A[X(i)] \exp\,[(a_i\xi+\eta)X(i)+B(a_i\xi+\eta)],$$

where, subject to integrability (or summation) conditions, the function $A(x)$ is arbitrary; the function $B(\varphi)$ is determined by $A(x)$ and the fact that this expression is a frequency function. Other examples of populations yielding joint frequency functions of this form are those with χ^2, binomial, or Poisson distributions.

Fixed Material for Section

Data 2 Order of symbol assignment to observations appropriate for testing randomness properties **4** $m=1$ **Description 1** Three types of sig. tests **2** Random sample null hyp.; implies that all possible arrangements of observation positions in the sequence considered are equally likely. Altern. hyp. defined in Introduction to this sect. The three types considered are $\xi>0$, $\xi<0$, $\xi\neq 0$ **Assumptions 1** None **2** None **3** None **Results 1** Randomization used to break ties, including ties among values of any fct. of observations which would have unequal values if data continuous **2** Each test has sig. level α **4** None **Characteristics 2** See pages 77–80 **3** Not used symmetrically, but independent of any procedure re-using the observations symmetrically **4** None **5** None **6** None.

Optimum Permutation Tests

Data 1 Univariate observations **3** $X(i)$ **Results 1** $t\{X(i)\}=\{\sum_{k=1}^{n}(a_k-Ma_i)X(k)\}/\{[\sum_{k=1}^{n}(a_k-Ma_i)^2/(n-1)][\sum_{k=1}^{n}(X(k)-M(i))^2]\}^{1/2}$ **2** *Tests*: Accept $\xi>0$ if $t\{X(i)\}>T_\alpha$. Accept $\xi<0$ if $-t\{X(i)\}>T_\alpha$. Accept $\xi\neq 0$ if $|t\{X(i)\}|>T_{\alpha/2}$ **3** Procedure for applying permutation tests stated on page 40. Class of permutations consists of all ways of assigning the symbols $X(i)$ to the observations. For $n\geqslant 20$, $1/n\leqslant\alpha\leqslant 1-1/n$, $\max_k (a_k-Ma_i)^2/\sum_{k=1}^{n}(a_k-Ma_i)^2\leqslant 5/2n$, and $\max_k [X(k)-M(i)]^2/nM_2(i)\leqslant 5/2n$, $T_\alpha\doteq\sqrt{n-1}t_\alpha(n-2)/\{n-2+t_\alpha(n-2)^2\}^{\frac{1}{2}}$ **Characteristics 1** Low if approx. used; upper low to high otherwise **Bibliography** Ref. 186, 244, 307, 575.

Most Powerful Rank Order Tests (*Terry*)

Data 1 Unequal univariate observations **3** $X\langle i\rangle$ **Results 1** $z=z\{X\langle i\rangle\}=\{\sum_{k=1}^{n}(a_k-Ma_i)EZ(n,X\langle i\rangle)\}\{[\sum_{k=1}^{n}(a_k-Ma_i)^2][\sum_{i=1}^{n}(EZ(n,i))^2]\}^{-1/2}$, where $Z(n,i)=i$th order statistic of sample of size n from std. normal pop. Also $Z=(z\sqrt{n-2})/\sqrt{1-z^2}$ **2** *Tests*: Accept $\xi>0$ if $Z>Z_\alpha$. Accept $\xi<0$ if $Z<-Z_\alpha$. Accept $\xi\neq 0$ if $|Z|>Z_{\alpha/2}$ **3** For $n\geqslant 15$ and $1/n\leqslant\alpha\leqslant 1-1/n$, $Z_\alpha\doteq t_\alpha(n-2)$. Ref. 511 contains values of $EZ(n,i)$ for $n\leqslant 20$ **Characteristics 1** Low to medium **Bibliography** Ref. 178 (Introduction), 186, 511, 513.

SEQUENTIAL TESTS (BIBLIOGRAPHY)

Discussion

Sequential tests of the random sample null hypothesis suffer from a basic difficulty. Namely, it is hazardous to accept the conclusion that an entire set of observations is a random sample without taking all of the observations into consideration. Except for unusual cases, a sequential procedure would not seem to be appropriate for testing randomness of univariate observations. Consequently, only a bibliography is given for the sequential tests of randomness that are of a nonparametric nature.

Bibliography Ref. 355, 390, 436.

MULTIVARIATE TESTS OF RANDOMNESS PROPERTY (BIBLIOGRAPHY)

Discussion

Since the assumption of a univariate random sample is used frequently in mathematical statistics, supplementary procedures for testing this assumption can be very valuable. The procedures presented in Chapter 5 are applicable to this problem. In some cases, however, randomness is itself the population property of interest. Agricultural field experiments where the influence of plant location is investigated fall under this heading. Due to the variety of types of situations encountered, and their specialized nature, no procedures are presented for the multidimensional case where randomness is itself the property investigated. However, a bibliography is given for some of the available nonparametric procedures of this type.

Bibliography Ref. 73, 74, 104, 173, 198, 199, 296, 297, 300, 357, 359, 494, 504, 514, 518.

RELATIVE EFFICIENCY SUMMARY

Discussion

Only a moderate amount of material is available concerning the relative efficiencies of the procedures presented in this chapter, and nearly all the results that have been obtained are for the asymptotic case. However, the results that are available should be helpful in selecting a randomness test which furnishes protection against a specified alternative hypothesis of the types considered. The alternative hypotheses considered involve one or a combination of shift, trend, and cycles. For trend, the special case of normal regression is examined separately. The case where the observations represent the outcome of a Markoff process with positive dependence corresponds roughly to a combination of trend and cycles. No one procedure is analyzed for all the alternative hypotheses considered but most of the procedures are investigated for at least one alternative hypothesis situation.

Protection Against Shift

A shift occurs when the average population value abruptly changes to a different level. None of the efficiency results given in the literature apply directly to the case of population shift. However, qualitative considerations are sufficient to indicate the relative desirability of the randomness tests presented.

The presence of a shift tends to result in long runs above and below the observation median. Consequently, the tests based on runs above and below the median should be sensitive to shifts which involve more than a small fraction of the observations, and therefore suitable for protecting against this alternative hypothesis.

When a shift occurs, pairs of consecutive observations tend to behave the same as for the randomness case except at the sequence location of the shift. Thus tests of the runs up and down type are not very sensitive to the presence of shift. Likewise for the circular serial correlation coefficient test and the runs of consecutive elements test.

If a shift occurs which is not near either end of the sequence of observations, the tests based on Kendall's rank correlation coefficient, Spearman's rank correlation coefficient, all those based on the signs of observation differences except the runs of consecutive elements test, and the two "most powerful" tests should be satisfactory. For these tests, a shift has the same general effect as a trend. Since all of these tests are designed to protect against trend, they should also furnish protection against shift.

Protection Against Trend

All the tests presented furnish some protection against a trend in average population values. However, the extent of the protection varies with the type of test considered. Although the only efficiency material available is for special cases and mainly of an asymptotic nature, it seems sufficient to indicate the relative desirability of the tests. The tests which appear to be most sensitive to trend are Kendall's rank correlation test, Spearman's rank correlation coefficient test, Mann's trend test, the curvilinear ranking test, and the two "most powerful" tests. The three Cox-Stuart tests and the comparison with median test appear to have a somewhat lower sensitivity, but are often easier to apply. These ten types of tests seem to be much more desirable for protecting against trend than the remaining randomness tests.

Normal Regression Case

A special trend situation where efficiencies have been obtained for a number of tests is that of normal regression. Explicitly, the type of normal regression considered is such that each observation of the sequence can be expressed in the form

$$X(i) = A + Bi + x_i, \qquad (i = 1, \ldots, n)$$

where A, B are constants and the x_i are a random sample from a normal population with zero mean and standard deviation σ. Then the null hypothesis of a random sample is equivalent to the relation $B = 0$.

Normal regression asymptotic efficiencies ($n \to \infty$) have been presented for twelve of the types of tests presented. These are the tests based on the number of plus signs in runs up and down, number of runs up and down, circular serial correlation coefficient, Kendall's rank correlation coefficient, Spearman's rank correlation coefficient, optimal weighting difference sign statistic, equal weighting difference sign statistic, equal weighting optimum subset statistic, comparison with median statistic, breaking of records statistic, and the statistics for the two "most powerful" tests. Table 5.5 lists the asymptotic efficiencies of these tests as compared with the corresponding "best" test for the normal regression case.

A very limited amount of efficiency information on normal regression is available for nonasymptotic sample sizes. Some partial results have been obtained for the case of the difference sign statistic using equal weighting and an optimum subset of the observations. Here, investigation shows that the asymptotic theory efficiency values are fairly accurate for $n \geqslant 60$ and $.01 \leqslant \alpha \leqslant .99$. For smaller sample sizes, the efficiency is less than the value for the asymptotic case and the deviation increases as the significance level decreases.

TABLE 5.5. ASYMPTOTIC EFFICIENCIES FOR NORMAL REGRESSION CASE*

Test Statistic	Efficiency (Expressed as Percentage)
No. +'s in runs up and down	0
No. runs up and down	0
Circ. serial corr. coeff.	0
Kendall's rank corr. coeff.	98
Spearman's rank corr. coeff.	98
Opt. wgt. diff. sign	86
Equal wgt. diff. sign	78
Equal wgt., opt. subset	83
Comparison with median	83
Breaking of records	0
"Most powerful" permutation	100
"Most powerful" rank order	100

* Based on material of ref. 112, 180, 186, 453, 501, 502.

Protection Against Cycles

In some cases the average population value may increase and decrease in a cyclical manner. For example, the same average population values may be repeated at regular intervals in the sequence of observations. Then the number of observations between repetitions is referred to as the cycle length. Only five of the types of randomness tests considered list cycles as an alternative hypothesis. Three of these apply to the case of runs up and down and are the tests based on the total number of runs, the Wallis-Moore chi-square statistic, and the chi-square, F-ratio statistics. The other two types are the circular serial correlation coefficient test and the runs of consecutive elements test. In addition, the curvilinear ranking test has a restricted type of cycle as part of its alternative hypothesis.

The consistency of the circular serial correlation coefficient test has been investigated for the case of repeated cycles. The results show that this test is not necessarily consistent against cycles. This possible lack of consistency also exists when the observations are replaced by their ranks. The test based on

$$\sum_{i=1}^{n} X(i)X(i+h)$$

is found to be consistent for the case where h equals the length of the cycles. However, the cycle length is virtually always unknown, and the use of $h=1$ seems to be as satisfactory as the use of any other value for h.

An asymptotic power function comparison has been made of the effect of using ranks for the case of repeated cycles. This investigation shows that the use of ranks can either increase or decrease the power of the circular serial correlation coefficient test, depending on the probability properties of the observations.

Markoff Chain Results

The power functions of tests of runs above and below the median have been investigated for the case of a Markoff chain with positive dependence. These investigations indicate that neither the test based on total number of runs nor the test based on the longest run is very powerful if $n \leqslant 20$. For the case of a simple Markoff chain, the test based on total number of runs seems to be more powerful than the test based on the longest run. However, this is not necessarily the case for double dependence Markoff chains.

Chapter 6

TCHEBYCHEFF TYPE INEQUALITIES

INTRODUCTION

Sometimes the only information available about a probability distribution consists of the values of a few of its probability constants (e.g., moments). In other cases additional properties such as continuity and a general type knowledge of the distribution shape are available. Although not complete, information of this nature has implications concerning the values of the distribution function considered and of relations among probability constants of this distribution. Specifically, bounds can be determined for probability values and for a probability constant in terms of other probability constants. Such bounds furnish what are referred to as Tchebycheff type inequalities in this handbook.

The types of situations considered are divided into six classes. For the first class, bounds are presented for the values of univariate probability expressions involving populations for which some specified probability constants are known but which are otherwise unrestricted. The second class differs from the first in that the populations satisfy some additional restrictions (e.g., they might be required to be continuous with a unimodal frequency function). In the third class, limits are given for probability expressions that involve the average (or sum) of two or more univariate observations. The fourth class considers bounds for absolute differences between two univariate distribution functions (perhaps for averages) that have specified properties in common. The fifth class of situations is concerned with bounds for the values of multivariate probability relations. For the sixth class, upper and/or lower limits are determined for expected values of the sample range and other functions of extreme order statistics, in terms of the population mean and standard deviation.

APPLICATIONS

Types of Procedures

Procedures where an upper and/or lower bound is determined for the value of a probability expression can be used to obtain confidence regions with bounded confidence coefficients and tests with bounded significance levels. This application is straightforward and, therefore, not explicitly considered in the presentations of the procedures.

For many nonparametric testing situations, some of the population probability constants (e.g., the first few moments) can be readily determined for the case of the null hypothesis even though the corresponding probability distribution is very difficult to evaluate. On the basis of these probability constants and the appropriate Tchebycheff type inequality, a bounded significance level test can be obtained for testing the null hypothesis. This is perhaps the most important nonparametric application of Tchebycheff type inequalities.

Usually the probability expressions considered involve two or more population probability constants. Unless all but one of these probability constants have known values, a joint confidence region is obtained which simultaneously involves all of the unknown probability constants. Although useful in some cases, joint confidence regions of this nature are often not of much value even if the confidence coefficient is precisely known. One situation where a single probability constant occurs is that where the random variable is the difference of two sample means (or two sample values), and only the first two population moments are used; then approximate confidence regions are obtained for the population variance.

The procedures that deal with expressions involving population probability constants furnish bounds for one population probability constant in terms of other probability constants. These procedures are useful for cases where the values of the probability constants occurring in the bounds are available but the other probability constant is not. For example, in some cases the population standard deviation is the measure of dispersion that is wanted, but the mean range (for a specified sample size) is all that is available. Then limits for the value of the standard deviation can sometimes be determined on the basis of the value for the mean range. To date, the only probability constants for which more than fragmentary results of this nature have been obtained are expected values of some functions of order statistics of a sample. Consequently these are the only type of probability constants for which bounds are presented in this chapter.

Advantages and Disadvantages

The principal advantage of Tchebycheff type inequalities is that they do not require much in the way of procedure assumptions. The population probability constants considered should exist for any reasonable type of practical situation. The assumptions made concerning distribution continuity, differentiability, and shape are of a general nature and should not be difficult to verify for many applications. When functions of observations are considered, an independence or random sample assumption is nearly always made. However, assumptions of this kind are not very stringent and occur for nearly all nonparametric procedures.

The major disadvantage of Tchebycheff type inequalities is that the bounds are virtually always of a very rough nature. Ordinarily, the significance level upper bound value is far in excess of the true significance level for the test considered. The confidence coefficient lower bound is usually appreciably smaller than the actual confidence coefficient value. Likewise, the upper and lower bounds for a probability constant nearly always differ by a substantial percentage. Consequently, Tchebycheff type inequalities are mainly of value for cases where more refined techniques are not available and where the problem is to investigate deviations of a gross nature.

Alternative Methods

Tchebycheff type inequalities are very conservative in the sense that the bounds obtained represent the most severe cases that can occur with respect to a rather general class of situations. For most practical type cases, the actual values should differ substantially from the bound values. Thus less conservative approximation methods may be more useful than Tchebycheff type inequalities for many applications.

Several approximation methods of this nature are discussed in Chapter 4. These are the Gram-Charlier A series, the Edgeworth series, generalizations of the Edgeworth series, the Pearson curves, etc. The methods outlined in Chapter 4 are for the univariate case but can be generalized to multivariate cases. Another approximation method for the univariate case that seems to have some desirable properties is that where $F(x)$ is represented by an expression of the form $1-(1+x^c)^{-b}$

For most situations of practical interest, these alternative methods have the advantage of furnishing values that are much nearer the true values than the bounds of the Tchebycheff type inequalities. Their primary disadvantage is that no limit is placed on the magnitude of the error that can occur through their use. Sometimes this disadvantage can be at least partially alleviated by using a relation that arises for an alternative method and also for a Tchebycheff type inequality. Then the "representative" value for the case considered is determined from the alternative method while an upper and/or lower bound for the actual value is determined from the Tchebycheff type inequality.

TYPES OF RESULTS AND SPECIAL NOTATION

The first section of the procedure presentations deals with probability expressions involving a single univariate observation, which is denoted by

$X(1)$; i.e., $m=1$ and $n=1$. The only conditions imposed are that specified probability constants exist for the population which yielded $X(1)$. The upper and/or lower bounds for a probability expression are then stated in terms of these specified probability constants. For nearly all cases, the probability expressions considered can be stated in the form

$$P[a \leqslant X(1) \leqslant b] = P(a, b),$$

and are represented by the abbreviated notation $P(a, b)$.

The special notation $P(a, b)$ is also used for the second section of presentations, which deals with the bounds obtained for univariate probability expressions when additional restrictions are imposed on the population yielding $X(1)$. These extra restrictions include convexity conditions on $P(a, b)$, conditions on the derivatives of the distribution function, monotonicity conditions including the requirement of continuity and a unimodal frequency function (modal value known for some cases and unknown for others), and the condition of a known finite range for the possible values of $X(1)$.

The third section of procedure presentations is concerned with cases where the univariate variable is $M(i)$ or $nM(i)$; that is, either an average or a sum of n univariate observations ($n > 1$). For the cases investigated, the probability expressions considered can be stated in the form

$$P[a \leqslant M(i) \leqslant b] = P_M(a, b),$$

and are represented by the special notation $P_M(a, b)$.

The fourth section is concerned with upper bounds for the maximum absolute deviation, at a stated point, between two univariate distribution functions which have specified properties in common. For example, both distributions might be symmetrical and have the same first two moments. The special case where one of the distributions has the normal form is considered here. Also distributions of averages are examined.

The fifth section of presentations deals with probability expressions involving a multivariate observation. Often the relation to be satisfied by this variable is lengthy and complicated. The notational procedure adopted for such cases is to represent the specified relation by a single symbol and use P(that symbol) to represent this probability in the statement of bounds. For example, if Z is used to represent the relation in the probability expression, then $P(Z)$ is used for this probability expression in the statement of bounds.

The sixth section of procedure presentations is concerned with determining bounds for $E(X[n]-X[1])$, $EX[i]$, $\sigma^2[n]$, $\sigma^2[1]$ for the case where the observations are a sample. These bounds are functions of $EX(i)$ and

$\sigma(i)$. No special notation is introduced for stating the results of the sixth section.

INFORMATION FROM ODD MOMENTS ABOUT MEAN

For situations of a general nature, knowledge of only the odd population moments about the mean furnishes virtually no information about the population distribution function. As shown in ref. 102, given any sequence of values for the odd moments about the mean and any distribution function, there exists a distribution function which has these odd moments about the mean and which is as nearly equal to the given distribution as desired. However, this does not necessarily imply that knowledge of odd moments can not be helpful when used in combination with other information. For example, in some situations knowledge of the first $2k$ population moments about the mean represents an improvement over knowledge of only the even moments of this group (i.e., the first k even moments).

GENERAL REMARKS

For given conditions, a Tchebycheff type inequality is said to be the best possible if it cannot be improved on. That is, there exists a situation satisfying the given conditions and for which the bound (or bounds) is attained, or there is a sequence of situations satisfying the given conditions and for which the bound (or bounds) is attained in the limit.

For some univariate cases, $P(a, b)$ is considered only for a at the extreme left-hand end of the distribution (e.g., $a=-\infty$); that is, only one-sided probability intervals are considered. Then two-sided intervals can be obtained by subtraction. Specifically, for $b'>b$,

$$P[b<X(1)\leqslant b']=P(a, b')-P(a, b).$$

However, inequalities obtained in this fashion will not, in general, be the best possible even if the one-sided results used in their derivation are the best possible.

Some general conclusions that apply to the results of the first, third, and sixth presentation sections were given by Hoeffding in ref. 246. Let the observations $X(i)$ be independent and such that each $X(i)$ has a given range (possibly infinite in one or both directions) and satisfies k conditions of the form

$$Eg_u^{(i)}[X(i)]=g_{ui}. \qquad (u=1, \ldots, k)$$

The problem is to determine the least upper bound (or the greatest lower bound) for the expected value

$$EG[X(1), \ldots, X(n)].$$

Hoeffding shows that under general conditions it is only necessary to consider discrete random variables $X(i)$ which take at most $k+1$ values.

The bounds obtained for cases where only the knowledge of specified moments is required cannot be improved by requiring the population to be continuous. These bounds are obtained for discrete populations with a finite number of possible values. Since discrete populations of this nature can be approximated as closely as desired by continuous populations, the bounds are not improved by limiting consideration to continuous populations.

PROBABILITIES FOR UNIVARIATE CASE—ARBITRARY POPULATION

Introduction

In this section, except for two cases, the probability expressions for which upper and/or lower bounds are obtained can be stated in the form $P(a, b)$ and the specified probability constants are population moments. For one of the two other cases, the variable $[X(1)-EX(1)]^2/\sigma^2(1)$ is investigated, instead of $X(1)$, and the probability considered is of the form $P\{a \leqslant [X(1)-EX(1)]^2/\sigma^2(1) \leqslant b\}$. In the remaining case, a different kind of probability relation is examined and the mean range of a sample of size n is the specified population probability constant.

The situations dealing with expressions of the form $P(a, b)$ fall under several headings. A two-way method of subdivision is used for describing the situation investigated. One of the subdivisions is with respect to nature of the specified population probability constants. Here moments, absolute moments, general type absolute moments, and the mean range are considered. The other subdivision is with respect to the type of probability expression being examined. For most cases, a single expression of the form $P(a, b)$ is considered. Then the interval whose probability is investigated is said to be one-sided if $a = -\infty$, symmetrical if $a = -b$, and unsymmetrical if a is not necessarily equal to $-b$. For two of the presentations, the magnitude of the deviation between two distribution functions with the same moments is examined. For one presentation, the least upper bound over x of an expression of the form

$$P\{x \leqslant X(1)_1 \leqslant x + dE(X[n_2]_2 - X[1]_2)\}$$

is evaluated, where $d > 0$ and the $X[i]_2$ are the order statistics of a random sample of size n_2 from the population that yielded $X(1)_1$.

For the cases where the specified population constants are absolute moments, the probability expressions are stated in the form $P(-b+x_0, b+x_0)$, where x_0 is arbitrary but specified. However, by suitable interpretation, various uses can be made of these results. For example, when the variable is known to be non-negative,

$$P(-b, b) = P(0, b)$$

so that $P(0, b)$ is being investigated for cases of this nature (here $x_0 = 0$).

Fixed Material for Section

Data 1 Arbitrary, univariate **2** None **Assumptions 1** None **Results 3** None **Characteristics 5** Satisfied for virtually all practical situations.

One General Type Absolute Moment—Symmetrical Interval (*Cantelli*)

Data 3 $X(1)$ **4** $m=1$; $n=1$ **Description 1** Lower bound for prob. expression **2** $P(-b+x_0, b+x_0)$, where x_0 is arbitrary but specified, in terms of specified fct. $g(x)$ and $Eg\{|X(1)-x_0|\}$, where $g(x)$ is positive, equals $g(-x)$, and is increasing for $x \geqslant b \geqslant 0$ **Assumptions 2** $Eg\{|X(1) - x_0|\}$ exists **3** None **Results 1** None **2** *Probability relation*: $P(-b+x_0, b+x_0) \geqslant 1 - Eg\{|X(1)-x_0|\}/g(b)$ **4** For Markoff inequalities, $g(x) = |x|^J$, $J>0$. For Tchebycheff's inequality, $g(x) = x^2$ and $x_0 = EX(1)$ **Characteristics 1** Low **2** Best possible **3** Single observation **4** $Eg\{|X(1) - x_0|\}$ must exist **6** Ref. 318 extends Markoff's inequality to case where one of several populations selected, with specified selection probabilities, and an observation drawn from this population. Ref. 259 shows that Tchebycheff's inequality can have more precision than any corresponding Markoff inequality using a higher order moment. Ref. 15 contains an extension of Tchebycheff's inequality to the case of stratification **Bibliography** Ref. 15, 52, 88, 208, 259, 318, 332, 407, 426, 510.

First Two Moments—Unsymmetrical Interval (*Selberg*)

Data 3 $X(1)$ **4** $m=1$; $n=1$ **Description 1** Lower bound for prob. expression **2** $P[EX(1)-a, EX(1)+b]$ in terms of $\sigma^2(1)$, where $b \geqslant a \geqslant 0$ **Assumptions 2** $\sigma^2(1)$ exists **3** None **Results 1** None **2** *Probability relation*: $P[EX(1)-a, EX(1)+b] \geqslant a^2/[a^2+\sigma^2(1)]$ if $a(b-a) \geqslant 2\sigma^2(1)$, $\geqslant 4[ab-\sigma^2(1)]/(a+b)^2$ if $a(b-a) \leqslant 2\sigma^2(1) \leqslant 2ab$, $\geqslant 0$ if $\sigma^2(1) \geqslant ab$ **4** Same lower bounds hold for $P[EX(1)-b, EX(1)+a]$ **Characteristics 1** Low **2** Best possible **3** Single observation **4** $\sigma^2(1)$ must exist **6** None **Bibliography** Ref. 208, 467.

Two General Type Absolute Moments—Symmetrical Interval (*von Mises*)

Data 3 $X(1)$ **4** $m=1$; $n=1$ **Description 1** Bounds for prob. expression **2** $P(-b+x_0, b+x_0)$, where x_0 arbitrary but specified, in terms of specified fcts. $U(x)$, $V(x)$ and $EU\{|X(1)-x_0|\}$, $EV\{|X(1)-x_0|\}$, where $U(x)$ and $V(x)$ are increasing for $x>0$, $U(0)=V(0)=0$, $U(x)=U(-x)$, $V(x) = V(-x)$, and the x, y curve with parametric equations $x=U(b)$, $y=V(b)$ is concave upwards **Assumptions 2** $EU\{|X(1)-x_0|\}$ and $EV\{|X(1)-x_0|\}$ exist **3** None **Results 1** $U=EU\{|X(1)-x_0|\}$, $V=EV\{|X(1)-x_0|\}$. Determine b_1 and b_2 from $[V(b_1)-V]/[U(b_1)-U]=[V-V(\infty)]/[U-U(\infty)]$ and $V(b_2)/U(b_2)=V/U$. For $b\leqslant b_1$ or $b\geqslant b_2$, determine b' from $[U-U(b)]/[U(b')-U(b)]=[V-V(b)]/[V(b')-V(b)]$ **2** *Probability relations*: $0\leqslant P(-b+x_0,\ b+x_0)\leqslant$ $[U-U(b)]/[U(b')-U(b)]$ for $b\leqslant b_1$; $\{[U-U(\infty)][V-V(b)]-[U-U(b)][V-V(\infty)]\}/[U(\infty)V(b)-V(\infty)U(b)]\leqslant$ $P(-b+x_0,\ b+x_0)\leqslant$ $[UV(b)-VU(b)]/[U(\infty)V(b)-V(\infty)U(b)]$ for $b_1\leqslant b\leqslant b_2$; $[U-U(b)]/[U(b')-U(b)]\leqslant$ $P(-b+x_0, b+x_0)\leqslant 1$ for $b\geqslant b_2$ **4** For Wald inequalities, ref. 534, $U(x)$ and $V(x)$ are $|x|^r$ and $|x|^s$ with $r<s$ positive integers ($s=2r$ for Cantelli inequalities). Then $\max[0, 1-E|X(1)-x_0|^r/b^r]\leqslant 1$ if $E|X(1)-x_0|^r/b^r\leqslant E|X(1)-x_0|^s/b^s$. If $E|X(1)-x_0|^r/b^r>E|X(1)-x_0|^s/b^s$, $1-\{E|X(1)-x_0|^s-Z_0^{s-r}E|X(1)-x_0|^r\}/[b^r(b^{s-r}-Z_0^{s-r})]\leqslant$ $P(-b+x_0,\ b+x_0)\leqslant 1$, where Z_0 is $+\text{root}\neq b$ of $E|X(1)-x_0|^r b^s-E|X(1)-x_0|^s b^r+Z^r[E|X(1)-x_0|^s-b^s]+Z^s[b^r-E|X(1)-x_0|^r]=0$. When $s=2r$, $Z_0=$ $\{[E|X(1)-x_0|^{2r}-b^rE|X(1)-x_0|^r]/[E|X(1)-x_0|^r-b^r]\}^{1/r}$; then $1-\{E|X(1)-x_0|^{2r}-[E|X(1)-x_0|^r]^2\}/\{(b^r-E|X(1)-x_0|^r)^2+E|X(1)-x_0|^{2r}-[E|X(1)-x_0|^r]^2\}\leqslant$ $P(-b+x_0, b+x_0)\leqslant 1$ **Characteristics 1** Low to medium **2** Best possible **3** Single observation **4** U and V must exist **6** None **Bibliography** Ref. 89, 208, 349, 426, 534.

Mean, Variance, Fourth Central Moment—Variable Squared (Guttman)

Data 3 $X(1)$ **4** $m=1$; $n=1$ **Description 1** Lower bound for prob. expression **2** $P\{a\leqslant[X(1)-EX(1)]^2/\sigma^2(1)\leqslant b\}$, for specific a and b, in terms of $EX(1)$, $\sigma^2(1)$, $\mu_4(1)$ **Assumptions 2** $\mu_4(1)$ exists **3** None **Results 1** $\gamma=[\mu_4(1)-1]^{1/2}$; $T=[X(1)-EX(1)]/\sigma(1)$; $\lambda>1$; $c\geqslant 0$ **2** *Probability relation*: $P[1-c-\lambda\sqrt{\gamma^2+c^2}\leqslant T^2\leqslant 1-c+\lambda\sqrt{\gamma^2+c^2}]$ $\leqslant 1-1/\lambda^2$ **4** $1-c-\lambda\sqrt{\gamma^2+c^2}$ max for $c=-\gamma/\sqrt{\lambda^2-1}$. $1-c+\lambda\sqrt{\gamma^2+c^2}$ min for $c=\gamma/\sqrt{\lambda^2-1}$. Distance between limits for T^2 min if $c=0$ **Characteristics 1** Low **2** Best possible if $1-c-\lambda\sqrt{\gamma^2+c^2}\geqslant 0$ **3** Single observation **4** $\mu_4(1)$ must exist **6** Furnishes lower bound for expression of form $P(a'\leqslant T\leqslant b')$ if $1-c-\lambda\sqrt{\gamma^2+c^2}\leqslant 0$ **Bibliography** Ref. 208, 220.

Mean Range of Sample—LUB for Intervals of Given Length (Winsten)

Data 3 $X(1)_1$ **4** $m=1$; $n_1=1$ **Description 1** Lower limit for least upper bound of prob. expression **2** LUB over x of $P\{x, x+dE(X[n_2]_2-X[1]_2)\}$, where $d>0$ and the $X[i]_2$ are order statistics of sample of n_2 from the population yielding $X(1)_1$ **Assumptions 2** $EX[n_2]_2-EX[1]_2$ exists **3** None **Results 1** u determined by $\sum_{v=1}^{u}[1-(v/u)^{n_2}-(1-v/u)^{n_2}]\leqslant$ $1/d<$ $\sum_{v=1}^{u+1}\{1-[v/(u+1)]^{n_2}-[1-v/(u+1)]^{n_2}\}$ and $p(d)$ determined by sol. for p of $1/d=\sum_{v=1}^{u}[1-(vp)^{n_2}-(1-vp)^{n_2}]$ **2** *Probability relation*: LUB_x

$P\{x, x+dE(X[n_2]_2-X[1]_2)\} \geqslant \quad p(d)$ **4** Maximizing x value unknown **Characteristics 1** Low to medium **2** Best possible **3** Single observation **4** $EX[n_2]_2-EX[1]_2$ must exist **6** Usefulness limited because maximizing x unknown. Might be useful in quality control work **Bibliography** Ref. 208, 593.

First k Absolute Moments—Symmetrical Interval

Data 3 $X(1)$ **4** $m=1$; $n=1$ **Description 1** Bounds for prob. expression **2** $P(-b+x_0, b+x_0)$, where x_0 arbitrary but specified, in terms of $E|X(1)-x_0|, \quad \ldots, E|X(1)-x_0|^k$ **Assumptions 2** $E|X(1)-x_0|^k$ exists **3** None **Results 1** $\nu_1=E|X(1)-x_0|, \quad \ldots, \nu_k=E|X(1)-x_0|^k$. $N=$largest integer in $k/2$. $\eta_1<\ldots<\eta_N$ are roots of

$$\begin{vmatrix} 1 & 1 & \nu_1 & \cdots & \nu_{N-1} \\ \eta & \nu_1 & \nu_2 & \cdots & \nu_N \\ \cdot & \cdot & \cdot & & \cdot \\ \cdot & \cdot & \cdot & & \cdot \\ \cdot & \cdot & \cdot & & \cdot \\ \eta^N & \nu_N & \nu_{N+1} & \cdots & \nu_{2N-1} \end{vmatrix} = 0. \text{ The roots of } \begin{vmatrix} \gamma & \nu_1 & \nu_2 & \cdots & \nu_N \\ \gamma^2 & \nu_2 & \nu_3 & \cdots & \nu_{N+1} \\ \cdot & \cdot & \cdot & & \cdot \\ \cdot & \cdot & \cdot & & \cdot \\ \cdot & \cdot & \cdot & & \cdot \\ \gamma^{N+1} & \nu_{N+1} & \nu_{N+2} & \cdots & \nu_{2N} \end{vmatrix} = 0$$

are $\gamma_1<\ldots<\gamma_N$. $0=\gamma_0<\eta_1<\gamma_1<\ldots<\eta_N<\gamma_N$. $H(x)$ is discrete dist. fct. which increases h_w at $x=x_w$. If $k=2N$, and $\gamma_{i-1}<b<\eta_i$ for some i or $\gamma_N<b$, the x_w are roots of

$$W(x)=\begin{vmatrix} 1 & 1 & 1 & \nu_1 & \cdots & \nu_{N-1} \\ x & b & \nu_1 & \nu_2 & \cdots & \nu_N \\ \cdot & \cdot & \cdot & \cdot & & \cdot \\ \cdot & \cdot & \cdot & \cdot & & \cdot \\ \cdot & \cdot & \cdot & \cdot & & \cdot \\ x^{N+1} & b^{N+1} & \nu_{N+1} & \nu_{N+2} & \cdots & \nu_{2N} \end{vmatrix}=0; \quad h_w=\textstyle\sum_{v=0}^N D_v^{(w)}\nu_v,$$

where the $D_v^{(w)}$ are determined by $\sum_{v=0}^N D_v^{(w)}x^v \equiv W(x)/W'(x_w)(x-x_w)$. If $k=2N$ and $\eta_i<b<\gamma_i$ for some i, the x_w consist of ∞ (infinitesimal prob. concentration at ∞) and the roots of

$$Z_{b,N}(x)=\begin{vmatrix} x & b & \nu_1 & \cdots & \nu_{N-1} \\ x^2 & b^2 & \nu_2 & \cdots & \nu_N \\ \cdot & \cdot & \cdot & & \cdot \\ \cdot & \cdot & \cdot & & \cdot \\ \cdot & \cdot & \cdot & & \cdot \\ x^{N+1} & b^{N+1} & \nu_{N+1} & \cdots & \nu_{2N-1} \end{vmatrix}=0; \quad h_w=\textstyle\sum_{v=0}^N d_v^{(w)}\nu_v,$$

where the $d_v^{(w)}$ are determined by $\sum_{v=0}^{N} d_v^{(w)} x^v \equiv Z_{b,N}(x)/Z'_{b,N}(x_w)(x-x_w)$. If $k=2N+1$, and $\gamma_{i-1}<b<\eta_i$ for some i or $\gamma_N<b$, the x_w consist of ∞ and the values for the corresponding $k=2N$ case, with the h_w being those for the $k=2N$ case. If $k=2N+1$ and $\eta_i<b<\gamma_i$ for some i, the x_w are the roots of $Z_{b,N+1}(x)=0$ and $h_w=\sum_{v=0}^{N+1} e_v^{(w)}\nu_v$, where the $e_v^{(w)}$ are determined by $\sum_{v=0}^{N+1} e_v^{(w)}x^v \equiv Z_{b,N+1}(x)/Z'_{b,N+1}(x_w)(x-x_w)$ **2** *Probability relation*: $H(b-) \leqslant P(-b+x_0,\ b+x_0) \leqslant H(b)$ **4** Markoff inequality obtained for $k=1$ and Cantelli inequalities for $k=2$. Solution also applicable if $\nu_1=E|X(1)-x_0|^\beta$, $\nu_2=E|X(1)-x_0|^{2\beta}$, ..., $\nu_k=E|X(1)-x_0|^{k\beta}$, for any $\beta>0$; bounds can be optimized (in various ways) by suitable selection of β **Characteristics 1** Low to high **2** Best possible **3** Single observation **4** $E|X(1)-x_0|^k$ must exist **6** Ref. 535 contains corresponding results for any k absolute moments **Bibliography** Ref. 89, 208, 426, 445, 535.

First 2k Moments—One-sided Interval

Data 3 $X(1)$ **4** $m=1$; $n=1$ **Description 1** Bounds for prob. expression **2** $P(-\infty, b)$ in terms of $EX(1),\ldots, EX(1)^{2k}$ **Assumptions 2** $EX(1)^{2k}$ exists **3** None **Results 1** $G(x)$ is discrete dist. fct. which increases g_u at $x=x_u$. The x_u are the roots of

$$\begin{vmatrix} 1 & 1 & 1 & EX(1) & \cdots & EX(1)^{k-1} \\ x & b & EX(1) & EX(1)^2 & \cdots & EX(1)^k \\ \cdot & \cdot & \cdot & \cdot & & \cdot \\ \cdot & \cdot & \cdot & \cdot & & \cdot \\ \cdot & \cdot & \cdot & \cdot & & \cdot \\ x^{k+1} & b^{k+1} & EX(1)^{k+1} & EX(1)^{k+2} & \cdots & EX(1)^{2k} \end{vmatrix} = 0.$$

$g_u=\sum_{v=0}^{k} C_v^{(u)}EX(1)^v$; the $C_v^{(u)}$ are determined by $\sum_{v=0}^{k} C_v^{(u)}x^v \equiv \prod_{h\neq u}(x-x_h)/(x_u-x_h)$ **2** *Probability relation*: $G(b-)\leqslant P(-\infty,\ b)\leqslant G(b)$ **4** Variable $X(1)-x_0$, where x_0 arbitrary but specified, could be used in place of $X(1)$; then, for $b+x_0$ fixed, bounds can be optimized (in various ways) through selection of x_0. For case of $k=1$ (Tchebycheff inequality), $0\leqslant P(-\infty,\ b)\leqslant \sigma(1)^2/\{\sigma(1)^2+[EX(1)-b]^2\}$ if $b\leqslant EX(1)$; $1-\sigma(1)^2/\{\sigma(1)^2+[EX(1)-b]^2\}\leqslant P(-\infty,\ b)\leqslant 1$ if $b>EX(1)$. For case of $k=2$, let $\mu'_3=EX(1)^3$, $\mu'_4=EX(1)^4$, $2\delta_1=\mu'_3-\sqrt{\mu'^2_3+4}$, $2\delta_2=\mu'_3+\sqrt{\mu'^2+4}$, $\varphi=\mu'_4-\mu'^2_3-1$; $q(x)=\Big(\{-[x-EX(1)]^2/\sigma^2(1)+[x-EX(1)]\mu'_3/\sigma(1)+1\}^2+\{1+[x-EX(1)]^2/\sigma^2(1)\}\varphi\Big)^{-1}\varphi$; $Q(y)=-y^2+\mu'_3y+1$. $r_1(y)<r_2(y)$ are the roots of $Q(y)r^2-[\mu'_3Q(y)+b\varphi]r-Q(y)-\varphi=0$. Then $0\leqslant P(-\infty,\ b)\leqslant q(b)$ if $b<\delta_1\sigma(1)+EX(1)$; $\Big\{1+r_2\Big([b-EX(1)]/\sigma(1)\Big)[b-EX(1)]/$

$\sigma(1)\Big\} \Big/ \Big\{r_1\Big([b-EX(1)]/\sigma(1)\Big)-[b-EX(1)]/\sigma(1)\Big\}\Big\{r_1\Big([b-EX(1)]/\sigma(1)\Big)-r_2\Big([b-EX(1)]/\sigma(1)\Big)\Big\} \leqslant P(-\infty, b) \leqslant 1-\Big\{1+r_1\Big([b-EX(1)]/\sigma(1)\Big)[b-EX(1)]/\sigma(1)\Big\} \Big/ \Big\{r_2\Big([b-EX(1)]/\sigma(1)\Big)-r_1\Big([b-EX(1)]/\sigma(1)\Big)\Big\}\Big\{r_2\Big([b-EX(1)]/\sigma(1)\Big)-[b-EX(1)]/\sigma(1)\Big\}$ if $\delta_1\sigma(1)+EX(1)<b<\delta_2\sigma(1)+EX(1)$; $1-q(b)\leqslant P(-\infty, b)\leqslant 1$ if $b>\delta_2\sigma(1)+EX(1)$ **Characteristics 1** Low to high **2** Best possible **3** Single observation **4** $EX(1)^{2k}$ must exist **6** Useful results for case of $|b|$ large given in ref. 324 **Bibliography** Ref. 208, 324, 426, 445, 472 (pages 77–80), 602.

PROBABILITIES FOR UNIVARIATE CASE—ADDITIONAL RESTRICTIONS

Discussion

When additional information is available about the univariate population considered, improved bounds (as compared with the corresponding "arbitrary population" cases) can nearly always be obtained for probability expressions. This section is concerned with procedures which utilize additional restrictions that are of practical importance. To be of practical value, the additional restrictions imposed should have an uncomplicated intuitive interpretation, so that acceptance (or rejection) ordinarily is not a difficult decision.

One easily interpreted condition states that the range of the random variable has specified finite upper and/or lower limits. This is not a very strong restriction since virtually all random variables associated with practical situations are subject to some type of limitation on the range of their possible values. Usually finite upper and lower limits can be specified on the basis of past experience and/or technical considerations. Even though such limits may be very conservative, their use furnishes some improvement in the bounds and also enlarges the class of available procedures. Several procedures are presented for which the only additional restriction is that one or both of the range limits has a known finite value. Further restrictions are imposed for the other presentations that have range limitations.

Symmetry about an identified point is a condition that sometimes can be verified without much difficulty. Several of the procedures are for the case of symmetry. In most cases, the population is assumed to be continuous for these procedures. Also the variable is assumed to have a known finite range for some of the cases involving symmetry. For one case, however, no additional restrictions are imposed besides that of symmetry about an identified point.

Many of the types of additional restrictions involve monotonicity conditions. When the population is not required to be continuous, this takes the form of a convexity condition on $P(-b, b)$. For the continuous cases, the monotonicity conditions ordinarily apply to the frequency function of the variable but can apply to derivatives of the frequency function. Some cases deal with monotonicity in the tails of the distribution while others specify monotonicity in the central part of the distribution. Most of the monotonicity conditions considered have uncomplicated intuitive interpretations.

A special type of monotonicity is that where the population is unimodal. Such a condition can often be verified on the basis of intuitive and/or technical considerations. This desirable feature, combined with the noticeable improvement obtained for bound values, has resulted in an emphasis on this type of assumption. Most of the procedures of this nature deal with the case where the modal value is an identified point, but this is not the case for all the procedures. For some presentations, further restrictions such as symmetry and/or a known finite range are imposed on the random variable.

All procedures but one are concerned with bounds for expressions of the form $P(a, b)$. This other procedure furnishes a lower bound for the maximum value of a continuous frequency function in terms of the population standard deviation.

Fixed Material for Section

Data 2 None **Assumptions 1** None **Results 3** None **Characteristics 1** Low

Known Finite Range—First Two Moments, Symmetrical Interval

Data 1 Arbitrary, univariate **3** $[X(1)-EX(1)]/\sigma(1)$ **4** $m=1$; $n=1$ **Description 1** Upper bound for prob. expression **2** $P(-b, b)$ in terms of finite range limits for $X(1)$ **Assumptions 2** None **3** $|X(1)-EX(1)| \leqslant B\sigma(1)$ **Results 1** None **2** *Probability relations*: For $b<1$, $P(-b, b) \leqslant 1-(1-b^2)/(B^2-b^2)$ **4** None **Characteristics 2** Best possible **3** Single observation **4** Effect of choosing too small a value for B can be determined; in any case, $B \geqslant 1$ **5** Virtually always satisfied if B conservatively chosen **6** None **Bibliography** Ref. 208, 317.

Known Range Limitations—First Two Moments, One-sided Interval

Data 1 Arbitrary, univariate **3** $X(1)$ **4** $m=1$; $n=1$ **Description 1** Bounds for prob. expression **2** $F(b)=P(-\infty, b)$ in terms of $EX(1)$, $\sigma(1)$ and range limitations for $X(1)$ **Assumptions 2** $EX(1)^2$ exists **3** $A \leqslant [X(1)-EX(1)]/\sigma(1) \leqslant B$, where one limit can be infinite **Results**

1 $T_b = [b - EX(1)]/\sigma(1)$ **2** *Probability relation*: $0 \leqslant F(b) \leqslant 1/(1+T_b^2)$ if $A < T_b \leqslant -1/B$; $(1+BT_b)/(A-B)(A-T_b) \leqslant F(b) \leqslant 1-(1+AT_b)/(B-A)(B-T_b)$ if $-1/B \leqslant T_b \leqslant -1/A$; $T_b^2/(1+T_b^2) \leqslant F(b) \leqslant 1$ if $-1/A \leqslant T_b < B$ **4** None **Characteristics 2** Best possible **3** Single observation **4** $EX(1)^2$ must exist. Effect of too small a value for B and/or too large a value for A can be determined; in any case, $B-A \geqslant 2$ **5** Virtually always satisfied if finite limits conservatively chosen **6** None **Bibliography** Ref. 472 (pages 77–80), 602.

Known Range Limitations—First Three Moments, One-sided Interval

Data 1 Arbitrary, univariate **3** $[X(1)-EX(1)]/\sigma(1)$ **4** $m=1$; $n=1$ **Description 1** Bounds for prob. expression **2** $F(b)=P(-\infty, b)$ in terms of $EX(1)$, $\sigma(1)$, $\mu_3(1)$ and range limitations for $X(1)$ **Assumptions 2** $EX(1)^3$ exists **3** $A \leqslant [X(1)-EX(1)]/\sigma(1) \leqslant B$, where one limit can be infinite **Results 1** $T=[X(1)-EX(1)]/\sigma(1)$; $g(b)=b^2-bET^3-1$; $z_1 = [ET^3-(A+b)]/(1+Ab)$; $z_2=[ET^3-(B+b)]/(1+Bb)$; $z_3=[ET^3-(A+B)]/(1+AB)$; $C(x, y, z)=(1+xy)/(z-x)(z-y)$ **2** *Probability relations*: $0 \leqslant F(b) \leqslant C(B, z_2, b)$ if $b<0$ and $g(b) \geqslant 0$; $C(b, z_1, A) \leqslant F(b) \leqslant C(b, z_1, A)+C(A, z_1, b)$ if $b \leqslant z_3$ and $g(b) \leqslant 0$; $C(b, B, z_2) \leqslant F(b) \leqslant C(b, B, z_2)+C(B, z_2, b)$ if $b \geqslant z_3$ and $g(b) \leqslant 0$; $1-C(A, z_1, b) \leqslant F(b) \leqslant 1$ if $b>0$ and $g(b) \geqslant 0$. The inequalities for $b<0$, $g(b) \geqslant 0$ and for $b \geqslant z_3$, $g(b) \leqslant 0$ hold if $A=-\infty$. The inequalities for $b \leqslant z_3$, $g(b) \leqslant 0$ and for $b>0$, $g(b) \geqslant 0$ hold if $B=\infty$ **4** None **Characteristics 2** Best possible **3** Single observation **4** $EX(1)^3$ must exist. Effect of too small a value for B and/or too large a value for A can be determined; in any case, $B-A \geqslant 2$ **5** Virtually always satisfied if finite limits conservatively chosen **6** None **Bibliography** Ref. 472 (pages 77–80), 602.

Known Range Limitations—First Four Moments, One-sided Interval

Data 1 Arbitrary, univariate **3** $[X(1)-EX(1)]/\sigma(1)$ **4** $m=1$; $n=1$ **Description 1** Bounds for prob. expression **2** $F(b)=P(-\infty, b)$ in terms of $EX(1)$, $\sigma(1)$, $\mu_3(1)$, $\mu_4(1)$ and range limitations for $X(1)$ **Assumptions 2** $EX(1)^4$ exists **3** $A \leqslant [X(1)-EX(1)]/\sigma(1) \leqslant B$, where one limit can be infinite **Results 1** $T=[X(1)-EX(1)]/\sigma(1)$; $g(x, y)=x^2+\{[y-ET^3+y(yET^3-ET^4)]x+yET^3-ET^4+(ET^3-y)^2\}/[1+y(ET^3-y)]$; $u_1<u_2$ are roots of $g(u, A)=0$; $v_1<v_2$ are roots of $g(v, B)=0$; $w_1<w_2$ are roots of $g(w, b)=0$. Then $A<v_1<u_1<v_2<u_2<B$. $w_3=[(A+B+b)ET^3-ET^4-AB-Ab-Bb]/(ABb+A+B+b-ET^3)$; $c=[ET^4-(ET^3)^2-1]/\{(1+b^2)[ET^4-(ET^3)^2-1]+(b^2-bET^3-1)^2\}$; $D(x, y, z)=[ET^3-(x+y+w_3)-xyw_3]/(z-x)(z-y)(z-w_3)$ **2** *Probability relations*: $0 \leqslant F(b) \leqslant c$ if $A<b \leqslant v_1$; $D(B, b, A) \leqslant F(b) \leqslant D(B, b, A)+D(A, B, b)$ if $v_1<b \leqslant u_1$; $(1+bw_2)/(w_1-b)(w_1-w_2) \leqslant F(b) \leqslant (1+bw_2)/(w_1-b)(w_1-w_2)+c$ if $u_1 \leqslant b \leqslant v_2$;

$1-D(A, B, b)-D(A, b, B) \leqslant F(b) \leqslant 1-D(A, b, B)$ if $v_2 \leqslant b \leqslant u_2$; $1-c \leqslant F(b) \leqslant 1$ if $u_2 \leqslant b < B$ **4** None **Characteristics 2** Best possible **3** Single observation **4** $EX(1)^4$ must exist. Effect of too small a value for B and/or too large a value for A can be determined; in all cases, $B-A \geqslant 2$ **5** Virtually always satisfied if finite limits conservatively chosen **6** None **Bibliography** Ref. 472 (pages 77–80), 602.

Symmetrical Distribution—First Two Moments, One-sided Interval (*Agnew*)

Data 1 Arbitrary, univariate **3** $X(1)$ **4** $m=1$; $n=1$ **Description 1** Bounds for prob. expression **2** $F(b)=P(-\infty, b)$ in terms of $EX(1)$ and $\sigma(1)$ **Assumptions 2** $EX(1)^2$ exists and population symmetrical **3** None **Results 1** None **2** *Probability relations*: $0 \leqslant F(b) \leqslant \sigma^2(1)/2[b-EX(1)]^2$ if $[b-EX(1)]/\sigma(1) \leqslant -1$; $0 \leqslant F(b) \leqslant \frac{1}{2}$ if $-1 \leqslant [b-EX(1)]/\sigma(1) \leqslant 0$; $\frac{1}{2} \leqslant F(b) \leqslant 1$ if $0 < [b-EX(1)]/\sigma(1) \leqslant 1$; $1-\sigma^2(1)/2[b-EX(1)]^2 \leqslant F(b) \leqslant 1$ for $[b-EX(1)]/\sigma(1) \geqslant 1$ **4** None **Characteristics 2** Best possible **3** Single observation **4** $EX(1)^2$ must exist **5** Moderately difficult to verify symmetry **6** None **Bibliography** Ref. 3.

von Mises Convexity Conditions—One Absolute Moment, Symmetrical Interval

Data 1 Arbitrary, univariate **3** $X(1)$ **4** m $=1$; $n=1$ **Description 1** Lower bound for prob. expression **2** $P(-b, b)$ in terms of $E|X(1)|^r$ and constants arising from convexity conditions **Assumptions 2** $E|X(1)|^r$ exists **3** For $x > b_0 > 0$ and positive x_1 defined by $(r+1)x_1^r(x_1-b)=x_1^{r+1}-b_0^{r+1}$, the graph of $P(-x, x)$ lies below the line joining $(x_1, 1)$ and $\big(b, P(-b, b)\big)$ **Results 1** $x_2 > 0$ defined by $(r+1)(x_2-b)E|X(1)|^r=x_2^{r+1}-b_0^{r+1}$ **2** *Probability relations*: In all cases, $P(-b, b) \geqslant 1-E|X(1)|^r/x_1^r$. If $E|X(1)|^r > b_0^r$ and $x_1 < x_2$, $P(-b, b) \geqslant (b-b_0)/(x_2-b_0)$ **4** van Dantzig results (ref. 124 and 208) represent special cases **Characteristics 2** Best possible **3** Single observation **4** $E|X(1)|^r$ must exist. Effects of moderate violations of convexity condition unknown **5** Moderately difficult to verify convexity assumption **6** Useful when variable $X(1)-EX(1)$ or $[X(1)-EX(1)]/\sigma(1)$ **Bibliography** Ref. 124, 208, 348.

"Unimodal" Convexity Conditions of Ulin—Unknown "Mode"

Data 1 Arbitrary, univariate **3** $X(1)$ **4** $m=1$; $n=1$ **Description 1** Lower bound for prob. expression **2** $P[EX(1)-b, EX(1)+b]$ in terms of $\sigma(1)$ **Assumptions 2** $EX(1)^2$ exists. Also there is an x' such that $F(x)$ convex for $x < x'$ and concave for $x > x'$ **3** None **Results 1** None **2** *Probability relations*: $P(-b, b) \geqslant 1-4\sigma^2(1)/9b^2$ if $\sqrt{3}\sigma(1)/b \leqslant \frac{5}{4}$; $\geqslant 16/9[1+\sigma^2(1)/b^2]^2$ if $\sqrt{3}\sigma(1)/b > \frac{5}{4}$ **4** None **Characteristics 2** Best possible **3** Single observation **4** $EX(1)^2$ must exist. Effects of moderate violations of "unimodal" conditions unknown **5** Not difficult to verify assumptions **6** Results for $\operatorname{sgn}(b-x')$ known given in ref. 529 **Bibliography** Ref. 529.

Unknown Mode—First Two Moments, One-sided Interval (Mallows)

Data 1 Continuous, univariate **3** $X(1)$ **4** $m=1$; $n=1$ **Description 1** Bounds for prob. expression **2** $F(b)=P(-\infty, b)$ in terms of $EX(1)$ and $\sigma(1)$ **Assumptions 2** $EX(1)^2$ exists. $f(x)$ continuous and unimodal **3** None **Results 1** None **2** *Probability relations*: $F(b) \leqslant 4/9\{1+[b-EX(1)]^2/\sigma^2(1)\}$ if $b-EX(1) < -\sqrt{5/3}\sigma(1)$; $\leqslant 1-4\{[b-EX(1)]^2/\sigma^2(1)\}/3\{1+[b-EX(1)]^2/\sigma^2(1)\}$ if $-\sqrt{5/3}\sigma(1) \leqslant b-EX(1) \leqslant 0$. $F(b) \geqslant 4\{[b-EX(1)]^2/\sigma^2(1)\}/3\{1+[b-EX(1)]^2/\sigma^2(1)\}$ if $0 \leqslant b-EX(1) \leqslant \sqrt{5/3}\sigma(1)$; $\geqslant 1-4/9\{1+[b-EX(1)]^2/\sigma^2(1)\}$ if $b-EX(1) > \sqrt{5/3}\sigma(1)$ **4** None **Characteristics 2** Best possible **3** Single observation **4** $EX(1)^2$ must exist. Effects of moderate violations of unimodal and/or continuity conditions unknown **5** Not difficult to verify assumptions **6** Method for extending results to case of first $2k$ moments given in ref. 324 **Bibliography** Ref. 324, 466.

Monotonicity Conditions of Camp and Meidell—Continuous, One Absolute Moment

Data 1 Continuous, univariate **3** $X(1)$ **4** $m=1$; $n=1$ **Description 1** Lower bound for prob. expression **2** $P(-b, b)$ in terms of $E|X(1)|^r$ **Assumptions 2** $E|X(1)|^r$ exists. $f(x)+f(-x)$ monotonically decreasing fct. of $|x|$ **3** None **Results 1** None **2** *Probability relation*: $P(-b, b) \geqslant 1-[r/(r+1)]^r E|X(1)|^r/b^r$ **4** Special case of van Dantzig results of ref. 124 and of tail monotonicity conditions considered in ref. 84 **Characteristics 2** Not necessarily best possible **3** Single observation **4** $E|X(1)|^r$ must exist. Effects of moderate violations of monotonicity condition unknown **5** Moderately difficult to verify monotonicity condition **6** Useful when variable is $X(1)-EX(1)$ or $[X(1)-EX(1)]/\sigma(1)$ **Bibliography** Ref. 84, 124, 208, 343.

Central Monotonicity Conditions of Narumi—Continuous, One Absolute Moment

Data 1 Continuous, univariate **3** $X(1)$ **4** $m=1$; $n=1$ **Description 1** Bounds for prob. expression **2** $P(-b, b)$ in terms of $E|X(1)|^h$ and range of monotonicity around origin, where h any positive real no. **Assumptions 2** Case (I): $f(x)+f(-x)$ nondecreasing for $0 \leqslant x \leqslant H$. Case (II): $f(x)+f(-x)$ nonincreasing for $0 \leqslant x \leqslant H$ **3** Case (I): $E|H(1)|^h < H^h < (h+1)E|X(1)|^h$. Case (II): $H^h > E|X(1)|^h$ **Results 1** h_1 is positive root of $b(H^h-b^h)/(H-b)=(h+1)E|X(1)|^h-H^h$ **2** *Probability relations.*

Case (I): $0 \leqslant P(-b, b) \leqslant b/H$ if $0 \leqslant b \leqslant h_1[E|X(1)|^h]^{1/h}$; $b/H-(H-b)[(h+1)E|X(1)|^h-H^h]/H(H^h-b^h) \leqslant P(-b, b) \leqslant b/H$ if $h_1[E|X(1)|^h]^{1/h} \leqslant b \leqslant H$; $1-[(h+1)E|X(1)|^h-H^h]/[(h+1)b^h-H^h] \leqslant P(-b, b) \leqslant 1$ if $b \geqslant H$. *Case (II)*: $(h+1)b[1-E|X(1)|^h/H^h]/hH \leqslant P(-b, b) \leqslant 1$ if $0 \leqslant b \leqslant hH/(h+1)$; $1-E|X(1)|^h/H^h \leqslant P(-b, b) \leqslant 1$ if $hH/(h+1) \leqslant b \leqslant H$; $1-E|X(1)|^h/b^h \leqslant P(-b, b) \leqslant 1$ for $b \geqslant H$ **4** Case (I): $H^h \leqslant (h+1)E|X(1)|^h$. If $H^h=(h+1)E|X(1)|^h$, $P(-b, b)=b/H$ for $0 \leqslant b \leqslant H$; $P(-b, b)=1$ for $b \geqslant H$. Case (II): The Camp-Meidell inequality is obtained for $H=\infty$ **Characteristics 2** Best possible **3** Single observation **4** $E|X(1)|^h$ must exist. Effects of moderate violations of monotonicity conditions unknown **5** Moderately difficult to verify monotonicity conditions (including value of H) **6** Useful when variable $X(1)-EX(1)$ or $[X(1)-EX(1)]/\sigma(1)$ **Bibliography** Ref. 208, 377.

Royden Unimodal Results—First Two Absolute Moments about Known Mode

Data 1 Continuous, univariate **3** $X(1)$ **4** $m=1$; $n=1$ **Description 1** Bounds for prob. expression **2** $P(x_0-b, x_0+b)$ in terms of $E|X(1)-x_0|$ and $E[X(1)-x_0]^2$, where x_0 modal value for $X(1)$ **Assumptions 2** $f(x)$ has unique max. for $x=x_0$ and $E[X(1)-x_0]^2$ exists **3** x_0 assumed known for some applications *Results* **1** $v_{10}=E|X(1)-x_0|$, $v_{20}=E[X(1)-x_0]^2$, $\Lambda=3v_{20}/4v_{10}^2$; z_0 determined from $b=4v_{10}(z^3-z^2)/(3z^2-4z+\Lambda)$ **2** *Probability relations*: $P(x_0-b,\ x_0+b) \leqslant 1-(2v_{10}-b)/(3v_{20}-2bv_{10})$ if $0 \leqslant b \leqslant 2v_{10}$; $\leqslant 1$ if $b \geqslant 2v_{10}$. $P(x_0-b, x_0+b) \geqslant b/2v_{10}$ if $0 \leqslant b \leqslant v_{10}$; $\geqslant 1-v_{10}/2b$ if $v_{10} \leqslant b \leqslant 3v_{20}/4v_{10}$; $\geqslant 1-(4v_{10}^2/3v_{20})+(8v_{10}^2b/9v_{20}^2)$ if $3v_{20}/4v_{10} \leqslant b \leqslant v_{20}/v_{10}$; $\geqslant 1-(\Lambda-1)/(3z_0^2-4z_0+\Lambda)$ if $b \geqslant v_{20}/v_{10}$ **4** None **Characteristics 2** Not necessarily best possible **3** Single observation **4** $E[X(1)-x_0]^2$ must exist. Effects of moderate violations of unimodal condition unknown **5** Unimodal condition not difficult to verify. Evaluating x_0 can be very difficult **6** None **Bibliography** Ref. 208, 445.

Smith "Unimodal" Conditions—One Absolute Moment, Known "Mode"

Data 1 Continuous, univariate **3** $X(1)$ **4** $m=1$; $n=1$ **Description 1** Lower bound for prob. expression **2** $P(-b, b)$ in terms of $EX(1)^{2r}$ and modal value of $|X(1)|$ **Assumptions 2** $EX(1)^{2r}$ exists (r positive integer) and freq. fct. of $|X(1)|$ has unique max. at $x=X_0$ **3** X_0 assumed known for some applications **Results 1** $v_{2r}=EX(1)^{2r}$; y_0 determined from $b=2r[b^{2r+1}-(X_0y)^{2r+1}]/(2r+1)y[b^{2r}-(X_0y)^{2r}]$ **2** *Probability relation*: For $b<X_0/P(-X_0, X_0)$, $P(-b, b) \geqslant 1-\{v_{2r}-X_0^{2r}[1-2rX_0/b(2r+1)]\}/\{(b/y_0)^{2r}-X_0^r[1-2rX_0/b(2r+1)]\}$ **4** Useful when variable $[X(1)-EX(1)]/\sigma(1)$ **Characteristics 2** Best possible **3** Single observation **4** $EX\ (1)^{2r}$ must exist. Effects of moderate violations of monotonicity condition unknown

5 Monotonicity property difficult to verify. Evaluation of X_0 can be very difficult **6** Requirement that $b<X_0/P(-X_0, X_0)$ somewhat restricts usefulness of results since this ratio often not known **Bibliography** Ref. 208, 483, 484, 485.

Symmetric, Unique Mode or Minimum, Known Finite Range (*Shohat*)

Data 1 Continuous, univariate **3** $X(1)$ **4** $m=1$; $n=1$ **Description 1** Bounds for prob. expression **2** $P[EX(1)-b, EX(1)+b]$ in terms of $\mu_{2r}(1)$ and limits for $X(1)$ **Assumptions 2** $f(x)$ symmetric. Case (I): $f(x)$ has unique max. at $x=EX(1)$. Case (II): $f(x)$ has unique min. at $x=EX(1)$ **3** $-B\leqslant X(1)-EX(1)\leqslant B$ **Results 1** None **2** *Probability relations*: *Case* (*I*): $1-(B/b)^{2r}/(2r+1) \leqslant P[EX(1)-b, EX(1)+b]\leqslant [B^{2r+1}-b^{2r+1}-(B-b)(2r+1)\mu_{2r}(1)]/B(B^{2r}-b^{2r})$. *Case* (*II*): $P[EX(1)-b, EX(1)+b]\geqslant [B^{2r+1}-b^{2r+1}-(B-b)(2r+1)\mu_{2r}(1)]/B(B^{2r}-b^{2r})$ **4** Infinite range results given in ref. 471 **Characteristics 2** Not necessarily best possible **3** Single observation **4** Effect of moderate violations of monotonicity conditions unknown. Effect of choosing too small a value for B can be determined **5** Unimodal condition not difficult to verify. Justification of unique minimum and of symmetry more difficult. Choice of conservative value for B not difficult **6** None **Bibliography** Ref. 471.

Asymmetric, Known Finite Range and Mode or Minimum (*Shohat*)

Data 1 Continuous, univariate **3** $X(1)$ **4** $m=1$; $n=1$ **Description 1** Bounds for prob. expression **2** $P(x_0-b, x_0+b)$, where x_0 value where $f(x)$ max or min (2 cases), from $E[X(1)-x_0]^{2r}$, r integer, and limits for $X(1)$ **Assumptions 2** Case (I): $f(x)$ has unique max at $x=x_0$. Case (II): $f(x)$ has unique min at $x=x_0$ **3** $A\leqslant X(1)-x_0\leqslant B$ **Results 1** $H_1=\max[(A^{2r+1}+b^{2r+1})/(A+b), (B^{2r+1}-b^{2r+1})/(B-b)]$, $H_2=\min[(A^{2r+1}+b^{2r+1})/(A+b), (B^{2r+1}-b^{2r+1})/(B-b)]$ **2** *Probability relations*: *Case* (*I*): $1-[\max(|A|, B)/b]^{2r}/(2r+1)\leqslant P(x_0-b, x_0+b)\leqslant \{H_1-(2r+1)E[X(1)-x_0]^{2r}\}/(H_1-b^{2r})$. *Case* (*II*): $P(x_0-b, x_0+b)\geqslant \{H_2-(2r+1)E[X(1)-x_0]^{2r}\}/(H_2+b^{2r})$ **4** One-sided results and infinite interval results given in ref. 471 **Characteristics 2** Not necessarily best possible **3** Single observation **4** Effects of moderate violations of monotonicity conditions unknown. Effect of too small a value for B and/or too large a value for A can be determined **5** Existence of unique mode not too difficult to verify. Justification of unique min more difficult. Determination of x_0 difficult for both cases. Choice of conservative values for A and B not difficult **6** None **Bibliography** Ref. 471.

Symmetrical and Unimodal—Mean Range of Sample (*Winsten*)

Data 1 Continuous, univariate **3** $X(1)_1$ **4** $m=1$; $n_1=1$ **Description 1** Lower bound for prob. expression **2** $P\{EX(1)_1-dE(X[n_2]_2-X[1]_2),$

$EX(1)_1 + dE(X[n_2]_2 - X[1]_2\}$, where $d > 0$ and the $X[i]_2$ are order statistics of sample of n_2 from population yielding $X(1)_1$ **Assumptions 2** $EX[n_2]_2$ and $EX[1]_2$ exist. Population symmetrical and unimodal **3** None **Results 1** $w_0 \leqslant \frac{1}{2}$ determined from $1/2d = 1 - w^{n_2} - (1-w)^{n_2}$ **2** *Probability relation*: For $d \geqslant 2^{n_2-2}/(2^{n_2-1}-1)$, $P\{EX(1)_1 - dE(X[n_2]_2 - X[1]_2), EX(1)_1 + dE(X[n_2]_2 - X[1]_2)\} \geqslant 1 + 4d\{w_0{}^{n_2+1} + w_0(1-w_0)^{n_2} - [1 + w_0{}^{n_2+1} - (1-w_0)^{n_2+1}]/(n_2+1)\}$ **4** None **Characteristics 2** Best possible **3** Single observation **4** $EX[n_2]_2$ and $EX[1]_2$ must exist. Not sensitive to symmetry and unimodal conditions if d large **5** Moderately difficult to verify symmetry **6** None **Bibliography** Ref. 208, 593.

Lower Bound for Maximum of Continuous Frequency Function (Stuart)

Data 1 Continuous, univariate **3** $X(1)$ **4** $m = 1$; $n = 1$ **Description 1** Lower bound for max of freq. fct. **2** $\sup_x f(x)$ in terms of $\sigma(1)$ **Assumptions 2** $EX(1)^2$ exists. $f(x)$ finite and continuous **3** None **Results 1** None **2** *Bound relation*: $\sup_x f(x) \geqslant 1/2\sqrt{3}\sigma(1)$ **4** None **Characteristics 2** Best possible **3** Not pertinent **4** $EX(1)^2$ must exist **5** Approx. satisfied for virtually all practical situations of continuous nature **6** None **Bibliography** Ref. 498.

PROBABILITIES FOR AN AVERAGE OR SUM—UNIVARIATE CASE

Introduction

As indicated by the Law of Large Numbers, increasing the number of observations for an average $M(i)$ virtually always leads to a closer determination of the probability distribution for this average. Thus the upper and lower bounds for a probability expression involving an average of several univariate observations should be improved in comparison with those for the same expression involving a single observation. This improvement in bound values should virtually always be substantial if the number of observations for the average is at least moderately large, and should increase as the number of observations increases.

Most of the procedures presented are concerned with bounds for probability expressions of the form $P_M(a, b) = P[a \leqslant M(i) \leqslant b]$. In every case but one, the univariate observations $X(1), \ldots, X(n)$ are considered to be statistically independent. A random sample assumption is made for many of the procedures. For a few cases the only properties assumed are that a few moments exist for the populations yielding the observations, and the bounds are expressed in terms of these moments. In other cases additional properties such as symmetry, finite range (known or unknown), unimodal conditions, non-negative variables, etc. are assumed.

One of the procedures furnishes a lower bound for the value U such that $P[|M(i)-EX(i)|<U]=1$, where the $X(i)$ are a sample and have an unknown finite range. Another procedure deals with possibly dependent variables which have a known finite range and for which $E[X(i)|X(i-1), \ldots, X(1)]=\mu$. An upper bound is obtained for $P\{|M(i)-\mu|\geqslant d$ for some $n\geqslant N\}$. Another procedure deals with sequential subtotals of the observations and finds bounds for the probability that at least one of these exceeds a given amount. Two procedures are concerned with one-sided probability expressions involving averages of non-negative variables.

Fixed Material for Section

Data 2 None **3** $X(i)$ **4** $m=1$ **Characteristics 1** Low **3** Used symmetrically.

Moment Conditions of Bernstein and Craig

Data 1 Arbitrary, univariate **Description 1** Lower bound for prob. expression **2** $P_M\{[-b+\sum_{i=1}^{n} EX(i)]/n, \ [b+\sum_{i=1}^{n} EX(i)]/n\}$, in terms of $\sum_{i=1}^{n} \sigma^2(i)$ and a parameter that occurs in the assumed moment conditions **Assumptions 1** Independent **2** Specified "moments" exist **3** Case (*I*): $2|\mu_v(i)|\leqslant H^{v-2}v!\mu_2(i)$ for $v\geqslant 2$ and all i. Here the ordinary moments $\mu_v(i)$ can be replaced by the corresponding moments taken over an arbitrarily large interval that is symmetrical about $EX(i)$. Case (II): $2|\lambda_v(i)|\leqslant H^{v-2}v!\lambda_2(i)$ for $v\geqslant 2$ and all i. Here the ordinary cumulants $\lambda_v(i)$ can be replaced by the corresponding cumulants taken over an arbitrarily large interval that is symmetrical about $EX(i)$. Cumulants and central moments are related by $\exp\,[\lambda_2(i)x^2/2!+\lambda_3(i)\,x^3/3!\ldots]\equiv 1+\mu_2(i)x^2/2!+\mu_3(i)x^3/3!+\ldots$ **Results 1** None **2** *Probability relation*: For both cases, $P_M\{[-b+\sum_{i=1}^{n} EX(i)]/n, \ [b+\sum_{i=1}^{n} EX(i)]/n\}\geqslant 1-2\exp\{-b^2/[2Hb+2\sum_{i=1}^{n}\sigma^2(i)]\}$ **3** None **4** Case (I) assumption satisfied for some H if for all i the variable $X(i)$ is continuous with frequency fct. $f_i(x)$ such that either $f_i[x-EX(i)]\geqslant f_i[-x+EX(i)]$ for all sufficiently large x or $f_i[x-EX(i)]\leqslant f_i[-x+EX(i)]$ for all sufficiently large x. In any case where the $X(i)$ have finite range such that $|X(i)-EX(i)|\leqslant B$, Case (I) assumption satisfied with $H=B/3$. Case (II) assumption satisfied for multinomial distribution and Pearson Type III distribution **Characteristics 2** Not necessarily best possible **4** Effect of choosing too small a value for H can be determined. Sensitivity to moderate violations of independence unknown. $EX(i)^2$ must exist; effect of nonexistence of higher order moments unknown **5** Not difficult to decide on independence. More difficult to choose conservative value for H (not always possible) **6** In ref. 48 independence condition removed by considering conditional expectations **Bibliography** Ref. 47, 48, 113, 208.

Offord's Moment Conditions—LUB for Intervals of Given Length

Data 1 Arbitrary, univariate **Description 1** Lower limit for least upper bound of probability expression **2** LUB over x of $P_M\{[x-b+\sum_{i=1}^{n} EX(i)]/n, \; [x+b+\sum_{i=1}^{n} EX(i)]/n\}$ **Assumptions 1** Independent **2** $E|X(i)-EX(i)|^3$ exists **3** $\sigma(i)/(E|X(i)-EX(i)|^3)^{1/3} \geqslant 2K^{1/3}$ for all i **Results 1** None **2** *Probability relation*: $\text{LUB}_x P_M\{[x-b+\sum_{i=1}^{n} EX(i)]/n, \; [x+b+\sum_{i=1}^{n} EX(i)]/n\} \leqslant 6(\log_e n)\{\log_e n + Kb/[\min_i \sigma(i)]\}/K^3\sqrt{n}$ **3** None **4** Maximizing x value unknown **Characteristics 2** Not necessarily best possible **4** $E|X(i)-EX(i)|^3$ must exist. Effect of choosing too large a value for K can be determined **5** Not difficult to verify independence. Moderately difficult to choose suitable value for K **6** Usefulness limited because maximizing x unknown **Bibliography** Ref. 208, 392.

First Two Moments—Random Sample (Guttman)

Data 1 Arbitrary, univariate **4** $n \geqslant 2$ **Description 1** Lower bound for prob. expression **2** $P_M\{EX(i)-[S^2(i)/n+\sigma^2(i)\sqrt{2(b^2-1)/n(n-1)}]^{1/2}, \; EX(i)+[S^2(i)/n+\sigma^2(i)\sqrt{2(b^2-1)/n(n-1)}]^{1/2}\}$ **Assumptions 1** Random sample **2** $EX(i)^2$ exists **3** None **Results 1** None **2** *Probability relation*: $P_M\{EX(i)-[S^2(i)/n+\sigma^2(i)\sqrt{2(b^2-1)/n(n-1)}]^{1/2}, \; EX(i)+[S^2(i)/n+\sigma^2(i)\sqrt{2(b^2-1)/n(n-1)}]^{1/2}\} \geqslant 1-1/b^2$ **3** None **4** None **Characteristics 2** Not necessarily best possible. $E[S^2(i)/n+\sigma^2(i)\sqrt{2(b^2-1)/n(n-1)}]/b^2[\sigma^2(i)/n] = [1+\sqrt{2(b^2-1)n/(n-1)}]/b^2$. Thus this method preferable to Tchebycheff's inequality (on the average) if $b \geqslant 2.3$; strongly preferable for large b **4** $EX(i)^2$ must exist. Effects of moderate violations of sample assumption unknown **5** Not difficult to decide on sample assumption **6** None **Bibliography** Ref. 208, 221.

Approximate Bounds—First Two Moments, Random Sample (Midzuno)

Data 1 Arbitrary, univariate **4** $n \geqslant 2$ for case involving $S^2(i)$ **Description 1** Theoretical-approximate lower bounds for prob. expressions

2 $P_M\Big[EX(i)-b\sigma(i)/\sqrt{n}, EX(i)+b\sigma(i)/\sqrt{n}\Big]$ $+O(n^{-1})$ and $P_M\Big[EX(i)-\sqrt{S^2(i)/n+b\sigma^2(i)/n}, EX(i)+\sqrt{S^2(i)/n+b\sigma^2(i)/n}\Big]$ $+O(n^{-1})$, in terms of a parameter λ **Assumptions 1** Random sample **2** $E|M(i)-EX(i)|^\lambda$ exists for λ a positive integer **3** None **Results 1** None **2** *Probability relations*: $P_M\Big[EX(i)-b\sigma(i)/\sqrt{n}, \quad EX(i)+b\sigma(i)/\sqrt{n}\Big] \geqslant \quad 1-[1\cdot 3\cdot 5\cdots(\lambda-1)][1+O(n^{-1})]/b^\lambda$, λ even. $P_M\Big[EX(i)-\sqrt{S^2(i)/n+b\sigma^2(i)/n}, \quad EX(i)+\sqrt{S^2(i)/n+b\sigma^2(i)/n}\Big] \geqslant \quad 1 \quad -b^{-\lambda}\sum_{h=0}^{\lambda}(-1)^h\binom{\lambda}{h}[2(\lambda-h)]![1+O(n^{-1})]/2^{\lambda-h}(\lambda-h)!$ **3** None **4** To $O(n^{-1})$, the lower bounds can be maximized with respect to λ **Characteristics 2** Not necessarily best possible **4** $E|M(i)-EX(i)|^\lambda$ must exist for λ values considered. Effects of moderate violations of sample assumption unknown. Min n such that $O(n^{-1})$ terms unimportant depends on population **5** Not difficult to decide on sample assumption. Difficult to determine min n such that $O(n^{-1})$ terms unimportant **6** Properties of tail prob. for this inequality furnished by ref. 433 **Bibliography** Ref. 345, 433.

Non-Negative Variables, First Moments (*Birnbaum, Raymond, Zuckerman*)

Data 1 Arbitrary, univariate **Description 1** Upper bound for prob. expression **2** $P[M(i)\geqslant b/n]$ in terms of the $EX(i)$ **Assumptions 1** Independent **2** The $EX(i)$ exist **3** $X(i)\geqslant 0$ for all i **Results 1** For $1\leqslant r<n$, $\gamma_1=\min\Big[\sum_{i=1}^{r} EX(i), \sum_{i=r+1}^{n} EX(i)\Big]$; $\gamma_2=\max\Big[\sum_{i=1}^{r} EX(i), \sum_{i=r+1}^{n} EX(i)\Big]$ **2** *Probability relations*: $P[M(i)\geqslant b/n]\leqslant 1$ if $b\leqslant\gamma_1+\gamma_2$; $\leqslant\gamma_2/(b-\gamma_1)$ if $\gamma_1+\gamma_2 \leqslant b \leqslant (\gamma_1+2\gamma_2+\sqrt{\gamma_1^2+4\gamma_2^2})/2$; $\leqslant(\gamma_1+\gamma_2)/b-\gamma_1\gamma_2/b^2$ if $b\geqslant(\gamma_1+2\gamma_2+\sqrt{\gamma_1^2+4\gamma_2^2})/2$ **3** None **4** Upper bound values can be minimized by choice of r and way of dividing the observations into two sets **Characteristics 2** Not necessarily best possible except for $n=2$ **4** $EX(1)\ldots, EX(n)$ must exist. Effects of moderate violations of independence unknown **5** Not difficult to verify independence and non-negative nature of variables **6** Useful when the $EX(i)$ differ by known factors **Bibliography** Ref. 58.

Non-Negative Variables, Equal First Moments (*Hoeffding and Shrikhande*)

Data 1 Arbitrary, univariate **Description 1** Upper bound for prob. expression **2** $P[M(i)\geqslant bEX(i)]$ **Assumptions 1** Case (I): Random sample. Case (II): Independent **2** The $EX(i)$ exist **3** $X(i)\geqslant 0$ for all i; $EX(1)=\ldots=EX(n)>0$ **Results 1** $w_I(b)=1/b-(1+\theta)(n-1)/4nb^2$, where $1/n\leqslant\theta<1$. $W_I(b)=1/b-(1+\theta')/4b^2$, where $0\leqslant\theta'\leqslant 1-4/n$. $w_{II}(b)=1/b-(n^2-1)/4n^2b^2$. $W_{II}(b)=1/b-4/b^2$ **2** *Probability relations. Case (I)*:

When $n=2$, $P[X(1)+X(2) \geqslant bEX(i)] \leqslant 1$ for $b \leqslant 2$; $\leqslant 4/b^2$ for $2 \leqslant b \leqslant \frac{5}{2}$; $\leqslant 2/b - 1/b^2$ for $b \geqslant \frac{5}{2}$. For all n and for $b \geqslant [3n+1+\sqrt{5n^2+6n+5}]/4n$, $P[M(i) \geqslant bEX(i)] \leqslant w_I(b)$. For even n and $b \geqslant \frac{5}{4}$, $P[M(i) \geqslant bEX(i)] \leqslant W_I(b)$. *Case (II)*: For all n and for $b \geqslant [3n+1+\sqrt{5n^2+6n+5}]/4n$, $P[M(i) \geqslant bEX(i)] \leqslant w_{II}(b)$. For even n and $b \geqslant (3+\sqrt{5})/4$, $P[M(i) \geqslant bEX(i)] \leqslant W_{II}(b)$ **3** None **4** θ and θ' unknown for $n > 2$ **Characteristics 2** Results for Case (I), which are best possible for some θ and θ' in indicated ranges, show that results for Case (II) nearly best possible for sufficiently large b. Results for Case (I) and $n=2$ are best possible **4** Effects of violation of Case (I) furnished by results for Case (II). Effects of violation of Case (II) furnished by preceding presentation, where first moments not necessarily equal. Effects of violating non-negative and independence assumptions unknown **5** Not difficult to verify sample condition and non-negative nature of variables. The $EX(i)$ must exist. Difficult to verify assumption of common mean value for Case (II) **6** For $n=2$, ref. 251 furnishes general results for non-negative variables in terms of k moments of the population sampled **Bibliography** Ref. 251.

Symmetrical, Unimodal, Known Finite Range—Random Sample (*Z. W. Birnbaum*)

Data 1 Continuous, univariate **Description 1** Lower bound for prob. expression **2** $P_M[EX(i)-b,\ EX(i)+b]$ in terms of upper limit for $|X(i)-EX(i)|$ **Assumptions 1** Random sample **2** Population symmetrical and $f(x)$ nonincreasing for $x > EX(i)$ **3** $-B \leqslant X(i)-EX(i) \leqslant B$ **Results 1** $\psi_n(b) = \frac{2}{n} \sum_{\frac{1}{2}n(1+b/B)<k\leqslant n} (-1)^k \binom{n}{k} [n(1+b/B)/2-k]^n$ **2** *Probability relation*: $P_M[EX(i)-b,\ EX(i)+b] \geqslant 1-\psi_n(b)$ **3** For $n \geqslant 15$ and $2/3n \leqslant \beta \leqslant 1-1/\sqrt{n}$, $\psi_n(b) \doteq \beta$, where $K_{\beta/2} = b\sqrt{3n}/B$ **4** None **Characteristics 2** Not necessarily best possible **4** Effect of using too small a value for B can be determined. Effects of moderate violations of other assumptions unknown **5** Not difficult to decide on sample assumption or choose conservative value for B. Moderately difficult to verify symmetry and monotonicity conditions **6** None **Bibliography** Ref. 54, 208.

Known Finite Range, Conditional First Moments—Sequential Probability (*Weingarten*)

Data 1 Arbitrary, univariate **4** n not fixed **Description 1** Upper bound for prob. expression **2** $P[|M(i)-\mu| \geqslant bB$ for some $n \geqslant N]$ in terms of N and b **Assumptions 1** None **2** None **3** $E[X(i)|X(i-1), \ldots, X(1)] = \mu$; $|X(i)-\mu| \leqslant B$, $(i=1, \ldots, n)$ **Results 1** None **2** *Probability relation*: $P[|M(i)-\mu| \geqslant bB$ for some $n \geqslant N] \leqslant 2[(1+b)^{-(1+b)/2}(1-b)^{-(1-b/2}]^N$ **3**

None **4** None **Characteristics 2** Best possible **4** Effect of choosing too small a value for B can be determined. Sensitivity to moderate violations of conditional first moment assumption unknown **5** Often not difficult to choose conservatively large value for B. Difficult to verify conditional first moment assumption if variables dependent **6** Useful for sequential analysis type schemes involving finite range variables **Bibliography** Ref. 576.

Kolmogoroff Inequalities for Cumulative Sums—Known Finite Range

Data 1 Arbitrary, univariate **Description 1** Bounds for prob. expression **2** $P\left\{\max_r \mid \sum_{i=1}^{r} X(i) - \sum_{i=1}^{r} EX(i)| \geqslant b\right\}$, $P\left\{\max_r \mid \sum_{i=1}^{r} X(i)| \leqslant b\right\}$, $P\{|M(i)| \geqslant b/n\}$ are types considered. Bounds given in terms of $\sigma^2\left[\sum_{i=1}^{n} X(i)\right] = \sum_{i=1}^{n} \sigma^2(i)$ and limit for $\max_i |X(i) - EX(i)|$ **Assumptions 1** Independent **2** None **3** $\max_i |X(i) - EX(i)| \leqslant B$ **Results 1** None **2** *Probability relations*: $P\left\{\max_r \mid \sum_{i=1}^{r} X(i) - \sum_{i=1}^{r} EX(i)| \geqslant b\right\} \leqslant \sum_{i=1}^{n} \sigma^2(i)/b^2$ $(b > B)$; $P\left\{\max_r \mid \sum_{i=1}^{r} X(i) - \sum_{i=1}^{r} EX(i)| \geqslant tb\right\} \leqslant \left[\sum_{i=1}^{n} \sigma(i)^2\right]^{1/2}/(b-B)^{2t}$ if t integer and $b > B$; $P\left\{\max_r \mid \sum_{i=1}^{r} X(i)| \leqslant b\right\} \leqslant 4(b+B)^2/\left[\sum_{i=1}^{n} \sigma^2(i)\right]$; $P\left\{|M(i)| \geqslant b/n\right\} \geqslant \left\{1 - (B^2 + 4b^2)/\left[\sum_{i=1}^{n} \sigma^2(i)\right]\right\}/1600$ and $P\left\{|M(i)| \geqslant \sum_{i=1}^{n} \sigma^2(i)/2n\right\} \geqslant 1/1600$ if $B \leqslant \left[\sum_{i=1}^{n} \sigma^2(i)\right]^{1/2}$ **3** None **4** Let $c(1) \geqslant \ldots \geqslant c(n) > 0$. Then, for specified r_1 and r_2 such that $1 \leqslant r_1 \leqslant r_2 \leqslant n$, $P\left\{\max_{r_1 \leqslant r \leqslant r_2} c(r)|\sum_{i=1}^{r} X(i) - \sum_{i=1}^{r} EX(i)| \geqslant b\right\} \leqslant \left[c(r_1)^2 \sum_{i=1}^{r_1} \sigma^2(i) + \sum_{i=r_1+1}^{r_2} c(i)^2\sigma^2(i)\right]/b^2$, from ref. 223 **Characteristics 2** Not necessarily best possible **4** Effect of choosing too small a value for B can be determined. Sensitivity to moderate violations of independence unknown **5** Not difficult to decide on independence or to choose conservatively large value for B **6** Useful for sequential analysis type schemes involving finite range variables **Bibliography** Ref. 208, 223, 285, 286.

Lower Bound for Range of Variable—First Two Moments, Sample (Rényi)

Data 1 Arbitrary, univariate **Description 1** Lower bound for range of random variable **2** Lower bound U_n for values U such that $P\{|M(i) - EX(i)| < U\} = 1$, in terms of $\int_{-\infty}^{EX(i)} F(x)dx$ and $\sigma(i)$ **Assumptions 1** Random sample **2** Variable has finite range **3** None **Results 1** $F(x)$ dist. fct. of $X(i)$ **2** *Probability relation*: $U_n \geqslant \sigma^2(i)/\left\{2\int_{-\infty}^{EX(i)} F(x)dx\right\}$ **3** None **4** None **Characteristics 2** Best possible **4** Effects of moderate violations of sample assumption unknown **5** Not difficult to decide on sample assumption. Less easy to decide on $\int_{-\infty}^{EX(i)} F(x)dx$ **6** Lower bound attained for binomial variable with success prob. 1/2 **Bibliography** Ref. 423.

DIFFERENCE OF UNIVARIATE DISTRIBUTION FUNCTIONS

Introduction

If a number of the corresponding moments of two distribution functions are equal, these distribution functions should not differ greatly. Four results are presented that furnish bounds for $|F_1(x)-F_2(x)|$ in terms of common moment values, and perhaps other properties. The first $2k$ moments are considered for two of the presentations. In one case, no additional restrictions are imposed; the other case is continuous, the variables have finite ranges, and the frequency function ratio $-f_1(x)/f_2(x)$ has known bounds. For another of the presentations of this type, only the first two moments are considered but the populations are assumed to be symmetrical. For the other presentation, one of the distribution functions is normal and the first two moments are considered.

As the sample size increases, the distribution of $M(i)$ ordinarily tends to normality. Consequently, for these cases it is possible to estimate $P_M(-\infty, x)$, the distribution function of $M(i)$, in terms of the normal probability integral. Three results are presented that furnish bounds for $|P_M(-\infty, x)-\Phi\{[x-EM(i)]/\sigma[M(i)]\}|$, where $\Phi(x)$ is the standard normal distribution function. Two of these presentations only require the observations to be independent and to be from populations for which the third absolute moment exists. The other presentation imposes the additional restriction that the observations are a sample.

Fixed Material for Section

Data 2 None **Description 1** Upper bound for absolute difference between two dist. fcts. **Results 3** None.

First 2k Moments—No Additional Restrictions (Khamis)

Data 1 Arbitrary, univariate **3** $X(1)_1$ from F_1 and $X(1)_2$ from F_2 **4** $m=2$; $n_1=n_2=1$ **Description 2** $F_1(x)$ and $F_2(x)$ have same first $2k$ moments about origin. $|F_1(x)-F_2(x)|$ in terms of x and these moments **Assumptions 1** None **2** Specified $2k$ moments exist and are same for both populations **3** Both F_1 and F_2 have at least $k+1$ points of increase **Results 1** Moments denoted by $\mu^{(1)}, \ldots, \mu^{(2k)}$.

$$D_k(x)=\begin{vmatrix} 0 & 1 & x & \cdots & x^k \\ 1 & 1 & \mu^{(1)} & \cdots & \mu^{(k)} \\ x & \mu^{(1)} & \mu^{(2)} & \cdots & \mu^{(k+1)} \\ . & . & . & & . \\ . & . & . & & . \\ . & . & . & & . \\ x^k & \mu^{(k)} & \mu^{(k+1)} & \cdots & \mu^{(2k)} \end{vmatrix} \qquad \Delta_k=\begin{vmatrix} 1 & \mu^{(1)} & \cdots & \mu^{(k)} \\ \mu^{(k)} & \mu^{(2)} & \cdots & \mu^{(k+1)} \\ . & . & & . \\ . & . & & . \\ . & . & & . \\ \mu^{(k)} & \mu^{(k+1)} & \cdots & \mu^{(2k)} \end{vmatrix}$$

2 *Probability relation*: $|F_1(x)-F_2(x)| \leqslant -\Delta_k/D_k(x)$ **4** For $k=1$, $|F_1(x)-F_2(x)| \leqslant 1/\{1+[x-EX(1)_1]^2/\sigma^2(1)_1\}$ **Characteristics 1** Low to medium (unless k large) **2** Best possible **3** Not pertinent **4** $EX(1)_1{}^{2k}$ and $EX(1)_2{}^{2k}$ must exist **5** Satisfied for virtually all practical situations **6** Related results for moments about arbitrary pt. given in ref. 280 **Bibliography** Ref. 3, 208, 280.

First 2k Moments—Finite Ranges, $-f_1(x)/f_2(x)$ Bounded (Khamis)

Data 1 Continuous, univariate **3** $X(1)_1$ from F_1 and $X(1)_2$ from F_2 **4** $m=2$; $n_1=n_2=1$ **Description 2** $F_1(x)$ and $F_2(x)$ have same first $2k$ moments about origin. $|F_1(x)-F_2(x)|$ in terms of x, the first $2k$ moments, and bounds for $-f_1(x)/f_2(x)$ **Assumptions 1** None **2** Specified $2k$ moments exist and are same for both populations **3** $a_1 \leqslant X(1)_1 \leqslant b_1$, $a_2 \leqslant X(1)_2 \leqslant b_2$; a_1 and/or a_2 can be $-\infty$ while b_1 and/or b_2 can be ∞ **Results 1** $a=\min(a_1, a_2)$, $b=\max(b_1, b_2)$; $A=\mathrm{LUB}_{a\leqslant x\leqslant b}[-f_1(x)/f_2(x)]$, $B=\mathrm{LUB}_{a\leqslant x\leqslant b}[-f_2(x)/f_1(x)]$; $K=(1+A)(1+B)/[2+A+B-(1+A)(1+B)]$; moments denoted by $\mu^{(1)}, \ldots, \mu^{(2k)}$;

$$D_k(x)=\begin{vmatrix} 0 & 1 & x & \cdots & x^k \\ 1 & 1 & \mu^{(1)} & \cdots & \mu^{(k)} \\ x & \mu^{(1)} & \mu^{(2)} & \cdots & \mu^{(k+1)} \\ . & . & . & & . \\ . & . & . & & . \\ . & . & . & & . \\ x^k & \mu^{(k)} & \mu^{(k+1)} & \cdots & \mu^{(2k)} \end{vmatrix} \qquad \Delta_k=\begin{vmatrix} 1 & \mu^{(1)} & \cdots & \mu^{(k)} \\ \mu^{(1)} & \mu^{(2)} & \cdots & \mu^{(k+1)} \\ . & . & & . \\ . & . & & . \\ . & . & & . \\ \mu^{(k)} & \mu^{(k+1)} & \cdots & \mu^{(2k)} \end{vmatrix}$$

2 *Probability relation*: $|F_1(x)-F_2(x)| \leqslant -K\Delta_k/D_k(x)$ **4** None **Characteristics 1** Low to medium (unless k large) **2** Best possible **3** Not pertinent **4** $EX(1)_1{}^{2k}$ and $EX(1)_2{}^{2k}$ must exist. Effect of using A, B values that are too small can be determined; in all cases $-1 \leqslant A, B \leqslant 0$ **5** Difficult to determine suitable values for A and/or B **6** Difficulty of evaluating A and/or B restricts usefulness. Related results given in ref. 280 **Bibliography** Ref. 280.

First Two Moments—Symmetrical Distributions (Agnew)

Data 1 Arbitrary, univariate **3** $X(1)_1$ from F_1 and $X(1)_2$ from F_2 **4** m$=2$; $n_1=n_2=1$ **Description 2** $F_1(x)$ and $F_2(x)$ have same first and second moments. $|F_1(x)-F_2(x)|$ in terms of x and these moments **Assumptions 1** None **2** $EX(1)_1{}^2$ and $EX(1)_2{}^2$ exist; $F_1(x)$ and $F_2(x)$ both symmetrical **3** $EX(1)_1=EX(1)_2$ and $\sigma^2(1)_1=\sigma^2(1)_2$ **Results 1** $\mu=EX(1)_1$, $\sigma^2=\sigma^2(1)_1$ **2** *Probability relations*: $|F_1(x)-F_2(x)|\leqslant\frac{1}{2}$ if $|(x-\mu)/\sigma|\leqslant 1$; $\leqslant 1/2[(x-\mu)/\sigma]^2$ if $|(x-\mu)/\sigma|\geqslant 1$ **4** None **Characteristics 1** Low **2** Best possible **3** Not pertinent **4** $EX(1)_1{}^2$ and $EX(1)_2{}^2$ must exist. Sensitivity to symmetry determined by comparison with result $|F_1(x)-F_2(x)|\leqslant 1/[1+(x-\mu)^2/\sigma^2]$, which is best possible if F_1 and F_2 not necessarily symmetrical **5** Moderately difficult to verify symmetry condition **6** None **Bibliography** Ref. 3.

Deviation From Normality—First Two Moments (Agnew)

Data 1 Arbitrary, univariate **3** $X(1)$ **4** $m=1$; $n=1$ **Description 2** $|F(x)-\Phi\{[x-EX(1)]/\sigma(1)\}|$ in terms of x, $EX(1)$, $\sigma(1)$; where $X(1)$ from F **Assumptions 1** None **2** $EX(1)^2$ exists **3** None **Results 1** None **2** *Probability relations*: $|F(x)-\Phi\{[x-EX(1)]/\sigma(1)\}|$ $-1/\{1+[x-EX(1)]^2/\sigma^2(1)\}\leqslant$ $-\Phi\{[x-EX(1)]/\sigma(1)\}$ if $x\leqslant EX(1)$; $\leqslant\Phi\{[x-EX(1)]/\sigma(1)\}-1$ if $x>EX(1)$ **4** None **Characteristics 1** Low **2** Best possible **3** Single observation **4** $EX(1)^2$ must exist **5** Satisfied for virtually all practical situations **6** None **Bibliography** Ref. 3.

Deviation From Normality For An Average—Berry's Inequality

Data 1 Arbitrary, univariate **3** $X(i)$ **4** $m=1$ **Description 2** $|P_M(-\infty,x)-\Phi\{[x-EM(i)]/\sigma[M(i)]\}|$ in terms of the $\sigma^2(i)$ and the $E|X(i)-EX(i)|^3$ **Assumptions 1** Independent **2** $E|X(i)|^3$ exists for all i **3** None **Results 1** None **2** *Probability relation*: $|P_M(-\infty,x)-\Phi\{[x-EM(i)]/\sigma[M(i)]\}|\leqslant 1.952\{\sigma[nM(i)]\}^{-1}\max_i[E|X(i)-EX(i)|^3/\sigma^2(i)]$ **4** None **Characteristics 1** Low **2** Not necessarily best possible **3** Used symmetrically **4** The $E|X(i)|^3$ must exist. Sensitivity to moderate violations of independence unknown **5** Verification of independence not difficult **6** Preferable to Bergström's inequality (see page 106) if distributions of variables at least roughly the same, but not necessarily preferable otherwise. The author is indebted to H. R. van der Vaart for pointing out that 1.952 factor furnished by ref. 497 **Bibliography** Ref. 49, 208, 497.

Deviation From Normality For An Average—Bergström's Inequality

Data 1 Arbitrary, univariate **3** $X(i)$ **4** $m=1$ **Description 2** $|P_M(-\infty,x)-\Phi\{[x-EM(i)]/\sigma[M(i)]\}|$ in terms of the $\sigma^2(i)$ and the $E|X(i)-EX(i)|^3$ **Assumptions 1** Independent **2** $E|X(i)|^3$ exists for all i **3** None **Results**

1 None **2** *Probability relation:* $|P_M(-\infty, x) - \Phi\{[x - EM(i)]/\sigma[M(i)]\}| \leqslant 4.8 \sum_{i=1}^{n} E|X(i) - EX(i)|^3/[\sum_{j=1}^{n} \sigma^2(j)]^{3/2}$ **4** None **Characteristics 1** Low **2** Not necessarily best possible **3** Used symmetrically **4** The $E|X(i)|^3$ must exist. Sensitivity to moderate violations of independence unknown **5** Verification of independence not difficult **6** Preferable to Berry's inequality (see page 106) for some cases where the variables have appreciably different distributions **Bibliography** Ref. 45, 208.

Deviation From Normality—Mean of Sample (Gurland)

Data 1 Arbitrary, univariate **3** $X(i)$ **4** $m = 1$ **Description 2** $|P_M(-\infty, x) - \Phi\{\sqrt{n}[x - EX(i)]/\sigma(i)\}|$ in terms of $\sigma^2(i)$ and $E|X(i) - EX(i)|^3$ **Assumptions 1** Random sample **2** $E|X(i)|^3$ exists **3** None **Results 1** None **2** *Probability relation:* $|P_M(-\infty, x) - \Phi\{\sqrt{n}[x - EX(i)]/\sigma(i)\}| \leqslant 2.89\ E|X(i) - EX(i)|^3/\sigma^3(i)\sqrt{n}$ **4** None **Characteristics 1** Low **2** Not necessarily best possible **3** Used symmetrically **4** $E|X(i)|^3$ must exist. Sensitivity to moderate violation of independence unknown. Comparison with Bergström's inequality (see page 106) shows that additional condition of same distribution reduces the factor for the bound from 4.8 to 2.89 **5** Not difficult to decide on random sample assumption **6** None **Bibliography** Ref. 219.

PROBABILITIES FOR MULTIVARIATE CASE

Discussion

For the multivariate case, the problem is to find a bound (or bounds) for the amount of probability falling in some specified region of the multidimensional space for the variable investigated. Owing to the variation in the types of regions considered, no attempt is made to develop a standard notation for the probability expressions. However, for cases where the relation to be satisfied is complicated, this relation is represented by a symbol and P(that symbol) is used to represent the probability that this relation is satisfied. In this section the sample size is m and the dimensionality of a random variable is n.

The data are the $\{X(i)_j\}_m$, with $m = 1$ in all but one case. For most of the presentations the value of n is arbitrary except that $n \geqslant 2$; also the case $n = 2$ occurs a few times. Most of the regions considered are of a "rectangular" or of an "elliptical" form. For several presentations, the data are independent univariate observations (e.g., a random sample), but the region cannot be expressed in a one-dimensional form; then $n = 1$ and the observations are $X(1)_1, \ldots, X(1)_m$. In one case the relation involves deviations from a regression line. For most of the presentations, the form of the data is arbitrary; sometimes the data are converted to a categorical form. However, a few continuous cases do occur. For nearly all the presentations, use of moments of higher than second order is not considered. The two presentations based on categorical data are applicable for testing distributions.

Fixed Material for Section

Data 2 None **3** $\{X(i)_j\}_m$ **4** $n \geqslant 2$ for multivariate cases **Results 3** None.

Bivariate, Rectangles, First and Second Order Moments (*Berge, Lal*)

Data 1 Arbitrary, bivariate **4** $m=1$; $n=2$ **Description 1** Lower bound for prob. expression **2** $P\Big\{|X(1)-EX(1)| \leqslant b_1\sigma(1),\ |X(2)-EX(2)| \leqslant b_2\sigma(2)\Big\}$ in terms of b_1, b_2, and $\rho[X(1), X(2)]$ **Assumptions 1** None **2** The second-order moments exist **3** None **Results 1** None **2** *Probability relation*: $P\Big\{|X(1)-EX(1)| \leqslant b_1\sigma(1), |X(2)-EX(2)| \leqslant b_2\sigma(2)\Big\} \geqslant \quad 1-\Big[b_1{}^2+b_2{}^2+\{(b_1{}^2+b_2{}^2)^2-4\rho[X(1), X(2)]^2 b_1{}^2 b_2{}^2\}^{1/2}\Big]\Big/2b_1{}^2b_2{}^2$ **4** Ref. 302 contains some results (may need typographical corrections) for $n \geqslant 3$ **Characteristics 1** Low **2** Best possible **3** Single observation **4** The second-order moments must exist **5** Satisfied for virtually all practical situations **6** None **Bibliography** Ref. 44, 302.

Bivariate, Ellipses, Moments of Specified Even Order (*K. Pearson*)

Data 1 Arbitrary, bivariate **4** $m=1$; $n=2$ **Description 1** Lower bound for prob. expression **2** $P(Y)$, where Y represents the relation $\gamma_{11}[X(1)-EX(1)]^2/\sigma^2(1)-2\gamma_{12}\rho[X(1), X(2)][X(1)-EX(1)][X(2)-EX(2)]/\sigma(1)\sigma(2)+\gamma_{22}[X(2)-EX(2)]^2/\sigma^2(2) \leqslant \quad b^2\{1-\rho[X(1),\ X(2)]^2\}$, in terms of the moments of order $2k$ **Assumptions 1** None **2** The moments of order $2k$ exist **3** $\gamma_{12}{}^2\rho[X(1), X(2)]^2<\gamma_{11}\gamma_{22}$ **Results 1** $I_k= \quad \{1-\rho[X(1), X(2)]^2\}^{-k}\int_{-\infty}^{\infty}\int_{-\infty}^{\infty}\Big\{\gamma_{11}[x_1-EX(1)]^2/\sigma^2(1)-2\gamma_{12}\rho[X(1),\ X(2)][x_1-EX(1)][y_1-EX(2)]/\sigma(1)\sigma(2)+\gamma_{22}[y_1-EX(2)]^2/\sigma^2(2)\Big\}^k dF(x_1, y_1)$, where F is joint dist. fct. of $X(1)$ and $X(2)$ **2** *Probability relation*: $P(Y) \geqslant 1-I_k/b^{2k}$ **4** The γ's are specified numbers. For special case of $\gamma_{11}=\gamma_{12}=\gamma_{22}=1$, $P(Y) \geqslant \quad 1-(2k)(2k-2)\cdots(2)/b^{2k}(1-1/2k)^{2k}$ and bound can be maximized by choice of k. This special inequality not necessarily best possible **Characteristics 1** Low to medium (unless k large) **2** Best possible **3** Single observation **4** The moments of order $2k$ must exist **5** Satisfied for virtually all practical situations **6** None **Bibliography** Ref. 208, 407, 485.

n-Variate, Ellipsoids, First and Second Order Moments (*Chapelon*)

Data 1 Arbitrary, multivariate **4** $m=1$ **Description 1** Lower bound for prob. expression **2** $P\Big\{\sum_{i_1, i_2=1}^{n} \operatorname{cov}\Big[X(i_1),X(i_2)\Big][X(i_1)-EX(i_1)][X(i_2)-$

$EX(i_2)] \leqslant b^2\}$ **Assumptions 1** None **2** The second-order moments exist **3** None **Results 1** None **2** *Probability relation*: $P\left\{ \sum_{i_1, i_2=1}^{n} \text{cov}\left[X(i_1), X(i_2)\right][X(i_1)-EX(i_1)][X(i_2)-EX(i_2)] \leqslant b^2\right\} \geqslant 1-n/b^n$, where $b \geqslant n^{1/n}$ **4** Related results for parallelopiped circumscribing this ellipsoid given in ref. 92 **Characteristics 1** Low **2** Not necessarily best possible **3** Single observation **4** The second-order moments must exist **5** Satisfied for virtually all practical situations **6** None **Bibliography** Ref. 92, 208.

Independent Univariate Variables, Ellipsoids (*Birnbaum, Raymond, Zuckerman*)

Data 1 Arbitrary, univariate **4** $n=1$ **Description 1** Upper bound for prob. expression **2** $P\left\{ \sum_{j=1}^{m} [X(1)_j - EX(1)_j]^2/b_j^2 \geqslant b\right\}$ in terms of the $\sigma(1)_j$ **Assumptions 1** The $X(1)_j$ are independent **2** The $EX(1)_j^2$ exist **3** None **Results 1** For $1 \leqslant r < m$, let $B_1 = \min\left[\sum_{j=1}^{r} \sigma^2(1)_j/b_j^2, \sum_{j=r+1}^{m} \sigma^2(1)_j/b_j^2\right]$, $B_2 = \max\left[\sum_{j=1}^{r} \sigma^2(1)_j/b_j^2, \sum_{j=r+1}^{m} \sigma^2(1)_j/b_j^2\right]$ **2** *Probability relations*: $P\left\{ \sum_{j=1}^{m} [X(1)_j - EX(1)_j]^2/b_j^2 \geqslant b\right\} \leqslant 1$ if $b \leqslant B_1 + B_2$; $\leqslant B_1 + B_2 - B_1(b - B_1 - B_2)/(b - B_1)$ if $B_1 + B_2 \leqslant b \leqslant (B_1 + 2B_2 + \sqrt{B_1^2 + 4B_2^2})/2$; $\leqslant B_1 + B_2 - B_1 B_2$ if $b \geqslant (B_1 + 2B_2 + \sqrt{B_1^2 + 4B_2^2})/2$ **4** Upper bound can be minimized by choice of r and way of dividing observations into two sets. If $\sigma^2(1)_1 = \ldots = \sigma^2(1)_m$, $P\left\{ \sum_{j=1}^{m} [X(1)_j - EX(1)_j]^2 \geqslant b^2\right\} \leqslant 1$ for $b^2 \leqslant m\sigma^2(1)_j$; $\leqslant 1 - [b^2 - m\sigma^2(1)_j]/[b^2 - m\sigma^2(1)_j/2]$ for $m\sigma^2(1)_j \leqslant b^2 \leqslant (3+\sqrt{5})m\sigma^2(1)_j/4$; $\leqslant m\sigma^2(1)_j[1 - m\sigma^2(1)_j/4b^2]b^{-2}$ for $b^2 \geqslant (3+\sqrt{5})m\sigma^2(1)_j/4$ **Characteristics 1** Low **2** Not necessarily best possible except for $m=2$ **3** Not necessarily used symmetrically **4** The $EX(1)_j^2$ must exist. Effects of moderate violations of independence unknown **5** Not difficult to verify independence **6** Useful when the $\sigma(1)_j$ differ by known factors **Bibliography** Ref. 58, 208.

n-Variate, Ellipsoids, Monotonicity Conditions (*Leser*)

Data 1 Continuous, multivariate **4** $m=1$ **Description 1** Lower bound for prob. expression **2** $P\left\{ \sum_{i=1}^{n} [X(i) - EX(i)]^2/b_i^2\sigma^2(i) \leqslant n\right\} = P(Z)$ in terms of parameter in monotonicity condition **Assumptions 1** None **2** The $EX(i)^2$ exist **3** Let $b_0 = [n/(1/b_1^2 + \ldots + 1/b_n^2)]^{1/2}$, $\sigma_0 = \{n/[1/\sigma^2(1) + \ldots + 1/\sigma^2(n)]\}^{1/2}$, $R = b_0\sigma_0\left\{ \sum_{i=1}^{n} [x_i - EX(i)]^2/b_i^2\sigma^2(i)\right\}^{1/2}$, $A(R_0) = \left[\int\cdots\int_{R=R_0} f(x_1, \ldots, x_n)dx_1\ldots dx_n\right]\Big/\left[\int\cdots\int_{R=R_0} dx_1\ldots dx_n\right]$, where f is the joint freq. fct. of the $\{X(i)\}_1 - E\{X(i)\}_1$. Then $A(R_0)$ is assumed to be nonincreasing fct. of R_0 for $R_0/\sqrt{n} \leqslant K\sigma_0$ **Results 1** None **2** *Probability relations. Case of* $K \leqslant 1$: $P(Z) \geqslant 0$ if $b_0 \leqslant 1$; $\geqslant 1 - 1/b_0{}^2$ if $b_0 \geqslant 1$. *Case of* $1 \leqslant K \leqslant \sqrt{(n+2)/n}$: $P(Z) \geqslant (n+2)(1-1/K^2)(b_0/K)^n/2$ if $b_0 \leqslant [2/(n+2)]^{1/n}K$; $\geqslant 1 - 1/K^2$ if $[2/(n+2)]^{1/n}K \leqslant b_0 \leqslant K$; $\geqslant 1 - 1/b_0{}^2$ if $b_0 \geqslant K$. *Case of* $K \geqslant \sqrt{(n+2)/n}$: $P(Z) \geqslant [n/(n+2)]^{n/2} b_0{}^n$ if $b_0 \leqslant [2/(n+2)]^{1/n} [(n+2)/n]^{1/2}$; $\geqslant 1 - [2/(n+2)]^{2/n}/b_0{}^2$ if $[2/(n+2)]^{1/n}[(n+2)/n]^{1/2} \leqslant b_0 \leqslant [2/(n+2)]^{1/n}K$; $\geqslant 1 - 1/K^2$ if $[2/(n+2)]^{1/n}K \leqslant b_0 \leqslant K$; $\geqslant 1 - 1/b_0{}^2$ if $b_0 \geqslant K$ **4** $K \geqslant K'$ if $f(x_1, \ldots, x_n)$ known to be decreasing fct. of $|x_i|$ for $|x_i| \leqslant K'b_i\sigma(i)/b_0$ and all i **Characteristics 1** Low to medium **2** Not necessarily best possible involving second order moments **3** Single observation **4** The $EX(i)^2$ must exist. For true $K > 1$, effect of using too large a value for K can be determined directly. For $n = 2$ and $\sigma(1) = \sigma(2)$, Berges' results (see page 108, also ref. 44) superior to these for $\rho[X(1), X(2)]$ near unity but inferior for $\rho[X(1), X(2)]$ near zero. Effects of continuity violation indicated by special case comparisons with results of Berge and Lal for $n = 2$ (see page 108, also ref. 302) **5** Difficult to determine K **6** None **Bibliography** Ref. 44, 208, 302, 309.

n-Variate, Continuous, Contour Moments (Camp)

Data 1 Continuous, multivariate **4** $m = 1$ **Description 1** Upper bound for prob. expression **2** $1 - P[\{X(i)\}_1 - E\{X(i)\}_1 \epsilon Q_\lambda]$, where Q_λ is set of points for which $f(x_1, \ldots, x_n) > \lambda$ and f is joint freq. fct. for $\{X(i)\}_1 - E\{X(i)\}_1$ **Assumptions 1** None **2** $f(x_1, \ldots, x_n) \leqslant L < \infty$. The prescribed moments exist **3** None **Results 1** Let $\tau(\lambda)$ be measure of Q_λ; then $y(\tau) = \min$ (over multiple values) of $\lambda(\tau) = \tau^{-1}(\lambda)$, $\hat{\mu}_k = \int_0^{\tau(0)} \tau^k y(\tau) d\tau$ **2** *Probability relation*: $1 - P[\{X(i)\}_1 - E\{X(i)\}_1 \epsilon Q_\lambda] \leqslant \hat{\mu}_{2k}[2k/(2k+1)]^{2k}/\tau(\lambda)^{2k}$ **4** If $\lambda = y(b\sqrt{\hat{\mu}_2})$, $1 - P[\{X(i)\}_1 - E\{X(i)\}_1 \epsilon Q_\lambda] \leqslant \hat{\mu}_{2k}[2k/(2k+1)]^{2k}/\hat{\mu}_2{}^k$ **Characteristics 1** Low to high **2** Best possible **3** Single observation **4** The prescribed moments must exist. f must exist and be bounded **5** Satisfied for virtually all continuous situations of practical nature **6** Usefulness limited by the utilization of an uncommon type of moment **Bibliography** Ref. 86, 208.

Bivariate—Deviation from Regression Line

Data 1 Arbitrary, bivariate **4** $m = 1$; $n = 2$ **Description 1** Upper bounds for prob. expression **2** Consider the regression line $x_2 = EX(2) + \rho[X(1), X(2)][\sigma(2)/\sigma(1)][x_1 - EX(1)]$; prob. expression investigated is $P\Big[\text{distance of } \{X(1), X(2)\} \text{ from regression line} \geqslant b\Big] = P(W)$. Bounds obtained in terms of $\sigma(2)$, $\rho[X(1), X(2)]$, and perhaps also $\alpha_4(1)$, $\alpha_4(2)$

Assumptions 1 None **2** The prescribed moments exist **3** None **Results 1** None **2** *Probability relations*: $P(W) \leqslant \sigma^2(2)\{1-\rho[X(1)X(2)]^2\}/b^2$; $P(W) \leqslant \left(\alpha_4(2)\left\{1-4\rho[X(1), X(2)]^2\right\}+6\rho[X(1), X(2)]^2\left\{1-\rho[X(1), X(2)]^2 - \rho[X(1), X(2)]^4/2\right\}\alpha_4(1)\right)\Big/b^4$ **4** Corresponding results hold if roles of $X(1)$ and $X(2)$ exchanged **Characteristics 1** Low **2** Not necessarily best possible **3** Single observation **4** Prescribed moments must exist **5** Satisfied for virtually all practical situations **6** None **Bibliography** Ref. 485.

n-Variate, Categorical Data, Tests for Distributions (Romanovskǐ)

Data 1 Arbitrary, multivariate **4** Case (I): $m=1$. Case (II): $m=2$ **Description 1** Lower bounds for prob. expressions **2** $P\left\{\sum_{t=1}^{T}[n'_t-En'_t]^2 < n^2b^2\right\}$ and $P\left[\sum_{t=1}^{T}(n'_t/n_1-n''_t/n_2)^2<b^2\right]$, where there are T categories, n'_t of the $X(i)_1$ fall in category t, and n''_t of the $X(i)_2$ fall in category t **Assumptions 1** The $X(i)_1$ and the $X(i)_2$ are independent random samples from same population **2** None **3** T known **Results 1** None **2** *Probability relations. Case (I)*: $P\left\{\sum_{t=1}^{T}[n'_t-En'_t]^2<n^2b^2\right\}\geqslant 1-(1-1/T)/nb^2$. *Case (II)*: $P\left[\sum_{t=1}^{T}(n'_t/n_1-n''_t/n_2)^2<b^2\right]\geqslant 1-(1-1/T)(1/n_1+1/n_2)/b^2$ **4** None **Characteristics 1** Low **2** Not necessarily best possible **3** Used symmetrically **4** Unknown sensitivity to sample conditions **5** Ordinarily not difficult to decide on sample conditions **6** Case (I) results can be used for goodness of fit tests. Case (II) results can be used to test whether two samples from same population **Bibliography** Ref. 208, 437.

n-Variate, Categorical Data, Chi-Square Type Variables (Vora)

Data 1 Arbitrary, multivariate **4** $m=1$ **Description 1** Bounds for prob. expressions **2** $P\left[\sum_{t=1}^{T}(n'_t-En'_t)^2/En'_t\leqslant b'\right]$ and $P\left\{\sum_{t=1}^{T}[n'_t+1/2-(1+T/2n)En'_t]^2/(1+T/2n)En'_t\leqslant b\right\}$, where there are T categories and n'_t of the $X(i)$ fall in category t **Assumptions 1** The $X(i)$ are random sample **2** None **3** T known. Categories assigned so that $En'_1\leqslant\ldots\leqslant En'_{T-2}\leqslant$ both En'_{T-1} and En'_T. Let $d_t=n/En'_t+n/(En'_{t+1}+\ldots+En'_T)$ for $t\leqslant T-2$ and $d_t=n/En'_t$ for $t=T-1, T$; also let $c_t=[b(-1+n/En'_t)/(n+T/2)]^{\frac{1}{2}}$, $G(z)=\frac{1}{2}+1/z-(1+z)[\log_e(1+z)]/z^2$, $D_1=6(n+T/2)\left\{1-\left[1-(\min_t d_t)[1-2G(c_1)]/3(n+T/2)\right]^{1/2}\right\}\Big/(\min_t d_t)$, $D_2=6(n+T/2)\left\{1-\left[1-(\max_t d_t)[1-2G(-c_1)]/3(n+T/2)\right]^{1/2}\right\}\Big/(\max_t d_t)$. Assumptions are: $c_1\leqslant 1-9/2(1+T/2n)En'_1$; $(\min_t d_t)[1-2G(c_1)]/3(n+T/2)\leqslant 1$; $(\max_t d_t)[1-2G(-c_1)]/3(n+T/2)\leqslant 1$; $(\max_t d_t)D_1/(n+T/2)<1$;

$(\max_t d_t)D_2/(n+T/2)<1$; $b(\max_t d_t)D_1{}^2/(n+T/2)\leqslant 1$; $b(\max_t d_t)D_2{}^2/(n+T/2)\leqslant 1$ **Results 1** $r_1=\Big[1+\sum_{t=1}^T (n/2)/(1-c_t)En'_t\Big]\Big/12(n+T/2)$; $r_2=\Big\{1/[1+1/2(n+T/2)]+(1-1/297)\sum_{t=1}^T (n/2)/(1+c_t)En'_t\Big\}\Big/12(n+T/2)$; $R_1=D_1\Big(\sum_{t=1}^T d_t\Big)/24(n+T/2)$ $+D_1{}^4(\max_t d_t)^2b^2/880(n+T/2)^2$; $R_2=D_2\Big(\sum_{t=1}^T d_t\Big)\Big/24(n+T/2)$ $-(\max_t d_t)\Big(\sum_{t=1}^T d_t\Big)D_2{}^2/264(n+T/2)^2$; $\lambda_1=(n+T/2)^{T/2}n!D_1{}^{-(T-1)/2}e^{r_1+R_1}\Big/\Gamma(n+1+T/2)$; $\lambda_2=(n+T/2)^{T/2}n!D_2{}^{-(T-1)/2}e^{r_2+R_2}\Big/\Gamma(n+1+T/2)$; $a_1=D_1\Big\{\sqrt{b}+\Big[\sum_{t=1}^T d_t/4(n+T/2)\Big]^{1/2}\Big\}^2$; $a_2=D_2\Big\{\sqrt{b}-\Big[\sum_{t=1}^T d_t/4(n+T/2)\Big]^{1/2}\Big\}^2$ if $b\geqslant\sum_{t=1}^T d_t/4(n+T/2)$ and $=0$ otherwise; b and b' are related by $b=\Big\{[b'/(1+T/2n)]^{1/2}+\Big[\Big(\sum_{t=1}^T n/En'_t-T^2\Big)/4(n+T/2)\Big]^{1/2}\Big\}^2$; $A_1=D_1\Big\{[b'/(1+T/2n)]^{1/2}+\Big[\sum_{t=1}^T d_t/4(n+T/2)\Big]^{1/2}\Big\}^2$; $A_2=D_2\Big\{[b'/(1+T/2n)]^{1/2}-\Big[\sum_{t=1}^T d_t/4(n+T/2)\Big]^{1/2}\Big\}^2$ if $b'\geqslant\sum_{t=1}^T d_t/4n$ and $=0$ otherwise; $\gamma^2=\Big[\sum_{t=1}^T n/En'_t-T^2\Big]D_2\Big/4(n+T/2)$; $F_{T-1}(x)=$ dist. fct. for χ^2 variable with $T-1$ degrees of freedom **2** *Probability relations*: $\lambda_2e^{-\gamma^2/2}F_{T-1}(A_2)\leqslant$ $P\Big[\sum_{t=1}^T (n'_t-En'_t)^2/En'_t\leqslant b'\Big]\leqslant$ $\lambda_1F_{T-1}(A_1)$; $\lambda_2F_{T-1}(a_2)\leqslant$ $P\Big\{\sum_{t=1}^T [n'_t+\tfrac{1}{2}-(1+T/2n)En'_t]^2\Big/(1+T/2n)En'_t\leqslant b\Big\}\leqslant$ $\lambda_1F_{T-1}(a_1)$ **4** None **Characteristics 1** Low to medium **2** Not necessarily best possible **3** Used symmetrically **4** Sensitivity to sample condition unknown **5** Ordinarily not difficult to decide on sample condition **6** Can be used for goodness of fit tests (see Chapter 11) **Bibliography** Ref. 531.

EXPECTATIONS OF SOME FUNCTIONS OF ORDER STATISTICS

Discussion

A bound (or bounds) for the value of a probability constant can sometimes be established in terms of the values for other probability constants. Such bounds can be of interest for situations where the probability constants in the bounds have known values and the value of the other probability constant is desired but is unknown. In some cases useful results can be obtained on the basis of such bounds, even though they are usually of a rough nature.

At present, the only class of probability constants that has received more than a token consideration in this respect is that dealing with expected values of functions of the order statistics of a sample. Hence presentation of bounds is limited to probability constants of this type. Explicitly, only $E(X[n]-X[1])$, $EX[i]$, $\sigma^2[n]$, and $\sigma^2[1]$ are considered, where the $X[i]$ are the order statistics of a univariate random sample. However, a bibliography is given for articles dealing with some of the results that have been obtained for other probability constants.

Procedures are presented for four types of situations. For one case, the population sampled is completely arbitrary except for the requirement that its variance exists. In another case the population is symmetrical but otherwise arbitrary except that $EX[n]^2$ (and thus also $EX[1]^2$) must exist. For another case the population has a known finite range. The bounds are expressed in terms of $EX(i)$ and $\sigma^2(i)$ for these three cases, where the $X(i)$ are the sample for which the $X[i]$ are the order statistics. The remaining situation deals with the case where the population consists of the sample values. Although this case can be interpreted in terms of population expectations, the practical implication is that bounds are obtained for $\{X[n]-X[1]\}/S(i)$, where the $X(i)$ are arbitrary numbers and the $X[i]$ are the order statistics of the $X(i)$.

Fixed Material for Section

Data 1 Arbitrary, univariate **2** None **3** $X[i], X(i)$ **4** $m=1$ **Characteristics 1** Low **2** Best possible **3** Used symmetrically.

Arbitrary Population (Plackett, Gumbel, Hartley-David)

Description 1 Bounds for prob. constants **2** $E(X[n]-X[1])$, $EX[n]-EX(i)$, $EX[1]-EX(i)$ in terms of $\sigma(i)$. Also $|EX[i]-EX(u)|/\sigma(u)$ **Assumptions 1** Random sample **2** $EX(i)^2$ exists **3** None **Results 1** $B(a, b)=(a-1)!(b-1)!/(a+b-1)!$ **2** *Bound relations*: $0<E(X[n]-X[1])\leqslant n\sigma(i)\left(2\{(2n-2)!-[(n-1)!]^2\}/(2n-1)!\right)^{1/2}$; $0<EX[n]-EX(i)\leqslant (n-1)\sigma(i)/\sqrt{2n-1}$; $-(n-1)\sigma(i)/\sqrt{2n-1}\leqslant EX[1]-EX(i)<0$; $0<|EX[i]-EX(u)|/\sigma(u)\leqslant [-1+B(2i-1, 2n-2i+1)/B(i, n-i+1)]^{1/2}$ **3** None **4** None **Characteristics 4** $EX(i)^2$ must exist **5** Satisfied for virtually all practical situations **6** Useful when $E(X[n]-X[1])$, $EX[n]-EX(i)$, or $EX[1]-EX(i)$ known but $\sigma(i)$ unknown **Bibliography** Ref. 216, 232, 416.

Arbitrary Symmetrical Population (Moriguti, Gumbel)

Description 1 Bounds for prob. constants **2** $E(X[n]-X[1])$, $EX[n]-EX(i)$, $\sigma^2[n]$, in terms of $\sigma(i)$. Also $\sigma^2[n]/\{EX[n]\}^2$ **Assumptions 1** Random sample **2** Population symmetrical and $EX[n]^2$ exists **3** None **Results 1** $\gamma_n=\int_{1/2}^{1} n[F^{n-1}-(1-F)^{n-1}]^2[F^{n-1}+(1-F)^{n-1}]^{-1}dF=1-\pi[1+O(n^{-1})]/2^n$ **2** *Bound relations*: $0<E(X[n]-X[1])\leqslant n\sigma(i)\left(2\{1-[(n-1)!]^2/(2n-2)!\}/(2n-1)\right)^{1/2}$; $0<EX[n]-EX(i)\leqslant n\sigma(i)$

$\left(\{1-[(n-1)!]^2/(2n-2)!\}/2(2n-1)\right)^{1/2}$; $\pi[1+O(n^{-1})]/2^n = \lambda_n \leqslant \sigma^2[n] \leqslant n\sigma^2(i)/2$; $-1+1/\gamma_n \leqslant \sigma^2[n]/\{EX[n]\}^2 < \infty$ **3** For $n \geqslant 6$, $\gamma_n \doteq 1-\pi/2^n$. For $n \geqslant 8$, $\lambda_n \doteq \pi/2^n$ **4** $EX(i)-EX[1] = EX[n]-EX(i)$; $\sigma[1]^2 = \sigma[n]^2$; $\sigma^2[1]/\{EX[1]\}^2$ has same bounds as $\sigma^2[n]/\{EX[n]\}^2$. Bounds for $\{E(X[n]-X[1])\}^2/\sigma^2(i)$, $\sigma^2(X[n]-X[1])/\sigma^2(i)$, and $\sigma(X[n]-X[1])/E(X[n]-X[1])$ are given in ref. 363 **Characteristics 4** $EX[n]^2$ must exist. The bounds for $E(X[n]-X[1])$ are the same as when symmetry not required. For $EX[n]-EX(i)$, effects of violating symmetry can be determined by comparison with corresponding results for a completely arbitrary population (see page 113). For $\sigma^2[n]$ and $\sigma^2[n]/\{EX[n]^2\}$, effects of symmetry violations unknown **5** Moderately difficult to verify symmetry **6** Useful when $E(X[n]-X[1])$ or $EX[n]-EX(i)$ known but $\sigma(i)$ unknown **Bibliography** Ref. 216, 232, 361, 363.

Population with Known Finite Range (Hartley and H. A. David)

Description 1 Bounds for prob. constant **2** $E(X[n]-X[1])/\sigma(i)$ in terms of bounds for $[X(i)-EX(i)]/\sigma(i)$ **Assumptions 1** Random sample **2** None **3** $-A \leqslant [X(i)-EX(i)]/\sigma(i) \leqslant B$ **Results 1** $U = \max(A, B)$; y_0 is the root of $y + \left\{(1-y)^{2n-1} - y^{2n-1} - [2I_{1-y}(n, n)-1]\binom{2n-1}{n-1}^{-1}\right\}\Big/ (2n-1)[(1-y)^{n-1}-y^{n-1}]^2 = 1/2U^2$, where $I_{1-y}(n, n)$ is Pearson's incomplete beta function. $V = U^2/(1+U^2)$ **2** *Bound relations*: If $U \leqslant \sqrt{2n-1}\Big/\left\{2\left[1-\binom{2n-2}{n-1}^{-1}\right]\right\}^{1/2}$, $E(X[n]-X[1])/\sigma(i) \leqslant n\left(2\{(2n-2)!-[(n-1)!]^2\}/(2n-1)!\right)^{1/2}$. Otherwise, $E(X[n]-X[1])/\sigma(i) \leqslant n(1-2y_0U^2)[(1-y_0)^{n-1}-y_0{}^{n-1}]/U + 2U[1-(1-y_0)^n - y_0{}^n]$. In any case, $E(X[n]-X[1])/\sigma(i) \geqslant \min\{2[1-(\tfrac{1}{2})^{n-1}], [1-V^2-(1-V)^2]/\sqrt{V(1-V)}\}$ **3** None **4** None **Characteristics 4** Effects of choosing A and/or B too small can be determined directly **5** Usually not difficult to choose conservatively large values for A and B **6** None **Bibliography** Ref. 232.

Arbitrary Set of Numbers (G. W. Thompson)

Description 1 Bounds for function of observations **2** $(X[n]-X[1])/S(i)$ **Assumptions 1** None **2** None **3** None **Results 1** None **2** *Bound relations*: *For n even*, $(X[n]-X[1])/S(i) \geqslant 2\sqrt{(n-1)/n}$. *For n odd*, $(X[n]-X[1])/S(i) \geqslant 2\sqrt{n/(n+1)}$. In any case, $(X[n]-X[1])/S(i) \leqslant \sqrt{2(n-1)}$ **3** None **4** None **Characteristics 4** None **5** Always satisfied **6** Useful when $X[n]-X[1]$ known but $S(i)$ unknown **Bibliography** Ref. 516.

Bibliography for Bounds on Probability Constants

Bounds have also been derived for a variety of other probability constants. Some general nature limits for moments are given by Shohat and

Tamarkin in ref. 472, by Combes in ref. 107, and by Richter in ref. 426. Following is a bibliography of some of the results in this direction: Ref. 16, 40, 61, 107, 118 (page 176), 190, 263, 278, 362, 415, 448, 523, 594.

Chapter 7

ESTIMATES AND TESTS FOR EXPECTED VALUES

INTRODUCTION

This chapter is concerned with procedures for investigating probability constants that are functions of the expected values of various statistics. However, only a portion of the presentations involving expected values are given in this chapter. If a statistic has specialized uses and is explicitly considered in at least one other chapter, the expected value results involving this statistic are given at one or more of the other places where this statistic occurs and are not considered in Chapter 7.

Point estimation procedures are presented for two types of situations. In one case, the estimation statistic has a specified type of representative value (e.g., its expected value) that exactly equals the function of expected values estimated. In the other case, the representative value of the statistic is only approximately equal to the probability constant estimated.

Exact tests and confidence intervals are presented for only one type of expected value and only apply to a special class of populations; namely, they are for the population mean and based on independent univariate observations from symmetrical populations with a common mean value (e.g., a sample from a symmetrical population). Approximate tests and confidence intervals are presented for several types of situations. Some of these approximate results are obtained on a judgment-empirical basis while others evolve from theoretical-approximate considerations (e.g., are based on the first few terms of an asymptotic expansion).

Presentations are also given for situations involving the expected values of statistics based on observations from binomial distributions. Although the binomial distribution is of a parametric character, it has many nonparametric applications. Consequently, procedures based on binomial data are of interest from a nonparametric viewpoint.

DISPERSAL OF EXPECTED VALUE PRESENTATIONS

Perhaps the most widely considered class of population probability constants is that involving expected values of statistics. Functions of expected values receive consideration in most of the chapters of this handbook. To avoid duplication, expected value results that are pertinent to other chapters are presented in those chapters rather than in Chapter 7. As an example, almost all of the Tchebycheff type inequalities presented in Chapter 6 involve expected values, but these results are not repeated in Chapter 7. As another example, results for the population correlation coefficient are considered to fall under the heading of independence of the components of a bivariate variable, and are given in the second volume of the handbook.

Several presentations are given which apply to the means of symmetrical univariate populations. Since the mean of a symmetrical population is also a median of that population, these presentations also apply to Chapter 8, which deals with population percentage points. To avoid repetition, the Chapter 7 presentations for the means of symmetrical populations are referenced but not restated in Chapter 8.

Nearly all of the material given in this chapter is concerned with expected values of univariate statistics. These expected value expressions include moments about the origin, moments about the mean, difference of means, expected values of order statistics, expected value of sample range, etc. Also considered are the mean value of a binomial population and the expected value of the number of successes for a set of random binomial events with possibly different success probabilities.

IMPLICATIONS OF MOMENTS

Although population moments and functions of population moments seem to constitute the most widely considered class of probability constants, these quantities do not necessarily represent anything more than rough index type numbers. Even the population mean, which has an important interpretation, is not very useful for some types of populations. As indicated by the material of Chapter 6, knowledge of the values of a few moments does not necessarily furnish more than very rough information about a probability distribution having these moments. In particular, knowledge limited to the values of odd moments about the mean furnishes virtually no definite information about a distribution function with these moments.

Fortunately, moments seem to have much stronger implications for special situations of the kind that tend to occur in practice than they do in general. In fact, many reasonably accurate probability results can be obtained on the basis of the first four population moments by use of

Pearson curves, from the first four terms of the standardized Edgeworth series, etc. Even results derived by interpolation–extrapolation from theoretical and/or experimental results for a few special cases expressed in terms of moments have been found to be useful in applications. Thus, the results presented in this chapter should have some usefulness from an applications viewpoint.

SITUATIONS CONSIDERED

Procedures at each of the three general levels of precision occur in this chapter. Although some of the results are of an exact nature, many are theoretical-approximate or judgment-empirical (see pages 36–39 for discussion of precision levels for procedures).

Continuous type data are assumed in most cases, especially those involving tests or confidence regions, but situations involving discrete data also occur. For nearly all of the cases considered, the observations are considered to be statistically independent, and frequently are assumed to be a random sample. Many of the procedures require symmetrical populations. The statistics utilized consist of observation moments, U statistics, various types of t statistics, order statistics, etc.

Five of the sections of this chapter are devoted to procedure presentations. The first of these sections, Exact Point Estimation, presents several types of exact point estimates, some of which apply to the means of symmetrical populations. The second such section, Approximate Point Estimation, contains some theoretical-approximate and judgment-empirical estimation procedures. The third presentation section is titled Exact Tests and Intervals for Mean–Symmetrical Populations; this section furnishes exact tests and confidence intervals for the mean of a symmetrical population and, in some cases, for the common mean of several symmetrical populations. The fourth such section is called Approximate Tests and Confidence Regions; the results of this section are of the theoretical-approximate and judgment-empirical types. The final presentation section, Binomial Distribution and Events, is concerned with point estimates, tests, and confidence intervals for the success probability of the binomial distribution, with approximations to the binomial distribution, and with corresponding results for the case of random binomial events. A supplementary bibliography for some other types of binomial results is also given.

Some of the statistical procedures presented are of an asymptotic character. However, many of the asymptotic results of a nonparametric nature which have been developed are not yet of practical value, due to a lack of knowledge about the minimum number of observations needed for at least rough accuracy. Because of their potential value, at least for special cases where empirical evidence can be gathered, a bibliography is given which lists some of these asymptotic results.

USE OF RANDOMIZATION FOR BREAKING TIES

As mentioned in Chapter 4, nearly all data can be converted to a continuous form such that the joint distribution of the converted data differs very slightly from the joint distribution of the original data. This conversion can be useful for situations where the only use of population continuity is to assure that no ties occur among the observations, or among specified functions of the observations. For some of these situations, the data can be converted to a form that can be considered continuous by use of an independent randomization process to break each group of ties, where the randomization is such that all orderings of the tied values are equally likely. These are the situations where the only use made of continuity is to establish an ordering among the values within one or more specified sets of observations or functions of observations. As an example, for the Wilcoxon signed-rank test and some of the other tests, the data can be converted to a form that can be considered continuous by using randomization to establish orderings in sets of the nonzero $|X(i)-\mu_0|$ that have the same value.

RESULTS FOR OTHER MOMENTS FROM RESULTS FOR MEAN

Much of the material presented is for investigation of the mean of a univariate population. Except for situations where symmetrical distributions are assumed, the results for the mean can be used to investigate other types of expected values. This is accomplished by combining sample values so as to obtain a set of observations from a univariate population whose mean equals the expected value that is to be investigated. As an example, let $X(1), \ldots, X(n)$ be the original sample values (n even) and form the observations $\frac{1}{2}[X(1)-X(2)]^2$, $\frac{1}{2}[X(3)-X(4)]^2, \ldots,$ $\frac{1}{2}[X(n-1)-X(n)]^2$. These observations are a sample of size $n/2$ from a population with mean $\sigma^2(i)$. As another example, let the $\{X(1)_j, X(2)_j\}$ be a sample of size m from a bivariate population and form the observations $X(1)_1X(2)_1, \ldots, X(1)_mX(2)_m$. These observations are a sample of size m from a univariate population with mean $E[X(1)_jX(2)_j]=\text{cov}\,[X(1)_j, X(2)_j]+[EX(1)_j][EX(2)_j]$.

REMARK ON MINIMUM LEVEL FOR ASSUMPTIONS

Although nonparametric methods are characterized by being valid without the imposition of strong conditions, they virtually always require something in the way of assumptions. Sometimes the assumption of a random sample is sufficient to yield worthwhile results. In cases involving expected values, however, some sort of knowledge about the population behavior in its tails should also be available. As pointed out in ref. 19, if the population tail properties are entirely unknown, a sample can yield virtually no information about the tails of the distribution, even if the sample is obtained sequentially. In ref. 19, problems of inference concerning the population mean are treated in some detail. It is shown that satisfactory point estimates, tests, or confidence intervals can not be obtained when there is no knowledge about the tail properties of the population sampled.

DISCUSSION OF ESTIMATE EFFICIENCY

The efficiency of an estimate is usually expressed in terms of its expected variation about the probability constant estimated, as measured by the mean square error (see page 32). That is, for fixed sample size and the same univariate constant estimated, one estimate is considered to be more efficient than another if it has a smaller mean square error about this constant (variance for the case of expected value estimates). Since the mean square error of an estimate usually depends on the population sampled, efficiency is ordinarily considered only for special classes of populations (e.g., the normal populations, all continuous populations with finite ranges, etc.). This is the case for most of the estimate efficiency results presented in this chapter.

Sometimes an estimate of a specified function of expected values is said to be minimum-variance unbiased for a stated class of populations. This implies that, among estimates of the specified probability constant which are unbiased for every population of the stated class, this estimate has minimum variance for all the populations of the class.

Estimate efficiency can have other interpretations besides that based on the mean square error of the estimate. For example, one statistic might be considered to be more efficient than another if, for all populations of the class considered, its risk function does not exceed the risk function for the other statistic and is smaller for at least one population. For this case a minimax estimate is most efficient (see page 32).

ADEQUATE SAMPLE SIZES FOR ESTIMATES

Although efficiencies are difficult to determine, even in a rough sense, approximate nonparametric methods are available for deciding on the suitability of point estimates based on samples and for determining adequate sample sizes. Namely, approximate estimates can be developed for the mean square error, and for the coefficient of variation, of a point estimate which is expressed in terms of sample moments and/or of order statistics. The basis for these approximate estimates are some expansions, with respect to sample size, of the expected values of functions of sample moments and of order statistics (see pages 136 and 137). When order statistics are involved, the population sampled is required to be continuous and have a frequency function that is reasonably well behaved. Expected values for order statistics usually involve the value of the frequency function at identified population percentiles; methods for estimating these frequency function values are given in Chapter 10.

Two-stage sampling can be used to approximately evaluate adequate sample sizes for point estimates (see page 34). Namely, the criterion (mean square error, coefficient of variation, etc.) used to determine an adequate sample size is estimated from the first stage of the sampling. For cases using the mean square error or the coefficient of variation, the sample size is adequate when the criterion has a specified value that is considered to be sufficiently small. In all cases, the criterion is an explicit function of the total sample size (first stage plus second stage).

In this chapter, no methods for determining adequate sample sizes are given in the presentations. Instead, a general approach, which is straightforward, is outlined here. The first step consists in exactly or approximately determining the expression for the criterion (mean square error, coefficient of variation, etc.) in terms of population constants. This determination relies on the expansions for expected values of functions of sample moments and for expected values of functions of order statistics. Next, the population constants occurring in the criterion are estimated. Ideally, the population constants should be jointly estimated. In many cases, however, joint estimation may only be feasible for subsets of the population constants; in some cases, each constant may be estimated individually. Finally, each of the population constants is replaced by its estimated value, yielding an estimate of the criterion. The estimated adequate sample size is the smallest size such that the estimate of the criterion is at most equal to a specified value.

As mentioned in Chapter 4, adequate sample sizes for confidence intervals can be obtained by considering each variable endpoint to be an estimate. An adequate sample size is determined for each such estimate and the maximum of these adequate sample sizes (there may be only one) is considered to be adequate for the confidence interval.

LIFE-TESTING AND CENSORED DATA APPLICATIONS

Many of the results given in this chapter are based on specified order statistics of a set of observations. As mentioned in Chapter 4, statistical procedures of this nature are useful for situations where only values of specified order statistics are available, whether the lack of availability of the remaining order statistics is accidental or deliberate. A censored set of observations is a special case of this situation. Life-testing situations are special cases where deliberate censoring can sometimes be exploited to save time and/or cost without loss of efficiency (see discussion in Chapters 4 and 8). Some of the results of this chapter are applicable for life-testing situations.

RESULTS FROM AVERAGES OF OBSERVATIONS

Two somewhat general approximate methods for investigating population moments can be developed on the basis of the Central Limit Theorem. Let the observations be divided into subsets of specified sizes in some unbiased manner (e.g., by randomization). For each subset, form the arithmetic average of its observations. If the number of observations in a subset is not too small, its observation mean should have a distribution that is at least roughly symmetrical. This distribution should be at least roughly normal when the observations are independent and their number is at least moderately large.

Ordinarily, the number of observations required for acceptance of approximate symmetry is noticeably less than that for acceptance of approximate normality. Averages of ten or more independent or mildly dependent observations should have nearly symmetrical distributions for most practical situations. Normality is of principal interest for the sample case. Approximate normality should be acceptable for averages of ten or more sample values for most populations of practical importance. Approximate symmetry should be acceptable for averages of seven or more sample values for most practical situations.

Part of the material of this chapter deals with situations where the observations are from symmetrical populations. These results are concerned with investigation of population means. The expected value of an observation mean equals the arithmetic average of the expected values of the observations on which it is based, irrespective of the dependences among the observations. Thus one approximate method of investigating the means of the populations yielding the observations is to form subsets of suitable sizes and apply an appropriate result based on symmetry to the observation means for the subsets. In particular, if the observations are a sample and the subsets are of equal size, the observation means are a sample from an approximately symmetrical population whose mean value equals the mean value of the population yielding the observations.

When the observations are a sample, the subsets are of the same size, and the subset size is large enough for a reasonable approximation to normality, a wide variety of procedures can be used to investigate the mean and the variance of the population yielding the sample. That is, the mean value of the distribution for a subset average equals the mean value of the population yielding the sample and its variance equals the reciprocal of the subset size times the variance of the population sampled. Moreover, the observation means for the subsets are a sample from an approximately normal distribution. Thus, the various procedures that have been developed for investigating the mean and variance of a normal population on the basis of a sample from that population are applicable (approximately).

EXACT POINT ESTIMATION

Introduction

This section is devoted to the presentation of point estimates that are of an exact nature. That is, a specified type of representative value for the estimation statistic is exactly equal to the expected value expression being estimated.

Three types of point estimation are considered (i.e., three types of representative values for an estimation statistic). These are expected value, median, and minimax estimation. The median estimation case occurs only when the expected values estimated are means of symmetrical univariate populations (and, therefore, also population medians). Then, for practical type situations, median estimation is virtually equivalent to expected value estimation. Minimax estimation occurs in three presentations but yields expected value estimates for two of these presentations and for part of the results of the third presentation. Thus expected value estimation receives the major emphasis in the material presented in this section.

Material Presented

First, some general results are given for the case of unbiased estimation on the basis of a univariate sample. The estimates presented are optimum in the sense of being minimum-variance unbiased for any class of populations which includes all the discontinuous populations and/or all the absolutely continuous populations for which unbiased estimates of the probability constant considered exist. These estimates include the U statistics (see page 49), which are also minimax estimates if the loss function used is convex. Similar but not so extensive results are obtained for the case of a sample from a multivariate population. Here each unbiased multivariate estimate presented is optimum in the sense that, among all estimates of the specified multivariate probability constant which are unbiased for all populations of the class considered, this estimate has minimum concentration ellipsoid (see page 32).

Estimation of the common mean (median) of symmetrical univariate populations on the basis of order statistics of independent observations from these populations is considered next. These order statistic estimates are selected so as to have reasonably high efficiencies for the case of random samples from specified types of populations. Also they have the property of being both median and expected value estimates.

The next presentation deals with minimax estimation of the average of the means for the univariate populations yielding the observations. Here the loss function is the square of the difference between the observed value of the estimate and the value of the probability constant estimated. For some of the results, the populations are assumed to have known finite ranges.

The next to last presentation is concerned with estimation of the difference between the means of two possibly different univariate populations. This is accomplished by a two-stage sampling procedure whose purpose is to minimize the variance of the estimate subject to the condition of fixed expense for the sampling. The statistic obtained is an exact expected value estimate but its minimum variance property is based on asymptotic considerations.

The final presentation contains an expansion (finite number of terms) which establishes relations among the expected values of differences of order statistics for various sample sizes. This expansion furnishes a basis for estimating expected values for differences of order statistics from one size sample in terms of differences of order statistics for other size samples.

Remarks on Estimating Mean of Symmetrical Population

Many statistics that are specially developed for estimation of the means for parametric classes of symmetrical univariate populations (e.g., the class of rectangular populations or the class of normal populations) have the property of being exact median and expected value estimates for sampling from any symmetrical population (discrete or continuous). The reason is that the distributions of these statistics can be shown to be symmetrical about the probability constant estimated subject only to the condition of population symmetry. Thus these estimates have favorable efficiencies for special classes of populations, but are valid for any symmetrical population. Hence, when any additional knowledge is available about the type of population sampled, this information can be exploited by using a nonparametric estimate which is known to be reasonably efficient for populations of this general type.

Many of the specialized estimates for the mean of a symmetrical univariate population utilize all the values of a sample. Sometimes, however, only specified order statistics of the sample are used. In some cases, this restriction on the use of the data may be unavoidable. For example, the sample may be censored; that is, a known number of the smallest order statistics and a known number of the largest order statistics are not available. Alternatively, the data deletion might be deliberate, motivated by time, cost, and/or computational considerations.

Two separate presentations are given for using linear functions of order statistics to estimate the mean of a symmetrical univariate population. One pertains to the case where the data are limited to a few order statistics. The other is for the case where the sample is symmetrically censored; the case where the entire sample is used represents an example of symmetrical censoring. For the case of a few order statistics, the coefficients in the linear function are all equal, and the situation of interest is that where the sample yielding the order statistics is from a normal population. In the censored sample case, the values for the coefficients are chosen so that a reasonably high efficiency is obtained for the situation considered to be important, which can vary over a wide range of possibilities.

For the estimates presented for the case of symmetry, validity holds for a situation that is more general than that of a sample from a symmetrical univariate population. Namely, these estimates are exact for the situation where the observations are only required to be statistically independent and from possibly different symmetrical populations having the same mean value.

Fixed Material for Section

Results 3 None.

Minimum-Variance Unbiased Univariate Estimation

Data 1 Arbitrary, univariate **2** Univariate observation obtainable as fct. of coordinates for multivariate observation **3** $X(i)$ **4** $m=1$; $n \geqslant 2$ in some cases **Description 1** Exact expected value (unbiased) point estimation **2** Univariate prob. constants for which unbiased estimates exist **Assumptions 1** Random sample **2** Class of populations considered includes all discrete populations and/or all absolutely continuous populations for which unbiased estimation possible for prob. constant considered **3** None **Results 1** None **2** *General Theorem*: For each eligible prob. constant and sample size, there is a unique unbiased estimate which is symmetrical in sample values. Among the set of estimates for this constant that are unbiased for every population of the class considered, this estimate has minimum variance. *First application*: Any U statistic is minimum-variance unbiased estimate of its expected value; e.g., $M'_t(i)$ is minimum-variance unbiased estimate of $EX(i)^t$. *Second application*: $\mu_t(i)$ estimated by expanding $E[X(i)-EX(i)]^t$ and unbiasedly estimating each term by symmetric statistic; e.g., $S^2(i)$ estimates $\sigma^2(i)$, $n^2M_3(i)/(n-1)(n-2)$ estimates $\mu_3(i)$, and $n(n^2-2n+3)M_4(i)/(n-1)$

$(n-2)(n-3) \quad -3n(2n-3)[M_2(i)]^2/(n-1)(n-2)(n-3)$ estimates $\mu_4(i)$; unbiased estimation of $\mu_t(i)$ impossible for $t > n$. *Third application*: Let H be a specified set of possible values for $X(i)$. The symmetric estimate of $P[H(i)\epsilon H]$ equals $1/n$ times no. of the $X(i)$ with values in H. *Other applications*: $\sum_{i_1 \neq i_2 = 1}^{n} X(i_1)X(i_2)/n(n-1)$ estimates $[EX(i)]^2$; $\sum_{i_1 \neq i_2 = 1}^{n} |X(i_1)-X(i_2)|/n(n-1)$ estimates $E|X(i_1)-X(i_2)|$ **4** Results applicable on basis of sample of multivariate observations. Here multivariate sample values first converted to univariate sample values in appropriate manner. For example, consider the bivariate sample $\{X(i)_j\}_2$ with $n_1 = n_2 = n$; then $M[X(i)_1 X(i)_2]$ is minimum variance unbiased estimate of $E[X(i)_1 X(i)_2]$, as is shown by converting $\{X(1)_j\}_2$ to $X(1)_1X(1)_2$; . . . ; $\{X(n)_j\}_2$ to $X(n)_1X(n)_2$ **Characteristics 1** Low to medium (unless n quite large) **2** Minimum-variance unbiased for any class of populations satisfying assumptions. U statistics also minimax estimates if loss fct. convex **3** Used symmetrically **4** Prob. constant must exist for populations considered. Sensitivity to random sample condition unknown for general case **5** Prob. constant exists for nearly all populations and constants of practical interest. Usually not difficult to decide on sample assumption **6** Conditions for prob. constant to be eligible for unbiased estimation given in ref. 186 and 229. Asymptotic dist. of U statistic is normal if its variance exists **Bibliography** Ref. 186, 229, 243, 372.

"Optimum" Multivariate Unbiased Estimation

Data 1 Arbitrary, multivariate **2** Data obtainable as fct. of coordinates of observations having arbitrary dimension **3** $\{X(i)_j\}_m$ **4** $n_1 = \ldots = n_m = n \geq 2$ ($m \geq 2$ in some cases) **Description 1** Exact expected value (unbiased) multivariate point estimation **2** n-dimensional prob. constants for which unbiased estimates exist **Assumptions 1** Random multivariate sample of size m **2** Class considered consists of all discrete populations and/or all absolutely continuous populations such that unbiased estimation of n-dimensional prob. constant possible for every population of class. Here ith coordinate of prob. constant estimated from $X(i)_1, \ldots, X(i)_m$ **3** None **Results 1** None **2** *General Theorem*: For each eligible n-dimensional prob. constant and sample size, there exists a unique unbiased n-variate estimate of this constant that, for each coordinate, is symmetrical in the sample values for that coordinate. Among the set of estimates of this constant that are unbiased for every population of the class considered, this estimate has minimum-concentration ellipsoid (see page 32). *Applications*: In particular, any n-variate U statistic is a minimum-concentration ellipsoid unbiased estimate of its expected value. First example: $\{M(i)_1, \ldots, M(i)_j\}$ is minimum-concentration ellipsoid unbiased estimate of $\{EX(i)_1, \ldots, EX(i)_m\}$. Second example: $\{M(i)_1, S^2(i)_2\}$ is estimate of $\{EX(i)_1, \sigma^2(i)_2\}$, etc. **4** For each coordinate, univariate considerations of Minimum-Variance Unbiased Univariate Estimation presentation (see page 125) apply **Characteristics 1** Low to medium (unless m and/or n quite large) **2** Minimum-concentration ellipsoid obtained for any class of populations satisfying assumptions. n-variate U statistics also minimax estimates for case of convex loss fct. **3** Used symmetrically **4** Prob. constant must exist for populations considered. Sensitivity to sample condition unknown for general case **5** Prob. constant exists for nearly all populations and constants of practical interest. Usually not overly difficult to decide on sample assumption **6** Conditions under which n-variate prob. constant eligible for unbiased estimation given in ref. 186. Asymptotic joint dist. for n-variate U statistic normal if second moments exist **Bibliography** Ref. 186, 243.

Mean of Symmetrical Populations—A Few Order Statistics

Data 1 Arbitrary, univariate **2** None **3** $X[i]$ for specified values of i **4** $m=1$ **Description 1** Exact expected value and median point estimates **2** $EX(i)$ **Assumptions 1** Independent **2** $X(i)$ from symmetrical population for which $EX(i)$ exists **3** $EX(1)=\ldots=EX(n)$ **Results 1** N = no. of order statistics used. $X[z]= X[\text{largest integer} \leqslant z+\frac{1}{2}]$ for $z<(n+1)/2$; $=X[\text{smallest integer} \geqslant z-\frac{1}{2}]$ for $z>(n+1)/2$; $=$observation median (see Chapter 2) for $z=(n+1)/2$ **2** *First estimate*: $\sum_{v=1}^{N} X[(n+1)(v-\frac{1}{2})/N]/N$. *Second estimate*: $\{X[(n+1)/6]+X[5(n+1)/6]\}/2$, where $n \geqslant 2$ **4** Second estimate approximately valid in expected value sense if symmetry condition violated but observations sample from population that is at least roughly normal (see page 134) **Characteristics 1** Low **2** Efficiency reasonably high for case of sample from normal population and no. of order statistics used not very small. For normality, asymptotic efficiency of first estimate, compared to $M(i)$, is approx. $100-[37-N(N-1)/7]/N$ percent for $N \leqslant 10$; for second estimate, this asymptotic efficiency is 75 percent. Ref. 95 and 189 contain some asymptotic dispersion comparisons between $M(i)$ and $X[(n+1)/2]$ for case of sample from unimodal population **3** Used symmetrically **4** Insensitive to mild violations of symmetry condition, especially for random sample case. $EX(i)$ must exist. Moderately sensitive to some types of independence violations except for first estimate and N/n near unity. Only moderately sensitive to moderate violations of equality of means condition **5** $EX(i)$ virtually always exists. Not difficult to verify independence. More difficult to verify symmetry; also to verify equality of means unless observations believed random sample **6** Mainly useful for random sample case where normality situation of principal interest. Estimates useful for some types of censored data situations **Bibliography** Ref. 43, 50, 95, 189, 366.

Mean of Symmetrical Populations—Censored Observations

Data 1 Arbitrary, univariate **2** None **3** $X[i]$ for $r \leqslant i \leqslant n+1-r$, where $0 \leqslant r \leqslant (n+1)/2$ **4** $m=1$ **Description 1** Exact expected value and median point estimates **2** $EX(i)$ **Assumptions 1** Independent **2** $X(i)$ from symmetrical population for which $EX(i)$ exists $(i=1, \ldots, n)$ **3** $EX(1) = \ldots = EX(n)$ **Results 1** Coefficients of order statistics in estimate denoted by $a(r), \ldots, a(n+1-r)$, where $a(z) = a$(largest integer in z). These satisfy $\sum_{i=r}^{n+1-r} a(i) = 1$, $a(i) = a(n+1-i)$, $a(r+1) = \ldots = a[(n+1+r)/A]$, $a[1+(n+1+r)/A] = \ldots = a[(n+1)/2]$, where $2(n+1+r)/(n-1) \leqslant A \leqslant (n+1+r)/(r+1)$ **2** *Estimate*: $\sum_{i=r}^{n+1-r} a(i)X[i]$ is expected value and median estimate of $EX(i)$. *Rules for choosing coefficients*: For situation of sample from U-shaped population, $a(r)$ is large and positive, $a(r+1)=0$, A increases as population shape becomes rectangular. For sampling from rectangular population, $a(r+1) = a[(n+1)/2] = 0$. For a triangular or parabolic population, all $a(i) > 0$, $a(r) = a(r+1)$, $a(r+1) > a[(n+1)/2]$, and A decreases as population shape becomes normal (develops tails). For a normal population, the $a(i)$ are equal. For a double exponential population (e.g., with freq. fct. $\frac{1}{2}e^{-|x-Ex|}$), all $a(i) > 0$, $a(r) = a(r+1)$, $a(r+1) < a[(n+1)/2]$, and A decreases as population shape becomes normal. For a population with heavy tails, $a(r) = a(r+1) = 0$ and A decreases as the tails become heavier. For discontinuous cases, freq. fct. shape approximately determined by forming histogram **4** Population shapes intermediate to types explicitly considered can be approximated by fixing $a(r)$, $a(r+1)$ and using A as interpolation parameter **Characteristics 1** Low **2** Reasonably high efficiency if observations sample from population of about the same shape as that used in determining the $a(i)$. Variance of estimate increases as population sampled changes from U-shaped to one with heavy tails **3** Used symmetrically **4** $EX(i)$ must exist. Insensitive to mild violations of symmetry condition, especially for random sample case. Moderately sensitive to some types of independence violations. Only moderately sensitive to moderate violations of equality of means condition **5** $EX(i)$ virtually always exists. Not difficult to verify independence. More difficult to verify symmetry; also to verify equality of means unless observations believed random sample **6** Mainly useful for random sample case. Ref. 404 and 430 consider efficiency of sample midrange as fct. of $\alpha_4(i)$. Useful for some types of life testing situations **Bibliography** Ref. 154, 265, 315, 404, 430, 449, 450, 451, 452.

Minimax Estimates for Average of Population Means (*Hodges and Lehmann*)

Data 1 Arbitrary, univariate **2** Univariate observation obtainable as fct. of coordinates for multivariate observation **3** $X(i)$ **4** $m=1$ **Description 1** Minimax point estimation, where loss fct. square of difference between estimate and constant estimated **2** Average of the $EX(i)$ values (possibly weighted) **Assumptions 1** Case (I): $\rho[X(i_1), X(i_2)] \leqslant 0$ for $i_1 \neq i_2$. Case (II): Random sample. Case (III): Observations uncorrelated **2** Case (I): Populations have known finite bounds. Case (II): Population absolutely continuous and has known finite bounds. Case (III): None **3** Case (I): $L(i) \leqslant X(i) \leqslant U(i)$. For all i, i_1, i_2, class of populations includes those for which $P[X(i)=L(i)]=1-P[X(i)=U(i)]$ and $P[X(i_1)=L(i_1)]=\mathrm{P}[X(i_2)=L(i_2)]$. Case (II): $L \leqslant X(i) \leqslant U$. Case (III): Class of populations considered includes those where observations from normal populations and have same variance; variance for this subclass $\geqslant$ variance for all other populations of class **Results 1** Case (I): $Y(i)=[X(i)-L(i)]/[U(i)-L(i)]$ **2** *Estimates. Case (I)*: $[\sqrt{n}MY(i)+\frac{1}{2}]/(1+\sqrt{n})$ is minimax estimate of $E[MY(i)]$. *Case (II)*: $[\sqrt{n}M(i)+(U+L)2]/(1+\sqrt{n})$ is minimax estimate of $EX(i) \quad = EM(i)$. *Case (III)*: $M(i)$ is minimax estimate of $EM(i)$ **4** In Case (I), $EM(i)$ can be estimated when populations have same bounds. $M(i)$ is also least squares estimate for $EM(i)$ in Case (III) **Characteristics 1** Low **2** Estimates are minimax (squared-difference loss fct.) **3** Used symmetrically when populations have same bounds or no specified bounds **4** Effect of incorrect choice for bounds determinable directly. Not very sensitive to mild violations of correlation and independence conditions. Effects of violating equal population part of random sample condition determinable by comparison of Case (II) with Case (I) **5** Not difficult to check on validity of assumptions **6** For Case (I), estimate most useful when populations have same bounds, so that $EM(i)$ can be estimated. This always possible by disregarding some of the information that may be available and using $\min_i L(i)$ and $\max_i U(i)$ as bounds for all the populations **Bibliography** Ref. 239.

Difference of Means, Two-Stage Sampling (*Ghurye and Robbins*)

Data 1 Arbitrary, univariate **2** Two-stage sampling involving two populations **3** $X(i)_j$ **4** $m=4$ **Description 1** Asymptotically minimum variance exact expected value estimation subject to cost restriction **2** Difference of means of two populations **Assumptions 1** The $X(i)_1$ and $X(i)_2$ are independent two-stage samples from one population while the $X(i)_3$ and $X(i)_4$ are independent two-stage samples from another population; also samples from first population independent of samples from second population **2** First eight moments exist for both populations **3** None **Results 1** $(n_1+n_2)c_1+(n_3+n_4)c_2 \leqslant c$, where c_1 is cost of sample value from first population, c_2 is this cost for second population, and c is total allowable cost. $u(n_1, n_3) = \sqrt{c_1}S(i)_1/[\sqrt{c_1}S(i)_1 + \sqrt{c_2}S(i)_2]$; $n'_2 = n_1$ if $cu(n_1, n_3)/c_1 < n_1$, $= (c - c_2n_3)/c_1$ if $(c - c_2n_3)/c_1 < cu(n_1, n_3)/c_1$, $= cu(n_1, n_3)/c_1$ if $n_1 \leqslant cu(n_1, n_3)/c_1 \leqslant (c - c_2n_3)/c_1$; $n'_4 = (c - c_1n'_2)/c_2$; n_2 = largest integer in $n'_2 - n_1$ and n_4 = largest integer in $n'_4 - n_3$ **2** *Estimation procedure*: Choose n_1, n_3 such that $c_1n_1 + c_2n_3 < c$ and take n_1 sample values from first population and n_3 from second population. On basis of first-stage samples, take n_2 more sample values from first population and n_4 more sample values from second population. Then $[n_1M(i)_1 + n_2M(i)_2]/(n_1 + n_2) - [n_3M(i)_3 + n_4M(i)_4]/(n_3 + n_4)$ is desired unbiased estimate of $EX(i)_1 - EX(i)_3$ **4** Selection of n_1 and n_3 important. Should be smallest sample sizes such that $S(i)_1$ and $S(i)_3$ reasonably stable estimates of $\sigma(i)_1$ and $\sigma(i)_3$, respectively **Characteristics 1** Low **2** Estimate has asymptotically minimum variance for the allowable sampling cost. Namely, let c_1, c_2 remain fixed while n_1, n_3, c become large so that n_1/n_3 bounded away from 0 and ∞, n_1/c and $n_3/c \to 0$, and $cn_1^{-(h+1)/2}$, $cn_2^{-(h+1)/2}$ bounded for $h > 1$. Then variance of estimate divided by minimum variance attainable tends to unity **3** Not necessarily used symmetrically; however, used symmetrically within each of four samples drawn **4** First eight moments of both populations must exist for efficiency relation to hold but estimate is exact unbiased if first moments exist. Violation of independence part of random sample conditions does not affect unbiased character of estimate but may strongly affect its efficiency **5** First eight moments virtually always exist for both populations. Not difficult to decide on random sample conditions **6** None **Bibliography** Ref. 202.

Expansion, Expectations of Differences of Order Statistics (Sillitto, Cole)

Data 1 Continuous, univariate **2** None **3** $X[i]_j$ **4** $n_j = n + 1 - j$ **Description 1** Exact expected value expression **2** Expansion relating expected values of differences of order statistics for various sample sizes **Assumptions 1** The sets $X(i)_j$ are m independent random samples from same population **2** $EX(i)_j$ exists **3** None **Results 1** s any integer such that $0 \leqslant s \leqslant i - 1$. $D(n_j, i) = EX[i+1]_j - EX[i]_j$, $(i = 1, \ldots, n_j - 1)$ **2** *Estimation relations*: $D(n_1, i) = [n!(i-s)!/(n-s)!i!]\Big\{D(n_{s+1}, i-s) - [(n-i+1)/(n-s+1)]D(n_s, i-s) + \left[\binom{s}{2}(n-i+1)(n-i+2)/(n-s+1)(n-s+2)\right] D(n_{s-1}, i-s) - \ldots + (-1)^s[(n-i+1)(n-i+2)\cdots(n-i+s)/(n-s+1)(n-s+2)\cdots n]D(n_1, i-s)\Big\}$ **4** Useful in estimating expected values for differences of order statistics from one size sample in terms of differences of order statistics for other sample sizes. Ref. 475 contains applications involving sample range, some measures of skewness, Gini's coefficient of mean difference, mean deviation about median, etc. **Characteristics** **1** Low **2** Unknown efficiency (when used for estimation) **3** Used symmetrically within samples **4** $EX(i)_j$ must exist. Moderately sensitive to random sample condition **5** $EX(i)_j$ virtually always exists. Not difficult to decide on random sample assumption **6** None **Bibliography** Ref. 106, 475.

APPROXIMATE POINT ESTIMATION

Discussion

This section is concerned with point estimates that are of a theoretical-approximate or a judgment-empirical nature. Most of the presentations deal with approximate estimation of the population mean and/or the population standard deviation. Expected values of order statistics and asymptotic expansions for expected values of sample moments are also considered.

The type of point estimation used cannot always be accurately defined. Most of the presentations involve expected value estimation. In some of the cases, however, the values of the estimates are determined on a judgment basis which cannot be directly related to any of the standard point estimation procedures. None of the material presented is concerned with median estimation or minimax estimation. In all cases, the data are a sample from a univariate population.

Nature of Methods and Approximations

All of the theoretical-approximate methods are based on approximations which result from using the first few terms of expansions for probability distributions or probability constants. Many of these expansions are of an asymptotic character, being made with respect to sample size. In some cases the distribution sampled is assumed to be expressible in a given form of a rather general nature; then the resulting error is of an implicit type, depending on how closely this assumption is satisfied. For other cases the error is explicitly isolated but only stated in an order of magnitude sense. However, if the order of magnitude for the error is small, e.g. $O(n^{-2})$ with $n \geqslant 20$, the results can usually be accepted as sufficiently accurate for most practical applications. Two of the asymptotic expansion presentations are of a general nature; these deal with expected values of sample moments and with expected values of sample order statistics. The general expansions given in these two presentations have many direct and indirect applications, although these are not explicitly stated in the presentations.

The two principal verification procedures used for the judgment-empirical cases are analytical analyses for distributions of a simplified nature and sampling from distributions which are of interest but not very amenable to analytical analysis. By one or both of these procedures, properties of an estimate are determined for a few special situations. Then, on the basis of judgment, these properties are interpolated and/or extrapolated to cover a somewhat general class of situations. Estimates obtained in this manner usually do not have precisely defined properties, even in an approximate sense. In particular, even rough evaluation of the efficiency for such an estimate can be difficult. Ordinarily, estimates determined by judgment-empirical methods are less desirable than those determined by theoretical-approximate methods.

In some cases, an estimate is determined on a theoretical-approximate basis and then the size of the error term is examined by judgment-empirical procedures. This combination of the theoretical-approximate and judgment-empirical methods tends to yield an estimate whose properties are reasonably well determined, and to represent a definite improvement over the use of either method alone.

For all the presentations of this section, any statement concerning the efficiency of an estimate refers to use of the ratio of mean square errors. That is, the efficiency of an estimate equals the mean square error of this estimate about the quantity estimated divided into the minimum mean square error of the estimates for this case.

The expansions for expected values of functions of sample moments and of sample order statistics can be used for at least roughly determining suitability and adequate sample sizes for estimates. Explicitly, these expansions furnish a basis for estimating mean square errors, etc. for point estimates based on order statistics and/or sample moments. By use of two-stage sampling, adequate sample sizes can be at least roughly determined by estimating the mean square error or coefficient of variation for the total sample from the first-stage sample (see page 120 for a more detailed discussion).

Situations Considered

The first two presentations are concerned with estimating the population standard deviation on the basis of the sample range or on the basis of estimates of the first two moments of the sample range. In both cases the results are of a judgment-empirical nature.

The next two presentations deal with estimates of the population mean and variance by use of sample order statistics. In one case the data for an estimate consist of two order statistics and for the other case all the values of a censored sample are available. The results are theoretical-approximate for both cases. The properties of the estimates based on two order statistics were also checked for a few special situations by judgment-empirical procedures.

When the only available data are a censored sample, there can be interest in estimating values of sample order statistics that were not observed (i.e., fall in the part of the sample that was censored). This is accomplished by estimating the expected values of the non-observed order statistics. A presentation is given which deals with this estimation problem for the situation where the order statistics estimated are not too far from the observed order statistics in the sequence of all the sample order statistics.

The final two presentations involve asymptotic expansions for expected values of functions of the sample values. In one case expected values of functions of sample moments are considered. In the other case the expansions are for expected values, variances, and covariances of sample order statistics.

Fixed Material for Section

Data 1 Univariate **2** None.

Population Standard Deviation from Sample Range

Data 1 Continuous **3** $X[i]$ **4** $m=1$; $2 \leqslant n \leqslant 10$ **Description 1** Judgment-empirical expected value estimation **2** $\sigma(i)$ on basis of $X[n]-X[1]$ **Assumptions 1** Random sample **2** $EX(i)^2$ exists **3** None **Results 1** d_n factor such that $E\{X[n]-X[1]\}/d_n=\sigma(i)$ for normal population **2** *Estimate*: $1.05\{X[n]-X[1]\}/d_n$ is estimate of $\sigma(i)$ **3** Table 7.1 contains values of d_n for $2 \leqslant n \leqslant 10$ **4** Based on analytical results and on empirical sampling for some cases where $\alpha_4(i)$ varies from near 1 to 9 **Characteristics 1** Low **2** Nearly as efficient as $S(i)$ for $\alpha_4(i)$ near 3, more efficient for values noticeably greater than 3, and less efficient for values noticeably less than 3 **3** Used symmetrically **4** $EX(i)^2$ must exist. Moderately sensitive to random sample condition **5** $EX(i)^2$ virtually always exists. Not difficult to decide on sample assumption **6** Except for $\alpha_4(i)$ near 1,

TABLE 7.1. VALUES OF d_n SUCH THAT $E\{X[n]-X[1]\}/d_n=\sigma(i)$ FOR NORMALITY*

n	2	3	4	5	6	7	8	9	10
d_n	1.12	1.70	2.06	2.32	2.54	2.70	2.84	2.98	3.08

* Abridged from Table XX of ref. 178: *Statistical tables for biological, agricultural, and medical research* (5th edition), R. A. Fisher and F. Yates, 1957, Oliver and Boyd Ltd., Edinburgh. Used with the kind permission of the authors, R. A. Fisher and F. Yates, and of the publisher.

bias of estimate small compared to its standard deviation **Bibliography** Ref. 110, 139, 404.

Population Variance From First Two Observed Moments of Sample Range (Shone)

Data 1 Continuous **3** $X[n]_j - X[1]_j$ **4** $2 \leqslant m \leqslant 5$; $n_1 = \ldots = n_m = n$ **Description 1** Judgment-empirical point estimation **2** $\sigma(i)_j$ on basis of $M_R = \sum_{j=1}^{m} \{X[n]_j - X[1]_j\}/m$ and $S_R{}^2 = \sum_{j=1}^{m} \{X[n]_j - X[1]_j - M_R\}^2/(m-1)$ **Assumptions 1** m independent random samples from populations differing only in mean value (if at all) **2** $EX(i)_j{}^2$ exists **3** None **Results 1** None **2** *Estimation results*: Estimates depend on n. For $n=2$, estimate of $\sigma(i)_j$ is $[(M_R{}^2 + S_R{}^2)/2]^{1/2}$. For $n=3$, estimate is $M_R{}^2/(2.10M_R - .81S_R)$. For $n=4$, estimate is $M_R{}^2/(2.29M_R - .69S_R)$. For $n=5$, estimate is $M_R{}^2/(2.41M_R - .46S_R)$ **3** None **4** Useful for situation (e.g., quality control) where only recorded dispersion data are sample ranges and nonparametric estimate of population standard deviation desired **Characteristics 1** Low **2** Should have reasonably high efficiency since M_R by itself tends to have high efficiency as estimate of $\sigma(i)_j$ **3** Used symmetrically within each sample **4** $EX(i)_j{}^2$ must exist. Moderately sensitive to independence and random sample conditions **5** $EX(i)_j{}^2$ virtually always exists. Not difficult to decide on independence and random sample assumptions **6** None **Bibliography** Ref. 473.

Population Mean and Variance—Two Order Statistics (Benson)

Data 1 Continuous **3** $X[i]$ **4** $m=1$; $n \geqslant 2$ **Description 1** Theoretical-approximate point estimation **2** $EX(i)$ and $\sigma(i)$, each from two order statistics **Assumptions 1** Random sample **2** $EX(i)^2$ exists **3** Population distribution approx. by first few terms of Gram-Charlier A series **Results 1** $X[z] = X$[largest integer $\leqslant z + \frac{1}{2}$] for $z < (n+1)/2$; $= X$ [smallest integer $\geqslant z - \frac{1}{2}$] for $z > (n+1)/2$ **2** *Estimates*: $\{X[(n+1)/6] + X[5(n+1)/6]\}/2$ is estimate of $EX(i)$, while $\{X[.93(n+1)] - X[.07(n+1)]\}/2.95$ is estimate of $\sigma(i)$ for $n \geqslant 9$ **3** None **4** Estimates also judgment-empirical since they were checked and found satisfactory for several non-normal populations of interest **Characteristics 1** Low **2** Should have high efficiency for small n. For case of normality, asymptotic efficiency of estimate for $EX(i)$ is 75 per cent while that of estimate for $\sigma(i)$ is 65 per cent **3** Used symmetrically **4** $EX(i)^2$ must exist. Moderately sensitive to random sample conditions. Moderately sensitive to Gram-Charlier A series assumption **5** $EX(i)^2$ virtually always exists. Not difficult to decide on random sample assumption. Moderately difficult to verify approximation by Gram-Charlier A series **6** Estimate of $EX(i)$ exact for case of symmetrical population. Useful for some kinds of censored data situations, including life-testing **Bibliography** Ref. 43.

Population Mean and Variance from Censored Sample

Data 1 Continuous **3** $X[i]$, $r_1<i<n-r_2$ **4** $m=1$; $n\geqslant 10\max(r_1, r_2)/3$ **Description 1** Theoretical-approximate point estimation **2** $EX(i)$ and $\sigma(i)$ by step-wise iterative procedure **Assumptions 1** Random sample **2** $EX(i)^2$ exists **3** $F(x)$ is of generalized Edgeworth form (see page 47); i.e., $F(x)=\Phi[(x-A)/B]+C\Phi^{(4)}[(x-A)/B]+D\Phi^{(6)}[(x-A)/B]+g[(x-A)/B]$ **Results 1** $\gamma=(1.2/n)\max(r_1, r_2)$, $x_1=K(\frac{3}{8}+\gamma/4)$, $x_2=K(\frac{1}{4}+\gamma/2)$, $x_3=K(\frac{1}{8}+3\gamma/4)$, $x_4=K(\gamma)=K_\gamma$. Using the censored data, form suitable histogram with area $1-(r_1+r_2)/n$; let X_1 be smallest abscissa and X_2 largest abscissa for which histogram nonzero; then $H(x)=r_1/n+$(area of histogram for abscissas $\leqslant x$), where $X_1\leqslant x\leqslant X_2$ **2** *Estimation procedure. Step* (1): For each combination of integers u, v, w such that $1\leqslant u<v<w\leqslant 4$, determine $a(u, v, w)$, $b(u, v, w)$, $c(u, v, w)$ from the three equations $a(u, v, w)[\Phi(x_u)-\Phi(-x_u)]+b(u, v, w)[\Phi(x_v)-\Phi(-x_v)]+c(u, v, w)[\Phi(x_w)-\Phi(-x_w)]=1$, $a(u, v, w)\Phi^{(4)}(x_u)+b(u, v, w)\Phi^{(4)}(x_v)+c(u, v, w)\Phi^{(4)}(x_w)=0$, $a(u, v, w)\Phi^{(6)}(x_u)+b(u, v, w)\Phi^{(6)}(x_v)+c(u, v, w)\Phi^{(6)}(x_w)=0$. *Step* (2): Subject to $X_1\leqslant A-Bx_4\leqslant A+Bx_4\leqslant X_2$, determine A, B such that $a(u, v, w)[H(A+Bx_u)-H(A-Bx_u)]+b(u, v, w)[H(A+Bx_v)-H(A-Bx_v)]+c(u, v, w)[H(A+Bx_w)-H(A-Bx_w)]=1$ at least roughly satisfied for all integers u, v, w such that $1\leqslant u<v<w\leqslant 4$; solution denoted by $\hat{A}$, $\hat{B}$. *Step* (3): If no A, B values at least roughly satisfy second step, increase γ and repeat first two steps. Estimation discontinued if successive increases reach $\gamma=(2/n)\max(r_1, r_2)$ without yielding acceptable values for $\hat{A}$, $\hat{B}$. *Step* (4): Given acceptable $\hat{A}$, $\hat{B}$ values, determine $\hat{C}$, $\hat{D}$ from the equations $2C\Phi^{(4)}(x_u)+2D\Phi^{(6)}(x_u)=H(\hat{A}+\hat{B}x_u)-H(\hat{A}-\hat{B}x_u)-\Phi(x_u)+\Phi(-x_u)$, $(u=1, \ldots, 4)$, by least-squares. If resulting $\hat{C}$, $\hat{D}$ do not at least roughly satisfy all four equations, estimation discontinued and $\hat{A}$, $\hat{B}$ discarded. *Step* (5): If $\hat{C}$, $\hat{D}$ acceptable and $\hat{A}$, $\hat{B}$ satisfy $[1+4(n-r_1-r_2)n^{-3/2}]\hat{B}^2>r_1(X_1-\hat{A})^2/n+r_2(X_2-\hat{A})^2/n+\frac{1}{n}\sum_{i=r_1+1}^{n-r_2}\{X[i]-\hat{A}\}^2$, $\hat{A}$ is estimate of $EX(i)$ and $\hat{B}$ is estimate of $\sigma(i)$ **3** None **4** Procedure yielding estimates partially self-checking with respect to distribution form assumption **Characteristics 1** Medium **2** Unknown in general. Should be at least moderate (say, 65 per cent or more) if distribution at least roughly normal **3** Used symmetrically **4** $EX(i)^2$ must exist. Moderately sensitive to random sample and generalized Edgeworth series assumptions **5** $EX(i)^2$ virtually always exists. Not difficult to decide on sample assumption. More difficult to decide on generalized Edgeworth series assumption but this partially offset by self-checking nature of procedure **6** Useful in life-testing and other situations involving deliberate or accidental censoring **Bibliography** Ref. 570.

Expected Values of Nonobserved Order Statistics

Data 1 Continuous **3** $X[r(h)]$ for $h=1,\ldots,H$, where $r(h)$ integer and $r(h_1)-r(h_2)=O(\sqrt{n+1})$ **4** m = 1; n restricted as stated in Results **Description 1** Theoretical-approximate expected value estimation **2** $EX[R]$, where R can differ a moderate amount from the $r(h)$ **Assumptions 1** Random sample **2** $f(x)$ and $EX(i)$ exist **3** $f(x)$ such that expansions of ref. 138 valid (i.e., $f(x)$ analytic, nonzero over range of def., etc.) **Results 1** $t=\sum_{h=1}^{H} r(h)/H$; $d(h)=t-r(h)$; $d(h_1)\neq d(h_2)$ if $h_1\neq h_2$; $p_T=T/(n+1)$; $q_T=1-p_T$; $A_k=$ $[(p_R-p_t)/2]^{k-1}/(k-1)!+p_Rq_R(k-1)(k-2)[(p_R-p_t)/2]^{k-2}/2(n+2)(k-1)!$; $B_k[d(h), (p_t-p_R)/2]=$ $[(p_t-p_R)/2]^{k-1}/(k-1)!-(k-1)[(p_t-p_R)/2]^{k-2}d(h)/(n+1)(k-1)!$ $+(k-1)(k-2)[(p_t-p_R)/2]^{k-3}[(n+1)p_tq_t+(p_t-q_t)d(h)+d(h)^2]/2(n+1)(n+2)(k-1)!$ $-(k-1)(k-2)(k-3)[(p_t-p_R)/2]^{k-3}d(k)[(n+1)p_tq_t+d(h)^2/3]/2(n+1)^2(n+2)(k-1)!$ **2** *Estimation procedure*: Choose H such that $H\geqslant 3$ and $H\geqslant \log_{10}[\max(n^{-3/2}, 10^{-4})]/\log_{10}|(p_R-p_t)/2|$. Given the $r(h)$, the estimate is $\sum_{h=1}^{H} a_hX[r(h)]$, where the a_h determined as simultaneous solution of $\sum_{h=1}^{H} a_hB_k[d(h), (p_t-p_R)/2]=A_k$, $(k=1,\ldots,H)$. $E\{\sum_{h=1}^{H} a_hX[r(h)]\}=$ $EX[R]$ $+$ $O(n^{-3/2})+O(|(p_R-p_t)/2|^H)$; if $H\geqslant 4$, $O(n^{-3/2})$ is replaced by $O(n^{-2})$ **3** Estimation method not used if either $\max_{1\leqslant h\leqslant H}|d(h)|>\frac{2}{3}p_tq_t(n+1)$ or $|p_R-p_t|>\frac{4}{3}\min(p_Rq_R, p_tq_t)$ **4** When $X[i]$ available for $1\leqslant i\leqslant r<R$, $r(h)=r-(H-h)D$, where $D=\max[1$, largest integer in $(n+1)^{1/2}/H]$ **Characteristics 1** Low to medium (unless H large) **2** Estimate has standard deviation $\sqrt{p_tq_t}/\sqrt{n}f(\theta_{p_t})+O(n^{-1})$. Method for approximately estimating value of $1/f(\theta_{p_t})$ given in Chapter 10 (also see ref. 571) **3** Used symmetrically **4** $EX(i)$ must exist. Moderately sensitive to random sample condition **5** $EX(i)$ virtually always exists. Not difficult to decide on random sample assumption **6** Useful for life-testing and other situations where sample order statistics are deliberately or accidentally deleted **Bibliography** Ref. 138, 571, 572.

Asymptotic Expansions for Expected Values of Sample Moments

Data 1 Arbitrary **3** $X(i)$ **4** $m=1$; $n\geqslant 2$ for some cases **Description 1** Some exact and theoretical-approximate expected value expressions **2** Expected values of functions of sample moments **Assumptions 1** Random sample **2** Expected values considered exist **3** None **Results 1** None **2** *Special Cases*: $EM(i)=EX(i)$; $\sigma^2M(i)=\sigma^2(i)/n$; $\mu_3M(i)=\mu_3(i)/n^2$; $\mu_4M(i)=3\sigma^4(i)/n^2+[\mu_4(i)-3\sigma^4(i)]/n^3$; $\mu_5M(i)=10\sigma^2(i)\mu_3(i)/n^3+O(n^{-4})$; $\mu_6M(i)=15\sigma^6(i)/n^3+O(n^{-4})$. $EM'_t(i)=\mu'_t(i)$; $\sigma^2M'_t(i)=[\mu'_{2t}(i)-\mu'_t(i)^2]/n$. $EM_2(i)=(n-1)\sigma^2(i)/n$; $\sigma^2M_2(i)=[\mu_4(i)-\sigma^4(i)]/n-2[\mu_4(i)-2\sigma^4(i)]/n^2+[\mu_4(i)-3\sigma^4(i)]/n^3$; $\mu_3M_2(i)=[\mu_6(i)-3\mu_4(i)\sigma^2(i)-6\mu_3(i)^2+2\sigma^6(i)]/n^2+O(n^{-3})$; $\mu_4M_2(i)=3[\mu_4(i)-\sigma^4(i)]^2/n^2+O(n^{-3})$;

cov $[M(i), M_2(i)] = (n-1)\mu_3(i)/n^2$; cov $\{M(i), [M_2(i)]^{1/2}\} = \mu_3(i)/2n\sigma(i) + O(n^{-3/2})$; $\sigma^2\{aM(i) + b[M_2(i)]^{1/2}\} = a^2\sigma^2(i)/n + b^2[\mu_4(i) + \sigma^4(i)]/4n\sigma^2(i) + O(n^{-3/2})$. $EM_t(i) = \mu_t(i) + O(n^{-1})$; $\sigma^2 M_t(i) = [\mu_{2t}(i) - 2t\mu_{t-1}(i)\mu_{t+1}(i) - \mu_t(i)^2 + t^2\mu_{t-1}(i)^2\sigma^2(i)]/n + O(n^{-2})$; cov $[M_V(i), M_W(i)] = [\mu_{V+W}(i) - V\mu_{V-1}(i)\mu_{W+1}(i) - W\mu_{V+1}(i)\mu_{W-1}(i) - \mu_V(i)\mu_W(i) + VW\mu_{V-1}(i)\mu_{W-1}(i)\sigma^2(i)]/n + O(n^{-2})$. $E\{[M_2(i)]^{1/2}\} = \sigma(i) + O(n^{-1})$; $\sigma^2\{[M_2(i)]^{1/2}\} = [\mu_4(i) - \sigma^4(i)]/4n\sigma^2(i) + O(n^{-2})$ *General case*: $H[M_V(i), M_W(i)]$ is fct. not containing n explicitly and for which second partial derivatives exist and are continuous in neighborhood of $[EM_V(i), EM_W(i)]$; also $|H[M_V(i), M_W(i)]| < an^b$ for all $M_V(i), M_W(i)$ and some $a, b \geqslant 0$. Then $EH[M_V(i), M_W(i)] = H[EM_V(i), EM_W(i)] + O(n^{-1})$ and $\sigma^2 H[M_V(i), M_W(i)] = \sigma^2 M_V(i)\{H_1[EM_V(i), EM_W(i)]\}^2 + 2$ cov $[M_V(i), M_W(i)]$ $H_1[EM_V(i), EM_W(i)]H_2[EM_V(i), EM_W(i)] + \sigma^2 M_W(i)\{H_2[EM_V(i), EM_W(i)]\}^2 + O(n^{-3/2})$, where H_1 partial derivative of H with respect to first coordinate and H_2 partial deriv. with respect to second coordinate. Case of single coordinate special case of these results. Extended to case of any specified number of coordinates for H in obvious manner **3** None **4** Further results obtainable from ref. 118 **Characteristics 1** Low **2** See presentations on exact unbiased estimation in Exact Point Estimation sect. of this chapt. Results of these presentations applicable since approximation occurs only with respect to prob. constant estimated **3** Used symmetrically **4** Expected values considered must exist. Moderately sensitive to random sample condition except for $EM(i)$ and $EM'_t(i)$ when $M[EX(i)]$ and $M[EX(i)^t]$ estimated, respectively **5** Expected values virtually always exist. Not difficult to decide on random sample assumption **6** Useful for estimating mean square errors and coefficients of variation for point estimates based on sample moments. Adequate sample sizes can be roughly determined by using two-stage sampling and estimating mean square error or coefficient of variation from first-stage sample **Bibliography** Ref. 118, 217.

Asymptotic Expansions for Expected Values of Order Statistics (*David and Johnson*)

Data 1 Continuous **3** $X[i]$ **4** $m = 1$ **Description 1** Theoretical-approximate expected value expansions **2** Expected values, variances, and covariances of the $X[i]$ **Assumptions 1** Random sample **2** $f(x)$ and $EX(i)^2$ exist **3** $f(x)$ such that expansions of ref. 138 valid (i.e., $f(x)$ analytic, nonzero over range of def., etc.) **Results 1** None **2** *Estimates*: $EX[U] = \theta_{U/(n+1)} - [U/(n+1)][1 - U/(n+1)]f'[\theta_{U/(n+1)}]/2(n+2) f[\theta_{U/(n+1)}]^3 + O[(n+2)^{-2}]$; $\sigma^2 X[U] = [U/(n+1)][1 - U/(n+1)]/(n+2)f[\theta_{U/(n+1)}]^2 + O[(n+2)^{-2}]$; for $U(1) < U(2)$, cov $\{X[U(1)], X[U(2)]\} = [U(1)/(n+1)][1 - U(2)/(n+1)]/(n+2)f[\theta_{U(1)/(n+1)}]f[\theta_{U(2)/(n+1)}]$

$+O[(n+2)^{-2}]$ **3** None **4** Additional terms in these expansions, also expansions for higher order moments of the $X[i]$, given in ref. 138 **Characteristics 1** Low for direct applications **2** Variance and covariance expansions allow approx. determination of variance for linear fct. of order statistics (in terms of pop. freq. fct. and n) **3** Used symmetrically **4** $EX(i)^2$ must exist. Moderately sensitive to random sample condition **5** $EX(i)^2$ virtually always exists. Not difficult to decide on random sample assumption **6** Useful for some types of censored data, including life-testing situations. Also useful for estimating mean square errors and coefficients of variation for point estimates based on order statistics. Adequate sample sizes can be roughly determined by using two-stage sampling and estimating mean square error, coefficient of variation, etc. from first-stage sample **Bibliography** Ref. 138, 274.

EXACT TESTS AND INTERVALS FOR MEAN—SYMMETRICAL POPULATIONS

Introduction

For all but one of the cases considered in this section, the data are n independent univariate observations from n symmetrical populations (possibly all different) with the same mean value. In the other case, the data are the coordinates of a multivariate observation. An important example of independent observations from symmetrical populations with a common mean is the situation of a random sample from a symmetrical population.

The presentations consist of exact tests and exact confidence intervals for the value of the common population mean. For some presentations the populations are required to be continuous, but many of the results are applicable whether the populations are continuous or discrete. Although the population means are stipulated to exist for the cases considered, the results furnish valid tests and confidence intervals for the common population median when one or more of the populations fail to have a finite first moment.

Nature of Material

Three levels of data specification occur among the tests that are presented. For one type of test, only the signs for the n differences of observation-value minus hypothesized-value-of-common-population-mean need to be considered. Both the signs of these differences and ranks of their absolute values are used for some of the other tests. The remaining types of tests use the actual values of the differences but are of a conditional character. That is, the absolute values of the differences are considered to be fixed values, and probability enters only with regard to the signs of the differences. These conditional tests are based on permutations of the signs of the differences and fall under the heading of permutation tests (see page 40).

For confidence intervals, the actual values of the observations are used in all cases, and population continuity is assumed for most of the results that are presented. In some cases, tests which can be obtained from confidence intervals are valid under weaker assumptions than are used for the confidence intervals. As an example, in many cases the strongest kind of population continuity assumed for a test is continuity of the distribution function at the population mean. For situations where the tests are valid under more general conditions than the corresponding confidence intervals, the tests are also given in the presentation.

In some presentations, only tests are considered for situations where confidence intervals exist and can be obtained on the basis of the tests (but are not given in a separate presentation). This occurs for the permutation tests and for some of the tests based on ranks. For these cases, the general method of obtaining confidence intervals from permutation and rank tests (see page 41) can be applied.

The presentations based on independent observations can be directly applied to situations which involve two or more sets of observations and where the value of the population mean can change from set to set. Here the totality of observations are independent and, for any given set, the symmetrical populations yielding the observations have the same mean value. The problem is to obtain confidence intervals and tests for an arbitrary but specified linear function of the population means for the sets. Let n_1 be the number of observations in the set with the smallest number of observations. Then by appropriate linear combinations and weightings of the observations in the various sets, n_1 univariate "observations" are obtained which are independent, symmetrically distributed, and all have expected value equal to the specified linear function of the population means for the sets. Here the observations are not necessarily used symmetrically, even within sets. A situation of this nature is also considered in Chapter 8.

Conversion of Data to Continuous Form

A conversion method that is always applicable for the symmetrical univariate situations considered in this section consists in adding very small ("infinitesimal") sample values from a continuous symmetrical population with zero mean to each of the observations. Then the converted observations are independent and from continuous symmetrical populations with the same mean value. Moreover, the converted observations are a sample if the original observations are a sample. Here no approximation is involved with respect to the quantity investigated, since the common mean for the converted populations exactly equals the common mean for the populations yielding the observations. Also, very little efficiency should be lost by the conversion since the converted populations differ very slightly from the actual populations.

In the case of tests, a combination of randomization and of an independent probability process in which a plus sign has the same probability as a minus sign can be used in place of adding a very small random value to each observation. Namely, randomization is used to assign orderings (with respect to magnitude) within sets where the absolute values of the differences between the observations and the hypothetical mean have the same value. After this, the differences with zero values are randomly given signs. Then the set consisting of the differences between the observations and the hypothetical mean contains no ties and, under the null hypothesis, can be considered to contain independent observations from continuous symmetrical populations with zero mean (with respect to use in the tests presented in this section).

Tests Obtained From Two-Sample and Randomness Tests

Let $X(1), \ldots, X(n)$ be independent observations from symmetrical populations such that $EX(1) = \ldots = EX(n)$ and consider testing the null hypothesis that $EX(i) = \mu_0$. Then, under the null hypothesis, the values of $|X(i) - \mu_0|$ are considered to be fixed and probability enters only with respect to the sign that is given $|X(i) - \mu_0|$ for $i = 1, \ldots, n$. For the unconditional case with respect to these signs, each of $|X(1) - \mu_0|, \ldots, |X(n) - \mu_0|$ that is nonzero receives a plus or minus sign in such a way that all possible combinations of signs are equally likely. However, the signs can also be allotted in a conditional manner, resulting in conditional tests of the null hypothesis. As an example, suppose that n_1 of the $X(i) - \mu_0$ are positive and n_2 are negative $(n_1 + n_2 \leqslant n)$. Then, under the null hypothesis, an allowable allotment of signs to the nonzero $|X(i) - \mu_0|$ is that where all possible combinations of n_1 plus signs and n_2 minus signs are equally likely.

Only the unconditional case occurs for the tests of this nature that are presented in this section. However, conditional tests with conditions of the type mentioned in the example can be easily obtained by making use of a class of two-sample tests. Namely, consider any two-sample test that is based on the principle that all ways of dividing $n_1 + n_2$ observations into sets of sizes n_1 and n_2 are equally likely under the two-sample null hypothesis. Then this test can be directly applied using the positive $X(i) - \mu_0$ as the values of a sample of size n_1 and the absolute values of the negative $X(i) - \mu_0$ as an independent sample of size n_2. Under the null hypothesis that $EX(i)=\mu_0$, and subject to the condition of n_1 plus signs and n_2 minus signs, all possible ways of dividing the $|X(i)-\mu_0|$ into sets of sizes n_1 and n_2, identified by the sign given the observations of a set, are equally likely (see, e.g., ref. 237).

As mentioned in Chapter 5, the randomness tests presented there can be used as two-sample tests. Since the two-sample tests yielded by the material of Chapter 5 belong to the class considered, they can be used to obtain conditional tests of $EX(i)=\mu_0$ for the case of independent observations from symmetrical populations with a common mean.

Use of Random Ranks—Discussion

As outlined in Chapter 4, random ranks can be useful in obtaining tests for cases where the use of ranks is appropriate. Nearly all of the tests presented in this section are based on ranks (necessarily non-negative) of the $|X(i)-\mu_0|$, $(i=1, \ldots, n)$; here the null hypothesis asserts that the common value of $EX(1), \ldots, EX(n)$ is μ_0. In some cases, the values of the $|X(i)-\mu_0|$ are treated as if they were ranks (i.e., the $|X(i)-\mu_0|$ are considered to be fixed numbers). The corresponding tests with the fixed rank values replaced by non-negative random ranks may be useful for some situations. Special alternative hypotheses can be emphasized by choice of the completely specified population yielding the random ranks. Moderately accurate determination of the null distribution for the test statistic is ordinarily not very difficult (see Chapter 4).

Applications to Two-Sample and Several-Sample Problems

The exact tests for the common central value of a set of symmetrical populations can be used for the univariate two-sample problem in many ways. The procedure is to develop several suitable statistics of specified observations of the two samples such that each sample value occurs in exactly (or at most) one statistic, and such that each of these statistics is symmetrically distributed about zero under the null hypothesis that the two independent samples are from the same population. Here one type of function is used to yield the statistic for a specified set of the sample values, a possibly different function is used for another specified set of the observations, etc.

To assure that a given statistic of sample values is symmetrically distributed about zero under the null hypothesis, it is sufficient to verify that exchanging an observation from the first sample and an observation from the second sample for one or more pairs of these observations changes the sign but not the magnitude of the statistic. As an example, for samples

$X(1)_1, \ldots, X(n_1)_1$ and $X(1)_2, \ldots, X(n_2)_2$ with $n_1 = 2$ and $n_2 = 1$, the statistic

$$h[X(1)_1, X(2)_1; X(1)_2] \\ = 5[X(2)_1 - X(1)_2]X(1)_1 - [X(2)_1 - X(1)_2]^3[X(1)_1 + X(1)_2 + X(2)_1]^2$$

is symmetrically distributed about zero under the null hypothesis since

$$h[X(1)_1, X(2)_1; X(1)_2] \equiv -h[X(1)_1, X(1)_2; X(2)_1].$$

In this case exchanging $X(2)_1$ and $X(1)_2$ left the magnitude of the statistic identically the same but changed its sign. As another example, with $n_1 = n_2 = 2$, the statistic

$$[X(1)_1 - X(2)_2]^{-1}[X(2)_1 + X(1)_2] + 2\{X(1)_2 - X(2)_1 + 3[X(2)_2 - X(1)_1]\}^5$$

is changed in sign but not magnitude if $X(1)_1, X(2)_2$ are exchanged and also $X(2)_1, X(1)_2$ are exchanged.

Since no two statistics contain the same observations, these statistics are independent and symmetrically distributed about zero under the null hypothesis. Thus the tests of this section are applicable. The choice of the test and the forms of the functions used to obtain the statistics determine the alternative hypotheses that are emphasized. Since there is a great amount of freedom in selecting the forms for the statistics, a wide variety of alternative hypotheses can be emphasized.

In order to have a reasonable selection of significance levels, the number of statistics determined in this manner should be at least seven or eight. Also, to avoid bias, the observations should be divided into sets without knowledge of their values, or by use of an independent randomization process.

The same approach can be used for the several-sample problem. Here the available data are several independent samples. The null hypothesis asserts that all these samples are from the same population. The procedure is to develop several suitable statistics such that each of the sample values occurs in exactly (or at most) one statistic, and such that each statistic is symmetrically distributed about zero under the null hypothesis. By their construction, the statistics are independent. A statistic is symmetrically distributed about zero under the null hypothesis if there exists an exchange procedure, among observations used in the statistic that are from different populations, which identically leaves the magnitude of the statistic the same but changes its sign. For example, let the observations be $X(1)_1, \ldots, X(1)_4$, where each observation is from a different sample. Then the statistic

$$2[X(1)_1 - X(1)_3]^3X(1)_2^2X(1)_4^2 - [X(1)_2 - X(1)_4][X(1)_1 + X(1)_3]$$

is symmetrically distributed about zero, since exchanging $X(1)_1$ with $X(1)_3$ and exchanging $X(1)_2$ with $X(1)_4$ leaves the magnitude of this statistic fixed but changes its sign.

By suitable choice of the forms of the statistics, and there is a very large amount of freedom in making this choice, alternative hypotheses of many types can be emphasized. As for the two-sample case, at least seven or eight statistics should be used for a test, so that a reasonable selection of significance levels is available.

Remark About a Sequential Test

Since the mean is also a median for symmetrical populations, the sequential tests for population percentiles given in Chapter 8 are applicable for testing the common value of the mean for independent observations from symmetrical populations. That is, the Chapter 8 sequential test for the null hypothesis that the common median of n populations has a specified value can be used as a test of the population mean for the case of symmetrical populations.

Extensions—Interpolation and Randomized-Exact

The randomized-exact and interpolation methods described in Chapter 8 (page 204) can also be applied to some of the results given in this section. In fact, one of the approximate presentations of the next section (page 170) is an interpolation application of the Broad Class of Confidence Intervals presentation of this section. Although no randomized-exact results are presented in Chapter 7, this method can be easily applied to the Sign Test, the Wilcoxon Signed-Rank Test, and the Broad Class of Confidence Intervals presentations. In addition to its application in the next section, the interpolation method can be easily applied to the Sign Test and the Wilcoxon Signed-Rank Test presentations. In principle, the interpolation and randomized-exact methods can also be applied to the other procedures given in this section where the available probability levels are of a discrete nature.

Use For Testing Population Symmetry

The tests presented in this section can be used to test population symmetry on the basis of a sample from the univariate population investigated. The first step of the procedure is to divide the sample values into groups of size three or larger, where this division is made without knowledge of the values of the observations, or by use of an independent randomization process (in which all possible divisions are equally likely). Then, for each group, a statistic with one-dimensional values is formed which is symmetrically distributed about zero when the population is symmetrical and which, in conjunction with the test used, should be chosen so as to emphasize the alternatives of interest. Population symmetry is investigated by testing the null hypothesis that these independent statistics have symmetrical distributions with zero means (here symmetry occurs as part of the null hypothesis).

For groups of size three, the only linear statistic available is of the form $x_1 + x_3 - 2x_2$ times a nonzero constant, where $x_1 \leqslant x_2 \leqslant x_3$ are the values of the observations for the group. However, a variety of nonlinear functions of $x_1 + x_3 - 2x_2$, and perhaps also of $x_3 - x_1$, can be used. Any function which identically has the same magnitude but the opposite sign when $x_1 \to 2\mu - x_3$, $x_2 \to 2\mu - x_2$, $x_3 \to 2\mu - x_1$, where μ is the mean of the population sampled, can be used as the statistic for a group. For example, the statistic

$$(x_3 - x_1)^2(x_1 + x_3 - 2x_2) - 5(x_1 + x_3 - 2x_2)^3 + 10|x_3 - x_1|/(x_1 + x_3 - 2x_2)$$

satisfies these conditions (the existence of the expected value of this statistic is not necessary if the test is considered to investigate the population median). By a suitable combined choice of the nonlinear functions for the groups and the test used, many different types of alternatives can be emphasized.

For groups of size four, the situation is also somewhat restricted. Namely, the only linear statistic available is of the form $x_1 + x_4 - x_2 - x_3$ times a nonzero constant. However, for groups of size five and larger, infinite classes of linear statistics are available. For example, when the group size is five, each of the linear statistics of the form $x_1 + x_5 + a(x_2 + x_4) - 2(a+1)x_3$ times a nonzero constant, where $-\infty < a < \infty$ and $x_1 \leqslant \ldots \leqslant x_5$ are the observations, can be used as the statistic for a group. Moreover, many types of nonlinear functions of one or more of the linear statistics, and perhaps also other functions of the observations, can be used as the statistic for a group. Let $x_1 \leqslant \ldots \leqslant x_N$ be the observations. Then any function which identically has the same magnitude but the opposite sign when $x_1 \to 2\mu - x_N$, $x_2 \to 2\mu - x_{N-1}, \ldots, x_N \to 2\mu - x_1$ can be used as the statistic for the group. Thus, if group sizes of at least five are used, the amount of freedom for emphasizing specified alternatives is very substantial.

Most of the tests presented in this section do not require the observations to be a sample. For use of these tests, the groups need not be of the same size and a different form of statistic could be used for each group. Thus, for these tests, none of the sample values need to be discarded in order to form the groups. Also, if the sample size is reasonably large, two or more different types of alternatives can be tested simultaneously.

The combination of the statistics selected for the groups and the test used determines the deviations from symmetry that are emphasized.

One type of deviation occurs when the statistics for the groups have distributions with nonzero means. Another type of deviation occurs when the statistics have zero means but their distributions are not symmetrical. By suitable choice of the statistics and the test, it should be possible to obtain a test which is sensitive to both of these types of deviations and emphasizes deviations of the second type at specified parts of the distribution. Greater emphasis on the first type of deviation can be obtained by combining a symmetry test of the kind described in Chapter 5 (page 61) with one of the tests considered here where the statistics constitute a random sample. The combined test would be considered significant if, and only if, at least one of the two tests is significant. Computation of the significance level of the combined test is easy since the two tests are independent under the null hypothesis. That is, only sequence order is used in one test, and the other test, based on the same statistics, uses these statistics in a symmetrical fashion.

Extensions Based on Transformations of Variable

As noted in the discussion of the use of the results of this section for testing population symmetry, suitable nonlinear transformations of variable can be helpful in obtaining tests which emphasize the alternative hypotheses that are of principal interest. This approach is also applicable for tests of $EX(i)$ when population symmetry is known to exist. Specifically, let the null hypothesis be $EX(i)=\mu_0$. Then, under the null hypothesis, the observed values $X(1)-\mu_0, \ldots, X(n)-\mu_0$ are n independent observations from symmetrical populations with zero mean. Each $X(i)-\mu_0$ can be replaced by a nonlinear function of $X(i)-\mu_0$ which does not depend on any of the $X(i')$ for $i' \neq i$ and which has a distribution that is symmetrical about zero. Any function which identically has the same magnitude but opposite sign when $X(i)-\mu_0$ is replaced by $\mu_0-X(i)$ can be used (the existence of the expected value of this function is not necessary if the test is considered to investigate the median of the distribution of the function). Then the null hypothesis that all the initial observations have zero means (or medians) is tested on the basis of these transformed observations.

By suitable choice of the nonlinear functions and of the test used, it should be possible to emphasize many different types of alternative hypotheses. For tests that do not require the observations to be a sample, a different form of nonlinear transformation could be used for each $X(i)-\mu_0$.

Outline of Presentations

The first presentation, Sign Test and Associated Confidence Intervals, furnishes the only type of test considered that is based entirely on the signs of the n differences between observation value and hypothesized mean value. Here the tests are valid under weaker assumptions than those used for the corresponding confidence intervals.

The next two presentations deal with rank tests. In one case the absolute values of the n differences are ranked in the usual way. This furnishes the Wilcoxon signed-rank test. In the other case, a special type of ranking is used. The values used for the ranks are the expectations of the order statistics for the absolute values of the observations of a random sample of size n from the standardized normal population. This method of selecting values for the ranks yields a test which is locally most powerful for the situation of specified normal alternative hypotheses.

Following these rank tests are three presentations which are concerned with permutation tests. For the first of these, the test statistic is a linear function of the sum of the observations. The second presentation consists of a family of tests for which the test statistic is a linear function of the order statistics of the observations. By suitable choice of the coefficients for the order statistics (on the basis of rough information concerning the shapes for the population distributions), the resulting permutation test should have a reasonably high efficiency. The third of these presentations furnishes a test that is oriented toward the case of a random sample from a continuous population. When the sample and continuity conditions hold, this test is asymptotically most powerful for a broad class of situations.

The next two presentations contain outlines of some rather general methods for constructing rank and permutation tests. The first of these presentations deals with tests that are obtained as a combination of the sign test and some tests for the two-sample problem. The second presentation contains a general procedure for developing tests; this procedure includes as special cases all the sign, rank, and permutation tests given in the other presentations.

The final two presentations are concerned with confidence intervals. The first of these presentations is devoted to the determination of confidence intervals directly from order statistics of the observations. This method yields an extensive class of confidence intervals, including those which correspond to the sign test and those which correspond to Wilcoxon's signed-rank test. For the second presentation, the data are the coordinates of an observation from a spherically symmetrical multivariate distribution. Use of the t statistic yields confidence intervals for the common expected value of these coordinates.

Fixed Material for Section

Data 4 $m=1$ **Assumptions 2** $EX(i)$ exists **Characteristics 3** Used symmetrically **4** $EX(i)$ must exist **5** $EX(i)$ virtually always exists.

Sign Test and Associated Confidence Intervals

Data 1 Arbitrary, univariate **2** None **3** $X(i)$ **4** Usually $n \geqslant 3$ **Description 1** Exact one-sided and two-sided tests and confidence intervals **2** $EX(i)$ **Assumptions 1** Independent **2** Populations symmetrical; also continuous at $EX(i)$ for confidence intervals case **3** $EX(1) = \ldots = EX(n)$ **Results 1** For tests: Null hyp. is $EX(i) = \mu_0$; $N =$ no. of $X(i) - \mu_0$ that are nonzero and $d =$ no. of $X(i) - \mu_0$ that are positive **2** *Tests*: Accept $EX(i) < \mu_0$ if $d \leqslant U$; has sig. level $\alpha_N(U) = (\frac{1}{2})^N \sum_{k=0}^{U} \binom{N}{k}$. Accept $EX(i) > \mu_0$ if $d \geqslant N - U$; has sig. level $\alpha_N(U)$. Accept $EX(i) \neq \mu_0$ if $d \leqslant U$ or $d \geqslant N - U$ $(U < N/2)$; has sig. level $2\alpha_N(U)$. *Confidence intervals defined by*: $P\{X[U+1] > EX(i)\} = P\{X[U+1] \geqslant EX(i)\} = P\{X[n-U] < EX(i)\} = P\{X[n-U] \leqslant EX(i)\} = \alpha_n(U) = (\frac{1}{2})^n \sum_{k=0}^{U} \binom{n}{k}$; for $U+1 < n-V$, $P\{X[U+1] < EX(i) < X[n-V]\} = \mathrm{P}\{X[U+1] \leqslant EX(i) \leqslant X[n-V]\} = 1 - \alpha_n(U) - \alpha_n(V)$ **3** Values of $\alpha_N(U)$, and $\alpha_n(U)$, obtainable from binomial dist. tables (e.g., ref. 378), or from incomplete beta fct. tables and the relation $\alpha_N(U) = I_{1/2}(N-U, U+1)$; when $N \geqslant 2$, $\alpha_N(U) \doteq \Phi(u_0)$, where $u_0 = \frac{1}{3}\{[(9U-1)/U][U/(N-U)+1]^{1/3} - [9(N-U)+8]/(N-U+1)\}/\{[U/(N-U+1]^{2/3}/U + 1/(N-U+1)\}^{1/2}$ **4** Interpolation furnishes confidence intervals with confidence coeff. (bounded) approx. equal to arbitrarily specified values (see page 143). Two-sided tests with unequal tails obtainable as combination of non-overlapping one-sided tests. Sign test of conditional nature when ties occur. If populations not continuous, $P\{X[U+1] > EX(i)\} = P\{X[n-U] < EX(i)\} \leqslant \alpha_n(U) \leqslant P\{X[U+1] \geqslant EX(i)\} = P\{X[n-U] \leqslant EX(i)\}$; also $P\{X[U+1] < EX(i) < X[n-V]\} \leqslant 1 - \alpha_n(U) - \alpha_n(V) \leqslant P\{X[U+1] \leqslant EX(i) \leqslant X[n-V]\}$ **Characteristics 1** Low **2** Null hyp. can be interpreted as asserting that $\mu_0 = \theta_{1/2}(i) = EX(i)$; for sample case, and altern. hyp. of form $\mu_0 = \theta_p$ with $p \neq \frac{1}{2}$, power fct. values given by ref. 321. Test with altern. $EX(i) > \mu_0$ consistent if $EX(i) > \mu_0$; test with altern. $EX(i) < \mu_0$ consistent if $EX(i) < \mu_0$; test with altern. $EX(i) \neq \mu_0$ consistent if $EX(i) \neq \mu_0$. Compared to t test, asymptotic rel. efficiency of sign test has no lower bound for sample from arbitrary continuous symmetrical population; lower bound is $33\frac{1}{3}$ per cent if population sampled also unimodal; asymptotic rel. efficiency is $200/\pi$ per cent if population normal; expression for computing asymptotic power fct. and rel. efficiencies given in ref. 290. For sample from normal population, efficiency of sign test (with $V = U$ for two-sided tests) approx. 95 per cent for $U = 0$, approx. 80 per cent for $U = 1$, approx. 75 per cent for $U = 2$, approx. 70 per cent for $U = 3$, and decreases to limit of 63.7 per cent as U increases. Sign test locally most powerful for case of sample from symmetrical exponential population with unknown mean, and has 100 per cent asymptotic efficiency **4** Moderately sensitive to symmetry and equality of means conditions when n (and N) of at least moderate size or one-sided results considered; only mildly sensitive if n (or N) small and equal-tail results considered. Moderately sensitive to independence condition and, for confidence intervals, can be sensitive to continuity condition **5** Not difficult to decide on independence or continuity assumptions. More difficult to verify symmetry; also to verify equality of means unless observations believed random sample **6** Also considered in Chapter 8 as test for $\theta_{1/2}(i)$. There exact tests and confidence intervals obtained by use of independent random process also considered; then most significance level and confidence coefficient values can be attained. Useful for some types of censored data, including life-testing situations **Bibliography** Ref. 76, 149, 150, 158, 159, 186, 222, 238, 241, 250, 290, 321, 418, 446, 552, 573.

Wilcoxon Signed-Rank Test

Data 1 Continuous, univariate **2** None **3** $X(i)$ **4** Usually $n \geqslant 3$ **Description 1** Exact one-sided and two-sided tests **2** $EX(i)$ **Assumptions 1** Independent **2** Populations continuous and symmetrical **3** $EX(1) = \ldots = EX(n)$ **Results 1** Null hyp. is $EX(i) = \mu_0$; $r_i =$ rank of $|X(i) - \mu_0|$ in $|X(1) - \mu_0|, \ldots, |X(n) - \mu_0|$; $T =$ sum of r_i over i such that $X(i) > \mu_0$; $T' =$ sum of r_i over i such that $X(i) < \mu_0$; $T'' = \min(T, T')$ **2** *One-sided tests*: Accept $EX(i) > \mu_0$ if $T \geqslant n(n+1)/2 - T_\alpha$; equivalently: Accept $EX(i) > \mu_0$ if $T'' \leqslant T_\alpha$ and $T' = T''$. Accept $EX(i) < \mu_0$ if $T \leqslant T_\alpha$; equivalently: Accept $EX(i) < \mu_0$ if $T'' \leqslant T_\alpha$ and $T = T''$. *Two-sided tests*: Accept $EX(i) \neq \mu_0$ if $T \geqslant n(n+1)/2 - T_{\alpha/2}$ or $T \leqslant T_{\alpha/2}$; equivalently: Accept $EX(i) \neq \mu_0$ if $T'' \leqslant T_{\alpha/2}$ **3** Table 7.2 lists T_α for $3 \leqslant n \leqslant 15$ and various α. For $n \geqslant 15$, $T_\alpha \doteq n(n+1)/4 - \{n(n+1)[nA(\alpha) + B(\alpha)]/4\}^{1/2}$, for α such that this quantity integral; here $A(\alpha)$ and $B(\alpha)$ obtained by interpolation from values listed in Table 7.3 and $\alpha = .05, .025, .01, .005$. When $n \geqslant 25$ and $1/5n \leqslant \alpha \leqslant 1 - 1/5n$, $T_\alpha \doteq -\frac{1}{2} + n(n+1)/4 - t_\alpha(n)$ $[n(n+1)(2n+1)/24]^{1/2}$, for α such that this quantity integral **4** Tests based on T'' often require less computation. Interpolation yields tests with signif. levels (bounded) approx. equal to arbitrarily specified values (see page 143). Discontinuous case can be handled by deleting observations for which $X(i) = \mu_0$ and randomly assigning ranks to ties among the $|X(i) - \mu_0|$; approx. method furnished by using midrank method of assigning ties. Also, method of converting data to continuous form (see page 139) can be used. General method for obtaining exact Wilcoxon signed-rank tests (population not necessarily continuous) given in ref. 158 and 159 **Characteristics 1** Low **2** Let $P = P[X(i) > \mu_0 | X(i) \neq \mu_0]$, $Q = 1 - P$, $\gamma =$ $P[X(u) > -X(v) + 2\mu_0 | X(u) > \mu_0, X(v) < \mu_0]$ $-$ $P[X(u) < -X(v) +$

TABLE 7.2. VALUES OF T_α FOR WILCOXON SIGNED-RANK TEST ($3 \leqslant n \leqslant 15$)*

n	α	T_α	n	α	T_α
3	.125	0	10	.0049	3
4	.062	0		.0098	5
5	.031	0		.024	8
	.062	1	11	.0046	5
6	.016	0		.0090	7
	.031	1		.027	11
	.047	2	12	.0046	7
7	.0078	0		.0105	11
	.016	1		.027	14
	.023	2	13	.0052	10
8	.0039	0		.0105	13
	.0078	1		.025	17
	.012	2	14	.0054	13
	.027	4		.0105	16
9	.0039	1		.027	21
	.0046	2	15	.0052	16
	.0098	3		.0095	19
	.027	6		.027	25

* Based on ref. 585: Probability tables for individual comparisons by ranking methods, F. Wilcoxon, *Biometrics*, Vol. 3, 1947, pages 119–20 and on ref. 526: *The simplest signed-rank tests*, J. W. Tukey, Memo. rept. 17, Statistical Research Group, Princeton Univ., 1949. Used with the kind permission of the authors, Frank Wilcoxon and John W. Tukey, and of the publishers.

TABLE 7.3. VALUES OF $A(\alpha)$, $B(\alpha)$ FOR $\alpha=.05, .025, .01, .005$*

α	$A(\alpha)$	$B(\alpha)$
.005	2.200	−.570
.01	1.790	.386
.025	1.269	1.050
.05	.882	1.310

* Based on ref. 526: *The simplest signed-rank tests*, J. W. Tukey, Memo rept. 17, Statistical Research Group, Princeton Univ., 1949. Used with the kind permission of the author, John W. Tukey, and of the publisher.

$2\mu_0|X(u)>\mu_0, X(v)<\mu_0]$. If the $X(i)$ are random sample from any population such that $P[X(i)\neq\mu_0]\neq 0$, then: Test with altern. $EX(i)>\mu_0$ consistent if $P-\frac{1}{2}+PQ\gamma>0$; test of $EX(i)<\mu_0$ consistent if $P-\frac{1}{2}+PQ\gamma<0$; test of $EX(i)\neq\mu_0$ consistent if $P-\frac{1}{2}+PQ\gamma\neq 0$; for sufficiently small α, none of these tests consistent if $P-\frac{1}{2}+PQ\gamma=0$; if population sampled symmetrical, $P-\frac{1}{2}+PQ\gamma>0$ equivalent to $EX(i)>0$, $P-\frac{1}{2}+PQ\gamma<0$ equivalent to $EX(i)<\mu_0$, and $P-\frac{1}{2}+PQ\gamma\neq 0$ equivalent to $EX(i)\neq 0$. For sample from normal population, efficiency approx. 95 per cent for all n. For sample from continuous dist. fct. of "shift in location" form $F[x-EX(i)]$, asymptotic relative efficiency never less than .864 compared to t test. If sample from "contaminated" population with dist. fct. of form $(1-\delta)F(x)+\delta G(x)$, $0\leqslant\delta\leqslant 1$, where $F(x)$ continuous and symmetrical about μ_0 and $G(x)$ continuous but not necessarily symmetrical or with mean μ_0, then lower bound for asymptotic rel. efficiency compared to the t test is zero; however, if $G(x)=F(x)^2$, test is locally most powerful rank test (for small δ), indicating that test sensitive to situations where population shape slips away from symmetry without changing value of population median. Expression for computing asymptotic power fcts. and rel. efficiencies given in ref. 290 **4** Moderately sensitive to independence, symmetry, and equality of means conditions. Lack of continuity unimportant since exact tests obtainable in presence of ties **5** Not difficult to decide on independence. More difficult to verify symmetry; also to verify equality of means unless observations believed random sample **6** Confidence intervals corresponding to this test given on page 157. Combination with sign test, also generalizations, given in ref. 158 and 159. **Bibliography** Ref. 158, 159, 186, 222, 241, 290, 446, 526, 527, 583, 584, 585, 586.

Locally Optimum Generalized Rank Test—Normal Alternative

Data 1 Continuous, univariate **2** None **3** $X(i)$ **4** Usually $n \geqslant 3$ **Description 1** Exact one-sided and two-sided tests **2** $EX(i)$ **Assumptions 1** Independent **2** Populations continuous and symmetrical **3** $EX(1) = \ldots = EX(n)$ **Results 1** Null hyp. is $EX(i) = \mu_0$. Let $|X(U_i) - \mu_0|$ be ith order statistic of $|X(1) - \mu_0|, \ldots, |X(n) - \mu_0|$; then $s_i = sgn[X(U_i) - \mu_0]$. R_i = expected value of ith order statistic of absolute values for observations of sample of n from standardized normal population. $\sigma_z{}^2 = \sum_{i=1}^n R_i{}^2$, $c_z = \min_i (R_{i+1} - R_i)/2$; min occurs for i near $(n+1)/2$. $Z = \sum_{i=1}^n s_i R_i$ **2** *Tests*: Accept $EX(i) > \mu_0$ if $Z > Z(\alpha)$. Accept $EX(i) < \mu_0$ if $Z < -Z(\alpha)$. Accept $EX(i) \neq \mu_0$ if $|Z| > Z(\alpha/2)$ **3** For $n \geqslant 15$ and $1/8n \leqslant \alpha \leqslant 1 - 1/8n$, $Z(\alpha) \doteq -c_z + t_\alpha(n)\sigma_z$. For smaller n, values of $Z(\alpha)$ furnished by method given in ref. 159. Ref. 511 contains values of R_i for $n \leqslant 20$ **4** Method of ref. 159 also furnishes exact tests when populations not necessarily continuous; deletion of observations for which $X(i) = \mu_0$ combined with random assignment of generalized ranks to ties another method of obtaining exact tests. Also, conversion of data to continuous form (see page 139) can be used. Corresponding confidence intervals obtainable from tests by general method outlined in Chapter 4 **Characteristics 1** Low **2** Locally most powerful generalized rank test (i.e., for $[EX(i) - \mu_0]/\sigma(i)$ small) when observations sample from normal population. When data sample from symmetrical population, test consistent if alternative specified in its statement holds **4** Moderately sensitive to independence, symmetry, and equality of means conditions. Lack of continuity unimportant since exact tests obtainable in presence of ties **5** Not difficult to decide on independence. More difficult to verify symmetry; also to verify equality of means unless observations believed random sample **6** None **Bibliography** Ref. 159, 185, 511.

Fisher Randomization Test

Data 1 Arbitrary, univariate **2** None **3** $X(i)$ **4** Usually $n \geqslant 3$ **Description 1** Exact one-sided and two-sided permutation tests **2** Null hyp. is $EX(i) = \mu_0$ **Assumptions 1** Independent **2** Populations symmetrical **3** $EX(1) = \ldots = EX(n)$; values of the $|X(i) - \mu_0|$ considered fixed **Results 1** $X(i) \neq \mu_0$ only for $i = i_1, \ldots, i_N$; $\sigma_w{}^2 = \sum_{k=1}^N [X(i_k) - \mu_0]^2$; $c_w = \min_{u \neq v} ||X(i_u) - \mu_0| - |X(i_v) - \mu_0||/2$; $W = \sum_{k=1}^N |X(i_k) - \mu_0| \operatorname{sgn}[X(i_k) - \mu_0] = \sum_{k=1}^N X(i_k) - N\mu_0$ **2** *Tests*: Accept $EX(i) > \mu_0$ if $W > W(\alpha)$. Accept $EX(i) < \mu_0$ if $W < -W(\alpha)$. Accept $EX(i) \neq \mu_0$ if $|W| > W(\alpha/2)$ **3** $W(\alpha) \doteq -c_w + t_\alpha(N)\sigma_w$ if $N \geqslant 10$, $\max_k [X(i_k) - \mu_0]^2/\sigma_w{}^2 \leqslant 5/2N$, and $1/4N \leqslant \alpha \leqslant 1 - 1/4N$. For other cases use permutation test procedure outlined in Chapter 4 (also see ref. 159) **4** Corresponding confidence intervals obtainable by general method outlined in Chapter 4.

Test essentially unconditional in implications **Characteristics 1** Low to medium **2** For random sample from arbitrary population such that $P[X(i) \neq \mu_0] \neq 0$ and $E\{[X(i)-\mu_0]^2|X(i) \neq \mu_0\} < \infty$: Test with altern. $EX(i) > \mu_0$ consistent if $E[X(i)|X(i) \neq \mu_0] > \mu_0$; test of $EX(i) < \mu_0$ consistent if $E[X(i)|X(i) \neq \mu_0] < \mu_0$; test of $EX(i) \neq \mu_0$ consistent if $E[X(i)|X(i) \neq \mu_0] \neq \mu_0$; for α sufficiently small, none of these tests consistent if $E[X(i)|X(i) \neq \mu_0] = \mu_0$. For sample from normal population, these are most powerful permutation tests and have asymptotic rel. efficiency of 100 per cent **4** Moderately sensitive to independence, symmetry, and equality of means conditions **5** Not difficult to decide on independence. More difficult to verify symmetry; also to verify equality of means unless observations believed random sample **6** Combination with sign test given in ref. 159. **Bibliography** Ref. 26, 158, 159, 176 (pages 43–47), 186, 244, 290, 307, 364, 446.

Permutation Tests Based on Linear Statistics

Data 1 Arbitrary, univariate **2** None **3** $X[i]$ **4** Usually $n \geqslant 3$ **Description 1** Exact one-sided and two-sided permutation tests **2** Null hyp. is $EX(i) = \mu_0$ **Assumptions 1** Independent **2** Populations symmetrical **3** $EX(1) = \ldots = EX(n)$; values of the $|X(i)-\mu_0|$ considered fixed **Results 1** $X[i] \neq \mu_0$ only for $i = i_1, \ldots, i_N$, where $i_1 < \ldots < i_N$; $L = \sum_{k=1}^{N} a(i_k)|X[i_k]-\mu_0|\text{sgn}\{X[i_k]-\mu_0\} = \sum_{k=1}^{N} a(i_k)X[i_k]-\mu_0 = \sum_{i=1}^{N} a(i)X[i]-\mu_0$, where $a(z) = a$(largest integer in z), $\sum_{i=1}^{n} a(i) = 1$, $a(i) = a(n+1-i)$, $a(2) = \ldots = a[(n+2)/A]$, $a[1+(n+2)/A] = \ldots = a[(n+1)/2]$, and $2(n+2)/(n-1) \leqslant A \leqslant (n+2)/2$; $\sigma_L{}^2 = \sum_{k=1}^{N} a(i_k)^2\{X[i_k]-\mu_0\}^2$; $c_L = \min_{u \neq v} ||a(i_u)\{X[i_u]-\mu_0\}| - |a(i_v)\{X[i_v]-\mu_0\}||/2$ **2** *Tests are*: Accept $EX(i) > \mu_0$ if $L > L(\alpha)$; accept $EX(i) < \mu_0$ if $L < -L(\alpha)$; accept $EX(i) \neq \mu_0$ if $|L| > L(\alpha/2)$. *Rules for selecting coeff. are*: For alternative of sampling from U-shaped population, $a(1)$ large and positive, $a(2) = 0$, and A increases as population shape approaches rectangular. For sampling from rectangular population, $a(2) = a[(n+1)/2] = 0$. For triangular or parabolic unimodal population, all $a(i) > 0$, $a(1) = a(2)$, $a(2) > a[(n+1)/2]$, and A decreases as pop. shape approaches normal form. For normal population, the $a(i)$ are all equal. For double exponential population (e.g., with freq. fct. $\frac{1}{2}e^{-|x-EX(i)|}$), all $a(i) > 0$, $a(1) = a(2)$, $a(2) < a[(n+1)/2]$, and A decreases as pop. shape approaches normality. For population with heavy tails, $a(1) = a(2) = 0$ and A decreases as tails become heavier. When population discontinuous, shape approx. determined by histogram **3** $L(\alpha) \doteq -c_L + t_\alpha(N)\sigma_L$ if $N \geqslant 25$, $\max_k a(i_k)^2 \{X[i_k]-\mu_0\}^2/\sigma_L{}^2 \leqslant 5/2N$, and $1/3N \leqslant \alpha \leqslant 1-1/3N$. For other cases, use permutation test procedure outlined in Chapter 4 (also see ref. 159) **4** Population shapes intermediate to types explicitly considered can be approximated by fixing $a(1)$, $a(2)$ and using A as interpolation parameter. Test essentially unconditional in its implications. Corresponding confidence intervals obtainable by general method outlined in Chapter 4 **Characteristics 1** Low to medium **2** Reasonably high efficiency for case of sample from population of approx. same shape as used in determining the $a(i)$ **4** Moderately sensitive to independence, symmetry, and equality of means conditions **5** Not difficult to decide on independence. More difficult to verify symmetry; also to verify equality of means unless observations believed random sample **6** Mainly useful for random sample case. Based on the presentation given on page 128. Fisher randomization test (see page 151) and Nair's randomization test (ref. 375) represent special cases. Can be applied to some types of censored data if the $a(i)$ are suitably selected **Bibliography** Ref. 159, 375.

Asymptotically Most Powerful Tests—Sample Case (Stein)

Data 1 Continuous, univariate **2** None **3** $X(i)$ **4** Usually $n \geqslant 10$ **Description 1** Exact one-sided and two-sided permutation tests **2** Null hyp. is $EX(i)=\mu_0$ **Assumptions 1** Random sample **2** Pop. freq. fct. $f(x)$ exists and is symmetrical **3** Values of the $|X(i)-\mu_0|$ considered fixed **Results 1** $F_n(x)$ = empirical dist. fct. of the $|X(i)-\mu_0|$. $\sigma_x{}^2=\sum_{i=1}^{n}[X(i)-\mu_0]^2/n$; $Y_i= 4\sqrt{n}\Big[F_n(|X(i)-\mu_0|+\sigma_x/2\sqrt{n})-2F_n(|X(i)-\mu_0|)+F_n(|X(i)-\mu_0|-\sigma_x/2\sqrt{n})\Big]\Big/\Big[F_n(|X(i)-\mu_0|+\sigma_x/2\sqrt{n})-F_n(|X(i)-\mu_0|-\sigma_x/2\sqrt{n})\Big]\sigma_x$. $c_y=\min_{u\neq v}|Y_u-Y_v|/2$. $\sigma_y{}^2=\sum_{i=1}^{n}Y_i{}^2$. $Y=\sum_{i=1}^{n}Y_i \operatorname{sgn}[X(i)-\mu_0]$ **2** *Tests*: Accept $EX(i)>\mu_0$ if $Y>Y(\alpha)$. Accept $EX(i)<\mu_0$ if $Y<-Y(\alpha)$. Accept $EX(i)\neq\mu_0$ if $|Y|>Y(\alpha/2)$ **3** $Y(\alpha)\doteq -c_y+t_\alpha(n)\sigma_y$ if $n\geqslant 25$, $\max_i Y_i{}^2/\sigma_y{}^2\leqslant 5/2n$, and $1/3n\leqslant\alpha\leqslant 1-1/3n$. For other cases, use permutation test procedure outlined in Chapter 4 **4** Test essentially unconditional in implications. Corresponding confidence intervals obtainable by general method outlined in Chapter 4. If $\max_i Y_i{}^2/\sigma_y{}^2\to 0$ as $n\to\infty$, dist. of Y asymptotically normal for all values of $\xi=EX(i)-\mu_0$, with $EY=\sum_{i=1}^{n}Y_i\Big[f(|X(i)-\mu_0|-\xi)-f(|X(i)-\mu_0|+\xi)\Big]\Big/\Big[f(|X(i)-\mu_0|-\xi)+f(|X(i)-\mu_0|+\xi)\Big]$ and $\sigma^2Y=\sum_{i=1}^{n}Y_i{}^2\Big\{1-\Big[f(|X(i)-\mu_0|-\xi)-f(|X(i)-\mu_0|+\xi)\Big]\Big/\Big[f(|X(i)-\mu_0|-\xi)+f(|X(i)-\mu_0|+\xi)\Big]\Big\}^2$. Tests valid if random sample condition replaced by independence and equality of means conditions **Characteristics 1** Low to medium **2** Asymptotically most powerful for situation considered. Efficiency moderately sensitive to random sample condition. For $n\geqslant 50$, $\max_i Y_i{}^2/\sigma_y{}^2\leqslant 5/2n$, and $\alpha\geqslant 1/2n$, approx. power fct. values in range $1/2n$ to $1-1/n$ obtainable by assuming normality for Y and estimating $f(|X(i)-\mu_0|\pm\xi)$ by

$\sqrt{n}\Big[F_n(|X(i)-\mu_0|\pm\xi+\sigma_x/2\sqrt{n}) \;-\; F_n(|X(i)-\mu_0|\pm\xi-\sigma_x/2\sqrt{n})\Big]/\sigma_x$ **4** Moderately sensitive to symmetry condition. Not very sensitive to sample and continuity assumptions if observations independent and from symmetrical populations with same mean; then permutation test procedure of Chapter 4 can be applied directly. Moderately sensitive to other types of violations of sample and continuity assumptions **5** Moderately difficult to verify symmetry. Not difficult to decide on sample and continuity assumptions **6** Member of family of tests considered on page 155. **Bibliography** Ref. 491.

Combination of Sign Test and Tests for Two-Sample Problem

Data 1 Arbitrary, univariate **2** None **3** $X(i)$ **4** Usually $n \geqslant 3$ **Description 1** Exact one-sided and two-sided tests (including permutation tests) **2** Null hyp. is $EX(i)=\mu_0$ **Assumptions 1** Independent **2** Populations symmetrical **3** $EX(i)=\ldots=EX(n)$; values of the $|X(i)-\mu_0|$ considered fixed for permutation tests **Results 1** $N_1=$no. of positive $[X(i)-\mu_0]$; $N_2=$no. of negative $[X(i)-\mu_0]$; N_1+N_2 considered fixed. $H=$test statistic for two-sample problem applied to positive $[X(i)-\mu_0]$ as first sample and absolute values of the negative $[X(i)-\mu_0]$ as second sample; this two-sample test based on principle that all ways of dividing the N_1+N_2 observations into sets of sizes N_1, N_2 equally likely under null hyp; large value for H indicates that mean of population yielding first sample greater than population mean for second sample, while small value for H indicates the reverse. Under the null hyp., $\alpha'=\alpha'(N_1+N_2)$ and $N(\alpha')=N(\alpha', N_1+N_2)$ satisfy $P[N_1\geqslant N(\alpha')|N_1+N_2]=\alpha'$; under the null hyp., $A_1(N_1)=A_1(N_1, N_1+N_2)$ and $H_1[A_1(N_1)]=H_1[A_1(N_1), N_1, N_1+N_2]$ satisfy $P\{H\geqslant H_1[A_1(N_1)]|N_1, N_1+N_2\}=A_1(N_1)$; under the null hyp., $A_2(N_2)=A_2(N_2, N_1+N_2)$ and $H_2[A_2(N_2)]=H_2[A_2(N_2), N_2, N_1+N_2]$ satisfy $P\{H\leqslant H_2[A_2(N_2)]|N_2, N_1+N_2\}=A_2(N_2)$ **2** *One-sided tests*: Accept $EX(i)>\mu_0$ if $N_1\geqslant N(\alpha')$ and/or $H\geqslant H_1[A_1(N_1)]$; test has sig. level $\alpha'+(\frac{1}{2})^{N_1+N_2}\sum_{r=0}^{N(\alpha')-1}\binom{N_1+N_2}{r}A_1(r)$. Accept $EX(i)<\mu_0$ if $N_2\geqslant N(\alpha')$ and/or $H\leqslant H_2[A_2(N_2)]$; sig. level$=$ $\alpha'+(\frac{1}{2})^{N_1+N_2}\sum_{r=0}^{N(\alpha')-1}\binom{N_1+N_2}{r}A_2(r)$. *Two-sided tests*: Accept $EX(i)\neq\mu_0$ if $N_1\geqslant N(\alpha')$ or $N_2\geqslant N(\alpha')$ and/or $H\geqslant H_1[A_1(N_1)]$ or $H\leqslant H_2[A_2(N_2)]$, where $\alpha'<\frac{1}{2}$ and $H_1[A_1(r)]>H_2[A_2(r)]$ for $r<N(\alpha')$; sig. level of this test$=$ $2\alpha'+(\frac{1}{2})^{N_1+N_2}\sum_{r=0}^{N(\alpha')-1}\binom{N_1+N_2}{r}[A_1(r)+A_2(r)]$ **3** Presentation on page 184 contains methods for determining $N(\alpha')$. General Class of Tests presentation of this sect., two-sample tests obtained

from the material of Chapter 5, and presentations to be given in the second volume for the two-sample problem, furnish methods of determining $A_1(N_1)$, $H_1[A_1(N_1)]$ and $A_2(N_2)$, $H_2[A_2(N_2)]$ for many two-sample tests of type considered. Joint dist. of N_1 (or N_2) and H asymptotically normal bivariate under null hyp. (see ref. 159); asymptotic joint dist. sometimes useful in determining sig. levels **4** Tests essentially unconditional in implications. Have computational advantage that H statistic need not be computed if sign test part significant. Combination of sign test and tests of General Class of Tests presentation (see page 155) included in class of tests considered. Corresponding confidence intervals obtainable by general method outlined in Chapter 4 **Characteristics 1** Low to medium (unless H test very complicated and/or n very large) **2** Test consistent if either sign test part or H test part furnishes consistent test when considered separately. Tests should have reasonably high efficiency if H test part suitably chosen. Power fct. values can be computed in same fashion as used to determine sig. level. E.g., consider situation where alternative hyp. considered such that observations independent, $P[X(i)>\mu_0]=p_a$ for all i, and $P\{H \geqslant H_1[A_1(N_1)]\}=A_a(N_1)$; then power fct. value for test of $EX(i)=\mu_0$ and this altern. hyp. is $\sum_{r=N(\alpha')}^{N_1+N_2} \binom{N_1+N_2}{r} p_a{}^r(1-p_a)^{N_1+N_2-r} + \sum_{r=0}^{N(\alpha')-1} \binom{N_1+N_2}{r} A_a(r)p_a{}^r(1-p_a)^{N_1+N_2-r}$ **4** Moderately sensitive to independence, symmetry, and equality of means conditions **5** Not difficult to decide on independence. More difficult to verify symmetry; also to verify equality of means unless observations believed random sample **6** Smirnov's test (ref. 481) and Hemelrijk's tests (ref. 235, 236, 237) of type considered here. Combination of sign test and Wilcoxon's signed-rank test examined in ref. 158 and 159; combination with Fisher randomization test considered in ref. 159 **Bibliography** Ref. 158, 159, 235, 236, 237, 446, 481, 573.

General Class of Tests

Data 1 Arbitrary, univariate **2** None **3** $X(i)$ **4** Usually $n \geqslant 3$ **Description 1** Exact one-sided and two-sided tests (including permutation tests) **2** Null hyp. is $EX(i)=\mu_0$ **Assumptions 1** Independent **2** Populations symmetrical **3** $EX(1)=\ldots=EX(n)$; values of the $|X(i)-\mu_0|$ considered fixed for permutation tests **Results 1** Nonzero values for the $|X(i)-\mu_0|$ are $u_1<\ldots<u_s$; value u_v occurs a_v times and value $-u_v$ occurs b_v times among the $[X(i)-\mu_0]$; $N_1=\sum_{v=1}^{s} a_v$; $N_2=\sum_{v=1}^{s} b_v$; $t_v=a_v+b_v$; $r_v=t_1+\ldots+t_v-(t_v-1)/2$; values of $s, t_1, \ldots, t_s, u_1, \ldots, u_s$, N_1+N_2 considered fixed; $\varphi_v=\varphi(u_v, r_v)=$specified non-negative fct.; $J=\sum_{v=1}^{s}(a_v-b_v)\varphi_v$; $c_j=\min_{v\neq w}\big||(a_v-b_v)\varphi_v|-|(a_w-b_w)\varphi_w|\big|/2$ **2** *One-*

sided Tests: Accept $EX(i) > \mu_0$ if $J \geqslant J_1(\alpha_1)$; sig. level of test $= \alpha_1$. Accept $EX(i) < \mu_0$ if $J \leqslant J_2(\alpha_2)$; sig. level $= \alpha_2$. *Two-sided test*: Accept $EX(i) \neq \mu_0$ if $J \geqslant J_1(\alpha_1)$ or $J \leqslant J_2(\alpha_2)$, where $J_1(\alpha_1) > J_2(\alpha_2)$; sig. level $= \alpha_1 + \alpha_2$ **3** $J_1(\alpha) \doteq c_j + t_\alpha(N_1+N_2)[\sum_{v=1}^{s} t_v\varphi_v{}^2]^{1/2}$ and $J_2(\alpha) \doteq -J_1(\alpha)$ if $N_1+N_2 \geqslant 30$, $\max_v (a_v - b_v)^2\varphi_v{}^2/\sum_{w=1}^{s}(a_w-b_w)^2\varphi_w{}^2 \leqslant 5/2(N_1+N_2)$, and $1/2(N_1+N_2) \leqslant \alpha \leqslant 1-1/2(N_1+N_2)$ **4** Tests essentially unconditional in implications. Corresponding confidence intervals obtainable by general method outlined in Chapter 4. J expressible as $2\sum_{v=1}^{s} a_v\varphi_v - \sum_{v=1}^{s} t_v\varphi_v$, where $\sum_{v=1}^{s} a_v\varphi_v$ general form for a class of statistics for two-sample problem with positive $[X(i)-\mu_0]$ as first sample and absolute values of negative $[X(i)-\mu_0]$ as second sample (all ways of dividing the nonzero $|X(i)-\mu_0|$ into sets of sizes N_1 and N_2 equally likely under null hyp.) **Characteristics 1** Low to medium (unless N_1+N_2 very large and/or φ_v very complicated) **2** Should have reasonably high efficiencies if φ_v suitably chosen (except possibly when large discrete prob. concentrated at μ_0). Asymptotic power fcts. and relative efficiency expressions and values given in ref. 290 for Mann-Whitney test, and for the median test for the two-sample problem. **4** Moderately sensitive to independence, symmetry, and equality of means conditions **5** Not difficult to decide on independence. More difficult to verify symmetry; also to verify equality of means unless observations believed random sample **6** With exception of those combining sign test and two-sample tests, all tests given in the preceding presentations of this sect. are special cases of general class considered here **Bibliography** Ref. 158, 159, 290, 446.

Broad Class of Confidence Intervals

Data 1 Continuous, univariate **2** Observations can be obtained by converting discontinuous data to continuous form (see page 139) **3** $X[i]$ **4** Usually $n \geqslant 3$ **Description 1** Exact one-sided and two-sided confidence intervals **2** $EX(i)$ **Assumptions 1** Independent **2** Populations continuous and symmetrical **3** $EX(1) = \ldots = EX(n)$ **Results 1** For any specified h of the $n(n+1)/2$ averages $\{X[u]+X[v]\}/2$, $u \geqslant v$, let $y_1 \leqslant \ldots \leqslant y_h$ denote their values. P_R is probability relation symbol which implies that stated relation holds given that $X(i)$ random sample from rectangular population with nonzero prob. range $-\frac{1}{2}$ to $\frac{1}{2}$ **2** *General results*: For any specified set of h averages, $P[y_r > EX(i)] = P_R(y_r > 0)$, $1 \leqslant r \leqslant h \leqslant n(n+1)/2$; $P[y_s < EX(i)] = P_R(y_s < 0)$, $1 \leqslant s \leqslant h \leqslant n(n+1)/2$; $P[y_r < EX(i) < y_s] = 1 - P_R(y_r > 0) - P_R(y_s < 0)$, $1 \leqslant r < s \leqslant h \leqslant n(n+1)/2$. *Other results*: Let s be h or 1 and $0 < n_g < \ldots < n_2 < n_1 \leqslant n$; then the one-sided confidence intervals $\max\{X[n-g], (X[n-g+1]+X[n-n_g-g+1])/2, \ldots, (X[n]+X[n-n_1])/2\} <$ $EX(i)$ and $\min\{X[g+1], (X[n_g+g]+X[g])/2, \ldots,$

$(X[n_1+1]+X[1])/2\} > EX(i)$, where terms $(X[n-d+1]+X[n-n_d-d+1])/2$ and $(X[n_d+d]+X[d])/2$ deleted if $n_d+d=n+1$, $(d=1,\ldots,g)$, both have confidence coeff. $2^{-n}\left[1+n_1+\sum_{i_1=1}^{n_2}(n_1-i_1)+\ldots+\sum_{i_{g-1}=1}^{n_g}\ldots\sum_{i_1=1}^{n_2-i_2-\cdots-i_{g-1}}(n_1-i_1-\ldots-i_{g-1})\right]$. Let $h=n(n+1)/2$ and $T=$ random variable having null hyp. dist. of Wilcoxon signed-rank statistic based on n observations from continuous symmetrical populations (see presentation on page 148 for def. and properties of T); then $P[y_r > EX(i)]=P[T\geqslant n(n+1)/2-r+1]$ and $P[y_s<EX(i)]=P[T\leqslant n(n+1)/2-s]$; these relations determine the one-sided confidence intervals that correspond to Wilcoxon signed-rank test; two-sided intervals are obtained as nonoverlapping combinations of one-sided intervals **3** Table 7.4 furnishes some specified one-sided confidence intervals for cases of $r=1$, $s=h$, $n\leqslant 15$; two-sided confidence intervals obtainable as nonoverlapping

TABLE 7.4. SOME ONE-SIDED CONFIDENCE INTERVALS FOR $EX(i)$ WHEN POPULATIONS SYMMETRICAL*

n	Confidence Coefficient	Upper Limit, One-sided Confidence Interval	Lower Limit, One-sided Confidence Interval
4	.938	$X[4]>EX(i)$	$X[1]<EX(i)$
5	.938	$(X[5]+X[4])/2>EX(i)$	$(X[2]+X[1])/2<EX(i)$
	.969	$X[5]>EX(i)$	$X[1]<EX(i)$
6	.953	$\max\{X[5],(X[6]+X[4])/2\}>EX(i)$	$\min\{X[2],(X[3]+X[1])/2\}<EX(i)$
	.969	$(X[6]+X[5])/2>EX(i)$	$(X[2]+X[1])/2<EX(i)$
	.984	$X[6]>EX(i)$	$X[1]<EX(i)$
7	.945	$\max\{X[5],(X[7]+X[4])/2\}>EX(i)$	$\min\{X[3],(X[4]+X[1])/2\}<EX(i)$
	.977	$\max\{X[6],(X[7]+X[5])/2\}>EX(i)$	$\min\{X[2],(X[3]+X[1])/2\}<EX(i)$
	.984	$(X[7]+X[6])/2>EX(i)$	$(X[2]+X[1])/2<EX(i)$
	.992	$X[7]>EX(i)$	$X[1]<EX(i)$
8	.957	$\max\{X[6],(X[8]+X[4])/2\}>EX(i)$	$\min\{X[3],(X[5]+X[1])/2\}<EX(i)$
	.973	$\max\{X[6],(X[8]+X[5])/2\}>EX(i)$	$\min\{X[3],(X[4]+X[1])/2\}<EX(i)$
	.988	$\max\{X[7],(X[8]+X[6])/2\}>EX(i)$	$\min\{X[2],(X[3]+X[1])/2\}<EX(i)$

TABLE 7.4. (*contd.*)

	.992	$(X[8]+X[7])/2>EX(i)$	$(X[2]+X[1])/2<EX(i)$
	.996	$X[8]>EX(i)$	$X[1]<EX(i)$
9	.949	$\max\{X[6], (X[9]+X[4])/2\}>EX(i)$	$\min\{X[4], (X[6]+X[1])/2\}<EX(i)$
	.978	$\max\{X[7], (X[9]+X[5])/2\}>EX(i)$	$\min\{X[3], (X[5]+X[1])/2\}<EX(i)$
	.990	$\max\{X[8], (X[9]+X[5])/2\}>EX(i)$	$\min\{X[2], (X[5]+X[1])/2\}<EX(i)$
	.994	$\max\{X[8], (X[9]+X[7])/2\}>EX(i)$	$\min\{X[2], (X[3]+X[1])/2\}<EX(i)$
	.996	$(X[9]+X[8])/2>EX(i)$	$(X[2]+X[1])/2<EX(i)$
10	.944	$\max\{X[6], (X[10]+X[4])/2\}>EX(i)$	$\min\{X[5], (X[7]+X[1])/2\}<EX(i)$
	.975	$\max\{X[7], (X[10]+X[5])/2\}>EX(i)$	$\min\{X[4], (X[6]+X[1])/2\}<EX(i)$
	.989	$\max\{X[8], (X[10]+X[6])/2\}>EX(i)$	$\min\{X[3], (X[5]+X[1])/2\}<EX(i)$
	.995	$\max\{X[9], (X[10]+X[6])/2\}>EX(i)$	$\min\{X[2], (X[5]+X[1])/2\}<EX(i)$
11	.952	$\max\{X[7], (X[11]+X[4])/2\}>EX(i)$	$\min\{X[5], (X[8]+X[1])/2\}<EX(i)$
	.972	$\max\{X[7], (X[11]+X[5])/2\}>EX(i)$	$\min\{X[5], (X[7]+X[1])/2\}<EX(i)$
	.989	$\max\{(X[11]+X[6])/2,$ $(X[9]+X[8])/2\}>EX(i)$	$\min\{(X[6]+X[1])/2,$ $(X[4]+X[3])/2\}<EX(i)$
	.995	$\max\{X[9], (X[11]+X[7])/2\}>EX(i)$	$\min\{X[3], (X[5]+X[1])/2\}<EX(i)$
12	.953	$\max\{(X[12]+X[4])/2,$ $(X[11]+X[5])/2\}>EX(i)$	$\min\{(X[9]+X[1])/2,$ $(X[8]+X[2])/2\}<EX(i)$
	.976	$\max\{X[8], (X[12]+X[5])/2\}>EX(i)$	$\min\{X[5], (X[8]+X[1])/2\}<EX(i)$
	.990	$\max\{X[9], (X[12]+X[6])/2\}>EX(i)$	$\min\{X[4], (X[7]+X[1])/2\}<EX(i)$
	.995	$\max\{(X[12]+X[7])/2,$ $(X[10]+X[9])/2\}>EX(i)$	$\min\{(X[6]+X[1])/2,$ $(X[4]+X[3])/2\}<EX(i)$
13	.953	$\max\{(X[13]+X[4])/2,$ $(X[12]+X[5])/2\}>EX(i)$	$\min\{(X[10]+X[1])/2,$ $(X[9]+X[2])/2\}<EX(i)$
	.977	$\max\{(X[13]+X[5])/2,$ $(X[12]+X[6])/2\}>EX(i)$	$\min\{(X[9]+X[1])/2,$ $(X[8]+X[2])/2\}<EX(i)$

TABLE 7.4. (*contd.*)

	.990	$\max\{(X[13]+X[6])/2, (X[10]+X[9])/2\} > EX(i)$	$\min\{(X[8]+X[1])/2, (X[5]+X[4])/2\} < EX(i)$
	.995	$\max\{X[10], (X[13]+X[7])/2\} > EX(i)$	$\min\{X[4], (X[7]+X[1])/2\} < EX(i)$
14	.953	$\max\{(X[14]+X[4])/2, (X[13]+X[5])/2\} > EX(i)$	$\min\{(X[11]+X[1])/2, (X[10]+X[2])/2\} < EX(i)$
	.977	$\max\{(X[14]+X[5])/2, (X[13]+X[6])/2\} > EX(i)$	$\min\{(X[10]+X[1])/2, (X[9]+X[2])/2\} < EX(i)$
	.990	$\max\{X[10], (X[14]+X[6])/2\} > EX(i)$	$\min\{X[5], (X[9]+X[1])/2\} < EX(i)$
	.995	$\max\{(X[14]+X[7])/2, (X[11]+X[10])/2\} > EX(i)$	$\min\{(X[8]+X[1])/2, (X[5]+X[4])/2\} < EX(i)$
15	.953	$\max\{(X[15]+X[4])/2(X[14]+X[5])/2\} > EX(i)$	$\min\{(X[12]+X[1])/2, (X[11]+X[2])/2\} < EX(i)$
	.977	$\max\{(X[15]+X[5])/2, (X[14]+X[6])/2\} > EX(i)$	$\min\{(X[11]+X[1])/2, (X[10]+X[2])/2\} < EX(i)$
	.990	$\max\{(X[15]+X[6])/2, (X[11]+X[10])/2\} > EX(i)$	$\min\{(X[10]+X[1])/2, (X[6]+X[5])/2\} < EX(i)$
	.995	$\max\{X[11], (X[15]+X[7])/2\} > EX(i)$	$\min\{X[5], (X[9]+X[1])/2\} < EX(i)$

* Based on material of ref. 554. Used with the kind permission of the Editor of the *Annals of Mathematical Statistics*.

combinations of one-sided intervals. Table 7.5 contains list of some probability relations that can be used to determine many one-sided and two-sided confidence intervals for case of $r=1$ and $s=h$ **4** Interpolation yields confidence intervals with confidence coeff. (bounded) approx. equal to arbitrarily specified values (see presentation on page 170). If populations not all continuous, $P[y_r > EX(i)] \leqslant P_R(y_r > 0) \leqslant P[y_r \geqslant EX(i)]$ and $P[y_s < EX(i)] \leqslant P_R(y_s < 0) \leqslant P[y_s \leqslant EX(i)]$; also $P[y_r < EX(i) < y_s] \leqslant 1 - P_R(y_r > 0) - P_R(y_s < 0) \leqslant P[y_r \leqslant EX(i) \leqslant y_s]$ **Characteristics 1** Low to medium **2** Confidence intervals corresponding to Wilcoxon signed-rank test have same type of efficiency and consistency properties as that test. For sample from normal population, confidence intervals of Table 7.4 at least 85 per cent efficient. If $d \leqslant 3n/4$, confidence intervals of Table 7.5 should have reasonably high efficiencies (say, 80 per cent or more), at least for case of sample from normal population **4** Moderately sensitive to independence, continuity, symmetry, and equality of means conditions **5** Not difficult to decide on continuity and independence. More difficult to verify symmetry; also to verify equality of means unless observations believed random sample **6** Confidence intervals corresponding to sign test special case of class considered here. Useful for some types of censored data, including life-testing situations **Bibliography** Ref. 446, 526, 554, 556.

TABLE 7.5. SOME PROBABILITY RELATIONS WHEN POPULATIONS ARE CONTINUOUS AND SYMMETRICAL ABOUT $EX(i)$*

Probability Expression	$2^n \times$ Value	
$P[(X[d]+X[1])/2 > EX(i)]$ $=P[(X[n]+X[n+1-d])/2 < EX(i)]$	2^{d-1}	
$P[\min\{X[2], (X[d]+X[1])/2\} > EX(i)]$ $=P[\max\{X[n-1], (X[n]+X[n+1-d])/2\} < EX(i)]$	d	
$P[\min\{(X[3]+X[2])/2, (X[d]+X[1])/2\} > EX(i)]$ $=P[\max\{(X[n-1]+X[n-2])/2, (X[n]+X[n+1-d])/2\} < EX(i)]$	$2(d-1)$	$(d>1)$
$P[\min\{X[3], (X[d]+X[1])/2\} > EX(i)]$ $=P[\max\{X[n-2], (X[n]+X[n+1-d])/2\} < EX(i)]$	$1+d(d-1)/2$	
$P[\min\{(X[4]+X[2])/2, (X[d]+X[1])/2\} > EX(i)]$ $=P[\max\{(X[n-1]+X[n-3])/2, (X[n]+X[n+1-d])/2\} < EX(i)]$	$4(d-2)$	$(d>2)$
$P[\min\{(X[4]+X[3])/2, (X[d]+X[1])/2\} > EX(i)]$ $=P[\max\{(X[n-2]+X[n-3])/2, (X[n]+X[n+1-d])/2\} < EX(i)]$	$2+(d-1)(d-2)$	$(d>1)$
$P[\min\{X[4], (X[d]+X[1])/2\} > EX(i)]$ $=P[\max\{X[n-3], (X[n]+X[n+1-d])/2\} < EX(i)]$	$d+d(d-1)(d-2)/6$	
$P[\min\{(X[5]+X[4])/2, (X[d]+X[1])/2\} > EX(i)]$ $=P[\max\{(X[n-3]+X[n-4])/2, (X[n]+X[n+1-d])/2\} < EX(i)]$	$2(d-1)+(d-1)(d-2)(d-3)/6$	$(d>1)$
$P[\min\{X[5], (X[d]+X[1])/2\} > EX(i)]$ $=P[\max\{X[n-4], (X[n]+X[n+1-d])/2\} < EX(i)]$	$1+d(d-1)/2 + d(d-1)(d-2)(d-3)/24$	
$P[\min\{X[6], (X[d]+X[1])/2\} > EX(i)]$ $=P[\max\{X[n-5], (X[n]+X[n+1-d])/2\} < EX(i)]$	$d[1+(d-1)(d-2)/6 + (d-1)(d-2)(d-3)(d-4)/120]$	

* Based on material of ref. 554. Used with the kind permission of the Editor of the *Annals of Mathematical Statistics*.

t Statistic, Spherical Symmetry (Multivariate Observation)

Data 1 Continuous, multivariate **2** Spherical symmetry can sometimes be imparted to observations by prior randomization **3** $\{X(i)\}_1$ **4** $n \geqslant 2$ **Description 1** Exact one-sided and two-sided confidence intervals **2** $EX(i)$ **Assumptions 1** None **2** n-variate observation from continuous populatior **3** $EX(1) = \ldots = EX(n)$; joint freq. fct. of form $f\{\sum_{i=1}^{n} [x_i - EX(i)]^2\}$ **Results 1** $t = t$-statistic $= \sqrt{n}[M(i) - EX(i)]/S(i)$, computed as if the $X(i)$ were a sample **2** *Confidence intervals determined from*: $P[t < t_\alpha(n-1)] = P[t > -t_\alpha(n-1)] = 1 - \alpha$; $P\Big[-t_{\alpha(1)}(n-1) < t < t_{\alpha(2)}(n-1)$; $\alpha(1) + \alpha(2) < 1\Big] = 1 - \alpha(1) - \alpha(2)$ **3** None **4** When independent, the $X(i)$ are necessarily random sample from normal population **Characteristics 1** Low **2** For case of sample from normal population, corresponding one-sided tests most powerful and corresponding equal-tail test most stringent (see Chapter 4) **4** Moderately sensitive to continuity, spherical symmetry, and equality of means conditions **5** Not difficult to decide on continuity. Moderately difficult to verify spherical symmetry and equality of means **6** Mainly useful for situations where spherical symmetry can be induced by randomization applied prior to obtaining the multivariate observation **Bibliography** Ref. 186, 307.

APPROXIMATE TESTS AND CONFIDENCE REGIONS

Introduction

This section presents several confidence regions and one significance test. These results are of a theoretical-approximate or judgment-empirical nature and based on univariate observations. Most of the presentations are concerned entirely with population means. The other material involves joint confidence regions for the population mean and standard deviation. Many of the results for population means are based on a Student t-statistic or some modification of a t statistic. Usually the populations are required to be continuous, but some of the results are also valid for discontinuous populations. In most cases the observations are a random sample.

Discussion of Presentations

Expansions for probability distributions furnish the basis for all but two of the theoretical-approximate methods; the other two methods furnish tests and confidence regions with bounded probability levels. All but three of the theoretical-approximate presentations require the data to be a random sample. For two of these nonsample cases, the population constant considered is the arithmetic average of the means of the populations which yielded the observations. For the other case, the populations are required to be symmetrical with a common mean value.

As usual, interpolations and extrapolations based on analytical analyses for a few elementary distributions and/or sampling results for a few distributions of interest furnish the basis for the judgment-empirical results. In all cases the data for a judgment-empirical presentation are a random sample, usually from a continuous type population.

The initial six presentations are concerned with t statistics or modifications of t statistics. The first of these contains judgment-empirical results for the ordinary t statistic based on a random sample while the second presents theoretical-approximate results for this situation. The third presentation deals with a modification of the t statistic and does not require a random sample or even independent observations; however, the number of observations must be large. Here the probability constant investigated is the average of the means for the populations from which the observations were obtained.

The fourth presentation requires a random sample and involves a modification of the t statistic in which the sample standard deviation is replaced by the mean range of one or more samples. The sample sizes considered are moderate to small, and the results are of a judgment-empirical nature. The fifth presentation is concerned with a modified t statistic in which the sample mean is replaced by the sample midrange, and the sample standard deviation is replaced by the sample range. These results are of a judgment-empirical character and only small sample sizes are considered. The sixth presentation deals with the use of a t statistic for the case of two independent samples from populations that can differ appreciably in shape. Here the probability constant investigated is the difference of population means and the procedure used is theoretical-approximate.

The seventh presentation is concerned with theoretical-approximate two-sided confidence intervals that have bounded confidence coefficients and are based on sign test type statistics. Statistical independence is required, but the observations need not be a random sample. The probability constant investigated is the average of the means for the populations from which the observations were drawn. However, the method is also applicable to other functions of the population means (e.g., their median).

The eighth and next to last presentation is of a theoretical-approximate nature and based on independent observations from symmetrical populations with the same mean value. Confidence intervals with confidence coefficients approximately equal to arbitrarily specified values are obtained by interpolation from exact results. In all cases, the true value for a confidence coefficient is bounded in terms of the values for the exact confidence intervals used for the interpolation.

The last presentation requires a random sample and the statistic used is the sample mean. The method is of a theoretical-approximate type and furnishes joint confidence regions (and tests) for the population mean and standard deviation.

Fixed Material for Section

Data 1 Univariate.

Judgment–Empirical Results for t Statistic

Data 1 Continuous **2** None **3** $X(i)$ **4** $m=1$; $n \geqslant 15$ **Description 1** Judgment-empirical two-sided confidence intervals **2** $EX(i)$ **Assumptions 1** Random sample **2** Population continuous and unimodal with finite moments **3** None **Results 1** $t = t$-statistic $= \sqrt{n}[M(i) - EX(i)]/S(i)$ **2** *Confidence interval relation*: $P[|t| < t_\alpha(n-1)] \doteq 1 - 2\alpha$, where $n \geqslant 15$ and $1/3n \leqslant \alpha \leqslant \frac{1}{2} - 1/3n$ **3** None **4** Based on both analytical computations and empirical sampling from specific distributions (skewed and symmetrical). When sample condition violated only by inequality of population means and average of means investigated, magnitude of t statistic tends to be smaller; implies that actual confidence coeff. less than value for random sample **Characteristics 1** Low **2** Empirical sampling indicates that for moderate population deviation from normality, power of corresponding test tends to be comparable with but somewhat less than that for normality; here null hyp. is $EX(i) = \mu_0$ and altern. is $EX(i) \neq \mu_0$ **3** Used symmetrically **4** Moderately sensitive to random sample condition. Not very sensitive to moderate deviations from unimodal, continuity, and finite moments requirements **5** Finite moments condition virtually always satisfied. Not difficult to decide on continuity and random sample assumptions. More difficult to verify unimodal property **6** Additional information on accuracy of confidence coefficient furnished by presentation on page 163. **Bibliography** Ref. 373, 405, 427, 431, 488.

Theoretical-Approximate Results for t Statistic

Data 1 Arbitrary **2** None **3** $X(i)$ **4** $m=1$; $n \geqslant 2$ (usually much larger) **Description 1** Theoretical-approximate one-sided and two-sided confidence intervals and signif. tests **2** $EX(i)$. For tests, null hyp. is that $EX(i) = \mu_0$ **Assumptions 1** Cases (I) and (II): Random sample. Case (III): Independent observations **2** Case (I): Population continuous with finite moments. Case (II): $EX(i)^{12}$ exists. Case (III): Populations symmetrical **3** Case (I): $F(x)$ expressible in Edgeworth series form (infinite no. of terms). Case (II): $0 < F(x) < 1$ for some x. Case (III):

$EX(1) = \ldots = EX(n)$ **Results 1** $t = t$-statistic $= \sqrt{n}[M(i) - EX(i)]/S(i)$; $t'_\alpha(n) = \sqrt{n}t_\alpha(n-1)/[n-1+t_\alpha(n-1)^2]^{1/2}$. $B_2 = (n+2)\sum_{i=1}^{n}[X(i)-\mu_0]^4/\{\sum_{i=1}^{n}[X(i)-\mu_0]^2\}^2$; $J = 1+(B_2-3)/n[1+B_2/(n+2)]$ **2** *Confidence interval relations. Case (I)*: $P[t \leqslant t_\alpha(n-1)] = 1-\alpha+O(n^{-1/2}) = 1-\alpha + [M_3(i)/S^3(i)]\Big[1+(2n-1)t_\alpha(n-1)^2/(n-1)\Big]\Big/6\Big[1+t_\alpha(n-1)^2/(n-1)\Big]^{(n+1)/2}(2n\pi)^{1/2} + O(n^{-1})$. $P[t \geqslant t_\alpha(n-1)] = 1-P[t \leqslant t_\alpha(n-1)]$. $P[|t| \leqslant t_\alpha(n-1); \alpha < \frac{1}{2}] = 1-2\alpha + O(n^{-1}) = 1-2\alpha + [M_4(i)/S^4(i)-3]\Big[t_\alpha(n-1)^3 - 3(n-1)t_\alpha(n-1)/(n+1)\Big]\Gamma(n/2)\Big/6(n-1)[(n-1)\pi]^{1/2}\Gamma[(n-1)/2]\Big[1+t_\alpha(n-1)^2/(n-1)\Big]^{(n+2)/2} - [M_3(i)/S^3(i)]^2(2n+5)\Big[t_\alpha(n-1)^5 + 2(2n-7)(n-1)t_\alpha(n-1)^3/(n+1)(2n+5) - 3(2n+11)(n-1)^2t_\alpha(n-1)/(n+1)(n+3)(2n+5)\Big]\Gamma(n/2)\Big/18(n-1)^2[(n-1)\pi]^{1/2}\Gamma[(n-1)/2][1+t_\alpha(n-1)^2/(n-1)]^{(n+4)/2} + O(n^{-3/2})$. *Case (II)*: $P[t \leqslant t_\alpha(n-1)] = \Phi[t'_\alpha(n)] + O(n^{-1/2}) = \Phi[t'_\alpha(n)] - [M_3(i)/S^3(i)]\Big\{3t'_\alpha(n)\Phi^{(2)}[t'_\alpha(n)] + \Phi^{(3)}[t'_\alpha(n)]\Big\}\Big/6\sqrt{n} + O(n^{-1})$. $P[t > t_\alpha(n-1)] = 1-P[t \leqslant t_\alpha(n-1)]$. $P[-t_\alpha(n-1) < t \leqslant t_\alpha(n-1); \alpha < \frac{1}{2}] = \Phi[t'_\alpha(n)] - \Phi[-t'_\alpha(n)] + O(n^{-1}) = \Phi[t'_\alpha(n)] - \Phi[-t'_\alpha(n)] + [M_4(i)/S^4(i)-3]\Big\{\Phi^{(4)}[t'_\alpha(n)]/3 + 2t'_\alpha(n)\Phi^{(3)}[t'_\alpha(n)] - t'_\alpha(n)\Phi^{(1)}[t'_\alpha(n)] + t'_\alpha(n)^2\Phi^{(2)}[t'_\alpha(n)]\Big\}\Big/4n + [M_3(i)/S^3(i)]^2\Big\{\Phi^{(6)}[t'_\alpha(n)]/9 + t'_\alpha(n)\Phi^{(5)}[t'_\alpha(n)]/3 - t'_\alpha(n)\Phi^{(3)}[t'_\alpha(n)]/2 + t'_\alpha(n)^2\Phi^{(4)}[t'_\alpha(n)]/2\Big\}\Big/2n + O(n^{-3/2})$. *Tests. Case (III)*: Under null hyp., t statistic with $EX(i)$ replaced by μ_0 has approx. t-dist. with $(n-1)J$ degrees of freedom for $n \geqslant 10$ and signif. level between $1/2n$ and $1-1/2n$; for equal-tail tests, usable when $n \geqslant 8$. Equal-tail t-test approx. valid when symmetry conditions violated if observations random sample from continuous unimodal population, $n \geqslant 10$, and signif. level between $1/2n$ and $1-1/2n$ **3** Tables of ref. 192 useful in evaluating prob. for Case (I) **4** Case (II) based on correction of ref. 97. For Case (I): $P[t \leqslant t_\alpha(n-1)] = 1-\alpha + \alpha_3(i)\Big[1+(2n-1)t_\alpha(n-1)^2/(n-1)\Big]\Big/6\Big[1+t_\alpha(n-1)^2/(n-1)\Big]^{(n+1)/2}(2n\pi)^{1/2} + [\alpha_4(i) - 3]\Big[t_\alpha(n-1)^3 - 3(n-1)t_\alpha(n-1)/(n+1)\Big]\Gamma(n/2)\Big/12(n-1)[(n-1)\pi]^{1/2}\Gamma[(n-1)/2][1+t_\alpha(n-1)^2/(n-1)]^{(n+2)/2} - [\alpha_3(i)]^2(2n+5)\Gamma(n/2)\Big[t_\alpha(n-1)^5 + 2(2n-7)(n-1)t_\alpha(n-1)^3/(n+1)(2n+5) - 3(2n+11)(n-1)^2t_\alpha(n-1)/(n+1)(n+3)(2n+5)\Big]\Gamma(n/2)\Big/36(n-1)^2[(n-1)\pi]^{1/2}\Gamma[(n-1)/2][1+t_\alpha(n-1)^2/(n-1)]^{(n+4)/2} + [\text{even fct. of } t_\alpha(n-1)]n^{-3/2} + O(n^{-2})$; if $F(x)$ equals sum of first four terms of its Edgeworth series expansion, the terms of order $n^{-3/2}$ (and higher) are zero. For Case (II): $P[t \leqslant t_\alpha(n-1)] = \Phi[t'_\alpha(n)] - \alpha_3(i)\Big\{3t'_\alpha(n)\Phi^{(2)}[t'_\alpha(n)] + \Phi^{(3)}[t'_\alpha(n)]\Big\}\Big/6\sqrt{n}$

$+[\alpha_4(i)-3]\Big\{\Phi^{(4)}[t'_\alpha(n)]/3+2t'_\alpha(n)\Phi^{(3)}[t'_\alpha(n)]-t'_\alpha(n)\Phi^{(1)}[t'_\alpha(n)]+t'_\alpha(n)^2\Phi^{(2)}[t'_\alpha(n)]\Big\}\Big/8n \quad +[\alpha_3(i)]^2\Big\{\Phi^{(6)}[t'_\alpha(n)]/9+t'_\alpha(n)\Phi^{(5)}[t'_\alpha(n)]3-t'_\alpha(n)\Phi^{(3)}[t'_\alpha(n)]/2+t'_\alpha(n)^2\Phi^{(4)}[t'_\alpha(n)]/2\Big\}\Big/4n \quad +[\text{even fct. of } t'_\alpha(n)]n^{-3/2} \quad +O(n^{-2})$ **Characteristics 1** Low to medium **2** If $F(x)$ equals first two terms of its Edgeworth series, power of one-sided tests approx. that for normality when $|\alpha_3(i)|\leqslant .4$ (null hyp. is $EX(i)=\mu_0$). For alternative $EX(i)>\mu_0$, positive $\alpha_3(i)$ tends to decrease power in region where value of power small and to increase it elsewhere (compared to value for normality), while opposite effect obtained from negative $\alpha_3(i)$ **3** Used symmetrically **4** Moderately sensitive to random sample and independence conditions. $EX(i)^{12}$ must exist for Case (II). Effects of some violations of Case (I) assumptions determinable from results for Case (II). For Case (III), not very sensitive to symmetry requirement if observations sample from continuous univariate population and n not too small. **5** Not difficult to decide on continuity, independence, and random sample conditions. More difficult to verify symmetry. Finite moments of all orders virtually always exist. Moderately difficult to justify Edgeworth series assumption of Case (I) **6** For extreme situations, very large n might be required for remainder terms that are $O(n^{-1})$ or $O(n^{-3/2})$ to be negligible; ordinarily larger n needed for discrete cases than for continuous cases. When sample condition violated only by inequality of population means and average of means investigated, magnitude of t statistic tends to be smaller; implies that actual values for signif. levels high and for confidence coefficients low compared to values for random sample. **Bibliography** Ref. 26, 75, 97, 192, 194, 195, 201, 248, 420, 530.

t Statistic, Nonsample Case, Large n

Data 1 Arbitrary **2** Sources of observations grouped according to distance and/or time considerations; groups so separated in distance and/or time that stipulated conditions on covariances and expected values hold **3** $X(i)$ **4** $m=1$; n large (say, $\geqslant 200$) **Description 1** Theoretical-approximate one-sided and two-sided confidence intervals **2** $EM(i)$ **Assumptions 1** Restrictions imposed on covariances **2** $EX(i)^4$ exists for all i **3** Observations divided into N subsets such that (*1*): Sum of covariances for all possible pairs approx. equals sum of covariances for pairs where both observations from same subset. (*2*): For each subset, a group of pairs of observations from that subset can be chosen so that: Sum of covariances for pairs of group approx. equals sum of covariances for pairs of subset; sum of squares of differences of expected values for observations of pair, over all pairs of group, very much less than sum of variances for observations of the subset; each observation of the subset occurs same number of times r in group of pairs, and value of r same for all the N groups corresponding to the N subsets; total number of pairs in the N groups $\leqslant 5n$. *(3)*: Each group can be increased by adding more pairs from the subset to form an augmented group such that: each observation of the subset occurs same number of times s in augmented group of pairs, and value of s same for all the N augugmented groups corresponding to the N subsets $(s > r)$; sum of variances for observations of subset very much greater than $(r+1)/(s-r)$ times sum of squares of differences of expected values for observations of pair over-all pairs added in increasing group to augmented group; total no. of pairs in the N augmented groups $\leqslant 10n$ **Results 1** $S_1{}^2(k)$ = sum of the squares of differences of observations of pair taken over all pairs of group for kth subset; $S_2{}^2(k)$ = sum of the squares of differences of observations of pair taken over all pairs of augmented group for kth subset; note that $[X(i_1), X(i_2)]$ and $[X(i_2), X(i_1)]$ considered to be same pair. $S_3{}^2 = \left| -(s+1)\sum_{k=1}^{N} S_1{}^2(k)/n(s-r) + (r+1)\sum_{k=1}^{N} S_2{}^2(k)/n(s-r)\right|$ **2** *Confidence interval relations*: $P\{\sqrt{n}[M(i)-EM(i)]/S_3 > K_\alpha\} \doteq P\{\sqrt{n}[M(i)-EM(i)]/S_3 < -K_\alpha\} = \alpha$, where $1/2n \leqslant \alpha \leqslant 1-1/2n$. $P\{-K_{\alpha(1)} < \sqrt{n}[M(i)-EM(i)]/S_3 < K_{\alpha(2)};\ \alpha(1)+\alpha(2) < 1\} \doteq 1 - \alpha(1) - \alpha(2)$, where $1/2n \leqslant \alpha(1)+\alpha(2) \leqslant 1-1/2n$ in general and $1/3 \leqslant \alpha(1)+\alpha(2) \leqslant 1-1/3n$ if $\alpha(1) \doteq \alpha(2)$ **3** None **4** Often conditions assumed approximately obtainable by appropriate prior division of observation sources into subsets on basis of distance and/or time considerations. Ordinarily two observations from "nearby" sources much more highly correlated than two observations from "distant" sources. Also "nearby" observations on same type of quantity should have expected values which are very nearly equal **Characteristics 1** Medium to high **2** Situation of asymptotic character. Efficiency of confidence intervals and corresponding tests has same magnitude and properties as efficiency of $M(i)$ as estimate of $EM(i)$ **3** Not used symmetrically **4** $S_3{}^2$ must converge to $\sigma^2 M(i)$ in prob., which is case of $EX(i)^4$ exists. Moderately sensitive to approx. equality of means and magnitude of covariances assumptions **5** $S_3{}^2$ almost always reasonably close to $\sigma^2 M(i)$ if $n \geqslant 200$. If experiment carefully planned, covariance and approx. equality of means conditions usually acceptable on intuitive grounds **6** Useful in agricultural, industrial, and social science fields **Bibliography** Ref. 560.

Modified t Statistic Using Sample Mean Range (*D. R. Cox*)

Data 1 Continuous **2** None **3** $X(i)_1$ and, for $j \geqslant 2$, $X[n_j]_j - X[1]_j$ **4** $n_2 = \ldots = n_m = n$; $2 \leqslant n \leqslant 5$; $n_1 \geqslant 15$ for two-sided results and $\geqslant 20$

for one-sided results. $m \geqslant 1+25c_n(6)^2$, where $c_n(6)$ listed in Table 7.6 **Description 1** Judgment-empirical one-sided and two-sided confidence intervals **2** $EX(i)_1$ **Assumptions 1** The $X(i)_1$ are random sample; the $X[n]_j - X[1]_j$ are independent of the $X(i)_1$ and based on independent samples from the same population, which is the same as that for the $X(i)_1$ except possibly with respect to mean value ($j \geqslant 2$) **2** Populations continuous and unimodal with finite moments **3** $1.5 \leqslant \alpha_4(i)_j \leqslant 7.0$ **Results 1** d_n such that $E\{X[n]_j - X[1]_j\}/d_n = \sigma(i)_j$ for case of normal population; $\bar{w}(n, m-1) = \sum_{j=2}^{m} \{X[n]_j - X[1]_j\}/(m-1)d_n$ **2** *Confidence interval relations*: $P\Big\{.95\sqrt{n_1}[M(i)_1 - EX(i)_1]/\bar{w}(n, m-1)[1-c_n(6)^2/2] < t_\alpha[(m-1)/2c_n(7)^2]\Big\} \doteq P\Big\{.95\sqrt{n_1}[M(i)_1 - EX(i)_1]/\bar{w}(n, m-1)[1-c_n(6)^2/2] > t_\alpha[(m-1)/2c_n(7)^2]\Big\} \doteq 1-\alpha$, where $1/2(n_1+.1mn) \leqslant \alpha \leqslant 1 - 1/2(n_1+.1mn)$. $P\Big\{-t_\alpha[(m-1)/2c_n(7)^2] < .95\sqrt{n_1}[M(i)_1 - EX(i)_1]/\bar{w}(n, m-1)[1-c_n(6)^2/2] < t_\alpha[(m-1)/2c_n(7)^2];\ \alpha < 1/2\Big\} \doteq 1-2\alpha$, where $1/3(n_1+.1mn) \leqslant \alpha \leqslant \frac{1}{2} - 1/3(n_1+.1mn)$ **3** Values of $c_n(6)$ and $c_n(7)$ listed in Table 7.6. For fractional $(m-1)/2c_n(7)^2$, value of $t_\alpha[(m-1)/2c_n(7)^2]$ obtained by interpolation. Values of d_n listed in Table 7.1 on p. 133 **4** If $\alpha_4(i)_j$ known, more refined results of ref. 110 can be used **Characteristics 1** Low **2** Efficiency should exceed that of t statistic based on sample of size n_1 when $(m-1)n$ noticeably greater than n_1 **3** The $X(i)_1$ used symmetrically **4** Moderately sensitive to condition that each $X[n]_j - X[1]_j$ based on random sample. Not very sensitive to independence of samples and, if populations have same variance, to requirement that samples from same population for $j \geqslant 2$. Not sensitive to moderate deviations from unimodal, continuity, and finite moments conditions. Effects of violating $\alpha_4(i)_j$ condition can be evaluated from results of ref. 110 **5** Finite moments condition virtually always satisfied. Not difficult to decide on continuity, independence, random sample, and $\alpha_4(i)_j$ conditions. More difficult to verify unimodal property **6** Useful in quality control situations where ranges only dispersion information recorded from previous samples **Bibliography** Ref. 110, 404, 488.

TABLE 7.6. VALUES OF $c_n(6)$ AND $c_n(7)$ FOR $2 \leqslant n \leqslant 5$*

n	$c_n(6)$	$c_n(7)$
2	.89	.93
3	.665	.70
4	.58	.60
5	.52	.54

* Based on ref. 110: The mean and coefficient of variation in small samples from non-normal populations, D. R. Cox, *Biometrika*, vol. 41, 1954, pages 469–81. Used with the kind permission of the author, David R. Cox, and of the Editor of *Biometrika*.

Range–Midrange Statistic, Population Mean

Data 1 Continuous **2** None **3** $X[n]$ and $X[1]$ **4** $m=1$; $3 \leqslant n \leqslant 5$ **Description 1** Judgment-empirical two-sided confidence intervals **2** $EX(i)$ on basis of $(X[n]+X[1])/2$ and $X[n]-X[1]$ **Assumptions 1** Random sample **2** Population continuous, has finite moments of all orders, and is unimodal with shape not hugely different from that for normality **3** None **Results 1** D_α determined by $P\{[(X[n]+X[1])/2-EX(i)]/(X[n]-X[1])>D_\alpha\}=\alpha$ for normal population **2** *Confidence interval relation*: $P\{(X[n]+X[1])/2-D_\alpha(X[n]-X[1])<EX(i)<(X[n]+X[1])/2+D_\alpha(X[n]-X[1])\} \doteq 1-2\alpha$, where $.04-.03\min(n-3, 1.15) \leqslant \alpha \leqslant .4$ **3** Table 7.7 furnishes D_α for $3 \leqslant n \leqslant 5$ and $\alpha = .005, .01, .025, .05$ (some α values listed are only for interpolation use) **4** Approx. validity indicated by computations for six non-normal populations (ref. 555). Confidence coeff. only roughly accurate for $D_\alpha > .9$; improved accuracy for $D_\alpha \leqslant .9$ and good accuracy for $.3 \leqslant D_\alpha \leqslant .6$ **Characteristics 1** Low **2** Efficiency approx. 95 per cent for normality and $\alpha \leqslant .05$ (compared to t statistic) **3** Used symmetrically **4** Moderately sensitive to continuity and random sample conditions; also to large deviations of population shape from normal form (e.g., U-shape, several modes, etc.). However, sensitivity not very great when $.3 \leqslant D_\alpha \leqslant .6$ and the observations are independent and from symmetrical populations that are continuous at the mean and have a common mean value **5** Finite moments of all orders virtually always exist. Not difficult to decide on continuity and random sample assumptions. Often moderately difficult to verify that population unimodal and not hugely different from normal **6** Useful in quality control and other places where large number of small sample tests encountered **Bibliography** Ref. 555.

TABLE 7.7. VALUES OF D_α FOR $3 \leqslant n \leqslant 5$ AND $\alpha = .005, .01, .025, .05$*

	n		
α	3	4	5
.005		1.37	.85
.01	2.11	1.04	.71
.025	1.30	.74	.52
.05	.90	.555	.425

* Based on material of ref. 555. Used with the kind permission of the Editor of the *Annals of Mathematical Statistics*.

Confidence Intervals for Difference of Means (Gronow)

Data 1 Continuous **2** None **3** $X(i)_j$ **4** $m=2$; $n_1, n_2 \geqslant 10$, $\frac{3}{4} \leqslant n_1/n_2 \leqslant \frac{4}{3}$ **Description 1** Theoretical-approximate two-sided confidence intervals **2** $EX(i)_1 - EX(i)_2$ **Assumptions 1** The $X(i)_1$ and the $X(i)_2$ are independent random samples **2** Populations continuous, symmetrical, and have finite moments **3** Dist. function for $X(i)_j$ adequately represented by first few terms (including fourth order moments) of symmetrical (all odd moments about mean are zero) Gram-Charlier type A series $(j=1, 2)$; here $\frac{2}{3} \leqslant \sigma(i)_1/\sigma(i)_2 \leqslant \frac{3}{2}$; $1.5 \leqslant \alpha_4(i)_j \leqslant 7$ **Results 1** $s(n_1, n_2) = \left\{(n_1+n_2)[(n_1-1)S^2(i)_1 + (n_2-1)S^2(i)_2]/n_1 n_2(n_1+n_2-2)\right\}^{\frac{1}{2}}$ **2** *Confidence interval relation*: $P\left\{|M(i)_1 - M(i)_2 - EX(i)_1 + EX(i)_2| < s(n_1, n_2)t_\alpha(n_1+n_2-2)\right\} \doteq 1-2\alpha$, where $[(n_1-1)(n_2-1)]^{-1/2}/2 \leqslant \alpha \leqslant \frac{1}{2} - [(n_1-1)(n_2-1)]^{-1/2}/2$ **3** None **4** Case where $\sigma(i)_1 = \sigma(i)_2$ but $\alpha_3(i)_j$ not necessarily zero considered in ref. 193 **Characteristics 1** Low **2** For power values in the range 2α to $1-[(n_1-1)(n_2-1)]^{-1/2}$, power functions of tests obtained from confidence intervals approx. same as that for case of normality and equal variances having value $[\sigma^2(i)_1 + \sigma^2(i)_2]/2$. Useful in determining how large samples must be in order to establish given difference in population means **3** Used symmetrically within each sample **4** Not very sensitive to requirement of symmetry (i.e., that $\alpha_3(i)_j = 0$ in expression for dist. fct.). Moderately sensitive to bounds for $\sigma(i)_1/\sigma(i)_2$ and $\alpha_4(i)_j$; also to moderate violations of form for dist. functions. Moderately sensitive to independence and random sample conditions **5** Not difficult to decide on independence and random sample assumptions. Not very difficult to verify bounds for $\alpha_4(i)_j$; more difficult to verify bounds for $\sigma(i)_1/\sigma(i)_2$. Moderately difficult to verify form for dist. functions except when populations believed symmetrical and unimodal **6** Useful for testing difference of means when populations known to be symmetrical and to not deviate greatly from normality **Bibliography** Ref. 193, 213.

Two-Sided Confidence Intervals for Means, From Sign Test Statistics

Data 1 Arbitrary **2** None **3** $X[i]$ **4** $m=1$; $4 \leqslant n \leqslant 15$ **Description 1** Theoretical-approximate two-sided confidence intervals with bounded confidence coefficients **2** $EM(i)$ **Assumptions 1** Independent **2** Case (I): The $EX(i)$ exist. Case (II): The $EX(i)$ exist and populations continuous at $EM(i)$ **3** $\max_{i_1} |P[X(i_1) < EM(i)] - \frac{1}{2}| \leqslant \beta$, $\max_{i_1} |P[X(i_1) > EM(i)] - \frac{1}{2}| \leqslant \beta$ **Results 1** None **2** *Confidence interval relations. Case* (I): $L(w,n,\beta) \leqslant P\{X[w] \leqslant EM(i) \leqslant X[n+1-w]\} \leqslant U(w, n, \beta)$. *Case (II)*: $L(w,n,\beta) \leqslant P\{X[w] \leqslant EM(i) \leqslant X[n+1-w]\} \leqslant U'(w, n, \beta)$ **3** Table 7.8 contains values of $U(w, n, \beta)$, $U'(w, n, \beta)$, and $L(w, n, \beta)$ for $4 \leqslant n \leqslant 15$, $\beta = 0$, .02, .05, .08,

.10, .15, .20, and various values of w **4** $EM(i)$ can be replaced by other fcts. of the $EX(i)$; any fct. used should reduce to common value of mean when $EX(1) = \ldots = EX(n)$; difficult to decide on β if complicated fct. used to replace $EM(i)$ **Characteristics 1** Low **2** For case of sample from normal population, efficiency approx. 95 per cent for $w=1$, approx. 80 per cent for $w=2$, approx. 75 per cent for $w=3$, approx. 70 per cent for $w=4$. Other efficiency results given in presentation on page 147 **3** Used symmetrically **4** The $EX(i)$ must exist. Moderately sensitive to independence condition. Comparison of $U(w, n, \beta)$ with $U'(w, n, \beta)$ shows sensitivity to continuity requirement of Case (II). Effect of wrong choice for β directly determinable by examination of $L(w, n, \beta)$, $U'(w, n, \beta)$, and $U(w, n, \beta)$ **5** The $EX(i)$ virtually always exist. Moderately difficult to decide on continuity at $EM(i)$ unless the $X(i)$ believed continuous variables. Often not difficult to choose conservatively large value for β **6** Also mentioned in Chapter 8 as tests and confidence intervals for $M\theta_{\frac{1}{2}}(i)$ **Bibliography** Ref. 559.

Bounded Probability Level Intervals for Mean—Symmetrical Populations

Data 1 Continuous **2** None **3** $X[i]$ **4** $m=1$; usually $n \geqslant 3$ **Description 1** Theoretical-approximate one-sided and two-sided confidence intervals with bounded confidence coeff. **2** $EX(i)$ **Assumptions 1** Independent **2** $EX(i)$ exists. Populations continuous and symmetrical **3** $EX(1) = \ldots = EX(n)$ **Results 1** The values of the $\{X[u]+X[v]\}/2$, $u \geqslant v$, denoted by $y_1 \leqslant \ldots \leqslant y_{n(n+1)/2}$; $r(\alpha) = r(\alpha, n)$ is no., determined by α and n, such that $1 \leqslant r(\alpha) \leqslant n(n+1)/2$ and $s(\alpha)$ is the integer such that $s(\alpha) \leqslant r(\alpha) < s(\alpha)+1$; $y_{r(\alpha)} = y_{s(\alpha)} + [r(\alpha)-s(\alpha)](y_{s(\alpha)+1} - y_{s(\alpha)})$; $y_{n+1-r(\alpha)} = y_{n+1-s(\alpha)} + [s(\alpha)-r(\alpha)](y_{n+1-s(\alpha)} - y_{n-s(\alpha)})$ **2** *First class of confidence intervals*: $P[y_{r(\alpha)} < EX(i)] = P[y_{n+1-r(\alpha)} > EX(i)] \doteq 1-\alpha$. $P[y_{r(\alpha_1)} < EX(i) < y_{n+1-r(\alpha_2)};\ n \geqslant r(\alpha_1)+r(\alpha_2)] = 1 - P[y_{r(\alpha_1)} > EX(i)] - P[y_{n+1-r(\alpha_2)} < EX(i)] = 1 - \alpha_1 - \alpha_2$. These results represent interpolations from confidence intervals corresponding to Wilcoxon signed-rank test. Bounds for these interpolated probabilities furnished by $P[y_{s(\alpha)+1} < EX(i)] = P[y_{n-s(\alpha)} > EX(i)] \leqslant P[y_{r(\alpha)} < EX(i)] = P[y_{n+1-r(\alpha)} > EX(i)] \leqslant P[y_{s(\alpha)} < EX(i)] = P[y_{n+1-s(\alpha)} > EX(i)]$. *Second class of confidence intervals*: For $1 \leqslant u \leqslant n-1$ and $0 \leqslant a \leqslant 1$, another class of interpolated confidence intervals given by: $P\Big[(1/2)\min\{2X[2],\ X[1]+(1-a)X[u]+aX[u+1]\} < EX(i)\Big] = P\Big[(1/2)\max\{2X[n-1],\ X[n]+(1-a)X[n+1-u]+aX[n-u]\} > EX(i)\Big] \doteq 1-(u+a)/2^n$; for $n \geqslant 4$, $1 \leqslant u_1, u_2 \leqslant n-1$, and $0 \leqslant a_1, a_2 \leqslant 1$, $P\Big[(1/2)\min\{2X[2],\ X[1]+(1-a_1)X[u_1]+a_1X[u_1+1]\} < EX(i) < (1/2)\max\{2X[n-1],\ X[n]+(1-a_2)X[n+1-u_2]+a_2X[n-u_2]\}\Big] = 1 - P\Big[(1/2)\min

	β	0	.02								
n	w	All Bounds	$U(w, n, \beta)$	$U'(w, n, \beta)$	$L(w, n, \beta)$	$U(w, n, \beta)$	$U'(w, n, \beta)$	$L(w, n, \beta)$	$U(w, n, \beta)$	$U'(w, n, \beta)$	$L(w, n, \beta)$
4	1	.8750	.8938	.8754	.8738	.9180	.8775	.8675	.9378	.8813	.8557
5	1	.9375	.9490	.9377	.9365	.9631	.9387	.9312	.9739	.9407	.9213
6	1	.9688	.9755	.9689	.9680	.9834	.9697	.9640	.9890	.9711	.9564
7	1	.9844	.9883	.9844	.9838	.9925	.9848	.9810	.9954	.9855	.9756
	2	.8750	.8992	.8753	.8729	.9286	.8769	.8619	.9508	.8798	.8414
8	1	.9922	.9944	.9922	.9918	.9966	.9925	.9899	.9981	.9930	.8862
	2	.9296	.9455	.9299	.9279	.9638	.9312	.9187	.9767	.9337	.9013
9	1	.9961	.9973	.9961	.9959	.9985	.9962	.9946	.9992	.9965	.9922
	2	.9610	.9709	.9611	.9596	.9818	.9619	.9524	.9891	.9633	.9387
10	2	.9786	.9846	.9786	.9775	.9910	.9792	.9722	.9949	.9802	.9620
	3	.8906	.9161	.8909	.8878	.9452	.8925	.8730	.9656	.8956	.8457
11	2	.9883	.9919	.9883	.9876	.9956	.9887	.9839	.9977	.9893	.9764
	3	.9346	.9517	.9348	.9322	.9704	.9359	.9200	.9826	.9379	.8968
12	3	.9614	.9726	.9616	.9596	.9842	.9624	.9500	.9914	.9640	.9315
13	3	.9776	.9847	.9776	.9762	.9917	.9782	.9690	.9958	.9792	.9547
	4	.9076	.9325	.9080	.9044	.9593	.9093	.8867	.9767	.9118	.8539
14	3	.9870	.9915	.9871	.9861	.9957	.9875	.9808	.9979	.9882	.9703
	4	.9426	.9596	.9428	.9399	.9771	.9439	.9254	.9877	.9460	.8978
15	3	.9926	.9954	.9927	.9919	.9978	.9929	.9882	.9990	.9933	.9806
	4	.9650	.9762	.9650	.9627	.9873	.9657	.9513	.9937	.9671	.9291
	5	.8814	.9140		.8771	.9491		.8541	.9715		.8118

TABLE 7.8. VALUES OF $U(w, n, \beta)$, $U'(w, n, \beta)$, $L(w, n, \beta)$ FOR $4 \leqslant n \leqslant 15$ AND VARIOUS β AND w*—*continued*

	β	0	.10			.15			.20		
n	w	All	$U(w, n, \beta)$	$U'(w, n, \beta)$	$L(w, n, \beta)$	$U(w, n, \beta)$	$U'(w, n, \beta)$	$L(w, n, \beta)$	$U(w, n, \beta)$	$U'(w, n, \beta)$	$L(w, n, \beta)$
4	1	.8750	.9488	.8848	.8448	.9700	.8965	.8076	.9838	.9118	.7518
5	1	.9375	.9795	.9424	.9120	.9895	.9481	.8787	.9951	.9559	.8295
6	1	.9688	.9918	.9724	.9492	.9963	.9765	.9227	.9985	.9815	.8816
7	1	.9844	.9967	.9862	.9704	.9987	.9882	.9503	.9996	.9907	.9174
	2	.8750	.9623	.8825	.8225	.9820	.8918	.7572	.9924	.9047	.6668
8	1	.9922	.9987	.9934	.9825	.9995	.9947	.9679	.9999	.9961	.9423
	2	.9296	.9830	.9359	.8851	.9929	.9433	.8273	.9974	.9531	.7434
9	1	.9961	.9995	.9967	.9897	.9998	.9973	.9792	1.0000	.9981	.9596
	2	.9610	.9924	.9646	.9257	.9972	.9690	.8775	.9991	.9746	.8036
10	2	.9786	.9966	.9812	.9520	.9989	.9842	.9135	.9997	.9879	.8505
	3	.8906	.9754	.8984	.8204	.9904	.9081	.7336	.9968	.9215	.6156
11	2	.9883	.9985	.9898	.9690	.9996	.9915	.9392	.9999	.9935	.8870
	3	.9346	.9882	.9398	.8752	.9959	.9462	.7978	.9988	.9547	.6867
12	3	.9614	.9944	.9654	.9137	.9983	.9702	.8479	.9996	.9763	.7470
13	3	.9776	.9974	.9800	.9408	.9993	.9830	.8865	.9999	.9867	.7974
	4	.9076	.9844	.9141	.8236	.9950	.9221	.7192	.9987	.9331	.5787
14	3	.9870	.9988	.9888	.9596	.9997	.9908	.9159	.9999	.9932	.8391
	4	.9426	.9922	.9478	.8718	.9978	.9541	.7784	.9995	.9625	.6446
15	3	.9926	.9994	.9937	.9726	.9999	.9949	.9382	1.0000	.9963	.8732
	4	.9650	.9961	.9683	.9076	.9990	.9725	.8268	.9998	.9779	.7030
	5	.8814	.9813		.7734	.9943		.6452	.9987		.4838

* Based on material of ref. 559. Used with the kind permission of the Editor of the *Annals of Mathematical Statistics*.

$\{2X[2], \quad X[1]+(1-a_1)X[u_1]+a_1X[u_1+1]\}> \quad EX(i)\Big] \quad -P\Big[(1/2)$ max $\{2X[n-1], \quad X[n]+(1-a_2)X[n+1-u_2]+a_2X[n-u_2]\}< \quad EX(i)\Big] \doteq 1-(u_1+a_1+u_2+a_2)/2^n$; these results mainly useful for $n \leqslant 15$. Bounds for this second class of interpolated probabilities furnished by $1-(u+1)/2^n \leqslant P\Big[\frac{1}{2}\min\{2X[2], \quad X[1]+(1-a)X[u]+aX[u+1]\}< \quad EX(i)\Big] = P\Big[\frac{1}{2}\max\{2X[n-1], \quad X[n]+(1-a)X[n+1-u]+aX[n-u]\}> \quad EX(i)\Big] \leqslant 1-u/2^n$ **3** Table 7.9 contains values of $r(\alpha)$ for $5 \leqslant n \leqslant 20$ and $\alpha = .05, .025, .01, .005$. For $n \geqslant 15$, $r(\alpha) \doteq 1+n(n+1)/4-\{n(n+1)[nA(\alpha)+B(\alpha)]/4\}^{1/2}$, for α such that this quantity integral; here $A(\alpha)$ and $B(\alpha)$ obtained by interpolation from values listed in Table 7.3 on page 150 for $\alpha = .05, .025, .01, .005$. When $n \geqslant 25$ and $1/5n \leqslant \alpha \leqslant 1-1/5n$, $r(\alpha) \doteq \frac{1}{2}+n(n+1)/4-t_\alpha(n)[n(n+1)(2n+1)/24]^{1/2}$, for α such that this quantity integral. For $n \geqslant 35$, replacing $r(\alpha)$ by nearest integer and using exact results should be satisfactory if $1/2n \leqslant \alpha \leqslant 1-1/2n$. When $1 \leqslant s(\alpha) \leqslant n(n+1)/2$, values of $P[y_{s(\alpha)} < EX(i)]$ obtainable from presentation on page 156 **4** Prob. bounds satisfy inequalities stated in presentation on page 159 when populations not necessarily continuous. If populations continuous at mean, $1-(n+1)/2^n \leqslant \quad P\Big[(1/2)\min\{2X[2], \quad X[1]+(1-a)X[u]+aX[u+1]\}< \quad EX(i)\Big] = P\Big[(1/2)\max\{2X[n-1], \ X[n]+(1-a)X[n+1-u]+aX[n-u]\}> \ EX(i)\Big] \leqslant 1-1/2^n$ **Characteristics 1** Low to medium **2** Confidence intervals interpolated from those corresponding to Wilcoxon signed-rank test have same efficiency and consistency properties as that test. If u, u_1, $u_2 \leqslant 3n/4$, the second class of interpolated confidence intervals should usually have moderately high efficiency (say, 85 per cent or more), at least for case of sample from normal population **3** Used symmetrically **4** $EX(i)$ must exist; however, existence of $EX(i)$ not required when $\theta_{1/2}(i)$ investigated instead of $EX(i)$. Moderately sensitive to independence, continuity, symmetry, and equality of means conditions **5** $EX(i)$ virtually always exists. Not difficult to decide on continuity and independence. More difficult to verify symmetry; also to verify equality of means unless observations believed random sample **6** Interpolated probability values should be reasonably accurate if populations also unimodal. Useful for some types of censored data, including life-testing situations **Bibliography** Ref. 526, 555.

Joint Confidence Regions for Mean and Standard Deviation

Data 1 Arbitrary **2** None **3** $X(i)$ **4** $m=1$; $n \geqslant 2$ (usually much larger) **Description 1** Theoretical-approximate joint confidence regions **2** $EX(i)$ and $\sigma(i)$ on basis of $M(i)$ **Assumptions 1** Random sample **2** Case (I):

TABLE 7.9. VALUES OF $r(\alpha)$ FOR $5 \leqslant n \leqslant 20$ AND $\alpha = .05, .025, .01, .005$*

n	α			
	.05	.025	.01	.005
5	1.60			
6	3.12	1.60		
7	4.70	3.12	1.28	
8	6.75	4.70	2.60	1.28
9	9.09	6.73	4.06	2.60
10	11.79	9.09	6.07	4.06
11	14.92	11.76	8.25	6.07
12	18.48	14.78	10.82	8.25
13	22.37	18.24	13.67	10.82
14	26.71	22.06	16.93	13.67
15	31.45	26.29	20.58	16.87
16	36.60	30.90	24.58	20.47
17	42.2	35.91	28.95	24.42
18	48.2	41.3	33.70	28.73
19	54.6	47.1	38.8	33.40
20	61.4	53.3	44.4	38.5

* Based on ref. 526: *The simplest signed-rank tests*, J. W. Tukey, Memo rept. 17, Statistica Research Group, Princeton Univ., 1949. Used with the kind permission of the author John W. Tukey, and the publisher.

$EX(i)^6$ exists. Case (II): $EX(i)^{12}$ exists and $X(i)$ nontrivially takes value over set of positive measure **3** None **Results 1** Lattice population is discrete population such that every value with nonzero prob. expressible in form $A+kb$, where $b>0$ and k an integer; $B = \max b$ for which this possible where $B=0$ for nonlattice populations. $\delta, \delta_1, \delta_2$ are values such tha $-1 \leqslant \delta, \delta_1, \delta_2 \leqslant 1$ **2** *Confidence region relations. Case (I)*: $P[M(i) - EX(i) \leqslant K_\alpha \sigma(i)/\sqrt{n}] = 1-\alpha+O(n^{-1/2}) = 1-\alpha + \{[M_3(i)/S^3(i)](1-K_\alpha^2) \varphi(K_\alpha)/6 + \delta B/2S(i)\sqrt{2\pi}\}n^{-1/2} + o(n^{-1/2})$. $P[-K_{\alpha/2}\sigma(i)/\sqrt{n} < M(i) - EX(i) \leqslant K_{\alpha/2}\sigma(i)/\sqrt{n}] = 1-\alpha+O(n^{-1/2}) = 1-\alpha + (\delta_2-\delta_1)B/2S(i)\sqrt{2\pi} + o(n^{-1/2})$. *Case* (II): $P[M(i)-EX(i) \leqslant K_\alpha\sigma(i)/\sqrt{n}] = 1-\alpha+O(n^{-1/2}) = 1-\alpha + [M_3(i)/S^3(i)](1-K_\alpha^2)\varphi(K_\alpha)/6\sqrt{n} + O(n^{-1})$. $P[-K_{\alpha/2}\sigma(i)/\sqrt{n} < M(i)-EX(i) \leqslant K_{\alpha/2}\sigma(i)/\sqrt{n}] = 1-\alpha+O(n^{-1}) = 1-\alpha + [M_4(i)/S^4(i)-3]K_{\alpha/2}(K_{\alpha/2}^2-3)\varphi(K_{\alpha/2})/12n + [M_3(i)/S^3(i)]^2 K_{\alpha/2}(K_{\alpha/2}^4 - 10K_{\alpha/2}^2 + 15)\varphi(K_{\alpha/2})/36n + O(n^{-3/2})$ **3** None **4** Furnishes one-sided confidence intervals for $EX(i)+K_\alpha\sigma(i)/\sqrt{n}$. For Case (II), $P[-\sqrt{3}\sigma(i)/\sqrt{n} < M(i) - EX(i) \leqslant \sqrt{3}\sigma(i)/\sqrt{n}] = .9167 - .0257[M_3(i)/S^3(i)]^2/n + O(n^{-3/2})$. In general, for Case (I), $P[M(i)-EX(i) \leqslant K_\alpha\sigma(i)/\sqrt{n}] = 1-\alpha + [\alpha_3(i)(1-K_\alpha^2)\varphi(K_\alpha)/6 + \delta B/2\sigma(i)\sqrt{2\pi}]n^{-1/2} + o(n^{-1/2})$; for Case (II), $P[M(i)-EX(i) \leqslant K_\alpha\sigma(i)/\sqrt{n}] = 1-\alpha + \alpha_3(i)(1-K_\alpha^2)\varphi(K_\alpha)/6\sqrt{n} + [\alpha_4(i)-3]K_\alpha(K_\alpha^2-3)\varphi(K_\alpha)/24n + [\alpha_3(i)]^2 K_\alpha(K_\alpha^4 - 10K_\alpha^2 + 15)\varphi(K_\alpha)/72n + O(n^{-3/2})$ **Characteristics 1** Low **2** Efficiency unknown i eneral but, for one-sided confidence intervals for $EX(i)+K_\alpha\sigma(i)/\sqrt{n}$, hould be of same level as efficiency of $M(i)$ as estimate of $EX(i)$; e.g., this ne-sided confidence interval has very high efficiency for case of normality would be 100 per cent if confidence coeff. precisely known) **3** Used ymmetrically **4** $EX(i)^6$ must exist for Case (I) and $EX(i)^{12}$ for Case (II). Ioderately sensitive to violations of random sample condition. Some ffects from violations of Case (II) assumptions determinable from results or Case (I) **5** Finite moments of all orders virtually always exist. Not lifficult to decide on random sample assumption; also to verify set of ositive measure condition for Case (II) **6** Useful for tests where null hyp. pecifies $EX(i)$ and $\sigma(i)$. In extreme situations, very large n might be equired for remainder terms that are $O(n^{-1/2})$, $o(n^{-1/2})$, $O(n^{-1})$, or even $O(n^{-3/2})$ to be negligible. However, judgment-empirical results indicate hat approx. probability values usually reasonably accurate for $n \geqslant 15$, and early always reasonably accurate $n \geqslant 30$, if population continuous and nimodal (here α not too near 0 or 1; say, $1/n \leqslant \alpha \leqslant 1-1/n$). Ref. 118 pages 363–67) furnishes rather general method for obtaining asymptotic oint confidence region for any specified set of population moments. Ref. 581 contains some results for special case of Pearson curves **Bibliog-raphy** Ref. 118, 206, 488, 567, 581.

BINOMIAL DISTRIBUTION AND EVENTS

Introduction

The binomial distribution is superficially parametric since its functional form is explicit, uncomplicated, and depends on only two parameters. However, this distribution is of nonparametric interest in the sense that very weak assumptions are often sufficient to establish its validity in applications. Also the binomial and related distributions have many ndirect nonparametric applications. Thus consideration of binomial listribution results seems to be appropriate for this handbook. The binomial event material was included in this chapter because, for a given number of trials, the expected number of successes can usually be considered to be the probability constant of interest. Also, many of the binomial results are used in following chapters.

The presentations that deal directly with the binomial distribution are concerned with approximations to this distribution and with both sequential and nonsequential point estimates, confidence intervals, and tests for the binomial success probability. The more general situation of binomial events with possibly different success probabilities is also considered. Methods are presented for obtaining approximations to the distribution of the number of successes for this more general case. Point estimates and confidence intervals are presented for the arithmetic average of the success probabilities of the binomial events which yielded the observations. The results given are not extensive. To partially cover other material in the same general area, a short bibliography dealing with additional subjects is given at the end of this section.

Discussion of Random Binomial Events

The most elementary nontrivial type of random variable is that which has only two possible values (say, 0 and 1, where 0 might be considered to represent failure and 1 to represent success). This random variable can be interpreted as the outcome of a random biomial event. If p is the probability that the outcome of a random binomial event is success, then $q=1-p$ is the probability of failure. When a number of outcomes of random binomial events are considered (e.g., several outcomes for the same event), the number of successes is usually the random variable of interest. If the n outcomes considered are statistically independent and have the same probability p for success, the distribution function for the number of successes is

$$F(x)=\sum_{i=0}^{x}\binom{n}{i}p^{i}q^{n-i}, \qquad (x=0, 1, \ldots, n)$$

where $0, 1, \ldots, n$ is the set of possible values. This is the well-known binomial distribution.

A more general nonsequential situation involving random binomial events is that where each event can have a different probability for success. Then the distribution function for the number of successes can be very complicated. If the events are statistically independent, this distribution function can be expanded into a series form on the basis of the average of the success probabilities and increasing integral powers, starting with the second, of the deviations of these probabilities from their average. If these deviations are not too large, the distribution function is very nearly equal to the first two terms of its expansion. The first and predominant term equals the binomial distribution function that is obtained when the probability of success is the average of the probabilities for the events. The second term depends on the sum of the squares of the deviations of the probabilities from their average.

Normal and Poisson approximations can be obtained for the distributions of the number of successes if the events are statistically independent and their number is sufficiently large. Results of this nature can also be obtained for some restricted cases where the outcomes are not necessarily independent. If the events and the statistical dependence are such that the event probabilities (conditional and unconditional) are sufficiently small, the distribution of the number of successes is approximately Poisson.

Discussion of Sequential Results

Since the sequential estimates and tests presented here have applications in Chapters 8 and 11, a description of their uses and properties seems to be worthwhile. Also, an interpretation whereby the one-sided tests can be considered to have one-sided composite null hypotheses is discussed here.

The purpose of a test is to compare the (unknown) parameter p of a binomial distribution with a specified value $p(0)$. The null hypothesis asserts that $p=p(0)$. For the one-sided test with alternative $p<p(0)$, a value $p(1)<p(0)$ is selected such that a true value of p less than $p(1)$ has important implications. The test has a specified significance level, and there is a specified probability lower bound (usually high) that the null hypothesis will be rejected if $p \leqslant p(1)$. For one-sided tests of $p>p(0)$, a value $p(2)$ greater than p is suitably selected. The test has a specified significance level and there is a specified probability lower bound that the null hypothesis will be rejected if $p \geqslant p(2)$.

The one-sided tests can also be interpreted as tests of composite null hypotheses. The test with alternative $p>p(0)$ can be considered to have the composite null hypothesis $p \leqslant p(0)$ and (generalized) significance level α (the value is α when $p=p(0)$ is the null hypothesis). Likewise, the test with alternative $p<p(0)$ can be considered to have the composite null hypothesis $p \geqslant p(0)$ and (generalized) significance level α. The generalized significance level of a test is determined by considering the set of possible values for p allowed by the composite null hypothesis. Letting the test remain fixed, each of these possible values is considered to be a simple null hypothesis, and the corresponding significance level is determined. The supremum of these values is the generalized significance level of the test.

In the case of two-sided tests, two suitable values $p(1)$ and $p(2)$ are selected such that $p(1)<p<p(2)$. Two types of tests are presented. Each type has alternative $p \neq p(0)$ and emphasizes situations where $p \leqslant p(1)$ or $p \geqslant p(2)$. In one case the two alternatives $p(1)$, $p(2)$ are averaged, independently for each sample value, by randomly, with probabilities w_1 and w_2, selecting one of these alternatives. For the other case a geometric mean type of average of the binomial distributions with probabilities $p(1)$ and $p(2)$ is used, with the weights w_1 and w_2 chosen so that this average is also a binomial distribution. The geometric mean type of averaging seems to be more appropriate than the (conceptual) random selection type in

some cases, but appears to require more computational effort in evaluating w_1 and w_2.

Sequential point estimation of p seems to be most appropriate when this estimation is a supplementary part of a sequential test for p. Let $E_p(n)$ be the expected sample size (average sample number) for the sequential procedure considered. Then $p(1-p)/E_p(n)$ is a lower bound for the variance of the optimum unbiased sequential estimate of p. Since the variance of the optimum unbiased estimate of p is $p(1-p)/n$ for fixed sample size n, nothing seems to be gained by using a sequential procedure for estimating p. Moreover, the nonsequential estimate usually requires substantially less computational effort for its determination. However, if the sequential data have already been obtained for another purpose, using this data to also obtain a point estimate of p would seem desirable. Consequently, one of the presentations contains a procedure for sequential estimation of p.

The sequential confidence intervals presented for p have advantages and disadvantages. Their principal advantage is that two-sided intervals are obtained whose endpoints satisfy a specified relation, where this relation can be any member of a rather general class of relations. Their principal disadvantages are that expected sample sizes and operating characteristic properties are not determined for these sequential intervals. Also, since a somewhat complicated equation must be solved for each new sample value, the amount of computation required to determine a sequential confidence interval can be large. This last disadvantage can be partially overcome by only solving the complicated equation every few sample values (say, every five sample values); however, this tends to reduce the efficiency of the procedure.

Decision Theory Methods

In addition to the methods presented in this section, procedures based on statistical decision theory can be used to investigate the parameter of a binomial distribution. Various methods of this type, which are ordinarily based on the use of supplementary information, can be found in ref. 67 and 541.

One of the presentations of this section contains nonsequential Bayes estimates for the parameter p of a binomial distribution. Here the supplementary information is used in specifying an *a priori* distribution for p. As an example, if virtually no supplementary information is available about p, the *a priori* frequency function could be rectangular [0, 1]. If supplementary information indicates that values near 0 and 1 are less likely than the other values, the *a priori* frequency function could be $6\xi(1-\xi)$, where $0 \leqslant \xi \leqslant 1$. If small values are considered to be more likely than large values the *a priori* frequency function could be $2(1-\xi)$ or

$(1-\xi)^2$, where $0 \leqslant \xi \leqslant 1$. If the value of p is known to be less than ξ_0, but nothing else is known, the *a priori* distribution could be rectangular $[0, \xi_0]$, etc. Although the examples given involve a continuous *a priori* distribution for p, this need not be the case. In general, a specified distribution function $G(\xi)$, where $0 \leqslant \xi \leqslant 1$, is used to represent the *a priori* distribution of p.

Three different types of loss functions are considered. One type is of the form $\lambda(p)(p-h_n)^2$, where $\lambda(p) > 0$ and h_n is an estimate of p. Another type is of the form $\lambda(p)|p-h_n|$, while the third type has zero loss if $-C \leqslant p-h_n \leqslant D$ and unit loss otherwise, where C, D are nonnegative and specified. If $C=D=0$ and the *a priori* distribution of p is rectangular $[0, 1]$, the standard maximum likelihood estimate of p is obtained. An additional measure of the suitability of an estimate is obtained for the third type of loss function when C and D are positive. Namely, a probability (depending on the specified *a priori* distribution of p) is specified for the relation $-C \leqslant p-h_n \leqslant D$ when h_n is the Bayes estimate of p. If $\log p$ is estimated instead of p, the third type of loss function applies to the ratio of p to its estimate (actually, the Bayes estimate is obtained for $\log p$ rather than p).

Ref. 262 contains a method which can be used to estimate the *a priori* distribution of p on the basis of additional observations. However, if the *a priori* distribution is only introduced as a convenient way of incorporating supplementary information into the estimation, the additional observations would virtually always be additional sample values from the binomial population considered. Then it would seem that direct use of these observations to increase the sample size would nearly always be more desirable than the use outlined in ref. 262.

Situations Considered

The first presentation contains nonsequential point estimates for the average of the success probabilities for a set of random binomial events. Some of these estimates require the events to be independent and to have the same success probability (the binomial distribution case). The second presentation contains an unbiased sequential estimate for the success probability of a binomial distribution. Some nonsequential Bayes estimates of the binomial parameter are given next. The fourth presentation furnishes some approximations to the binomial distribution that are reasonably accurate and relatively easy to apply. Nonsequential confidence intervals for the success probability of the binomial distribution are given in the fifth presentation, while the sixth presentation deals with two-sided sequential confidence intervals for the value of this success probability; the seventh presentation contains one-sided and two-sided sequential tests for this probability.

The remaining four presentations are all nonsequential and concerned with the more general situation where the events can have different success probabilities. The first of these presents an expansion for the distribution of the number of successes when the events are independent. On the basis of this expansion, the next presentation furnishes approximate confidence intervals for the average of the success probabilities. The next to last presentation also requires independent events and contains normal approximations to the distribution of the number of successes. These approximations can be used to obtain confidence intervals for the average of the success probabilities. The final presentation is the only one that does not require independent events. Here the Poisson approximation is found to be useful when the success probabilities are small and the dependence among the events is not very extensive.

In the binomial distribution presentations, the population constant of principal interest is the probability of success. Functions of this probability, etc. can also be of interest. Results of this nature have some nonparametric characteristics but were considered to be too specialized for presentation here. However, references to some of these results seemed to be worthwhile and are given as additional bibliography at the end of this section.

Fixed Material for Section

Data 1 Possible values for each observation are 0 and 1 (0 represents failure and 1 represents success) **2** None **3** $X(i)$ **4** $m=1$ **Assumptions 2** None.

Nonsequential Unbiased and Minimax Estimates for Binomial Parameter

Data 4 n not fixed value for one of estimates **Description 1** Exact expected value and minimax estimates, where loss fct. for minimax estimation is square of difference between estimate and value estimated **2** $P[X(i)=1]$ on basis of $M(i)$ **Assumptions 1** Random sample **3** None **Results 1** $p=P[X(i)=1]$ **2** *Estimates*: $M(i)$ is minimum-variance unbiased estimate of p; also is max. likelihood estimate. The minimax estimate for p is $M(i)\sqrt{n}/(1+\sqrt{n})+1/2(1+\sqrt{n})$, where loss fct. is square of diff. between estimate and true value of p. Let sampling be stopped when $nM(i)=Z$; then $(Z-1)/(n-1)$ unbiased estimate of p and an average of Z/p sample values required **3** None **4** $M(i)$ is sufficient statistic for estimation of p. Median estimate of p obtainable as endpoint of one-sided confidence interval with .5 confidence coeff. (see presentation on page 185) **Characteristics 1** Low **2** 100 per cent efficiencies for types of estimates considered **3** Used symmetrically **4** $M(i)$ is expected value estimate of $EM(i)$ under any circumstances. However, the variances and expected losses for the estimates can be very sensitive to violations of independence of the $X(i)$; also moderately sensitive to condition that events have same success prob. **5** Not difficult to decide on independence but sometimes moderately difficult to verify that the $P[X(i)=1]$ are equal **6** Sequential unbiased estimation of p considered in next presentation and statistical decision theory estimation (Bayes estimates) considered on page 182 **Bibliography** Ref. 229, 239, 492.

Sequential Unbiased Estimation of Binomial Parameter (Girshick, Mosteller, Savage)

Data 4 n not a fixed value **Description 1** Exact unbiased sequential point estimates **2** $p=P[X(i)=1]$, on basis of the n observations evaluated in performing a nontruncated sequential test where observations obtained and used singly **Assumptions 1** Random sample **3** None **Results 1** Test based on $\sum_{t=1}^{i} X(t)$ and terminated first time $\sum_{t=1}^{i} X(t)$ equals the value of a boundary point. Test actually terminated when $i=n$ and with attainment of boundary pt. $(C_n, n-C_n)$, where first coordinate represents no. of successes and second coordinate no. of failures. When ith sample value used, $1 \leqslant i \leqslant n$, the accessible boundary pts. (specified by the test procedure) are $(b_i, i-b_i)$ for $b_i \leqslant i$ and $(a_i, i-a_i)$ when $a_i \geqslant 0$; here $b_i \geqslant a_i$, $b_i \leqslant b_{i+1}$, $a_i \leqslant a_{i+1}$, and the a_i, b_i are integers. Let the set $(A_1, A'_1), \ldots, (A_R, A'_R)$, where $R \leqslant 2n-1$ and the arrangement is such that $A_r + A'_r \leqslant A_{r+1} + A'_{r+1}$ with $A_r \leqslant A_{r+1}$, consist of $(C_n, n-C_n)$ and the accessible boundary pts. for $i<n$; when the same pt. occurs more than once, it is included only once in this set. Let $N(A_1, A'_1) =1$. If $A_1=0$, express $\sum_{r=1}^{R} N(A_r, A'_r)p^{A_r}(1-p)^{A'_r}$ in terms of increasing powers of p and equate the coeff. of each positive power of p to zero. Starting with coeff. of p and proceeding according to increasing powers of p, determine $N(A_r, A'_r)$ for $r=2, \ldots, R$ in a stepwise fashion. If $A'_1=0$ (either $A_1=0$ or $A'_1=0$), express $\sum_{r=1}^{R} N(A_r, A'_r)q^{A'_r}(1-q)^{A_r}$ in terms of increasing powers of q and equate the coeff. of each positive power of q to zero. Starting with coeff. of q and proceeding according to increasing powers of q, determine $N(A_r, A'_r)$ for $r=2, \ldots, R$ in a stepwise fashion. By one of these methods, $N(A_R, A'_R)=N(C_n, n-C_n)$ is evaluated. Let the set $(B_1, B'_1), \ldots, (B_W, B'_W)$, where $W<R$ and the arrangement is such that $B_w + B'_w \leqslant B_{w+1} + B'_{w+1}$ with $B_w \leqslant B_{w+1}$, consist of $(C_n, n-C_n)$ and the accessible boundary pts. for $i<n$ where the first coordinate is nonzero. Let $N^*(B_1, B'_1)=1$. If $B_1=1$, express $\sum_{w=1}^{W} N^*(B_w, B'_w)p^{B_w-1}(1-p)^{B'_w}$ in terms of increasing powers of p and equate the coeff. of each positive power of p to zero. Starting with the

coeff. of p and proceeding according to increasing powers of p, determin $N^*(B_w, B'_w)$ for $w=2, \ldots, W$ in a stepwise fashion. If $B'_1=0$ (eithe $B_1=1$ or $B'_1=0$), express $\sum_{w=1}^{W} N^*(B_w, B'_w)q^{B'_w}(1-q)^{B_w-1}$ in terms (increasing powers of q and equate coeff. of each positive power of q t zero. Starting with coeff. of q and proceeding according to increasin powers of q, determine $N^*(B_w, B'_w)$ for $w=2, \ldots, W$ in a stepwis fashion. By one of these methods, $N^*(B_W, B'_W)=N^*(C_n, n-C_n)$ i evaluated **2** *Estimate*: $\hat{p}=N^*(C_n, n-C_n)/N(C_n, n-C_n)$ is unbiase estimate of p. **3** None **4** For given i, any pt. $(c, i-c)$ with c an integer an $0 \leqslant c \leqslant i$ is said to be accessible and of index i. The estimate presented i the unique unbiased estimate of p if every two accessible pts. of inde i $(i=1, \ldots, n)$ which are not boundary pts. cannot be separated on th line $x_1+x_2=i$ (where x_1 is first coordinate and x_2 second coordinate fo pts.) by boundary pts. or pts. that are not accessible **Characteristic** **1** Low to high, depending on n. Low only for very small n **2** $\sigma^2(\hat{p}) \geqslant p(1-p)/E_p(n)$, where $E_p(n)$ is average sample number, for true value c p, for sequential test yielding observations on which estimate based Upper bound for $E_p(n)$ furnished by presentation on page 189 **3** Not use symmetrically **4** Sensitive to dependences involving more than sma percentage of observations. Moderately sensitive to variation amon values of the $P[X(i)=1]$ **5** Not difficult to decide on independence bu sometimes more difficult to verify that the $P[X(i)=1]$ are equal **6** Onl recommended for use when test also being applied (see page 186). Sequen tial methods useful in acceptance inspection **Bibliography** Ref. 66, 204 226, 264, 308, 417, 456, 598, 599.

Nonsequential Bayes Estimation of Binomial Parameter

Description 1 Exact point estimation on basis of statistical decisio theory **2** Bayes estimation of $p=P[X(i)=1]$ from sample values, specifie *a priori* dist. of p (best guess from supplementary information), an specified loss fct. **Assumptions 1** Random sample **3** None **Results** $\lambda(p)>0$; $0 \leqslant h_n \leqslant 1$, where h_n an estimate of p. Loss fcts. considered are $L_1(p, h_n)=\lambda(p)(p-h_n)^2$; $L_2(p, h_n)=\lambda(p)|p-h_n|$; $L_3(p, h_n)=0$ i $-C \leqslant p-h_n \leqslant D$, $=1$ otherwise, where $C, D \geqslant 0$; $L_4(p, h_n)=0$ i $-C \leqslant \log_e p-\log_e h_n \leqslant D$, $=1$ otherwise. $G(\xi)=$specified *a priori* dis fct. for unknown value of p $(0 \leqslant \xi \leqslant 1)$. $E[p^s\lambda(p)|nM(i)]=$ $[\int_0^1 \lambda(\xi$ $\xi^{nM(i)+s}(1-\xi)^{n[1-M(i)]}dG(\xi)]/[\int_0^1 \xi^{nM(i)}(1-\xi)^{n[1-M(i)]}dG(\xi)]$ for $s=0, 1, 2$ $\tau_1(h_n)=h_n{}^2E[\lambda(p)|nM(i)]-2h_nE[p\lambda(p)|nM(i)]+E[p^2\lambda(p)|nM(i)]$. G_2 $\xi'|nM(i)]=$ $[\int_0^{\xi'} \lambda(\xi)\xi^{nM(i)}(1-\xi)^{n[1-M(i)]}dG(\xi)]/[\int_0^1 \lambda(\xi)\xi^{nM(i)}(1-\xi)^{n[1-M(i)]}$ $dG(\xi)]$. $\tau_2(h_n)=\int_0^1 |\xi-h_n|dG_2[\xi|nM(i)]$. Fcts. occurring in def. of $\tau_1(h)$ and $\tau_2(h_n)$ such that these quantities finite for all h_n or, for given $nM(i)$, only finite for one value of h_n. $G_3[\xi'|r] = [\int_0^{\xi'} \xi^r(1-\xi)^{n-r}dG(\xi)]/[\int_0^1 \xi^r(1-\xi)^{n-r}dG(\xi)]$. $\tau_3[h_n|r] = G_3[\min(h_n+D, 1)|r] - G_3[\max(h_n-C, 0)|r]$. $\tau_4[h_n|r] = G_3\{\exp[\min(\log_e h_n + D, 1)]|r\} - G_3\{\exp[\max(\log_e h_n - C, 0)]|r\}$ **2** *General Bayes estimates. Case of* L_1: Estimate is $t_1[nM(i)] = E[p\lambda(p)|nM(i)]/E[\lambda(p)|nM(i)]$ when $\tau_1(h_n) < \infty$ for all h_n, $=$ value of h_n for which $\tau_1(h_n) < \infty$ otherwise. *Case of* L_2: Estimate $t_2[nM(i)]$ is median of $G_2[\xi|nM(i)]$ when $\tau_2(h_n) < \infty$ for all h_n, is value of h_n for which $\tau_2(h_n) < \infty$ otherwise. *Case of* L_3: Estimate $t_3[nM(i)]$ is value of h_n which maximizes $\tau_3[h_n|nM(i)]$. For given $G(\xi)$, $P\{-C \leqslant p - t_3[nM(i)] \leqslant D\} = \sum_{r=0}^{n} \tau_3\{t_3[r]|r\}\binom{n}{r} \int_0^1 \xi^r(1-\xi)^{n-r}dG(\xi) =$ subjective prob. that furnishes measure of extent to which estimate is so close to true value that no loss occurs. *Case of* L_4: Estimate $\log_e t_4[nM(i)]$ of $\log_e p$ is value of $\log_e h_n$ which maximizes $\tau_4[h_n|nM(i)]$. For given $G(\xi)$, $P\{e^{-C} \leqslant p/t_4[nM(i)] \leqslant e^D\} = \sum_{r=0}^{n} \tau_4\{t_4[r]|r\}\binom{n}{r} \int_0^1 \xi^r(1-\xi)^{n-r}dG(\xi) =$ subjective prob. that furnishes measure of extent to which estimate is so close to true value (in sense of ratio) that no loss occurs. *Examples of Bayes estimates for* L_1 *and* L_2. Here $G(\xi)$ continuous with freq. fct. $A(a,b)\xi^a(1-\xi)^b$, where $a, b > -1$; $\lambda(p) = p^c(1-p)^d$, values of $-(a+c)$ and $-(b+d)$ not too large, and a, b, c, d not necessarily integers. Many important combinations of $G(\xi)$ and $\lambda(p)$ can be approximated by allowable selections of values for a, b, c, d. *Case of* L_1: Here both $-(a+c)$ and $-(b+d) < 3$. Then $t_1[nM(i)] = [nM(i)+a+c+1]/(n+b+d+1)$ for $-(a+c+1) \leqslant nM(i) \leqslant n+b+d+1$, $=0$ for $nM(i) < -(a+c+1)$, $=1$ for $nM(i) > n+b+d+1$. *Case of* L_2: Here both $-(a+c)$ and $-(b+d) < 2$. Then $t_2[nM(i)]$ is median of beta dist. with freq. fct. $[\Gamma(n+b+d+1)\xi^{nM(i)+a+c}(1-\xi)^{n+b+d-nM(i)-a-c}]/\Gamma[nM(i)+a+c+1]\Gamma[n+b+d-nM(i)-a-c]$ for $-(a+c+1) \leqslant nM(i) \leqslant n+b+d+1$, is 0 for $nM(i) < -(a+c+1)$, is 1 for $nM(i) > n+d+b+1$ **3** Median of beta dist. often obtainable from tables of incomplete beta fct. **4** If $C = D = 0$ and $G(\xi) = \xi$, $t_3[nM(i)]$ is max likelihood estimate of p and $\log_e t_4[nM(i)]$ is max likelihood estimate of $\log_e p$. Prob. relations stated for L_3 and L_4 do not represent probabilities in usual sense because they depend on *a priori* dist. of p. Except in special cases, estimates not unbiased. For the case of L_1, the risk equals $\sum_{r=0}^{n} \tau_1[t_1(r)]\binom{n}{r} \int_0^1 \xi^r(1-\xi)^{n-r}dG(\xi)$. The risk equals $\sum_{r=0}^{n} \tau_2[t_2(r)]\binom{n}{r} \int_0^1 \xi^r(1-\xi)^{n-r}dG(\xi)$ for the case of L_2. For L_3, the risk is $1 - P\{-C \leqslant p - t_3[nM(i)] \leqslant D\}$, and the risk is $1 - P\{e^{-C} \leqslant p - t_4[nM(i)] \leqslant e^D\}$ for the case of L_4 **Characteristics 1** Low to upper low for examples for L_1 and L_2. Low to high for general situations **2** 100 percent efficient in sense of minimizing risk for given $G(\xi)$ and loss fct. **3** Used symmetrically **4** In general, risk fct. properties can be very sensitive to dependences involving more than small percentage of observations. However, since $M(i)$ is expected value estimate of p irrespective of dependence, p still estimated in at least rough sense for most cases where independence part of sample assumption violated. Only mediumly sensitive to moderate variation among values of the $P[X(i)=1]$ if their arithmetic average considered to be estimated, since $M(i)$ is estimate of $MP[X(i)=1]$; here too independence can have large effect on risk fct. properties but $MP[X(i)=1]$ still estimated in at least rough sense for most situations **5** Not so difficult to decide on independence but sometimes more difficult to verify that the $P[X(i)=1]$ are equal **6** Useful when supplementary information available for selecting $G(\xi)$. Bayes estimates also obtainable sequentially and this considered in some of references **Bibliography** Ref. 20, 67, 203, 205, 262, 408, 412, 457 (Sect. 13.4), 492, 541, 542.

Approximations to Binomial Distribution

Description 1 Approximations to binomial prob. distribution; also exact expression in terms of F-dist. **2** $P[nM(i)\leqslant k]$, $0\leqslant k\leqslant n$ (k integer), where $nM(i)=$ observed no. of successes **Assumptions 1** Random sample **3** $0<P[X(i)=1]<1$ **Results 1** $p=P[X(i)=1]$, $q=1-p$ **2** *Approximations. For $p\leqslant .5$ and $np\leqslant .8$,* $P[nM(i)<k]\doteq \frac{1}{2}p(k-np)e^{-np}(np)^k/k! + e^{-np}\sum_{u=0}^{k}(np)^u/u!$ *For $p\leqslant .5$ and $np\geqslant .8$,* $P[nM(i)\leqslant k]\doteq\Phi(k_1/3\sqrt{k_2})$, where $k_1=[(n-k)p/(k+1)q]^{1/3}[9-1/(n-k)]+1/(k+1)-9$ and $k_2=[(n-k)p/(k+1)q]^{2/3}/(n-k)+1/(k+1)$. *For $p\geqslant .5$ and $nq\leqslant .8$,* $P[nM(i)\leqslant k]\doteq 1-\frac{1}{2}(n-k-1-nq)e^{-nq}(nq)^{n-k-1}/(n-k-1)! \; -e^{-nq}\sum_{u=0}^{n-k-1}(nq)^u/u!$. *For $p\geqslant .5$ and $nq\geqslant .8$,* $P[nM(i)\leqslant k]\doteq 1-\Phi(k'_1/3\sqrt{k'_2})$, where $k'_1=[(k+1)q/(n-k)p]^{1/3}[9-1/(k+1)]+1/(n-k)-9$ and $k'_2=[(k+1)q/(n-k)p]^{2/3}/(k+1)+1/(n-k)$. *Exact expression:* $P[nM(i)\leqslant k]=P[F>(n-k)p/(k+1)(1-p)]$, where F has F-dist. with $2(k+1)$ and $2(n-k)$ degrees of freedom **3** Applied by use of tables of Poisson, normal, and F-dists. **4** For $npq\geqslant 9$, $nM(i)$ approx. normally distributed with mean $np+(p-\frac{1}{2})$ and variance npq (continuity correction of $\frac{1}{2}$); also for $npq\geqslant 15$, $2\sin^{-1}\sqrt{M(i)}$ approx. normally distributed with mean $2\sin^{-1}\sqrt{p}$ and variance $1/n$. For np sufficiently small (say, at most $\frac{3}{2}$), or p sufficiently small (say, at most .03), dist. of $nM(i)$ approx. Poisson with mean np. Exact expression based on F-dist. of somewhat approx. nature since determination of α for given $F_\alpha(k_1, k_2)$ usually based on interpolation **Characteristics 1** Low **2** Approximations have excellent accuracy **3** Used symmetrically **4** Not pertinent **5** Not pertinent **6** None **Bibliography** Ref. 7, 87, 115, 168, 191, 224 (pages 673–75, 698), 234, 368, 421.

Approximate Confidence Intervals for Binomial Parameter

Description 1 Approx. one-sided and two-sided confidence intervals **2** $p = P[X(i)=1]$ **Assumptions 1** Random sample **3** $0<p<1$ **Results 1** $p'_\alpha[H]$ determined by $\sum_{h=0}^{H}\binom{n}{h} p'_\alpha[H]^h\{1-p'_\alpha[H]\}^{n-h}=\alpha$ for $H=0, 1, \ldots, n-1$ and $p'_\alpha[n]=1$; $p''_\alpha[H]$ determined by $\sum_{h=H}^{n}\binom{n}{h} p''_\alpha[H]^h\{1-p''_\alpha[H]\}^{n-h}=\alpha$ for $H=1, \ldots, n$ and $p''_\alpha[0]=0$. Explicitly, in terms of F-dist., $p'_\alpha[H]= (H+1)F_\alpha[2(H+1), 2(n-H)]/\{n-H+(H+1)F_\alpha[2(H+1), 2(n-H)]\}$ for $H<n$ and $p''_\alpha[H]= H/\{H+(n-H+1)F_\alpha[2(n-H+1), 2H]\}$ for $H>0$ **2** *One-sided relations*: $P\{p'_\alpha[nM(i)]\leqslant p\}\leqslant\alpha$ and equals α for some value(s) of p; thus $P\{p'_\alpha[nM(i)]>p\}\geqslant 1-\alpha$ and equals $1-\alpha$ for some value(s) of p. $P\{p''_\alpha[nM(i)]\geqslant p\}\leqslant\alpha$ and equals α for some value(s) of p; thus $P\{p''_\alpha[nM(i)]<p\}\geqslant 1-\alpha$ and equals $1-\alpha$ for some value(s) of p. *Two-sided relations*: $P\{p''_{\alpha/2}[nM(i)]<p<p'_{\alpha/2}[nM(i)]\}= 1-P\{p'_{\alpha/2}[nM(i)]\leqslant p\}-P\{p''_{\alpha/2}[nM(i)]\geqslant p\}\geqslant 1-\alpha$; $P\{p'_{1-\alpha/2}[nM(i)]\leqslant p\leqslant p''_{1-\alpha/2}[nM(i)]\}= 1-P\{p''_{1-\alpha/2}[nM(i)]<p\}-P\{p'_{1-\alpha/2}[nM(i)]>p\}\leqslant 1-\alpha$ **3** In addition to their expression in terms of the F-dist., values of $p'_\alpha[nM(i)]$ and $p''_\alpha[nM(i)]$ can be determined from table for binomial dist., table for incomplete beta fct., and from approx. to binomial dist. (see this sect.) **4** Probabilities for the two-sided intervals do not necessarily attain value $1-\alpha$ for some p. Various modifications yield two-sided intervals such that probability attains bound value of $1-\alpha$ and which have shorter average lengths than those presented (see ref. 119, 496); also modifications available such that average confidence coeff. over all p has exact value for both one-sided and two-sided intervals (see ref. 230). If $nM(i)[1-M(i)]\geqslant 9$ and $1/5n\leqslant\alpha\leqslant 1-1/5n$, the relation $(K_\alpha/|K_\alpha|)\{[(n+1)^2+nK_\alpha^2/2]p-(n+1)nM(i)-nK_\alpha^2/2\}/\sqrt{n}\leqslant K_\alpha[(n+1)nM(i)+nK_\alpha^2/4-1]^{1/2}$ and the relation $(K_\alpha/|K_\alpha|)\{[(n+1)^2+nK_\alpha^2/2]p-(n+1)[nM(i)+1]-nK_\alpha^2/2\}/\sqrt{n}\geqslant -K_\alpha\{(n+1)[nM(i)+1]+nK_\alpha^2/4-1\}^{1/2}$ both have prob. $\doteq 1-\alpha$ $(K_\alpha/|K_\alpha|=1$ for $\alpha=\frac{1}{2})$ **Characteristics 1** Low **2** Very high efficiency. One-sided tests based on $M(i)$ uniformly most powerful in sense of Tocher's extension of Neyman-Pearson lemma (see ref. 517). One-sided and equal-tail two-sided tests asymptotically optimum in an information theory sense **3** Used symmetrically **4** If n large, very sensitive to dependences involving sizable percentage of observations. Not very sensitive to moderate variation among the $P[X(i)=1]$ if confidence intervals for their average value considered **5** Not difficult to decide on the independence of the $X(i)$ but more difficult to verify that the $P[X(i)=1]$ are equal **6** Tests directly obtainable from confidence intervals; however, tests obtained for two-sided case not necessarily uniformly most powerful. Form of uniformly most powerful randomized unbiased test for two-sided case given in ref. 68. **Bibliography** Ref. 68, 103, 119, 168, 224 (pages 673–75, 698), 230, 301, 314, 368, 378, 387, 408, 459, 496, 517.

Sequential Confidence Intervals for Binomial Parameter

Data 4 n not a fixed value **Description 1** Theoretical-approx. two-sided confidence intervals **2** $p=P[X(i)=1]$ **Assumptions 1** Random sample **3** $0<p<1$ **Results 1** $X(0)=$guess for value of p from supplementary information available at beginning of experiment ($\neq 0, 1$); $X(0)=\frac{1}{2}$ if no supplementary information available. p'_{1i} and p'_{2i} are smaller and larger values of p', respectively, which satisfy $(p')^{X(1)+\ldots+X(i)}(1-p')^{i-X(1)-\ldots-X(i)}= (1-\epsilon)\{[X(0)+X(1)+\ldots+X(i-1)]/i\}^{X(1)+\ldots+X(i)}\{1-[X(0)+\ldots+X(i-1)]/i\}^{i-X(1)-\ldots-X(i)}$, where ϵ is lower limit for confidence coeff. of seq. confidence interval. $p'_{Ln}=\max_{1\leqslant i\leqslant n}p'_{1i}$; $p'_{Un}=\min_{1\leqslant i\leqslant n}p'_{2i}$. $r(p'_{Ln}, p'_{Un})$ is specified relation that is always satisfied for $p'_{Un}-p'_{Ln}$ sufficiently small. Example is $p'_{Un}-p'_{Ln}\leqslant D_1+D_2p'_{Un}+D_3p'_{Ln}$ with D_1, D_2, D_3 suitably chosen such that $D_1+D_2p'_{Un}+D_3p'_{Ln}$ is positive and does not $\to 0$ as $p'_{Un}\to p'_{Ln}$; $p'_{Un}-p'_{Ln}\leqslant D_1$ and $p'_{Un}-p'_{Ln}\leqslant D(p'_{Un}+p'_{Ln})$, with D_1, D positive and $\leqslant\frac{1}{10}$, are special cases **2** *Two-sided confidence interval*: Starting with $n=1$, continue taking observations (singly) until $r(p'_{Ln}, p'_{Un})$ satisfied. For final n, $P(p'_{Ln}\leqslant p\leqslant p'_{Un})\geqslant\epsilon$ **3** None **4** Based on pages 145–56 of ref. 539. Advantage of these intervals is that endpoints satisfy specified relation, which can be selected with moderate generality. Expected sample size not determined, but it should not be excessively large unless $p(1-p)$ near zero and/or $r(p'_{Ln}, p'_{Un})$ not satisfied except when $p'_{Un}-p'_{Ln}$ very small **Characteristics 1** Upper low to high, depending on final n, since p'_{1i} and p'_{2i} must be evaluated for each new sample value. Computation reduced by only determining new values for p'_{Un} and p'_{Ln} every five observations, etc. **2** Unknown efficiency, but intuitive considerations indicate that efficiency at least moderately high; in fact, for many situations this is only available procedure **3** Not used symmetrically **4** Can be sensitive to dependences involving more than small percentage of observations. Moderately sensitive to variation among values of the $P[X(i)=1]$ **5** Not difficult to decide on independence but more difficult to verify that the $P[X(i)=1]$ are equal **6** Useful when important that endpoints of two-sided confidence interval satisfy a specified relation of $r(p'_{Ln}, p'_{Un})$ type **Bibliography** Ref. 539.

Sequential Tests for Binomial Parameter

Data 4 n not a fixed value **Description 1** Approx. (nearly exact) one-sided and two-sided sequential signif. tests **2** $p=P[X(i)=1]$ **Assump-**

tions **1** Random sample **3** $0<p<1$ **Results 1** $p(0), p(1), p(2)$ specified such that $p(1)<p(0)<p(2)$. Null hyp. H_0 is $p=p(0)$. Altern. hyp. for one-sided tests are $p<p(0)$ with emphasis on situations where $p \leqslant p(1)$, and $p>p(0)$ with emphasis on $p \geqslant p(2)$. For the two types of two-sided tests, altern. hyp. is $p \neq p(0)$ with emphasis on situations where $p \leqslant p(1)$ or $p \geqslant p(2)$. To a reasonable approx., all tests have signif. level α $(\alpha<\frac{1}{2})$. For one-sided tests, β is max prob. of type II error for situations emphasized. For one type of two-sided test, $\beta=$prob. of type II error when $p=w_1p(1)+w_2p(2)$, where w_1 and w_2 non-negative, $w_1+w_2=1$, and w_1 chosen so that larger of prob. of type II error at $p(1)$ and at $p(2)$ minimized. For other type of two-sided test, $\beta=$prob. of type II error when $p=p(1)^{w_1}p(2)^{w_2}$, where w_1 and w_2 such that $0<p(1)^{w_1}p(2)^{w_2}<1$, $p(1)^{w_1}p(2)^{w_2}+[1-p(1)]^{w_1}[1-p(2)]^{w_2}=1$, and w_1 chosen so that larger of prob. of type II error at $p(1)$ and at $p(2)$ minimized. For both types of two-sided tests, method of evaluating w_1 stated in part 4 of Results. In all cases, $\alpha+\beta<1$. Notation: $q=1-p$, $q(0)=1-p(0)$, $p'=1-p'$, etc. $a_J[p', p'']$ is largest integer $\leqslant$ $\{\log_{10}[B/(1-\alpha)]\}/|\log_{10}(p''q'/p'q'')|$ $+J[\log_{10}(q'/q'')]/\log_{10}(p''q'/p'q'')$ and $b_J[p', p'']$ is smallest integer $\geqslant -\frac{1}{3}+\{\log_{10}[(1-\beta)/\alpha]\}/|\log_{10}(p''q'/p'q'')|+(J+\frac{2}{3})[\log_{10}(q'/q'')]/\log_{10}(p''q'/p'q'')$. Let $h_1=h_1[p'']=\{\log_{10}[p''/p(0)]\}/\log_{10}[q(0)/q'']$, $h_2=h_2[p'']=\{\log_{10}[(1-\alpha)/\beta]\}/\log_{10}[q(0)/q'']$, and $h_3=h_3[p'']=\{\log_{10}[(1-\beta)/\alpha]\}/\log_{10}[q(0)/q'']+\frac{2}{3}-(h_1+1)/3$. When $p(0), \alpha, \beta, p''$ such that h_1, h_2, h_3, and $(h_2+h_3)/(h_1+1)$ positive integers with $(h_2+h_3)/(h_1+1) \geqslant 2$, $V[p'']=h_1+1$ and $V_0[p'']=h_2-(h_1+1)$[largest integer in $h_2/(h_1+1)$]; otherwise $V[p'']=V_0[p'']=1$. For J, V integers $\geqslant 1$, $N_J=\sum_{t=1}^{(J-1)V+V_0} X(t)$ **2** *Tests*: Sequential sampling procedure starts with group of $n=V_0$ sample values and continues in groups of sample values with $n=V_0+V, V_0+2V, \ldots$ until a decision reached. No prior conditions are imposed on tests when $J=1$. Notation: $J(n)=1+(n-V_0)/V$. *One-sided test of* $p<p(0)$: Here $(V, V_0)=$ (1, 1) or $(V[p(1)], V_0[p(1)])$. Given that $a_J[p(0), p(1)]<N_J<b_J[p(0), p(1)]$ for $J \leqslant J(n)-1$, accept H_0 if $N_{J(n)} \leqslant a_{J(n)}[p(0), p(1)]$; accept $p<p(0)$ with emphasis on $p \leqslant p(1)$ if $N_{J(n)} \geqslant b_{J(n)}[p(0), p(1)]$; otherwise take another V sample values and repeat procedure for increased sample size. *One-sided test of* $p>p(0)$: Here $(V, V_0)=$ (1, 1) or $(V[p(2)], V_0[p(2)])$. Given that $a_J[p(0), p(2)]<N_J<b_J[p(0), p(2)]$ for $J \leqslant J(n)-1$, accept H_0 if $N_{J(n)} \leqslant a_{J(n)}[p(0), p(2)]$; accept $p>p(0)$ with emphasis on $p \geqslant p(2)$ if $N_{J(n)} \geqslant b_{J(n)}[p(0), p(2)]$; otherwise take another V sample values and repeat procedure for increased sample size. *Two-sided test using* $w_1p(1)+w_2p(2)$: Here $(V, V_0)=$ (1, 1) or $(V[w_1p(1)+w_2p(2)], V_0[w_1p(1)+w_2p(2)])$. Given that $a_J[p(0), w_1p(1)+w_2p(2)]<N_J<b_J[p(0), w_1p(1)+w_2p(2)]$ for $J \leqslant J(n)-1$, accept H_0 if $N_{J(n)} \leqslant a_{J(n)}[p(0), w_1p(1)+w_2p(2)]$; accept

$p \neq p(0)$ with emphasis on $p \leqslant p(1)$ or $p \geqslant p(2)$ if $N_{J(n)} \geqslant b_{J(n)}[p(0), w_1 p(1) + w_2 p(2)]$; otherwise take another V sample values and continue. *Two-sided test using* $p(1)^{w_1} p(2)^{w_2}$: Here $(V, V_0) = (1, 1)$ or $(V[p(1)^{w_1} p(2)^{w_2}], V_0[p(1)^{w_1} p(2)^{w_2}])$. Given that $a_J[p(0), p(1)^{w_1} p(2)^{w_2}] < N_J < b_J[p(0), p(1)^{w_1} p(2)^{w_2}]$ for $J \leqslant J(n) - 1$, accept H_0 if $N_{J(n)} \leqslant a_{J(n)}[p(0), p(1)^{w_1} p(2)^{w_2}]$; accept $p \neq p(0)$ with emphasis on $p \leqslant p(1)$ or $p \geqslant p(2)$ if $N_{J(n)} \geqslant b_{J(n)}[p(0), p(1)^{w_1} p(2)^{w_2}]$; otherwise take another V sample values and continue **3** None **4** The two-sided test using $w_1 p(1) + w_2 p(2)$ is based on the conceptual situation where, independently for each sample value, the altern. $p(1)$ occurs with prob. w_1 and the altern. $p(2)$ occurs with prob. w_2. For this test, subject to the restrictions stated in part 1 of Results, value for w_1 is that which minimizes $\max\{B_1[w_1, p(1)], B_1[w_1, p(2)]\}$, where $B_1[w_1, p] = \{[(1-\beta)/\alpha]^{r_1(w_1, p)} - 1\}/\{[(1-\beta)/\alpha]^{r_1(w_1, p)} - [\beta/(1-\alpha)]^{r_1(w_1, p)}\}$ and $r_1(w_1, p)$ is sol. for r of $p\{[w_1 p(1) + w_2 p(2)]/p(0)\}^r + (1-p)\{[1 - w_1 p(1) - w_2 p(2)]/[1-p(0)]\}^r = 1$. The two-sided test using $p(1)^{w_1} p(2)^{w_2}$ is based on a geometric-mean type averaging of the binomial distribution with parameter $p(1)$ and that with parameter $p(2)$. For this test, subject to restrictions stated in part 1 of Results, value for w_1 is that which minimizes $\max\{B_2[w_1, p(1)], B_2[w_1, p(2)]\}$, where $B_2[w_1, p] = \{[(1-\beta)/\alpha]^{r_2(w_1, p)} - 1\}/\{[(1-\beta)/\alpha]^{r_2(w_1, p)} - [\beta/(1-\alpha)]^{r_2(w_1, p)}\}$ and $r_2(w_1, p)$ is sol. for r of $p[p(1)^{w_1} p(2)^{w_2}/p(0)]^r + (1-p)\{[1 - p(1)^{w_1} p(2)^{w_2}]/[1-p(0)]\}^r = 1$. *Truncation*: Let $n'[p]$ be the largest integer contained in $3h_2[p]h_3[p](1 + h_1[p])^2/h_1[p] + 3V/2$ which equals V_0 + integral multiple of V. Then, with only slight change in operating characteristics, one-sided test of $p < p(0)$ can be truncated when $n'[p(1)]$ sample values obtained, one-sided test of $p > p(0)$ can be truncated when $n'[p(2)]$ sample values obtained, two-sided test using $w_1 p(1) + w_2 p(2)$ can be truncated when $n'[w_1 p(1) + w_2 p(2)]$ sample values obtained, and two-sided test using $p(1)^{w_1} p(2)^{w_2}$ can be truncated when $n'[p(1)^{w_1} p(2)^{w_2}]$ sample values obtained. In all truncation cases, if no decision reached from sequential method by final sample value, H_0 rejected if value of final N_J nearer rejection boundary than acceptance boundary, and H_0 accepted otherwise. Whether truncated or not, one-sided test with altern. $p < p(0)$ can also be considered as test of composite null hyp. $p \geqslant p(0)$ and one-sided test of $p > p(0)$ can also be considered as test of composite null hyp. $p \leqslant p(0)$; both of these tests have a (generalized) signif. level of approx. α. Some decision theory implications of the sequential tests are considered in ref. 67 and 541 **Characteristics 1** Low for one-sided tests; lower medium for two-sided test using $w_1 p(1) + w_2 p(2)$; medium for two-sided test using $p(1)^{w_1} p(2)^{w_2}$ **2** For test of $p < p(0)$, operating characteristic (OC) fct. (prob. of accepting H_0 given p) is $B_1[1, p]$; for test of $p > p(0)$, OC fct. is $B_1[0, p]$; for test using $w_1 p(1) + w_2 p(2)$, OC fct. is $B_1[w_1, p]$; for test using $p(1)^{w_1}p(2)^{w_2}$, OC fct. is $B_2[w_1, p]$. For the corresponding four tests, let $p_a = p(1), p(2), w_1p(1)+w_2p(2), p(1)^{w_1}p(2)^{w_2}$, respectively, and let $B[p]$ be the general notation for the OC fct. of a test; here the test considered is identified by the expression for p_a. Then $B[0]=1$, $B[1]=0$, $B[p(0)]=1-\alpha$, $B[p_a]=\beta$, $B\{1/(h_1[p_a]+1)\} = \{\log_{10}[(1-\beta)/\alpha]\}/\{\log_{10}[(1-\beta)/\alpha]+|\log_{10}[\beta/(1-\alpha)]|\}$ furnish five pts. for OC fct. of each test; interpolation furnishes other pts. To attain specified α and β, much smaller sample sizes needed, on the average, for sequential tests than for corresponding fixed sample size tests; often expected sample size (average sample number) less than $\frac{1}{2}$ of corresponding fixed sample size. For test of $p<p(0)$, $E(n) \leqslant n'[p(1)]/3$ for all p; for test of $p>p(0)$, $E(n)\leqslant n'[p(2)]/3$; for test using $w_1p(1)+w_2p(2)$, $E(n)\leqslant n'[w_1p(1)+w_2p(2)]/3$; for test using $p(1)^{w_1}p(2)^{w_2}$, $E(n)\leqslant n'[p(1)^{w_1}p(2)^{w_2}]/3$ **3** Not used symmetrically **4** Can be sensitive to dependences involving more than small percentage of observations. Moderately sensitive to variation among values of the $P[X(i)=1]$ **5** Not difficult to decide on independence but more difficult to verify that the $P[X(i)=1]$ are equal **6** Results when sample values obtained in groups of other sizes outlined in ref. 264 and 539. Useful in acceptance inspection **Bibliography** Ref. 11, 13, 22, 25, 67, 82, 142, 264, 417, 490, 537, 539, 541, 547.

Approximate Probabilities—Independent Binomial Events

Description 1 Approximations to prob. distributions (yield approx. confidence intervals) **2** $P[s_1 \leqslant nM(i) \leqslant s_2]$, $0\leqslant s_1\leqslant s_2\leqslant n$ (s_1, s_2 integers), in terms of the $p_i = P[X(i)=1]$, $\bar{p}=\sum_{i=1}^{n} p_i/n$, $\sigma_p{}^2 = \sum_{i=1}^{n}(p_i-\bar{p})^2/n$, and $C_v(s_1, s_2) = \sum_{a=1}^{2}\sum_{b=1}^{v}(-1)^{b+(v-1)a}P_{n-v}(a-b-1+s_a)$, where $P_d(c) = \binom{d}{c}\bar{p}^c(1-\bar{p})^{d-c}$ for $0\leqslant c\leqslant d$ (c, d integers) and $=0$ otherwise

Assumptions 1 Independent **3** Case (I): None. Case (II): Values σ_L and σ_U known such that $0\leqslant\sigma_L\leqslant\sigma_p\leqslant\sigma_U$. Also, for the values of s_1 and s_2 considered, the Results stated for Case (II) hold if $n\sigma_U{}^2|C_2(s_1, s_2)| \leqslant \min[\sum_{k=s_1}^{s_2}\binom{n}{k}\bar{p}^k(1-\bar{p})^{n-k}, 1-\sum_{k=s_1}^{s_2}\binom{n}{k}\bar{p}^k(1-\bar{p})^{n-k}]$; and, in addition, $n\sigma_U{}^2|C_4(s_1, s_2)|/8+\sigma_U|C_3(s_1, s_2)|/3 \leqslant |C_2(s_1, s_2)|/20$ and/or $5n^2\sigma_U{}^4|C_4(s_1, s_2)|/2 + 20n\sigma_U{}^3|C_3(s_1, s_2)|/3 + 10n\sigma_U{}^2|C_2(s_1, s_2)| \leqslant \min[\sum_{k=s_1}^{s_2}\binom{n}{k}(\bar{p})^k(1-\bar{p})^{n-k}, 1-\sum_{k=s_1}^{s_2}\binom{n}{k}\bar{p}^k(1-\bar{p})^{n-k}]$ **Results 1** None

2 *Approximations. Case* (I): $P[s_1\leqslant nM(i)\leqslant s_2] = \sum_{k=s_1}^{s_2}\binom{n}{k}\bar{p}^k(1-\bar{p})^{n-k} + n\sigma_p{}^2C_2(s_1, s_2)/2 + C_3(s_1, s_2)\sum_{i=1}^{n}(p_i-\bar{p})^3/3 + [\sum_{i=1}^{n}(p_i-\bar{p})^4 - n^2\sigma_p{}^4/2]C_4(s_1, s_2)/4 + [\sum_{i=1}^{n}(p_i-\bar{p})^5 - 5n\sigma_p{}^2\sum_{i=1}^{n}(p_i-\bar{p})^3/6]C_5(s_1, s_2)/5 + \{\sum_{i=1}^{n}(p_i-\bar{p})^6 - 3n\sigma_p{}^2\sum_{i=1}^{n}(p_i-\bar{p})^4/4 - [\sum_{i=1}^{n}(p_i-\bar{p})^3]^2/3 + n^3\sigma_p{}^6/8\}$

$C_6(s_1, s_2)/6 + \ldots$. *Case* (II): $P[s_1 \leqslant nM(i) \leqslant s_2] \doteq \sum_{k=s_1}^{s_2} \binom{n}{k} \bar{p}^k(1-\bar{p})^{n-k} + n(\sigma_U{}^2+\sigma_L{}^2)C_2(s_1, s_2)/4$, with max error of approx. $n(\sigma_U{}^2-\sigma_L{}^2)|C_2(s_1, s_2)|/4$ **3** None **4** Case (II) furnishes approx. confidence intervals for $\bar{p}$. Normal and Poisson approximations to dist. of $nM(i)$ given in following two presentations. When $s_1 \leqslant n\bar{p} \leqslant s_2$, $\sum_{k=s_1}^{s_2} \binom{n}{k} \bar{p}^k(1-\bar{p})^{n-k} \leqslant P[s_1 \leqslant nM(i) \leqslant s_2] \leqslant 1$, with both limits attainable; bounds for special case where $s_1=0$ and s_2 unrestricted given in ref. 247 **Characteristics 1** Low to medium **2** Use of all terms stated for Case (I) should furnish excellent approx. to $P[s_1 \leqslant nM(i) \leqslant s_2]$ unless the p_i values vary greatly **3** Used symmetrically **4** If n large, very sensitive to dependences involving sizeable percentage of observations. Only moderately sensitive to situations of mild dependence where each observation independent of all but a few of the other observations. Only mildly sensitive to error from use of σ_U moderately less than σ_p, or σ_L moderately greater than σ_p, for Case (II) **5** Not difficult to decide on independence condition and to choose conservatively accurate values for σ_U and σ_L **6** Case (II) results useful in testing $\bar{p}$ **Bibliography** Ref. 247, 378, 408, 566.

Normal Approximation—Independent Binomial Events

Data 4 n has lower bound **Description 1** Approximation to value of probability relation (also approx. confidence intervals) **2** $P[M(i) \leqslant -1/2n + EM(i) - K_\alpha \sigma M(i)]$ in terms of the $p_i = P[X(i)=1]$, $\bar{p} = \sum_{i=1}^{n} p_i/n$, and $\sigma_p{}^2 = \sum_{i=1}^{n} (p_i - \bar{p})^2/n$ **Assumptions 1** Independent **3** $n[\bar{p}(1-\bar{p}) - \sigma_p{}^2] \geqslant 20$ and $1/n \leqslant \alpha \leqslant 1-1/n$ **Results 1** None **2** *Relations*: $P\{M(i) \leqslant -1/2n + \bar{p} - K_\alpha[\bar{p}(1-\bar{p}) - \sigma_p{}^2]^{1/2}/\sqrt{n}\} \doteq P\{M(i) < 1/2n + \bar{p} - K_\alpha[\bar{p}(1-\bar{p}) - \sigma_p{}^2]^{1/2}/\sqrt{n}\} \doteq \alpha$, for α such that $-\frac{1}{2} + n\bar{p} - \sqrt{n}K_\alpha[\bar{p}(1-\bar{p}) - \sigma_p{}^2]^{1/2}$ integral **3** None **4** If A, B known and such that $0 \leqslant A \leqslant \sigma_p{}^2/\bar{p}(1-\bar{p}) \leqslant B \leqslant .5$ with $B - A \leqslant .05$, $P\{|M(i) - \bar{p}| \leqslant K_{\alpha/2}[\bar{p}(1-\bar{p})(1-A/2-B/2)/n]^{1/2}\} \doteq 1-\alpha$ and furnishes approx. two-sided confidence intervals for $\bar{p}$ (by solving quadratic equation), subject to part 3 of assumptions; when $nM(i)[1-M(i)](1-A/2-B/2) \geqslant 25$ and $2/n \leqslant \alpha \leqslant 1-2/n$, the relation $P\Big[M(i) \leqslant \bar{p} - K_\alpha\{M(i)[1-M(i)](1-A/2-B/2)/n\}^{1/2}\Big] \doteq \alpha$ furnishes approx. one-sided and two-sided confidence intervals for $\bar{p}$. Similar results obtainable for special situation involving mild dependence among the observations (see ref. 569) **Characteristics 1** Low **2** Approximations explicitly using $\sigma_p{}^2$ reasonably accurate; approximations with $\sigma_p{}^2$ replaced by $(A+B)\bar{p}(1-\bar{p})/2$ only roughly accurate for extreme case of $A=.45$, $B=.5$ **3** Used symmetrically **4** If n large, very sensitive to dependences involving sizable percentage of observations. Only moderately sensitive to situations of mild dependence where each observation independent of all but a few of the other observations. Only mildly sensitive to error from use of A moderately less, or B moderately greater, than $\sigma_p^2/\bar{p}(1-\bar{p})$ **5** Not difficult to decide on independence assumption and to choose conservatively accurate values for A and B **6** Results involving A and B useful in testing $\bar{p}$ **Bibliography** Ref. 118 (pages 217–18), 561, 569.

Poisson Approximation—Possibly Dependent Binomial Events

Data 4 n has lower bound **Description 1** Approximation to probability distributions (yields approx. confidence intervals) **2** $P[nM(i) \leqslant k]$, $0 \leqslant k \leqslant n$ (k integer), where $nM(i)$ = observed no. of successes, in terms of the $p_i = P[X(i) = 1]$ and $\bar{p} = \sum_{i=1}^{n} p_i/n$ **Assumptions 1** Case (I): Independent. Case (II): Each $X(i)$ independent of at least $n-L-1$ of other observations **3** Case (I): $\max_i p_i \leqslant .08$; also $\bar{p} \leqslant .02$ or $n\bar{p} \leqslant 1$. Case (II): Consider conditional prob. of value 1 for an observation (depending on outcomes for zero or more other observations); $(L+1)$ times this conditional prob. at most .1 for all possible conditions; also $\bar{p} \leqslant .01$ **Results 1** None **2** *Relations*: $P[nM(i) \leqslant k] \doteq \sum_{u=0}^{k} e^{-n\bar{p}}(n\bar{p})^u/u!$ for both cases **3** None **4** Useful in obtaining approx. confidence intervals for $\bar{p}$ (see, e.g., ref. 563). Discussion of methods for verifying assumptions for Case (II) given in ref. 565. For independent observations, the asymptotic theorem corresponding to Case (I) is: A necessary and sufficient condition for the limiting dist. ($n \to \infty$) of $nM(i)$ to be Poisson with parameter λ is that $\max_i p_i \to 0$ and $n\bar{p} \to \lambda$. For possibly dependent observations, the asymptotic theorem corresponding to Case (II) is: A sufficient condition for the limiting dist. ($n \to \infty$) of $nM(i)$ to be Poisson with parameter λ is that each $X(i)$ is independent of at least $n-L-1$ of the other observations, $\lim_{n\to\infty} (L+1)\{\max P[X(i)=1|X(1), \ldots, X(i-1)]\} = 0$, where the max is taken over all possible values for $X(1), \ldots, X(i-1)$ and all i ($1 \leqslant i \leqslant n$, with the prob. being unconditional for $i=1$), and $\lim_{n\to\infty} n\bar{p} = \lambda$ **Characteristics 1** Low **2** Approximation only moderately accurate for some cases **3** Used symmetrically **4** Very sensitive to moderate or strong dependences involving sizable percentage of observations. Moderate violations of quantitative restrictions on event probabilities have only moderate effects on accuracy of prob. dist. approx. Not sensitive to violation of independence condition of Case (I) if conditional prob. condition of Case (II) satisfied **5** Not difficult to decide whether observations independent. More difficult to decide on value of L and upper bound for conditional prob. relation of Case (II) **6** Useful in testing $\bar{p}$ for set of binomial events with small success probabilities **Bibliography** Ref. 291, 563, 565.

Bibliography of Additional Binomial Distribution Results

The following set of references is not intended to be complete. However, many results of potential usefulness in the nonparametric statistics field are included. This bibliography consists of: Ref. 12, 27, 41, 70, 77, 120, 239, 307, 367, 368, 399, 422, 434, 493, 509.

BIBLIOGRAPHY FOR ASYMPTOTIC RESULTS

Remarks

Many asymptotic results have potential use in the nonparametric statistics field but, due to lack of knowledge about the minimum numbers of observations needed for acceptable accuracy, have not yet reached a stage where they are of practical importance. Following is a list of references to some of the asymptotic material of this nature. Depending on the case considered, the populations yielding the observations can be arbitrary, continuous, or discrete. For some situations the observations are a random sample, in others they are independent, and in some they can have a limited form of dependence. The statistics whose asymptotic properties are derived fall under the two general headings of standard type statistics and of successive cumulative sums. The standard statistics include observation moments, observation range and midrange, ratios of observation means, U statistics, etc. The results for successive sums have application in the sequential analysis field.

Bibliography

Ref. 2, 8, 26, 49, 91, 98, 99, 130, 147, 148, 169, 171, 186, 206, 249, 254, 256, 257, 268, 322, 333, 335, 413, 414, 424, 506, 522, 538, 540.

Chapter 8

ESTIMATES AND TESTS FOR POPULATION PERCENTILES

INTRODUCTION

Many important population properties can be represented in terms of population percentage points. This chapter contains procedures for obtaining point estimates, confidence intervals, and significance tests for population percentiles and differences of population percentiles. In all cases the data are univariate observations. Additional material of this nature, which applies to the special case of medians for populations with symmetrical distributions, is given in Chapter 7.

DESIRABLE PROPERTIES OF POPULATION PERCENTILES

A univariate probability distribution is completely determined by the totality of its percentage points. That is, all available information, from a mathematical statistics viewpoint, is furnished by the values of the population percentiles. In many cases knowledge about a few suitably chosen population percentiles can furnish a substantial amount of information. In fact, knowledge about a single appropriately selected population percentage point is often very valuable.

A useful property of population percentiles is that they maintain their identity under a continuous monotonic transformation of variable. That is, let one univariate random variable be transformed into another univariate random variable by use of a specified continuous monotonic function. Then there is a direct correspondence between the percentage points of the original population and those of the transformed population. If $y=h(x)$, continuous and strictly increasing, is the transformation function, if $h^{-1}(y)$ is its inverse, and if θ''_p is a $100p$ per cent point of the transformed population, then $h^{-1}(\theta''_p)$ is a $100p$ per cent point of the original population. Likewise, if θ'_p is a $100p$ per cent point of the original population, then $h(\theta'_p)$ is a $100p$ per cent point of the transformed population.

An advantage of population percentiles over population moments is that moments do not, in general, maintain their identity under transformations of variable. Knowledge about moments of the transformed population is very difficult to interpret in terms of moments of the original population, and vice versa. Sometimes a desirable property can be imparted to the transformed population by use of a suitable continuous monotonic change of variable (e.g., approximate symmetry). This property can be exploited if population percentiles are considered but is not very useful when population moments are considered. Populations percentage points are the only population probability constants which maintain their identity for all continuous monotonic transformations of variable and all populations.

Functions of population percentiles can be used to measure dispersion, skewness, peakedness, etc. For example, dispersion can be measured from $(\theta_{3/4}-\theta_{1/4})/2$, skewness from $(\theta_{9/10}+\theta_{1/10}-2\theta_{1/2})/(\theta_{9/10}-\theta_{1/10})$, and peakedness from $.263-(\theta_{3/4}-\theta_{1/4})/2(\theta_{9/10}-\theta_{1/10})$.

A problem of practical importance is that of comparing percentage points of two populations. As an example, investigation of whether two populations have the same median value can be of interest. As another example, procedures for investigating whether a specified upper percentile of one population is less than a specified lower percentile of another population have many worthwhile applications.

MEDIAN-SYMMETRY RESULTS OF CHAPTER 7

A number of the procedures presented in Chapter 7 involve the means of symmetrical populations. Since the mean of a symmetrical population is a median of that population, these procedures also apply to the medians of symmetrical populations. In fact, when applied to population medians they are valid under weaker conditions than when applied to population means.

Most of the median-symmetry results of Chapter 7 are not considered again in this chapter. No restatement occurs if the procedures are only applicable to population medians. However, if a procedure can be generalized to population percentiles other than the median, the resulting modification is stated in Chapter 8 (symmetry is not required for these generalized procedures).

CENSORED DATA APPLICATIONS

As mentioned in Chapter 4, sometimes only the values of specified order statistics of a set of observations are available. Then statistical procedures based exclusively on the available order statistics are the only ones that are applicable. Many of the results given in this chapter are based on a few specified order statistics of one or two sets of observations and are therefore applicable for situations of this type. In particular, they are applicable for censored data, whether the censoring is accidental or deliberate. Deliberate censoring can be used to advantage for life-testing situations and one section is concerned with the efficiency of some of the statistical procedures for this case.

OUTLINE OF MATERIAL PRESENTED

The first presentation section is concerned with point estimation of a specified population percentile. Considered are expected value estimation, median estimation, expected value estimation from nearby data, and estimation from response, no-response data. In all cases the results are of a theoretical-approximate nature and the populations are continuous at the value of the percentile considered. Random sampling from a continuous population is assumed for the two cases involving expected value estimates.

The next section contains confidence intervals for a specified population percentile. Exact, randomized-exact, and theoretical-approximate results are presented for arbitrary population percentage points. None of these procedures requires random sampling but the populations are required to be continuous at the common value of the percentile considered.

The following section is concerned with significance tests for a specified population percentile point. Tests of composite hypotheses, theoretical-approximate tests for discrete populations, and sequential tests are considered.

The next to last section does not contain presentations of new procedures. Instead, the efficiencies of some of the nonparametric procedures already presented are examined for life-testing situations. Smaller percentage points of the time-to-failure distribution are considered and the experiment is stopped when the statistics for the nonparametric procedure are determined. Lower bounds for the efficiency of the nonparametric results are determined for the case of sampling from gamma distributions and from normal distributions.

The final section contains some exact and some theoretical-approximate confidence intervals and tests for the difference of two population percentage points. In some of the cases these percentage points are from the same population; in the other cases they are from different populations. In all cases, the populations are continuous.

POINT ESTIMATION OF POPULATION PERCENTILES

Introduction

This section is concerned with point estimation of a specified population percentile. General methods are presented for expected value estimation and for median estimation. A method of medium generality and a method of less generality are given for estimating some of the population percentiles that fall in the censored part of a sample. The less general method is applicable for estimating population percentiles that are moderately far from the available data. Also a procedure is given for estimating population percentiles on the basis of response, no-response data. Additional point estimation procedures, which apply to medians of symmetrical populations, are given in Chapter 7.

Estimation from Nearby Data

In some cases, not all the values for a sample are known. That is, the values are not known for some of the order statistics of the sample. For example, this is the case if the sample is censored in one or both tails. When not all the sample values are known, the general estimation methods may not be applicable, due to unavailability of values for some of the order statistics used in the estimates. This poses the problem of obtaining suitable estimates from the nearby data with known values.

The order statistic $X[i]$ can be thought of as a sample percentage point, namely the $100[i/(n+1)]$ per cent point of the sample of size n. Using this viewpoint, the order statistic $X[i]$ is considered to be nearby to θ_p if p is sufficiently near to $i/(n+1)$ in value. A rather general method for estimating θ_p, based on expected value considerations, is given for cases where several order statistics are available which are nearby to θ_p and have known values. In particular, this method is applicable for estimating population percentiles which are not very far into the censored part of a sample.

If the data are a censored sample and the population percentile to be estimated is not nearby the data in the sense of the general method, some other type of estimation procedure is needed. When the population is continuous and has a probability distribution that can be approximately represented in a generalized Edgeworth series form, "nearby" can be given a much more liberal interpretation. For this case, estimates of θ_p can be obtained where the value of p differs from $i/(n+1)$ by at least .29 for all $X[i]$ with known values. The procedure used is a continuation of the method given in the presentation on page 135, and the estimate for θ_p is determined on the basis of these estimates.

Estimation from Response, No-Response Data

For some situations, the random variable is response or no-response for an experiment carried out at a controlled level (which is at the discretion of the experimenter). The problem is to determine a level with the property that response has probability p of occurring. Then, if the probability of response increases with level value, this level with probability p for response can be considered a $100p$ per cent point of the population of levels. That is, the probability of response is at most equal to p for all lower levels and is at least equal to p for all higher levels. Cases where the probability of response decreases with level value can be converted to cases where this probability increases with level value by applying a continuous monotonically decreasing change of variable to the level value.

Robbins and Monro (ref. 435) developed a stochastic approximation method for estimating a specified percentage point of the population of levels. The method consists in starting with some arbitrarily specified level, experimentally determining the outcome for this level, selecting a new level on the basis of the initial level and the experimental outcome, determining the outcome for the second level, selecting another level on the basis of the second level and the outcome for this level, etc. When this method is used in an appropriate manner, the sequentially obtained new levels converge, in a probability sense, to the value of the population percentile being estimated.

This estimation procedure encounters several difficulties from an applications viewpoint. First, there is no established rule for selecting a suitable initial value to start the process. Second, a sequence of constants is used in the determination of new levels but no completely specified method is given for suitable selection of the values for these constants. Finally, a rule that is not highly conservative is needed for deciding when a level is reached which is a reasonably accurate estimate of the population percentile, so that the process can be stopped; the material of ref. 81 represents a step in this direction. In spite of their application difficulties, Robbins–Monro type estimation processes seem to furnish the most satisfactory nonparametric method of estimating population percentiles on the basis of response, no-response data. Observations of this nature occur in sensitivity testing, fatigue trials, bioassay work, etc.

Adequate Sample Sizes

The general approach outlined on pages 34–36 can be used to determine adequate sample sizes for the first three estimation methods presented in this section. That is, two-stage sampling can be used and the criterion estimated from the first-stage sample. Then an adequate total sample size is determined from this estimate of the criterion. Each of these three presentations contains an approximate expression for the mean square error and the only unknown population constant in these expressions is of the form $1/f(\theta_p)$; methods for estimating this constant (p specified but θ_p unknown) are given in Chapter 10. If the coefficient of variation is used as the criterion, θ_p is also estimated from the first-stage sample (by the estimation method being considered or by any other available method).

No method for determining adequate sample sizes is available for the estimation method based on generalized Edgeworth series. An upper bound for adequate sample sizes is stated for the estimation method based on response, no-response data.

Adequate sample sizes for confidence intervals can be obtained by considering each variable endpoint to be an estimate (see Chapter 4). An adequate sample size is determined for each such estimate and the maximum of these adequate sample sizes (there may be only one) is considered to be adequate for the confidence interval.

A Related Problem

For a given value x_0, a problem that is sometimes of interest is to estimate what percentage point this represents for a population from which a random sample is available. That is, the problem is to estimate p such that $\theta_p = x_0$ for the population sampled. If the population is continuous at x_0, this problem is equivalent to estimating the value of $F(x_0)$, where $F(x)$ is the population distribution function. Methods of estimating $F(x)$ for a specified value of x are given in Chapters 10 and 11.

Outline of Presentations

The first presentation is concerned with expected value estimation of a specified percentile of a continuous population on the basis of order statistics of a sample from that population. In general, exact expected value estimates do not exist for percentage points of continuous populations. However, with mild restrictions, estimates that are very nearly unbiased can be obtained. In addition, a method can be obtained for estimating the standard deviations of these estimates for θ_p.

The second presentation contains median estimates for percentiles of populations that are continuous at the value estimated. These estimates are based on one or two order statistics. When only one order statistic occurs in the estimation expression, the estimate is exact; for the other cases, the estimate is theoretical-approximate. The observations yielding the order statistics are required to be independent and to have a common value for the population percentile estimated; however, these observations are not necessarily a random sample. Thus the median estimates are valid under more general conditions than the expected value estimates.

The third and fourth presentations are concerned with estimating a specified percentile of a continuous population on the basis of nearby sample data. The estimates are of a theoretical-approximate nature for both cases. The third presentation is applicable under moderately general conditions but requires that the population percentile estimated be rather close to order statistics with known values. The fourth presentation allows the percentile to be moderately far from the order statistics with known values but requires that, to an acceptable approximation, the population distribution is of a generalized Edgeworth series form.

The fifth and final presentation furnishes a general method for estimating a specified population percentile from response, no-response data. The percentage point estimated is required to be unique and the population of control levels must be continuous at this percentile. The estimates presented are of a theoretical-approximate nature.

Fixed Material for Section

Data 1 Univariate **2** None.

General Expected Value Estimation

Data 1 Continuous **3** $X[r(h)]$; $h=1,\ldots,s$ **4** $m=1$; lower bound for n contained in Results **Description 1** Theoretical-approximate expected value estimation **2** θ_p from linear combination of the $X[r(h)]$, where $s\leqslant 3$ and the integers $r(h)$ all differ from $(n+1)p$ by $O(\sqrt{n+1})$ **Assumptions 1** Random sample **2** $f(x)$ exists **3** $f(x)$ such that expansions of ref. 138 valid (i.e., $f(x)$ analytic, nonzero over range of def., etc.) **Results 1** $r(h)=(n+1)p+c_h\sqrt{n+1}=\text{integer}$, where the c_h are specified constants and $c_1<\ldots<c_s$; suitable values for the c_h obtained by first determining smallest integer H that is $\geqslant$ $\sqrt{n+1}[10\prod_{h_1>h_2=1}^{s}(h_1-h_2)]^{-1/s}$; next, number c determined by requirement that $(n+1)p+c\sqrt{n+1}$ is one of $1,\ldots,n$ and c^2 is minimum; then $c_h=c+(hH+H')/\sqrt{n+1}$, where H' is integer (possibly negative) which minimizes $\max_{1\leqslant h\leqslant s}|c+(hH+H')/\sqrt{n+1}|$ subject to $1/(n+1)-p\leqslant c+(hH+H')/\sqrt{n+1}\leqslant n/(n+1)-p$. Method considered applicable if $\max_{1\leqslant h\leqslant s}|c_h|\leqslant p(1-p)(n+1)^{1/2}/3$. Constants $a_1,\ldots,a_s$ evaluated by simultaneous solution of first s of equations $\sum_{h=1}^{s}a_h=1$, $\sum_{h=1}^{s}a_hc_h=0$, $\sum_{h=1}^{s}a_hc_h{}^2=-p(1-p)$ **2** *Estimate is*: $\sum_{h=1}^{s}a_hX[r(h)]$, which has expected value $\theta_p+O(n^{-s/2})$ **3** None **4** If $r(h)=(n+1)p$, $EX[r(h)]=\theta_p+O(n^{-1})$; asymptotic dist. of $X[r(h)]$ normal if $f(\theta_p)>0$ and $f'(x)$ continuous at θ_p. Similar results for $4\leqslant s\leqslant 7$ given in ref. 571 **Characteristics 1** Low **2** All estimates have standard deviations of form $\sqrt{p(1-p)}/\sqrt{n}f(\theta_p)+O(n^{-1})$. Let $s=2$; then statistic $\sqrt{p(1-p)/n}\sum_{h=1}^{2}b_hX[r(h)]$ has expected value $\sqrt{p(1-p)}/\sqrt{n}f(\theta_p)+$

$O(n^{-1})$ and variance that is $O(n^{-3/2})$, where the b_h determined by $\sum_{h=1}^{2} b_h = 0$, $\sum_{h=1}^{2} b_h c_h = \sqrt{n+1}$ (also see ref. 571 and Chapter 10). Approx. confidence intervals for $\sqrt{p(1-p)}/\sqrt{n}f((\theta_p)$ obtainable from ref. 562; also see Chapter 10 **3** Used symmetrically **4** Sensitive to random sample condition and requirement that expansions of ref. 138 valid **5** Not difficult to decide on sample assumption. Expansions valid for most continuous situations of practical interest **6** Use of $s=3$ furnishes protection against errors, due to neglected terms, in expected value for estimate. In general, population percentiles do not have exact expected value estimates. **Bibliography** Ref. 118 (pages 367–70), 138, 562, 571.

Median Method of Estimation

Data 1 Arbitrary **3** $X[i]$ **4** $m=1$; lower bound for n stated in Results **Description 1** Theoretical-approximate median estimation **2** Common value of $\theta_p(1), \ldots, \theta_p(n)$ by linear combination of two consecutive order statistics **Assumptions 1** Independent **2** Each population continuous at at $100p$ per cent point **3** $\theta_p(1) = \ldots = \theta_p(n) = \theta_p$ **Results 1** Method applicable if $np(1-p) \geqslant 1$. Integer u is such that $P(X[u] < \theta_p) = \alpha(1)$ and $P(X[u+1] < \theta_p) = \alpha(2)$, where $\alpha(2) \leqslant \frac{1}{2} < \alpha(1)$ **2** *Approx. median estimate* for θ_p is $[K_{\alpha(1)}/(K_{\alpha(1)} - K_{\alpha(2)})]X[u+1] - [K_{\alpha(2)}/(K_{\alpha(1)} - K_{\alpha(2)})]X[u]$ **3** $P(X[u] < \theta_p) = \sum_{i=u}^{n} \binom{n}{i} p^i (1-p)^{n-i}$ **4** Exact median estimate obtained if $\alpha(2) = \frac{1}{2}$. A randomized estimate that is an exact median estimate can always be obtained on basis of presentation on page 206 **Characteristics 1** Low **2** If observations random sample from population with freq. fct. $f(x)$ such that $f(\theta_p) > 0$ and $f'(x)$ continuous at θ_p, estimate has mean square error that is approx. of form $p(1-p)/nf(\theta_p)^2 + O(n^{-3/2})$ and estimate is asymptotically normal with mean θ_p. Estimate of $p(1-p)/nf(\theta_p)^2$ obtainable from ref. 571 (also see presentation on page 305) and approximate confidence intervals for this quantity obtainable from ref. 562; some of these estimates and intervals given in Chapter 10 **3** Used symmetrically **4** Moderately sensitive to independence condition; highly sensitive if n large and sizable fraction of observations dependent. Sensitive to continuity assumption unless n not too large and prob. concentrated at θ_p small for nearly all the populations. Only moderately sensitive to condition of common value for the $\theta_p(i)$ if $M\theta_p(i)$ investigated **5** Not difficult to decide on independence and continuity assumptions. More difficult to verify common value for the $\theta_p(i)$ unless observations believed random sample **6** Median estimates approx. valid under more general conditions than corresponding expected value estimates. Exact median estimates can be obtained by use of randomization (see page 206) **Bibliography** Ref. 76, 94, 118 (pages 367–70), 562, 571.

General Estimation of Percentiles from Nearby Data

Data 1 Continuous **3** $X[s(v)]$; $v=1,\ldots,V$; $s(v_1)-s(v_2)=O(\sqrt{n+1})$ for $v_1 \neq v_2$ **4** $m=1$; n restricted as stated in Results **Description 1** Theoretical-approximate expected value estimation **2** θ_p **Assumptions 1** Random sample **2** $f(x)$ exists **3** $f(x)$ such that expansions of ref. 138 valid [i.e., $f(x)$ analytic, nonzero over range of definition, etc.] **Results 1** $t=\sum_{v=1}^{V} s(v)/V$; $d(v)=t-s(v)$; $p_T=T/(n+1)$, $q_T=1-p_T$. Estimation method not used if $\max_{1\leqslant v\leqslant V}|d(v)|>\frac{2}{3}p_tq_t(n+1)$ or if $|p-p_t|>\frac{4}{3}\min[p(1-p),p_tq_t]$. $A_k=[(p-p_t)/2]^{k-1}/(k-1)!$; $B_k[d(v),(p_t-p)/2]=[(p_t-p)/2]^{k-1}/(k-1)!-(k-1)[(p_t-p)/2]^{k-2}d(v)/(n+1)(k-1)!+(k-1)(k-2)[(p_t-p)/2]^{k-3}[(n+1)p_tq_t+(p_t-q_t)d(v)+d(v)^2]/2(n+1)(n+2)(k-1)!-(k-1)(k-2)(k-3)[(p_t-p)/2]^{k-4}d(v)[(n+1)p_tq_t+d(v)^2/3]/2(n+1)^2(n+2)(k-1)!$. $V\geqslant$ max of 3 and $\log_{10}[\max(n^{-3/2},10^{-4})]/\log_{10}|(p-p_t)/2|$. $D_1,\ldots,D_V$ determined as simultaneous solution of $\sum_{v=1}^{V} D_vB_k[d(v),(p_t-p)/2]=A_k$, $(k=1,\ldots,V)$ **2** *Estimate is*: $\sum_{v=1}^{V} D_vX[s(v)]$, which has expected value $\theta_p+O(n^{-3/2})+O[|(p-p_t)/2|^V]$; here $O(n^{-3/2})$ replaced by $O(n^{-2})$ if $V\geqslant 4$ **3** None **4** When $X[i]$ known for $1\leqslant i\leqslant s<(n+1)p$, suitable value for $s(v)$ is $s-(V-v)\{\max[1,$ largest integer in $(n+1)^{1/2}V^{-1}]\}$ **Characteristics 1** Low (unless V large) **2** Estimate has variance $p_tq_t/nf(\theta_{p_t})^2+O(n^{-3/2})$ and is asymptotically normally distributed; method of estimating quantities of type $p_tq_t/nf(\theta_{p_t})^2$ given in ref. 571 (also see presentation on page 305) and method of obtaining approx. confidence intervals given in ref. 562; some of these estimates and confidence intervals given in Chapter 10 **3** Used symmetrically **4** Sensitive to random sample condition and to requirement that expansions of ref. 138 valid **5** Not difficult to decide on sample assumption. Expansions valid for most situations of practical interest **6** Useful in life-testing and other situations involving deliberate or accidental censoring **Bibliography** Ref. 118 (pages 367–70), 138, 562, 571, 572.

Estimation in Censored Part of Sample—Generalized Edgeworth Series

Data 1 Continuous **3** $X[i]$ for $R_1<i<n-R_2$ **4** $m=1$; $n\geqslant 10\max(R_1,R_2)/3$ **Description 1** Theoretical-approximate point estimation **2** θ_p, where $.01\leqslant p\leqslant .99$ and $(n+1)p\leqslant R_1$ or $(n+1)p\geqslant n-R_2$ (also see Results) **Assumptions 1** Random sample **2** None **3** $F(x)$ of generalized Edgeworth form (see page 47); i.e., $F(x)=\Phi[(x-A)/B]+C\Phi^{(4)}[(x-A)/B]+D\Phi^{(6)}[(x-A)/B]+g[(x-A)/B]$ **Results 1** Histogram $H(x)$ with nonzero limits X_1, X_2 $(X_1<X_2)$ and suitable estimates $\hat{A}$, $\hat{B}$, $\hat{C}$, $\hat{D}$ of A,B,C,D

obtained by method stated in presentation on page 135 $T_1=(\hat{A}-X_1)/\hat{B}$, $T_2=(X_2-\hat{A})/\hat{B}$; only p such that $n \geqslant [1+3(1-p-R_2/n)]/(1-p)$ considered when $T_1 \geqslant T_2$ and only p such that $n \geqslant 3[1+3(R_1/n-p)]/p$ when $T_1<T_2$; if $T_1 \geqslant T_2$, $p \leqslant R_1/n+\Phi(T_1)-\Phi(-T_1)+2\hat{C}\Phi^{(4)}(T_1)+2\hat{D}\Phi^{(6)}(T_1)$; if $T_1<T_2$, $p \geqslant 1-R_2/n-\Phi(T_2)+\Phi(-T_2)-2\hat{C}\Phi^{(4)}(T_2)-2\hat{D}\Phi^{(6)}(T_2)$. For allowable $p>1-R_2/n$, t_p determined from $H(\hat{A}-\hat{B}t_p)+\Phi(t_p)-\Phi(-t_p)+2\hat{C}\Phi^{(4)}(t_p)+2\hat{D}\Phi^{(6)}(t_p)= p$; for allowable $p<R_1/n$, t'_p determined from $H(\hat{A}+\hat{B}t'_p)-\Phi(t'_p)+\Phi(-t'_p)-2\hat{C}\Phi^{(4)}(t'_p)-2\hat{D}\Phi^{(6)}(t'_p)= p$ **2** *Estimates*: For allowable $p>1-R_2/n$, estimate of θ_p is $\hat{A}+\hat{B}t_p$. For allowable $p<R_1/n$, estimate of θ_p is $\hat{A}-\hat{B}t'_p$ **3** None **4** Method can be applicable even if $\hat{A}$ not suitable estimate of $EX(i)$ and $\hat{B}$ not suitable estimate of $\sigma(i)$. Estimation procedure partially self-checking with respect to distribution form assumption **Characteristics 1** Low to medium **2** Unknown in general. Should be at least moderately efficient if distribution at least roughly normal **3** Used symmetrically **4** Moderately sensitive to random sample and generalized Edgeworth series conditions **5** Not difficult to decide on sample assumption. More difficult to decide on generalized Edgeworth series assumption but this partially offset by self-checking nature of procedure **6** Useful in life-testing and other situations involving deliberate or accidental censoring **Bibliography** Ref. 570.

Stochastic Estimation from Response, No-Response Data (Robbins–Monro)

Data 1 Binomial ($1 \equiv$ response, $0 \equiv$ no-response) **3** $X(i)_j$ **4** $m=1$ if single observation evaluated at ith step, $=2$ if two observations evaluated at ith step; $n_1=n_2=n$ and upper limits for required size of n stated in Results (limit depends on the $X(i)_2$ for $m=2$ case) **Description 1** Theoretical-approximate estimates for percentiles of the population of control levels that determines probabilities for response and no-response; i.e., $P[X(i)_j=1|\text{control level is } x]= F(x)$, where $F(x)$ dist. fct. of population of control levels. Choice of control levels at option of experimenter **2** Control level θ_p, where $F(\theta_p)=p$. Estimation based on sequential type scheme in which next control level to be experimentally investigated for response, no-response determined by preceding control level investigated and outcome for that level; thus, for $i>1$, each binomial observation $X(i)_j$ is associated with a control level that is random variable **Assumptions 1** Independent, with the $X(i)_1$ being independent of the $X(i)_2$ **2** $F'(\theta_p)$ exists [thus $F(x)$ continuous at θ_p] **3** $F'(\theta_p) \geqslant p(1-p)/(U-L)$, where $F(x) \doteq 0$ for $x \leqslant L$ and $F(x) \doteq 1$ for $x \geqslant U$ (U and L obtained from judgment-experience considerations); implies that θ_p unique **Results 1** Process stopped at end of nth step (i.e., when $i=n$), where n such that variance of estimate $\leqslant W^2$ (value of W specified from technical or other considerations); use of $W=(U-L)/10$ may be satisfactory (based on coeff. of variation considerations) if $(U+L)/2$ sufficiently different from zero and believed to lie between $\theta_p/2$ and $2\theta_p$ **2** *Estimate and procedure*: Control level x_{n+1} is estimate of θ_p for both $m=1$ and $m=2$. Starting with $x_1=(U+L)/2$, sequentially obtain value of x_{n+1} by procedure of evaluating binomial observation $X(i)_1$ for control level x_i and determining the successive control level values from $x_{i+1}= x_i+[(U-L)/ip(1-p)][p-X(i)_1]$, $(i=1,\ldots,n)$. *For* $m=1$, $(U-L)^2/W^2p(1-p)$ is upper limit for required size of n. *When* $m=2$, improved upper limit for required size of n obtained by evaluating additional observation $X(i)_2$ at each step; here $X(i)_2$ is the response, no-response outcome for the control level nearest to $x_i+i^{-1/4}$ that does not equal x_i; then process stopped at smallest n such that $n \geqslant [(U-L)^2/W^2p(1-p)] \min\left\{1, \max\left[\frac{1}{5}, |1-2\sum_{i=1}^{n} [X(i)_2-X(i)_1](U-L)/n^{3/4}p(1-p)|^{-1}\right]\right\}$; this use of two observations per step will often result in a substantially smaller total no. of observations for the experiment **3** None **4** This stochastic process approx. same as minimax process given in ref. 69 and 156 for special case $f_1=p(1-p)/(U-L)$ and $f_2=2f_1$, where $F(x)$ required to be such that $(x-\theta_p)f_1 \leqslant F(x)-p \leqslant (x-\theta_p)f_2$ for $x \geqslant \theta_p$ and such that $(x-\theta_p)f_1 \geqslant F(x)-p \geqslant (x-\theta_p)f_2$ for $x \leqslant \theta_p$. Use of $[(U-L)/ip(1-p)]$ for coeff. of $[p-X(i)_1]$ based on criterion that this coeff. be $\geqslant 1/iF'(\theta_p)$. Upper limits for required size of n determined on basis of variance for asymptotic dist. of x_{n+1} (see ref. 242) and from the material of ref. 81. Situations where more than one response, no-response observation evaluated at each step considered in ref. 69 and 81. Situation where $F(x)$ discrete considered in ref. 146 **Characteristics 1** Low to high (depending on n) **2** Asymptotic dist. of x_{n+1} normal with mean θ_p and variance $[(U-L)^2/np(1-p)]/[-1+2(U-L)F'(\theta_p)/p(1-p)]$. Process approx. minimax in sense of yielding min for $E(x_{n+1}-\theta_p)^2$ subject to $f_1=p(1-p)/(U-L)$, $f_2=2f_1$, and requiring coeff. of $[p-X(i)_1]$ to be of form $f_1c^2/[p(1-p)+ic^2f_1{}^2]$ with $|x_1| \leqslant c \leqslant [2p(1-p)/f_1(f_2-f_1)]^{1/2}$ **3** Not used symmetrically **4** Moderately sensitive to conditions of independence and existence of $F'(\theta_p)$. Usually not very sensitive to moderate violations of properties to be satisfied by values used for U and L. Sensitive to situations where $F'(\theta_p) < < p(1-p)/(U-L)$; however, a weakened form of estimation is possible even when θ_p not unique (see ref. 81) **5** Not difficult to select conservative values for U, L and to decide on independence. In practice, verification of continuity of $F(x)$ usually sufficient to establish existence of $F'(\theta_p)$. For most continuous populations of practical interest, $F'(\theta_p) \geqslant p(1-p)/(U-L)$ **6** Useful in sensitivity testing, fatigue trials, and bioassay work **Bibliography** Ref. 69, 81, 101, 145, 146, 156, 242, 435.

CONFIDENCE INTERVALS FOR POPULATION PERCENTILES

Discussion

This section contains exact, randomized-exact, and interpolated confidence intervals for arbitrary population percentage points. A procedure for obtaining approximate confidence intervals for an arbitrary population percentile on the basis of response, no-response data is also given. None of these procedures requires a random sample but population continuity at the percentage point value is required in all cases. Additional confidence interval results, which apply to medians of symmetrical populations, are given in Chapter 7.

Exact, Randomized-Exact, and Interpolation Methods

The exact confidence intervals presented are of the form $(X[i_1], X[i_2])$, where $i_1 < i_2$ with $0 \leqslant i_1 \leqslant n$ and $1 \leqslant i_2 \leqslant n+1$. These confidence intervals have exact confidence coefficients whose values depend on i_1, i_2, n, and the population percentage point considered.

Unless n is at least moderately large, the confidence coefficients of the exact confidence intervals for a specified population percentile fail to approximate many values of interest. However, by use of a controlled independent probability process, randomized confidence intervals are obtained which can have any specified confidence coefficient value. These intervals are referred to as randomized-exact confidence intervals.

In this chapter the only randomized-exact one-sided confidence intervals considered are those of the form where the random endpoint is an order statistic $X[i]$ with specified probability p and is $X[i+1]$ with probability $1-p$ $(0 \leqslant i \leqslant n)$. The only randomized-exact two-sided confidence intervals considered are those of the form where the interval is $[X[i_1], X[i_2]]$ with probability p_1, is $[X[i_1], X[i_2+1]]$ probability p_2, is $[X[i_1+1], X[i_2]]$ with probability p_3, and is $[X[i_1+1], X[i_2+1]]$ with probability p_4, where all of these intervals are closed. Here $p_1+p_2+p_3+p_4=1$, $i_1 < i_2$, $0 \leqslant i_1 \leqslant n-1$, and $1 \leqslant i_2 \leqslant n$.

The introduction of a controlled independent probability process has the advantage of yielding exact confidence intervals with coefficients that can be equal to all values of interest. However, use of this method has some drawbacks. First, corresponding confidence intervals with approximately determined confidence coefficients may be available which have higher efficiencies than the randomized-exact results for important situations. Second, procedures based on randomizing schemes performed after the data values are available tend to be less convincing than corresponding procedures without this characteristic; namely, the choice and application of the independent probability process might inadvertently be influenced by the knowledge of the specific results that can be attained.

The interpolated confidence intervals presented have confidence coefficients whose values are only approximately determined; however, the true value is bounded between two known values which are usually at least moderately close together. For samples of small sizes, the interpolated confidence intervals tend to have higher efficiencies than the corresponding exact-randomized confidence intervals, at least when the population is approximately normal and the median is the population percentage point considered. The interpolation method used is such that each random endpoint for a confidence interval is of the form $aX[i]+(1-a)X[i+1]$, where $0 \leqslant a \leqslant 1$ and $1 \leqslant i \leqslant n-1$.

Generalizations of Chapter 7 Results

The only presentation of this section that is a direct generalization of a presentation in Chapter 7 is that concerned with exact and interpolated confidence intervals for arbitrary population percentiles. However, other generalizations of the Chapter 7 material can also be made. First, the randomized-exact method of this chapter is directly applicable to the case of symmetrical populations with a common median. Second, the results of the Chapter 7 presentation furnishing two-sided confidence intervals for population means on the basis of sign test statistics are applicable to the situation of medians of populations which are not necessarily symmetrical.

Description of Presentations

The first presentation contains exact confidence intervals and interpolated confidence intervals for arbitrary population percentage points. The second presentation contains randomized-exact confidence intervals for arbitrary population percentage points. In both cases the observations need not be a random sample but are required to be independent and to have a common value for the population percentile estimated; also the populations must be continuous at this percentage point value.

The third and final presentation is concerned with obtaining approximate confidence intervals for a specified population percentile on the basis of response, no-response data. The population percentile considered is required to be unique and the population must be continuous at the value of this percentage point.

Fixed Material for Section

Data 1 Univariate **2** None **Assumptions 1** Independent.

Exact and Interpolated Confidence Intervals

Data 1 Arbitrary **3** $X[i]$ **4** $m=1$ **Description 1** Exact and bounded-confidence-coefficient one-sided and two-sided confidence intervals

2 Common value of $\theta_p(1), \ldots, \theta_p(n)$ **Assumptions 2** Each population continuous at $100p$ per cent point **3** $\theta_p(1) = \ldots = \theta_p(n) = \theta_1$ **Results 1** $b(u) = b(u; n, p) = \sum_{i=u}^{n} \binom{n}{i} p^i(1-p)^{n-i}$; $X(u, \alpha) = [(K_\alpha - K_{b(u+1)})/(K_{b(u)} - K_{b(u+1)})]X[u] + [(K_{b(u)} - K_\alpha)/(K_{b(u)} - K_{b(u+1)})]X[u+1]$, where $b(u+1) \leqslant \alpha \leqslant b(u)$ **2** *Confidence intervals. Exact*: $P(X[u] < \theta_p) = b(u)$; $P(X[u] > \theta_p) = 1 - b(u)$; $P(X[u] \leqslant \theta_p \leqslant X[v];\ u < v) = b(u) - b(v)$. *Interpolated*: $P[X(u, \alpha) < \theta_p] \doteq \alpha$ and $b(u+1) \leqslant P[X(u, \alpha) < \theta_p] \leqslant b(u)$; $P[X(u, \alpha) \geqslant \theta_p] \doteq 1 - \alpha$ and $P(X[u] > \theta_p) \leqslant P[X(u, \alpha) > \theta_p] \leqslant P(X[u+1] > \theta_p)$; $P[X(u, \alpha') \leqslant \theta_p \leqslant X(v, \alpha'');\ v \geqslant u+1] \doteq \alpha' - \alpha''$ ($\alpha' \geqslant \alpha''$ since $v \geqslant u+1$) and $b(u+1) - b(v) \leqslant P[X(u, \alpha') \leqslant \theta_p \leqslant X(v, \alpha'');\ v \geqslant u+1] \leqslant b(u) - b(v+1)$ **3** $b(u)$ can be evaluated by methods in binomial dist. sect. of Chapter 7 **4** If $b(u)$ not near zero or unity, $X[u]$ is asymptotically normally distributed with variance $p(1-p)/nf(\theta_p)^2$ when observations sample from population with $f(\theta_p) > 0$ and $f'(x)$ continuous at θ_p. If populations not necessarily continuous at θ_p, $P(X[u] < \theta_p) \leqslant b(u) \leqslant P(X[u] \leqslant \theta_p)$ and $P(X[u] > \theta_p) \leqslant 1 - b(u) \leqslant P(X[u] \geqslant \theta_p)$; also $P(X[u] < \theta_p < X[v]) \leqslant b(u) - b(v) \leqslant P(X[u] \leqslant \theta_p \leqslant X[v])$ **Characteristics 1** Low **2** Exact one-sided results most powerful for case of sample from arbitrary absolutely continuous population. For $p = \frac{1}{2}$ and sample from normal population, all intervals have asymptotic efficiencies of 63.7 per cent; efficiency tends to increase as n decreases and can reach 95 per cent for small n **3** Used symmetrically **4** Moderately sensitive to independence condition; highly sensitive if n large and sizable percentage of observations dependent. Sensitive to continuity assumption unless n not too large and prob. concentrated at θ_p small for nearly all the populations. Only moderately sensitive to condition of common value for the $\theta_p(i)$ if $M\theta_p(i)$ investigated **5** Not difficult to decide on independence and continuity assumptions. More difficult to verify common value for the $\theta_p(i)$ unless observations believed random sample **6** Interpolated confidence intervals tend to be more efficient than corresponding randomized-exact intervals, at least for $p = \frac{1}{2}$, n not too large, and sample from normal population **Bibliography** Ref. 76, 94, 118 (pages 367–70), 184, 386.

Randomized-Exact Confidence Intervals

Data 1 Arbitrary **3** $X[i]$ **4** $m = 1$ **Description 1** Randomized-exact one-sided and two-sided confidence intervals **2** Common value of $\theta_p(1), \ldots, \theta_p(n)$ **Assumptions 2** Each population continuous at $100p$ per cent point **3** $\theta_p(1) = \ldots = \theta_p(n) = \theta_p$ **Results 1** $b(u) = b(u; n, p) = \sum_{i=u}^{n} \binom{n}{i} p^i(1-p)^{n-i}$ for $u = 0, \ldots, n$ and $b(n+1; n, p) = b(n; n-1, p) = 0$, $b(-1; n-1, p) = 1$; $p(u, \alpha) = [\alpha - b(u+1)]/[b(u) - b(u+1)]$, where α must satisfy

$b(u+1) \leqslant \alpha \leqslant b(u)$; $b'(u) = n[b(u-1; n-1, p) - b(u; n, p)]/(1-p)$. Values of p_1, p_2, p_3, p_4, U, V determined from requirements that U and V integers such that $0 \leqslant U < V \leqslant n$, the p's are nonnegative, $p_1+p_2+p_3+p_4=1$, $[b(U)-b(V)]p_1+[b(U+1)-b(V)]p_2+[b(U)-b(V+1)]p_3+[b(U+1)-b(V+1)]p_4 = 1-\alpha$, $[b'(U)-b'(V)]p_1+[b'(U+1)-b'(V)]p_2+[b'(U)-b'(V+1)]p_3+[b'(U+1)-b'(V+1)]p_4 = 0$; if $p_1, \ldots, p_4, U, V$ not uniquely determined by stated requirements, additional requirement that $[b(U)+b(V)]p_1+[b(U+1)+b(V)]p_2+[b(U)+b(V+1)]p_3+[b(U+1)+b(V+1)]p_4$ as near unity as possible is imposed. $Y(u, \alpha)$ = random variable that equals $X[u]$ with prob. $p(u, \alpha)$ and equals $X[u+1]$ with prob. $1-p(u, \alpha)$; $[Y_1(U, V, \alpha), Y_2(U, V, \alpha)]$ = random variable that is the closed interval $[X[U], X[V]]$ with prob. p_1, is $[X[U+1], X[V]]$ with prob. p_2, is $[X[U], X[V+1]]$ with prob. p_3, and is $[X[U+1], X[V+1]]$ with prob. p_4 (all of these intervals closed) **2** *Confidence intervals*: $P[Y(u, \alpha) < \theta_p] = \alpha$; $P[Y(u, \alpha) > \theta_p] = 1-\alpha$; $P[Y(u, \alpha') \leqslant \theta_p \leqslant Y(v, \alpha''); u<v] = 1 - P[Y(u, \alpha') > \theta_p] - P[Y(v, \alpha'') < \theta_p] = \alpha' - \alpha''$ ($\alpha' \geqslant \alpha''$ since $u < v$); $[Y_1(U, V, \alpha), Y_2(U, V, \alpha)]$ unbiased confidence interval with coeff. $1-\alpha$ **3** $b(u; n, p)$ can be evaluated by methods in binomial dist. sect. of Chapter 7 **4** If observations sample from population with $f(\theta_p) > 0$ and $f'(x)$ continuous at θ_p, $Y(u, \alpha)$ asymptotically normal with variance $p(1-p)/nf(\theta_p)^2$. When populations not necessarily continuous at θ_p, $P[Y(u, \alpha) < \theta_p] \leqslant \alpha \leqslant P[Y(u, \alpha) \leqslant \theta_p]$ and $P[Y(u, \alpha) > \theta_p] \leqslant 1-\alpha \leqslant P[Y(u, \alpha) \geqslant \theta_p]$; also $P[Y(u, \alpha') < \theta_p < Y(u, \alpha'')] \leqslant \alpha' - \alpha'' \leqslant P[Y(u, \alpha') \leqslant \theta_p \leqslant Y(u, \alpha'')]$ and confidence coeff. of $[Y_1(U, V, \alpha), Y_2(U, V, \alpha)]$ is $\geqslant 1-\alpha$ **Characteristics** **1** Low for one-sided and two-sided intervals based on $Y(u, \alpha)$. Medium for unbiased intervals **2** For sample from arbitrary absolutely continuous population, one-sided intervals most powerful randomized similar (see ref. 184). Unbiased intervals most powerful unbiased randomized similar; also most stringent when $p=\frac{1}{2}$. For sample from normal population and $p=\frac{1}{2}$, all intervals have asymptotic efficiencies of 63.7 per cent; efficiency tends to increase as n decreases and can be 95 per cent for small n **3** Used symmetrically **4** Moderately sensitive to independence condition; highly sensitive if n large and sizable percentage of observations dependent. Sensitive to continuity assumption unless prob. concentrated at θ_p small for nearly all populations and n not very large. Only moderately sensitive to condition of a common $100p$ per cent point if $M\theta_p(i)$ investigated **5** Not difficult to decide on independence and continuity assumptions. More difficult to verify a common $100p$ per cent point for all populations unless observations believed random sample **6** Interpolated confidence intervals tend to be more efficient than corresponding randomized-exact intervals, at least for $p=\frac{1}{2}$, n not too large, and sample from normal population **Bibliography** Ref. 118 (pages 367–70), 184.

Approximate Confidence Intervals from Response, No-Response Data

Data 1 Binomial ($1 \equiv$ response, $0 \equiv$ no-response) **3** $X(i)_j$ **4** $m=1$ if single observation evaluated at ith step, $=2$ if two observations evaluated at ith step; $n_1=n_2=n$ and upper limits for required size of n stated in Results (limit depends on the $X(i)_2$ for $m=2$ case) **Description 1** Theoretical-approximate one-sided and two-sided confidence intervals for percentiles of the population of control levels that determines probabilities for response and no-response; i.e., $P[X(i)_1=1|$ control level is $x]=F(x)$, where $F(x)$ dist. fct. of population of control levels. Choice of control levels at option of experimenter **2** Control level θ_p, where $F(\theta_p)=p$. Confidence intervals based on sequential type scheme in which next control level to be experimentally investigated for response, no-response determined by preceding control level investigated and outcome for that level; thus, for $i>1$, each binomial observation $X(i)_j$ associated with control level that is random variable **Assumptions 1** Independent, with the $X(i)_1$ independent of the $X(i)_2$ **2** $F'(\theta_p)$ exists (thus $F(x)$ continuous at θ_p) **3** $F'(\theta_p) \geqslant p(1-p)/(U-L)$, where $F(x) \doteq 0$ for $x \leqslant L$ and $F(x) \doteq 1$ for $x \geqslant U$ (U and L obtained from judgment-experience considerations) **Results 1** x_i is control level at which value of $X(i)_1$ determined. Process stopped at end of nth step (i.e., when $i=n$), where n such that $\sigma x_{n+1} \leqslant W$ (value of W specified from technical or other considerations); use of $W=(U-L)/10$ may be satisfactory (based on coeff. of variation considerations) if $(U+L)/2$ sufficiently different from zero and believed to lie between $\theta_p/2$ and $2\theta_p$. Starting with $x_1=(U+L)/2$, control levels $x_2, \ldots, x_{n+1}$ determined by evaluating $X(i)_1$ for level x_i and using relation $x_{i+1}= x_i+[(U-L)/ip(1-p)][p-X(i)_1]$, $(i=1, \ldots, n)$; $X(i)_2$ is evaluated at control level nearest to $x_i+i^{-1/4}$ that does not equal x_i. $Z= [np(1-p)]^{1/2}(x_{n+1}-\theta_p) |1-2\sum_{i=1}^{n}[X(i)_2-X(i)_1](U-L)/n^{3/4}p(1-p)|^{1/2}/(U-L)$ **2** *Confidence Intervals*: *When* $m=1$, and $1/4n \leqslant \alpha \leqslant \frac{1}{2}$ (i.e., only the $X(i)_1$ evaluated), $(U-L)^2/W^2p(1-p)$ is upper limit for required size of n and, to a reasonable approx., $P[x_{n+1}-\theta_p \geqslant -K_\alpha(U-L)/\sqrt{np(1-p)}] \geqslant 1-\alpha$ and $P[x_{n+1}-\theta_p \leqslant K_\alpha(U-L)/\sqrt{np(1-p)}] \geqslant 1-\alpha$; if $1/4n \leqslant \alpha(1), \alpha(2) \leqslant \frac{1}{2}-1/4n$, $P[-K_{\alpha(1)}(U-L)/\sqrt{np(1-p)} < x_{n+1}-\theta_p < K_{\alpha(2)}(U-L)/\sqrt{np(1-p)}] \geqslant 1-\alpha(1)-\alpha(2)$. *When* $m=2$ (both $X(i)_1$ and $X(i)_2$ evaluated for each i), process stopped at smallest n that is $\geqslant [(U-L)^2/W^2p(1-p)]$ min $\left\{1, \max\left[\frac{1}{5}, |1-2\sum_{i=1}^{n}[X(i)_2-X(i)_1](U-L)/n^{3/4}p(1-p)|^{-1}\right]\right\}$ and, for $2/n \leqslant \alpha \leqslant 1-2/n$, $P(Z \leqslant -K_\alpha) \doteq P(Z \geqslant K_\alpha) \doteq \alpha$; for $2/n \leqslant \alpha(1), \alpha(2) \leqslant \frac{1}{2}-2/n$, $P(-K_{\alpha(1)} < Z < K_{\alpha(2)}) \doteq 1-\alpha(1)-\alpha(2)$; this use of two observations per step will often result in a substantially smaller total number of observations for the experiment **3** None **4** This stochastic process approx. same as minimax process given in ref. 69 and 156 for special case $f_1=$

$p(1-p)/(U-L)$ and $f_2=2f_1$, where $F(x)$ required to be such that $(x-\theta_p)f_1 \leqslant F(x)-p \leqslant (x-\theta_p)f_2$ for $x \geqslant \theta_p$ and such that $(x-\theta_p)f_1 \geqslant F(x)-p \geqslant (x-\theta_p)f_2$ for $x \leqslant \theta_p$. Use of $(U-L)/ip(1-p)$ for coeff. of $[p-X(i)_1]$ based on criterion that this coeff. be $\geqslant 1/iF'(\theta_p)$. Rules for stopping process (upper limits for required size of n) determined on basis of material of ref. 81 and 242 **Characteristics 1** Low to high (depending on n) **2** Asymptotic dist. of x_{n+1} normal with mean θ_p and variance $[(U-L)^2/np(1-p)]/[-1+2(U-L)F'(\theta_p)/p(1-p)]$. Process approx. minimax in sense of yielding min for $E(x_{n+1}-\theta_p)^2$ subject to $f_1=p(1-p)/(U-L)$, $f_2=2f_1$, and requiring coeff. of $[p-X(i)_1]$ to be of form $f_1c^2/[p(1-p)+ic^2f_1{}^2]$ with $|x_1| \leqslant c \leqslant [2p(1-p)/f_1(f_2-f_1)]^{1/2}$ **3** Not used symmetrically **4** Moderately sensitive to conditions of independence and existence of $F'(\theta_p)$. Usually not very sensitive to moderate violations of relations to be satisfied by values used for U and L. Sensitive to situations where $F'(\theta_p) < < p(1-p)/(U-L)$ **5** Not difficult to select conservative values for U, L and to decide on independence. In practice, verification of continuity of $F(x)$ usually sufficient to establish existence of $F'(\theta_p)$. For most continuous populations of practical interest, $F'(\theta_p) \geqslant p(1-p)/(U-L)$ **6** Useful in sensitivity testing, fatigue trials, and bioassay work **Bibliography** Ref. 69, 81, 101, 145, 156, 242.

TESTS FOR POPULATION PERCENTILES

Introduction

The confidence interval results given in the preceding section can be converted to tests for population percentage points. However, direct development of tests is more appropriate for some situations of interest. This section contains tests for continuous cases where both the null and the alternative hypotheses can be composite. Also considered are the case of sampling from a discrete population and the case of sequential tests for populations that are continuous at the hypothetical value tested. Further tests, which apply to medians of symmetrical populations, are stated in Chapter 7.

Tests for Composite Hypotheses

Here a composite null hypothesis asserts that the population percentage point considered has one of a specified set of values. A composite alternative hypothesis asserts that the population percentile value is in some specified set which has no values in common with the null hypothesis set.

A test is one-sided if all the values for the null hypothesis set are on the same side of the set of values for the alternative hypothesis considered; otherwise the test is two-sided. Only one-sided tests are considered in the composite hypotheses presentation of this section. Two-sided tests can also be devised but their properties are more difficult to establish and to interpret.

Consider the set of possible values for the population percentile considered that is furnished by a composite null hypothesis. Let each of these potential values be considered as a simple hypothesis and determine the significance levels of the test, which is fixed, for these simple null hypotheses. That is, the critical region for the test is fixed and the simple null hypothesis considered is varied. Then the (generalized) significance level of the test considered equals the supremum of the significance levels obtained for this totality of simple null hypotheses.

The one-sided tests given are applicable to situations where the observations are independent but not necessarily a sample. Then the null hypothesis values are not required to represent the same percentage points for every population when this hypothesis is true. All that is required is that, for each population, the value of the percentile considered is in the null hypothesis set when the null hypothesis holds.

Tests for Discrete Cases

In general, θ_p is said to be a $100p$ per cent point of the population yielding $X(i)$ when it satisfies the relations $P[X(i) < \theta_p] \leqslant p$ and $P[X(i) > \theta_p] \leqslant 1-p$. Thus, for the discrete case, θ_p is not associated with a unique value for p. In fact, each permissible value of θ_p is a $100p$ per cent point for an interval of values for p.

For nonparametric situations, this ambiguity causes difficulties. Namely, the experimenter is interested in the value of θ_p for a specified value p. However, there is an unknown interval of probability values which have the same percentage point value as θ_p. Let p_1 be the lower endpoint of this interval and p_2 the upper endpoint. Then $P[X(i) < \theta_p] = p_1$ and $P[X(i) > \theta_p] = 1-p_2$. Unless the values of p_1 and p_2 are rather close together, significance levels computed under the assumption that $P[X(i) < \theta_p] = p$ and $P[X(i) > \theta_p] = 1-p$ can differ substantially from the actual values.

The null hypothesis asserts that θ_p has a specified value $\theta_p^{(0)}$ and the three alternative hypotheses considered are $\theta_p > \theta_p^{(0)}$, $\theta_p < \theta_p^{(0)}$, and $\theta_p \neq \theta_p^{(0)}$. The tests are based on the signs of the n values $X(i) - \theta_p^{(0)}$, where the $X(i)$ are a random sample. Here zero values for the $X(i) - \theta_p^{(0)}$ are eliminated in conducting a test. Two ways of eliminating zero values are considered. In one case, the test is based entirely on the signs of the nonzero values (i.e., the zero values are omitted from consideration). In the other case, each zero value is independently given a plus or a minus sign, with probability $\frac{1}{2}$ for each sign; then the test is based on the resulting n plus and minus signs.

Neither method of handling zero values yields exact tests. Instead, bounded significance level tests are obtained, where the significance level bounds depend on p_1 and p_2. If the number of plus and minus signs is large, the value of $p_2 - p_1$ must be quite small to yield significance level bounds that differ substantially from the trivial values of zero and unity.

An alternative method of obtaining tests for the discrete case consists in using the confidence interval results for the first two presentations of the preceding section. When the populations yielding the independent observations are arbitrary, the confidence intervals for the common value of the $100p$ per cent points have confidence coefficients that are bounded on one side by the values that occur for the case of continuous populations. One-sided and two-sided tests are easily developed which have significance levels that are bounded from above by the significance level for the continuous case. Thus this alternative method has the advantages that no observations are discarded, no independent probability process is used, and the significance levels have specified upper bounds. Its major disadvantage is that, in some cases, the power may be substantially decreased because the actual (unknown) significance level is much lower than the value of the upper bound. The tests presented in this section tend to have significance levels that are nearer the value for continuity than the significance levels of the corresponding tests based on confidence intervals, but have the disadvantage that the upper bound tends to unity as the number of observations increases.

Exact tests can be obtained by use of the method of converting data to a continuous form that is described in Chapter 4. Namely, an independent value from a continuous population with infinitesimally small range could be added to each observation value. Then the population for the modified sample values is continuous and tests based on the confidence intervals for the case of continuity at θ_p can be used. Also θ_p for the modified population only differs from θ_p for the discrete population by an infinitesimal amount. Besides this, the requirement of a random sample need not be imposed; it is sufficient that the observations be independent and from populations with a common value for θ_p. In most cases, an infinitesimal random value can be obtained as, say, 10^{-100} times an approximately random value (ten decimal places is usually sufficient) from the rectangular distribution with range $-\frac{1}{2}$ to $\frac{1}{2}$, which is easily determined from a random digit table.

In spite of the attractiveness of the procedure of converting the data to a continuous form, in the sense that exact results are obtained, this procedure can be undesirable in some cases. Namely, introduction of an independent probability process can be considered undesirable; also, the discrete nature of the data is sometimes of basic importance for the situation being considered.

Basis for Sequential Tests

For the sequential cases, the tests have valid significance levels if the observations are independent and from populations which have a common value for the percentage points considered; also these populations are continuous at the hypothetical value tested. However, the tests are constructed using the assumption that the observations are a random sample from a continuous population. The tests presented are sequential forms of the sign test. That is, if the null hypothesis is $\theta_p = \theta_p^{(0)}$, the test is based on the signs of the $X(i) - \theta_p^{(0)}$.

For the one-sided test with alternative $\theta_p > \theta_p^{(0)}$, the first step is to select a value $p(1)$ which is less than p and such that the test has a specified high probability of accepting the alternative hypothesis if $\theta_p^{(0)} = \theta_{p(1)}$. Then, if a negative sign for $X(i) - \theta_p^{(0)}$ is denoted by 1 and a positive sign by 0, the standard one-sided binomial sequential test of the null hypothesis that $P[X(i) - \theta_p^{(0)} < 0] = p$ and the alternative hypothesis that $P[X(i) - \theta_p^{(0)} < 0] < p$ can be applied directly to test $\theta_p = \theta_p^{(0)}$ against the alternative $\theta_p > \theta_p^{(0)}$, with special emphasis on situations where $\theta_p^{(0)} \leqslant \theta_{p(1)}$. In a similar manner, the one-sided binomial sequential test of $P[X(i) - \theta_p^{(0)} < 0] = p$ against the alternative $P[X(i) - \theta_p^{(0)} < 0] > p$ can be used directly to test $\theta_p = \theta_p^{(0)}$ against the alternative $\theta_p < \theta_p^{(0)}$, with special emphasis on situations where $\theta_p^{(0)} \geqslant \theta_{p(2)}$, with $p < p(2)$.

The one-sided tests can also be interpreted as tests of composite null hypotheses. Namely, the test with alternative $\theta_p^{(0)} < \theta_p$ can be considered to have the composite null hypothesis $\theta_p^{(0)} \geqslant \theta_p$ and (generalized) significance level equal to α (which is the value when $\theta_p = \theta_p^{(0)}$ is the null hypothesis). The test with alternative $\theta_p^{(0)} > \theta_p$ can be considered to have the composite null hypothesis $\theta_p^{(0)} \leqslant \theta_p$ and (generalized) significance level α. Here, as for the one-sided nonsequential tests with composite null hypotheses, the generalized significance level of a test is determined by considering the set of possible values for θ_p that is specified by the composite null hypothesis. Letting the test remain fixed, each of these possible values is considered to be a simple null hypothesis and the resulting significance level is determined. The supremum of these values is said to be the generalized significance level of the test.

In the case of two-sided tests, two values $p(1)$ and $p(2)$ are selected such that $p(1) < p < p(2)$. The problem is to test $\theta_p = \theta_p^{(0)}$ against the alternative $\theta_p \neq \theta_p^{(0)}$, with emphasis on situations where $\theta_p^{(0)} \leqslant \theta_{p(1)}$ or $\theta_p^{(0)} \geqslant \theta_{p(2)}$. This test is performed by use of a two-sided binomial sequential test of the null hypothesis that $P[X(i) - \theta_p^{(0)} < 0] = p$ against the alternative hypothesis that $P[X(i)-\theta_p^{(0)}<0]\neq p$ with emphasis on $P[X(i)-\theta_p^{(0)}<0]\leqslant p(1)$ or $P[X(i)-\theta_p^{(0)}<0]\geqslant p(2)$. Two types of two-sided tests are presented. A statement of their basis and properties is given in the presentation.

The three kinds of binomial sequential tests used in testing $\theta_p=\theta_p^{(0)}$ are given in the sequential test presentation (page 186) of Chapter 7. The principal notational difference between the binomial sequential test presentation of Chapter 7 and the sequential test presentation of this section is that here the null hypothesis value is p rather than $p(0)$.

Outline of Presentations

The first presentation is concerned with one-sided tests for population percentage points where both the null hypothesis and the alternative hypothesis can be composite. The observations are not necessarily a sample but are independent and from populations that are continuous at their $100p$ per cent points.

The second presentation contains some approximate tests for an arbitrary percentage point of a discrete population. These tests are of a bounded significance level nature. However, determination of the bound values depends on some additional knowledge about the nature of the discrete population.

The third and last presentation furnishes one-sided and two-sided sequential tests for population percentage points. In deriving the tests, the observations are considered to be a random sample from a continuous population. However, these tests have valid significance levels for situations where this condition is not satisfied.

Fixed Material for Section

Data 1 Univariate **2** None **4** $m=1$.

One-Sided Tests Involving Composite Hypotheses

Data 1 Arbitrary **3** $X[i]$ **Description 1** Exact one-sided signif. tests with composite null hyp. set of values S_0 and composite alternative hyp. set of values S_a **2** $\theta_p(1),\ldots,\theta_p(n)$; null hyp. asserts that $\theta_p(i)\epsilon S_0$ for all i **Assumptions 1** Independent **2** Each population continuous at its $100p$ per cent pt. **3** None **Results 1** Altern. hyp. asserts that nearly all $\theta_p \epsilon S_a$ and specifies the relative locations of S_0 and S_a. $b(u)=\sum_{i=u}^{n}\binom{n}{i}p^i(1-p)^{n-i}$ **2** *Tests*: For altern. hyp. that sup $S_0<\inf S_a$, test with (generalized) sig. level $1-b(u)$ is: Reject null hyp. if $X[u]>\sup S_0$. For altern. hyp. that inf. $S_0>\sup S_a$, test with (generalized) sig. level $b(u)$ is: Reject null hyp. if $X[u]>\inf S_0$ **3** $b(u)$ can be evaluated by methods in binomial dist. sect. of Chapter 7 **4** Examples of S_0, S_a combinations for case of $\theta_p(1)=\ldots=\theta_p(n)=\theta_p$ are S_0: $\theta_p \leqslant \theta_p^{(0)}$, S_a: $\theta_p > \theta_p^{(0)}$; S_0: $\theta_p \geqslant \theta_p^{(0)}$, S_a: $\theta_p < \theta_p^{(0)}$. If observations sample from population with $f(\theta_p) > 0$ and $f'(x)$ continuous at θ_p, $X[u]$ asymptotically normally distributed with variance $p(1-p)/nf(\theta_p)^2$ when signif. level fixed **Characteristics 1** Low **2** Most powerful for case of sample from arbitrary absolutely continuous population **3** Used symmetrically **4** Moderately sensitive to independence condition; highly sensitive if n large and sizable percentage of observations dependent. Value of generalized signif. level sensitive to continuity assumption unless n not too large and prob. concentrated at $100p$ per cent pt. small for nearly all populations **5** Not difficult to decide on independence and continuity assumptions **6** Useful for life-testing and other censored data situations **Bibliography** Ref. 118 (pages 367–70), 184.

Tests for Arbitrary Percentiles of Discrete Populations

Data 1 Discrete **3** $X(i)$ **Description 1** Theoretical-approximate one-sided and two-sided signif. tests **2** θ_p **Assumptions 1** Random sample **2** None **3** $\theta_p = \theta_\xi$ for ξ in interval of length at most δ **Results 1** Null hyp. is $\theta_p = \theta_p^{(0)}$. N_1 = no. of positive $[X(i)-\theta_p^{(0)}]$; N_2 = no. of negative $[X(i)-\theta_p^{(0)}]$. n' = no. of positive signs for the $[X(i)-\theta_p^{(0)}]$ when, independently and with prob. $\frac{1}{2}$ for $+$ and for $-$, signs are randomly given to the $[X(i)-\theta_p^{(0)}]$ that are zero. $b(u;p,N)=\sum_{i=u}^{N}\binom{N}{i}p^i(1-p)^{N-i}$. One type of tests is conditional and based on N_1, N_2; the other type is unconditional and based on n' **2** *Conditional tests*: Accept $\theta_p < \theta_p^{(0)}$ if $N_1 \geqslant u$; has sig. level with nominal value $b(u;p,N_1+N_2)$ and bounded between $b[u;(p-\delta)/(1-\delta),N_1+N_2]$ and $b[u;p/(1-\delta),N_1+N_2]$. Accept $\theta_p > \theta_p^{(0)}$ if $N_1 \leqslant u-1$; has sig. level with nominal value $1-b(u;p,N_1+N_2)$ and bounded between $1-b[u;p/(1-\delta),N_1+N_2]$ and $1-b[u;(p-\delta)/(1-\delta),N_1+N_2]$. Accept $\theta_p \neq \theta_p^{(0)}$ if $N_1 \leqslant u-1$ or $N_1 \geqslant v$, where $v \geqslant u$; has sig. level with nominal value $1-b(u;p,N_1+N_2)+b(v;p,N_1+N_2)$ and bounded between $\inf_{-\delta\leqslant p'\leqslant 0}\{1-b[u;(p+p')/(1-\delta),N_1+N_2]+b[v;(p+p')/(1-\delta),N_1+N_2]\}$ and $\sup_{-\delta\leqslant p'\leqslant 0}\{1-b[u;(p+p')/(1-\delta),N_1+N_2]+b[v;(p+p')/(1-\delta),N_1+N_2]\}$. *Unconditional tests*: Accept $\theta_p < \theta_p^{(0)}$ if $n' \geqslant u$; has sig. level with nominal value $b(u;p,n)$ and bounded between $b(u;p-\delta/2,n)$ and $b(u;p+\delta/2,n)$. Accept $\theta_p > \theta_p^{(0)}$ if $n' \leqslant u-1$; has sig. level with nominal value $1-b(u;p,n)$ and bounded between $1-b(u;p+\delta/2,n)$ and $1-b(u;p-\delta/2,n)$. Accept $\theta_p \neq \theta_p^{(0)}$ if $n' \leqslant u-1$ or $n' \geqslant v$, where $v \geqslant u$; has sig. level with nominal value $1-b(u;p,n)+b(v;p,n)$ and bounded between $\inf_{-\delta/2\leqslant p'\leqslant\delta/2}[1-b(u;p+p',n)+b(v;p+p',n)]$ and $\sup_{-\delta/2\leqslant p'\leqslant\delta/2}[1-b(u;p+p',n)+b(v;p+p',n)]$ **3** $b(u;p,N)$ can be evaluated by methods in binomial dist. sect. of Chapter 7 **4** In all cases, $0 \leqslant p-\delta \leqslant p+\delta \leqslant 1$. If α is nominal sig. level and N_1+N_2 large, sig. level bounds quite far apart for conditional tests when $\delta \geqslant .1|K_\alpha|[p(1-p)(N_1+N_2)]^{-1/2}$; likewise bounds quite far apart for unconditional tests if $\delta \geqslant .4|K_\alpha| [p(1-p)/n]^{1/2}$; here p such that normal approx. to binomial dist. reasonably accurate. Tests also applicable for case of arbitrary population that can be discrete at θ_p. Tests with upper bound for signif. level equal to value for continuous case obtainable from confidence intervals in first two presentations of preceding sect. Exact tests that are appropriate for some situations can be obtained by converting discrete data to approx. equivalent continuous form (see page 211). **Characteristics 1** Low to medium **2** Unknown; however, results for corresponding continuous cases furnish indication of efficiency properties. **3** Used symmetrically **4** Not very sensitive to random sample condition when populations have common value for θ_p. Effect on prob. bounds of using too small for δ can be determined directly **5** Not difficult to decide on sample assumption or to choose conservatively large value for δ **6** Has many applications; in practice all populations discrete due to measurement accuracy limitations. Form useful for life-testing and other censored data situations obtained by expressing tests in terms of order statistics **Bibliography** Ref. 238, 418, 573.

One-Sided and Two-Sided Sequential Tests

Data 1 Arbitrary **3** $X(i)$ **4** n not a fixed value **Description 1** Approx. (nearly exact) one-sided and two-sided signif. tests **2** θ_p; null hyp. H_0 is $\theta_p=\theta_p^{(0)}$ **Assumptions 1** Random sample **2** Population continuous at all percentiles considered **3** None **Results 1** $p(1)$, $p(2)$ specified such that $p(1)<p<p(2)$. Altern. hyp. for one-sided tests are $\theta_p^{(0)}<\theta_p$ with emphasis on $\theta_p^{(0)} \leqslant \theta_{p(1)}$, and $\theta_p^{(0)}>\theta_p$ with emphasis on $\theta_p^{(0)} \geqslant \theta_{p(2)}$. For the two types of two-sided tests, altern. hyp. is $\theta_p^{(0)} \neq \theta_p$ with emphasis on $\theta_p^{(0)} \leqslant \theta_{p(1)}$ or $\theta_p^{(0)} \geqslant \theta_{p(2)}$. To a reasonable approx., all tests have signif. level α ($\alpha<\frac{1}{2}$). For one-sided tests, β is max prob. of type II error for situations emphasized. For one type of two-sided test, $\beta=$prob. of type II error when $\theta_p^{(0)}=\theta_{w_1 p(1)+w_2 p(2)}$, where w_1 and w_2 are nonnegative, $w_1+w_2=1$, and w_1 chosen so that larger of prob. of type II error at $\theta_{p(1)}$ and at $\theta_{p(2)}$ is minimized. For other type of two-sided test, $\beta=$probability of type II error when $\theta_p^{(0)}=\theta_{p(w_1,w_2)}$, where $p(w_1, w_2)= p(1)^{w_1}p(2)^{w_2}$, w_1 and w_2 are such that $0<p(w_1, w_2)<1$, $p(w_1, w_2)+[1-p(1)]^{w_1}[1-p(2)]^{w_2}=1$, and w_1 chosen so that larger of prob. of type II error at $\theta_{p(1)}$ and at $\theta_{p(2)}$ is minimized. For both types of two-sided tests, method of evaluating w_1 stated in part 4 of Results. In all cases $\alpha+\beta<1$.

Notation: $q=1-p$, $q(1)=1-p(1)$, $q'=1-p'$, etc. $a_J[p',p'']$ is largest integer $\leqslant$ $\{\log_{10}[\beta/(1-\alpha)]\}/|\log_{10}(p''q'/p'q'')|$ $+J[\log_{10}(q'/q'')]/\log_{10}(p''q'/p'q'')$ and $b_J[p',p'']$ is smallest integer $\geqslant$ $-\frac{1}{3}+\{\log_{10}[(1-\beta)/\alpha]\}/|\log_{10}(p''q'/p'q'')|$ $+(J+\frac{2}{3})[\log_{10}(q'/q'')]/\log_{10}(p''q'/p'q'')$. Let $h_1=h_1[p'']=[\log_{10}(p''/p)]/\log_{10}(q/q'')$, $h_2=h_2[p'']=\{\log_{10}[(1-\alpha)/\beta]\}/\log_{10}(q/q'')$, $h_3=h_3[p'']=\{\log_{10}[(1-\beta)/\alpha]\}/\log_{10}(q/q'')+\frac{2}{3}-(h_1+1)/3$. When p, α, β, p'' such that $h_1, h_2, h_3, (h_2+h_3)/(h_1+1)-1$ positive integers, $V[p'']=h_1+1$ and $V_0[p'']=h_2-(h_1+1)$[largest integer in $h_2/(h_1+1)$]; otherwise $V[p'']=V_0[p'']=1$. $s(t)=1$ if $X(t)-\theta_p^{(0)}<0$ and $=0$ otherwise. For J, V integers $\geqslant 1$, $T_J=\sum_{t=1}^{(J-1)V+V_0} s(t)$ **2** *Tests*: Sequential sampling procedure starts with $n=V_0$ and continues in groups of sample values with $n=V_0+V, V_0+2V, \ldots$ until a decision is reached. No conditions are imposed on tests when $J=1$. Notation: $J(n)=1+(n-V_0)/V$. *One-sided test of* $\theta_p^{(0)}<\theta_p$: Here $(V, V_0)=(1, 1)$ or $(V[p(1)], V_0[p(1)])$. Given that $a_J[p, p(1)]<T_J<b_J[p, p(1)]$ for $J\leqslant J(n)-1$, accept H_0 if $T_{J(n)}\leqslant a_{J(n)}[p, p(1)]$; accept $\theta_p^{(0)}<\theta_p$ with emphasis on $\theta_p^{(0)}\leqslant\theta_{p(1)}$ if $T_{J(n)}\geqslant b_{J(n)}[p, p(1)]$; otherwise take another V sample values and repeat procedure for increased sample size. *One-sided test of* $\theta_p^{(0)}>\theta_p$: Here $(V, V_0)=(1, 1)$ or $(V[p(2)], V_o[p(2)])$. Given that $a_J[p, p(2)]<T_J<b_J[p, p(2)]$ for $J\leqslant J(n)-1$, accept H_0 if $T_{J(n)}\leqslant a_{J(n)}[p, p(2)]$; accept $\theta_p^{(0)}>\theta_p$ with emphasis on $\theta_p^{(0)}\geqslant\theta_{p(2)}$ if $T_{J(n)}\geqslant b_{J(n)}[p, p(2)]$; otherwise take another V sample values and continue. *Two-sided test using* $\theta_{w_1p(1)+w_2p(2)}$: Here $(V, V_0)=(1, 1)$ or $(V[w_1p(1)+w_2p(2)], V_0[w_1p(1)+w_2p(2)])$. Given that $a_J[p, w_1p(1)+w_2p(2)]<T_J<b_J[p, w_1p(1)+w_2p(2)]$ for $J\leqslant J(n)-1$, accept H_0 if $T_{J(n)}\leqslant a_{J(n)}[p, w_1p(1)+w_2p(2)]$; accept $\theta_p^{(0)}\neq\theta_p$ with emphasis on $\theta_p^{(0)}\leqslant\theta_{p(1)}$ or $\theta_p^{(0)}\geqslant\theta_{p(2)}$ if $T_{J(n)}\geqslant b_{J(n)}[p, w_1p(1)+w_2p(2)]$; otherwise take another V sample values and continue. *Two-sided test using* $\theta_{p(w_1,w_2)}$: Here $(V, V_0)=(1, 1)$ or $(V[p(w_1, w_2)], V_0[p(w_1, w_2)])$. Given that $a_J[p, p(w_1, w_2)]<T_J<b_J[p, p(w_1, w_2)]$ for $J\leqslant J(n)-1$, accept H_0 if $T_{J(n)}\leqslant a_{J(n)}[p, p(w_1, w_2)]$; accept $\theta_p^{(0)}\neq\theta_p$ with emphasis on $\theta_p^{(0)}\leqslant\theta_{p(1)}$ or $\theta_p^{(0)}\geqslant\theta_{p(2)}$ if $T_{J(n)}\geqslant b_{J(n)}[p, p(w_1, w_2)]$; otherwise take another V sample values and continue **3** None **4** The two-sided test using $\theta_{w_1p(1)+w_2p(2)}$ is based on the conceptual situation where, independently for each sample value, the altern. $\theta_{p(1)}$ occurs with prob. w_1 and the altern. $\theta_{p(2)}$ occurs with prob. w_2; then $P[X(i)-(\text{altern. occurring})<0]=$ $w_1P[X(i)-\theta_{p(1)}<0]+w_2P[X(i)-\theta_{p(2)}<0]=$ $w_1p(1)+w_2p(2)=$ $P[X(i)-\theta_{w_1p(1)+w_2p(2)}<0]$. For this test, subject to restrictions stated in part 1 of Results, value for w_1 is that which minimizes $\max\{B_1[w_1, p(1)], B_1[w_1, p(2)]\}$, where $B_1[w_1, p']=\{[(1-\beta)/\alpha]^{r_1(w_1,p')}-1\}/\{[(1-\beta)/\alpha]^{r_1(w_1,p')}-[\beta/(1-\alpha)]^{r_1(w_1,p')}\}$ and $r_1(w_1,p')$ is sol. for r of $p'\{[w_1p(1)+w_2p(2)]/p\}^r+(1-p')\{[1-w_1p(1)-w_2p(2)]/(1-p)\}^r=$ 1. The two-sided test using $\theta_{p(w_1,w_2)}$ is based on a geometric mean type averaging of the dist. of $s(t)$ when $\theta_p^{(0)}=\theta_{p(1)}$ and the dist. when $\theta_p^{(0)}=\theta_{p(2)}$. For this test, subject to restrictions stated in part 1 of Results, value for w_1 is that which minimizes max $\{B_2[w_1, p(1)], B_2[w_1, p(2)]\}$, where $B_2[w_1, p']=\{[(1-\beta)/\alpha]^{r_2(w_1, p')}-1\}/\{[(1-\beta)/\alpha]^{r_2(w_1, p')}-[\beta/(1-\alpha)]^{r_2(w_1, p')}\}$ and $r_2(w_1, p')$ is sol. for r of $p'[p(w_1, p_2)/p]^r+(1-p')\{[1-p(w_1, w_2)]/(1-p)\}^r=1$. *Truncation*: Let $n'[p']$ be the largest integer contained in $3h_2[p']h_3[p'](1+h_1[p'])^2/h_1[p']+3V/2$ which equals V_0+integral multiple of V. Then, with only slight change in operating characteristics, one-sided test of $\theta_p^{(0)}<\theta_p$ can be truncated when $n'[p(1)]$ sample values obtained, one-sided test of $\theta_p^{(0)}>\theta_p$ can be truncated when $n'[p(2)]$ sample values obtained, two-sided test using $\theta_{w_1 p(1)+w_2 p(2)}$ can be truncated when $n'[w_1p(1)+w_2p(2)]$ sample values obtained, and two-sided test using $\theta_{p(w_1, w_2)}$ can be truncated when $n'[p(w_1, w_2)]$ sample values obtained. In all truncation cases, if no decision reached from sequential method by final sample value, H_0 rejected if value of final T_J nearer rejection boundary than acceptance boundary, and H_0 accepted otherwise. Whether truncated or not, one-sided test with altern. $\theta_p^{(0)}<\theta_p$ can also be considered as test of composite null hyp. $\theta_p^{(0)}\geqslant\theta_p$ and one-sided test of $\theta_p^{(0)}>\theta_p$ can also be considered as test of composite null hyp. $\theta_p^{(0)}\leqslant\theta_p$; both of these tests have a (generalized) signif. level of approx. α **Characteristics 1** Low for one-sided tests (unless sample size large); lower medium for two-sided test using $\theta_{w_1 p(1)+w_2 p(2)}$; medium for two-sided test using $\theta_{p(w_1, w_2)}$ **2** For test of $\theta_p^{(0)}<\theta_p$, operating characteristic (OC) fct. (prob. of accepting H_0 given p'', where p'' such that $\theta_{p''}=\theta_p^{(0)}$) is $B_1[1, p'']$; for test of $\theta_p^{(0)}>\theta_p$, OC fct. is $B_1[0, p'']$; for test using $\theta_{w_1 p(1)+w_2 p(2)}$, OC fct. is $B_1[w_1, p'']$; for test using $\theta_{p(w_1, w_2)}$, OC fct. is $B_2[w_1, p'']$. For the corresponding four tests, let $p_a=p(1)$, $p(2)$, $w_1p(1)+w_2p(2)$, $p(w_1, w_2)$, respectively, and let $B[p'']$ be the general notation for the OC fct. of a test; here the test considered is identified by the expression for p_a. Then $B[0]=1$, $B[1]=0$, $B[p]=1-\alpha$, $B[p_a]=\beta$, $B[1/(h_1[p_a]+1)]=\{\log_{10}[(1-\beta)/\alpha]\}/\{\log_{10}[(1-\beta)/\alpha]+|\log_{10}[\beta/(1-\alpha)]|\}$ furnish five pts. for OC fct. of each test; interpolation furnishes other pts. To attain specified α and β, much smaller sample sizes required, on the average, for sequential tests than for corresponding fixed sample size tests; often expected sample size (average sample no.) less than $\frac{1}{2}$ of corresponding fixed sample size. For test of $\theta_p^{(0)}<\theta_p$, $E(n)\leqslant n'[p(1)]/3$; for test of $\theta_p^{(0)}>\theta_p$, $E(n)\leqslant n'[p(2)]/3$; for test using $\theta_{w_1 p(1)+w_2 p(2)}$, $E(n)\leqslant n'[w_1p(1)+w_2p(2)]/3$; for test using $\theta_{p(w_1, w_2)}$ $E(n)\leqslant n'[p(w_1, w_2)]/3$ **3** Not used symmetrically **4** Test properties same as for random sample case if observations independent and from populations which are continuous at $\theta_p^{(0)}$and for which $\theta_p^{(0)}=\theta_{p''}(i)$, where p'' is the same for all i. Can be sensitive to dependences involving more than small percentage of the observations. Moderately sensitive to variations among the $P[X(i)-\theta_p^{(0)}<0]$. Can be sensitive to continuity requirement; however, significance level valid if $P[X(i)<\theta_p(i)]=p$ for all i and the observations are independent **5** Not difficult to decide on assumptions **6** Useful in sampling situations where observations can be obtained sequentially **Bibliography** Ref. 436.

EFFICIENCIES FOR LIFE-TESTING SITUATIONS—SMALLER PERCENTILES

Introduction

This section considers the efficiency properties of some nonparametric procedures (point estimates, confidence intervals, and tests) for investigating smaller population percentage points in life-testing situations. If θ_p is investigated and one of the nonparametric procedures is used, the experiment can be discontinued when only moderately more than np failures have occurred among the n items being life-tested. The efficiency of the nonparametric procedure, in comparison with the optimum parametric procedure based on the same number of items failed, is examined for the case of sampling from gamma distributions and from normal distributions. The nonparametric procedures are found to be highly efficient when p is at least moderately small.

Characteristics of Life-Testing Situations

As already mentioned, in life-testing the items of a group are simultaneously subjected to some conditions which will ultimately lead to the failure of all the items. For each item, the variable considered is its time to failure (or some continuous, monotonic, and increasing function of time to failure). A valuable property of this type of variable is that the r smallest order statistics of a set of observations can be determined without the necessity of evaluating any of the other observations. Thus statistical procedures based entirely on the r smallest order statistics of a set of observations have the advantage that the experiment can be stopped when the rth failure occurs. Then the extra cost and time involved in continuing the experiment are avoided.

Nonparametric Procedures Considered

The point estimates considered are those given in the General Expected Value Estimation and in the Median Method of Estimation presentations of this chapter. The confidence intervals are those stated in the Exact and Interpolated Confidence Intervals presentation and in the Randomized-Exact Confidence Intervals presentations of this chapter. The only significance tests considered are those that are obtained directly from these confidence intervals.

Discussion of Efficiency Concepts

For gamma and normal distributions, determination of efficiencies for the nonparametric procedures is difficult unless the sample size is large. Fortunately, consideration of asymptotic efficiencies seems to furnish lower bound values for the efficiencies at smaller sample sizes. For the normality case, this contention seems to be borne out by computational results, at least when the population median is investigated. Intuitively, the relative importance of a few order statistics, when compared to the totality of all smaller or equal sample values, would not seem to increase as the sample size increases. Consequently, efficiencies obtained for the asymptotic case are considered to be lower bounds for the actual values at all sample sizes.

In computing efficiencies, the optimum procedure used for comparison is the best that can be obtained (asymptotically) on the basis of the order statistics with values at most equal to the largest order statistic used by the nonparametric procedure. The optimum procedure varies with the distribution considered.

Generality of Efficiency Results

The efficiency lower bound values listed in this section are applicable to all gamma distribution functions and to all normal distribution functions (gamma distributions are defined on page 126 of ref. 118). That is, for a specified θ_p, the lower bound value stated is the minima of the asymptotic efficiencies of the nonparametric procedures (estimates, tests, and confidence intervals for the same percentile have the same asymptotic efficiency) over the class of all gamma distributions and all normal distributions. Here the normal distributions have unknown mean but can have known variance. For the gamma distributions, the minimum value for which the frequency function is nonzero can be known. Allowing this extra knowledge tends to decrease the efficiency of the nonparametric procedures, but increases the range of applicablity of the results.

The motivation for basing the efficiency investigation on the classes of gamma and normal distributions arises from the consideration that populations of this type seem to be capable of approximating many continuous life-testing situations of practical importance. Although they have infinite ranges in both directions, normal distributions furnish reasonably close approximations to many life-testing type distributions of interest.

Efficiency Lower Bound Values

The following table contains efficiency lower bounds that should be approximately valid for the classes of all gamma distributions and all normal distributions:

Value of p	.01	.02	.05	.1	.2	.3	.5	.7
Efficiency as %	99	98	97	95	92	88	78	61

Here θ_p is the percentage point considered and the data are the values of the sample which are less than or equal to the largest order statistic used by the nonparametric procedure. These lower bound efficiency values are the asymptotic efficiencies for a normal distribution with known variance. This table is based on the material of ref. 568.

Implications of Efficiency Lower Bounds

An efficiency of 100γ per cent implies that the nonparametric procedure based on $1/\gamma$ as many sample values furnishes the same "information" as the corresponding optimum procedure based on a sample of the original size. The efficiency lower bound values show that, for θ_p investigated, use of a nonparametric procedure and a slight percentage increase in the sample size furnishes about as much information as the optimum available procedure, when p is not too large and the population sampled is at least roughly of a gamma or a normal form. Often cost and/or time are saved if the number of items life-tested is increased by a moderate amount but the experiment is discontinued when only about $100p$ per cent of the items have failed. Thus, unless the situation is of a well-established parametric nature, the general validity and indicated high efficiency of the nonparametric procedures would seem to furnish a strong recommendation for their use in life-testing situations.

Section Bibliography

Ref. 164, 260, 557, 568.

DIFFERENCE OF TWO POPULATION PERCENTILES—CONTINUOUS CASE

Discussion

This section contains exact and theoretical-approximate confidence intervals and tests for the difference of two population percentage points. In one case these percentage points are from the same continuous population and the observations are a sample from that population. In another case, the percentage points are from separate continuous populations and the data are independent samples from these populations. For the remaining case, two independent sets of independent observations from continuous symmetrical populations are considered, where all the populations for one set have a common central value, and likewise for the other set. Exact confidence intervals and tests are obtained for the two-population situation where the populations differ only in location and the same population percentage points are compared (e.g., the medians); also for the nonsample situation where the common medians of two sets of symmetrical populations are compared. Point estimates for differences of percentiles are not considered. However, approximate expected value estimates can be obtained on the basis of the General Expected Value Estimation presentation of this chapter and some of the confidence interval results can be used to obtain approximate median estimates.

Desirability of Percentile Comparisons

For the case of a single population, percentage points furnish valuable information about the population properties. In particular, functions of differences of percentage points can be used to measure dispersion, skewness, peakedness, and other population properties of interest. In many situations, measures based on population percentiles are more suitable than the corresponding measures based on population moments, since percentiles are not so sensitive to the tail properties of the population.

For the case of two populations, a comparison of percentage points can yield useful information about the relative properties of these populations. As an example, the difference of corresponding percentage points furnishes a measure of how the populations differ in location at this percentage point. Such a comparison at several suitably spaced percentage points furnishes an indication of how the two populations differ in both location and shape. As another example, the information that an upper percentage point of one population is less than a lower percentage point of another population can be very valuable. In fact, information of this nature often is of much greater interest than the knowledge that one population has a smaller mean than the other.

For the case of two groups of continuous symmetrical populations, where the populations of a group have the same central value, a comparison of these two medians furnishes information about the relative locations of these groups of populations. A special case of this situation is a comparison of the medians of two arbitrary continuous symmetrical populations.

When two or more populations are involved, a comparison of percentiles can be considered to fall under the heading of the comparison results occurring in the second volume of the handbook. These comparison procedures are presented here, rather than in the second volume, because of their direct expression in terms of population percentiles.

Nature of Procedures

Four different types of situations are considered; namely, percentage points of the same population, the same percentage point of two populations that have the same shape, the medians of two sets of symmetrical populations, and arbitrary percentiles of two populations that can have quite different shapes. All the populations are continuous and all the observations are mutually independent.

The only situations for which exact confidence intervals are obtained are those where the medians of two populations that have the same shape, or of two sets of symmetrical populations, are compared. The exact tests presented are for the case of two populations with the same shape. However, these tests seem to be reasonably accurate, on the basis of judgment-experience considerations, when the shapes of the populations are allowed to differ a moderate amount. For the situation of percentiles of the same population, confidence intervals are given which have confidence coefficients whose values are bounded from below. For the situation of arbitrary percentiles of populations that can differ greatly in location and shape, the confidence coefficients are bounded from both below and above.

Distribution Approximation by Sum of Normal Functions

Many statistics have distributions that are approximately normal for large sample sizes. As the sample sizes become smaller, the nearness to normality of these distributions tends to decrease. To obtain statistical procedures that are applicable for these smaller sample sizes, methods are needed which are amenable to statistical derivations and which are capable of approximating distributions that are only roughly normal. The Gram-Charlier A series, the Edgeworth series, generalizations of the Edgeworth series, the Pearson curves, etc. have been found useful for this purpose. Another method consists in approximating the distribution considered by a positively weighted sum of normal distribution functions, subject only to the condition that all these distributions have the same (unknown) value for a specified population percentile say, the $100P$ per cent point. Since the number of normal distributions used, one parameter of each distribution, and the relative values of the weightings in the sum are all arbitrary, this method seems capable of furnishing reasonable approximations to virtually all distributions that are at least roughly normal and for which the value of P is appreciably different from $\frac{1}{2}$ (say, $P \leqslant \frac{1}{4}$ or $P \geqslant \frac{3}{4}$). That is, this type of approximation should be satisfactory for moderate as well as large sample sizes when P is not near $\frac{1}{2}$.

The procedure of approximating a roughly normal distribution by a sum of normal functions is used in obtaining approximate one-sided confidence intervals for the difference of arbitrary percentiles of two possibly different continuous populations. Here an independent sample is taken from each population and the confidence intervals are based on a single order statistic of each sample. With mild restrictions on the population distributions, these order statistics are approximately normally distributed for large sample sizes. For sample sizes that are not too small, the approximation method is assumed to be conceptually applicable for representing the distributions of these order statistics. That is, for each order statistic, some unknown summation of the specified type is assumed to furnish a reasonable approximation to the actual distribution. On this basis, upper and lower bounds that are reasonably close together can be obtained for the confidence coefficients of the intervals considered.

Use of Transformations of Variable

For the situations involving two populations, profitable use can sometimes be made of continuous monotonic changes of variable. As an example, the null hypothesis that a specified change of variable transforms one population into the other population can be tested on the basis of the exact results; here the emphasis would be on the hypothesis that the transformed population has the same median as the other population. More generally, the hypothesis that a specified function of a given percentage point of one population equals a specified function of a given percentage point of the other population could be tested, or confidence intervals could be obtained for the difference of these two functions.

Often a suitable selection of the transformations of variables for the two populations, perhaps the same transformation for both populations, will virtually assure that the procedure assumptions are satisfied. In fact, this may be the principal motivation for introducing changes of variable in many instances.

Outline of Presentations

The first presentation is concerned with confidence intervals for the difference of two arbitrary percentage points of the same population. The second presentation contains confidence intervals for the difference of the medians of two populations that have the same shape. Also a test is given for the null hypothesis that the two populations with identical shapes have medians that differ by a specified amount. The third presentation furnishes confidence intervals for the difference of the common central median of one set of symmetrical populations and the common central median of another set. The fourth and final presentation contains confidence intervals for the difference of arbitrary percentage points from populations that can be appreciably different in shape and location.

Fixed Material for Section

Data 1 Continuous, univariate **2** None **Characteristics 4** Moderately sensitive to all the assumptions.

Arbitrary Percentiles of Same Continuous Population (Chu)

Data 3 $X[i]$ **4** $m=1$; $n \geqslant 2$ **Description 1** Theoretical-approximate one-sided and two-sided confidence intervals with confid. coeff. having stated lower bounds **2** $\theta_{p(2)}-\theta_{p(1)}$, where $p(2)>p(1)$ **Assumptions 1** Random sample **2** Population continuous; both $\theta_{p(2)}$ and $\theta_{p(1)}$ unique **3** None **Results 1** $b[s,p]=b[s,p;n]=\sum_{i=s}^{n}\binom{n}{i}p^i(1-p)^{n-i}$. For specified α such that $\alpha \geqslant [1-p(1)]^n+p(2)^n$, t is largest integer $\leqslant$ $1+p(1)(n-w)/[1+p(1)-p(2)]$; $r=t+w$; w is smallest of $0,1,\ldots,n-1$ such that $b[t,p(1)]-b[r,p(2)] \geqslant 1-\alpha$. Likewise, for $\alpha \geqslant [1-p(2)]^n+p(1)^n$, t' is largest integer $\leqslant$ $1+p(1)(n-w')/[1+p(1)-p(2)]$; $r'=t'+w'$; w' is largest of $0,1,\ldots,n-1$ such that $b[r';p(2)]-b[t',p(1)] \geqslant 1-\alpha$ **2** *Probability relations*: *In general*, for $1 \leqslant v<u \leqslant n$ and $1 \leqslant v'<u' \leqslant n$, $P\{X[u]-X[v] \geqslant \theta_{p(2)}-\theta_{p(1)}\} \geqslant b[v,p(1)]-b[u,p(2)]$ and $P\{X[u']-X[v'] \leqslant \theta_{p(2)}-\theta_{p(1)}\} \geqslant b[u',p(2)]-b[v',p(1)]$. *Less generally*, for $0<\alpha<1$, $P\{X[r]-X[t] \geqslant \theta_{p(2)}-\theta_{p(1)}\} \geqslant 1-\alpha$ and $P\{X[r']-X[t'] \leqslant \theta_{p(2)}-\theta_{p(1)}\} \geqslant 1-\alpha$; for $\max\{\frac{1}{2},[1-p(1)]^n+p(2)^n\} \leqslant \alpha<1$, $r \leqslant r'$, and $t \geqslant t'$, $P\{X[r]-X[t] \leqslant \theta_{p(2)}-\theta_{p(1)} \leqslant X[r']-X[t']\} \geqslant 2\alpha-1$; intervals involving r,t and/or r',t' have desirable properties compared to other ways of obtaining same lower bounds for confid. coeff. (see ref. 96) **3** $b[s,p;n]$ can be evaluated by methods in binomial dist. sect. of Chapter 7 **4** Method of choosing r,t,r',t' implies that r and r' of form $np(2)+O(\sqrt{n})$ and t,t' of form $np(1)+O(\sqrt{n})$; then, if $f(\theta_{p(1)})>0$, $f(\theta_{p(2)})>0$, and $f'(x)$ continuous at $\theta_{p(1)}$ and $\theta_{p(2)}$, both $(X[r]-X[t])$ and $(X[r']-X[t'])$ have asymptotically normal distributions with variance $p(1)[1-p(1)]/nf(\theta_{p(1)})^2-2p(1)[1-p(2)]/nf(\theta_{p(1)})f(\theta_{p(2)})+p(2)[1-p(2)]/nf(\theta_{p(2)})^2$. See Chapter 10 for methods of estimating this variance **Characteristics 1** Low **2** Intervals involving r,t and/or r',t' consistent if $f(\theta_{p(1)}), f(\theta_{p(2)})>0$ and $f'(x)$ continuous at $\theta_{p(1)}$ and $\theta_{p(2)}$ **3** Used symmetrically **5** Not difficult to decide on random sample and continuity assumptions. Also not difficult to decide on uniqueness of $\theta_{p(1)}$ and $\theta_{p(2)}$; this uniqueness ordinarily verified if population believed unimodal **6** For results involving u, v, u', v', actual confid. coeff. can be much greater than stated lower bound; however, for intervals involving r,t and/or r',t', actual value and bound should be reasonably close together if n at least moderately large. Useful for life-testing and other censored data situations **Bibliography** Ref. 96, 118 (pages 367–70).

Exact Results—Medians of Populations Differing only in Location

Data 3 $X(i)_j$ and $X[i]_j$ **4** $m=2$ **Description 1** Exact one-sided and two-sided confidence intervals; also exact two-sided sig. tests **2** $\theta_{1/2}(i)_1-\theta_{1/2}(i)_2$ **Assumptions 1** The $X(i)_1$ random sample from population with dist. fct. $F^{(1)}(x)$ and the $X(i)_2$ independent random sample from pop. with dist. fct. $F^{(2)}(x)$ **2** $F^{(1)}(x)$ and $F^{(2)}(x)$ continuous **3** $F^{(1)}[x-\theta_{1/2}(i)_1]=F^{(2)}[x-\theta_{1/2}(i)_2]$ **Results 1** Null hyp. is $\theta_{1/2}(i)_1-\theta_{1/2}(i)_2=D$ for the tests; $a=(n_1+n_2)/2$ if n_1+n_2 even and $=(n_1+n_2+1)/2$ if n_1+n_2 odd; $Z_a=a$th largest of $X(1)_1-D, \ldots, X(n_1)_1-D, X(1)_2, \ldots, X(n_2)_2$; d_1=no. of the $X(i)_1-D$ exceeding Z_a and d_2=no. of the $X(i)_2$ exceeding Z_a; $X^2(d_1, d_2)= [|d_1(n_2-d_2)-d_2(n_1-d_1)|-(n_1+n_2)/2]^2(n_1+n_2)/(n_1+n_2-a)n_1n_2a$. $H(u, v)=\sum_{i=0}^{u-1}\binom{v+i-1}{v-1}\binom{n_1+n_2-v-i}{n_2-v}\Big/\binom{n_1+n_2}{n_1}$. For attainable α, integers U_α, V_α determined by $H(U_\alpha, V_\alpha)=\alpha$ and $(n_1/2-U_\alpha)/\sqrt{n_1}$ as nearly equal to $(V_\alpha-n_2/2)/\sqrt{n_2}$ as possible **2** *Test*: Accept $\theta_{1/2}(i)_1-\theta_{1/2}(i)_2\neq D$ if $|(n_2-d_2)d_1-(n_1-d_1)d_2|>(n_1+n_2)/2$ and $X^2(d_1, d_2)>X_\alpha^2(d_1, d_2)$, where sig. level α is $<\frac{1}{2}$. *Confidence Intervals*: $P\{X[u]_1-X[v]_2>\theta_{1/2}(i)_1-\theta_{1/2}(i)_2\}=H(u, v)$; $P\{X[u']_1-X[v']_1<\theta_{1/2}(i)_1-\theta_{1/2}(i)_2\}=1-H(u', v')$; $P\{X[u]_1-X[v]_2<\theta_{1/2}(i)_1-\theta_{1/2}(i)_2<X[u']_1-X[v']_2;\ u\leqslant u', v\geqslant v'\}= H(u', v')-H(u, v)$; for one-sided intervals and attainable confid. coeff. α $(0<\alpha<1)$, approx. preferable u, v combination is U_α, V_α and approx. preferable u', v' combination is $U_{1-\alpha}$, $V_{1-\alpha}$ **3** When $n_1, n_2\geqslant 10$ and $\frac{1}{2}>\alpha\geqslant[4 \min (n_1, n_2)]^{-1}$, $X_\alpha^2(d_1, d_2) \doteq \chi_\alpha^2(1)$; see ref. 352 for method of evaluating $X_\alpha^2(d_1, d_2)$ for other cases. When $n_1, n_2\geqslant 10$ and $[5 \min (n_1, n_2)]^{-1}\leqslant\alpha\leqslant 1-[5 \min (n_1, n_2)]^{-1}$, $U_\alpha \doteq$ largest integer $\leqslant \frac{1}{2}+n_1/2-K_\alpha[n_1(n_1+n_2)]^{1/2}/2(\sqrt{n_1}+\sqrt{n_2})$ and $V_\alpha \doteq$ largest integer $\leqslant \frac{1}{2}+n_2/2+K_\alpha[n_2(n_1+n_2)]^{1/2}/2(\sqrt{n_1}+\sqrt{n_2})$ **4** Intuitive considerations indicate that tests approx. valid when population shapes differ moderate amount (see ref. 352); also tests valid for discontinuous case if randomization used to break ties. Tests and intervals valid for $\theta_p(i)_1-\theta_p(i)_2$ with arbitrary p but tend to be less sensitive to assumption of same shape when $p=\frac{1}{2}$. If population shape known to be symmetrical, confidence intervals obtainable for $\theta_{1/2}(i)_1 + \theta_{1/2}(i)_2$. Basic relation is $P\{X[u]_1+X[n_2+1-v]_2>\theta_{1/2}(i)_1+\theta_{1/2}(i)_2\} = P\{X[n_1+1-u]_1+X[v]_2<\theta_{1/2}(i)_1+\theta_{1/2}(i)_2\} = H(u, v)$ **Characteristics 1** Low (except for tests with $\min (n_1, n_2)<10$) **2** For case of normal populations with known variance ratio, asymptotic efficiency of tests is 64 per cent; asymptotic efficiency of confidence intervals at least 65 per cent when preferable u, v and u', v' combinations used **3** Used symmetrically within each sample **4** For some cases, bounds for confidence coefficients obtainable from Arbitrary Percentiles of Possibly Different Continuous Populations presentation **5** Not difficult to decide on independence, random sample, and continuity assumptions. Rather difficult to verify that populations differ only in location **6** Useful when experience indicates that populations differ in location but not in shape. Useful for life-testing and other censored data situations **Bibliography** Ref. 32, 352 (pages 394–98).

Exact Confidence Intervals—Medians, Two Sets of Symmetrical Populations

Data 3 $X(i)_j$ **4** $m=2$; $n_1 \leqslant n_2$ **Description 1** Exact and approx. one-sided and two-sided confidence intervals and tests **2** $\theta_{1/2}(i)_1-\theta_{1/2}(i)_2$, where $\theta_{1/2}(i)_1$ central value of dist. of $X(i)_1$ and $\theta_{1/2}(i)_2$ central value of dist. of $X(i)_2$ **Assumptions 1** Observations are mutually independent **2** All populations are continuous and symmetrical; each observation from a possibly different population **3** $\theta_{1/2}(1)_1=\ldots=\theta_{1/2}(n_1)_1=\theta_{1/2}^{(1)}$ and $\theta_{1/2}(1)_2=\ldots=\theta_{1/2}(n_2)_2=\theta_{1/2}^{(2)}$ **Results 1** $n_2=An_1+B$, where A and B integers with $A\geqslant 1$ and $0\leqslant B<n_1$. Draw the $X(1)_2,\ldots,X(n_2)_2$ as B sets of $A+1$ observations and n_1-B sets of A observations. Let $\bar{X}_2(i)$ be mean of ith of these sets and let $Y(i)=X(i)_1-\bar{X}_2(i)$, $(i=1,\ldots,n_1)$ **2** *Confidence intervals and tests*: The $Y(i)$ are independent observations from continuous symmetrical populations with common median $\theta_{1/2}^{(1)}-\theta_{1/2}^{(2)}$. The exact and approx. results of Chapter 7 for investigating the common mean of symmetrical populations can be used to obtain confidence intervals and tests for $\theta_{1/2}^{(1)}-\theta_{1/2}^{(2)}$ **3** Confidence intervals obtainable from presentation on page 156. **4** Let $Z(i)=UX(i)_1+V\bar{X}_2(i)$, where U and V are arbitrary constants. Then the $Z(i)$ are independent observations from continuous symmetrical populations with common median $U\theta_{1/2}^{(1)}+V\theta_{1/2}^{(2)}$ **Characteristics 1** Low **2** Efficiency considered for some tests based on presentations of pages 156 and 168 when $n_1\leqslant 15$ and samples from two normal populations; compared to "best" t test solution to Behrens-Fisher problem (see ref. 458), efficiency is in range 90 to 95 per cent; compared to most powerful test when ratio of variances of two populations known, efficiency in range 75 to 85 per cent for $A=1$ and in range 45 to 75 per cent for $A=\infty$ **3** Observations not used symmetrically **5** Not difficult to decide on independence and continuity assumptions but usually difficult to decide on equality of central medians unless each set of observations believed to be sample **6** These are the only results presented for obtaining confidence intervals for difference of medians when each observation from possibly different population; also are only results for investigating arbitrary linear fct. of $\theta_{1/2}^{(1)}$ and $\theta_{1/2}^{(2)}$. Useful for life-testing and other censored data situations **Bibliography** Ref. 458, 558.

Arbitrary Percentiles of Possibly Different Continuous Populations

Data 3 $X[i]_j$ **4** $m=2$; lower bounds for n_1, n_2 specified in Assumptions **Description 1** Theoretical-approximate one-sided confidence intervals with bounded confid. coeff. **2** $\theta_{p(1)}(i)_1-\theta_{p(2)}(i)_2$ **Assumptions 1** Two independent random samples **2** Both populations continuous **3** For $n_1 \geqslant 3/p(1)[1-p(1)]$, freq. fct. of $X[i(1)]_1-\theta_{p(1)}(i)_1$ approx. expressible in form $\sum_{k=1}^{A[i(1)]} a_k{}^2 f_{i(1)}^{(k)}(x)$, where $\int_{-\infty}^{0} f_{i(1)}^{(k)}(x)dx = P\{X[i(1)]_1 < \theta_{p(1)}(i)_1\}$ for all k and the $f_{i(1)}^{(k)}(x)$ are normal freq. fcts. Likewise, for $n_2 \geqslant 3/p(2)[1-p(2)]$, freq. fct. of $X[i(2)]_2-\theta_{p(2)}(i)_2$ approx. expressible in form $\sum_{k=1}^{B[i(2)]} b_k{}^2 g_{i(2)}^{(k)}(x)$, where $\int_0^\infty g_{i(2)}^{(k)}(x)dx = P\{X[i(2)]_2 > \theta_{p(2)}(i)_2\}$ for all k and the $g_{i(2)}^{(k)}(x)$ are normal freq. fcts. **Results 1** $\alpha = \left\{\sum_{i=i(1)}^{n_1}\binom{n_1}{i} p(1)^i[1-p(1)]^{n_1-i} + \sum_{i=0}^{i(2)-1}\binom{n_2}{i} p(2)^i[1-p(2)]^{n_2-i}\right\}\Big/2$; values of $i(1)$, $i(2)$, n_1, n_2, $p(1)$, $p(2)$ are such that $\sum_{i=i(1)}^{n_1}\binom{n_1}{i} p(1)^i[1-p(1)]^{n_1-i} \doteq \sum_{i=0}^{i(2)-1}\binom{n_2}{i} p(2)^i[1-p(2)]^{n_2-i}$; α' determined by $K_{\alpha'}=\sqrt{2}K_\alpha$ **2** *Confidence interval relations*: *For* $\alpha \leqslant .25$, relation $\alpha' \leqslant P\{X[i(1)]_1 - X[i(2)]_2 < \theta_{p(1)}(i)_1-\theta_{p(2)}(i)_2\} \leqslant \alpha$ approx. satisfied. *For* $\alpha \geqslant .75$, $\alpha \leqslant P\{X[i(1)]_1 - X[i(2)]_2 < \theta_{p(1)}(i)_1-\theta_{p(2)}(i)_2\} \leqslant \alpha'$ approx. satisfied **3** None **4** Other type of one-sided confidence intervals obtained as complements of type presented. Two-sided confidence intervals obtained as nonoverlapping combinations of two one-sided intervals. Bound having value α valid under conditions more general than those assumed (see ref. 564); inequality $\alpha^2 \leqslant P\{X[i(1)]_1 - X[i(2)]_2 < \theta_{p(1)}(i)_1-\theta_{p(2)}(i)_2\} \leqslant 2\alpha-\alpha^2$ approx. satisfied even if freq. fcts. for order statistics not approx. expressible in forms assumed. If requirement that $P\{X[i(1)] < \theta_{p(1)}(i)_1\} \doteq P\{X[i(2)] > \theta_{p(2)}(i)_2\}$ not satisfied to reasonable approx., "interpolated" order statistics of type considered in Exact and Interpolated Confidence Intervals presentation can be used in place of $X[i(1)]$ and/or $X[i(2)]$ **Characteristics 1** Low **2** For case where populations sampled are normal with known variance ratio, asymptotic efficiency lies between .26 and .67 if $.01 \leqslant p(1), p(2) \leqslant .99$; between .50 and .67 if $.045 \leqslant p(1), p(2) \leqslant .955$; between .62 and .67 if $.1 \leqslant p(1), p(2) \leqslant .9$ **3** Used symmetrically within each sample **5** Not difficult to decide on the independence, random sample and continuity assumptions. More difficult to verify assumed form for freq. fcts. of order statistics **6** Useful in investigating whether upper percentile of one population less than lower percentile of another population. Useful for life-testing and other censored data situations **Bibliography** Ref. 334, 564.

Chapter 9

DISTRIBUTION-FREE TOLERANCE REGIONS

INTRODUCTION

This chapter is concerned with distribution-free tolerance regions that are based on random samples from univariate or multivariate populations. Some exact results can be obtained when the population sampled is continuous or partially continuous; exact randomized results, which greatly extend the available probability levels, are presented for continuous populations. Approximate results are obtained for discontinuous cases, and also for situations where interpolation is used to extend the forms of the tolerance regions and the available probability levels. The special situation of sampling from a multivariate population with a random variable whose coordinates are independent in known groups is also considered. Tolerance regions that are at least roughly of a desired form can be obtained through judicious use of the allowable methods for constructing these regions from the data. No sequential material is presented, although some results of this nature are discussed.

The presentation method used in this chapter differs from that for preceding chapters in several respects. First, much of the important material is stated prior to the presentations of statistical procedures. This is possible because many of the statistical procedures have properties in common, which are stated and discussed in preceding sections. Second, for one of the two major uses of tolerance regions, all the statistical procedure results are contained in a single section; this uncommon presentation situation occurs in the statistical prediction of the number of values of a second sample that will fall in a tolerance region determined by a first sample. Third, to treat both univariate and multivariate situations using the standard notation, n is given two separate meanings. For the univariate case, n is used to represent the sample size; however, for the multivariate case, the sample size is denoted by m, and n is used to represent the dimensionality of the random variable. If the situation considered can be univariate or multivariate, only m is used for the sample size.

GENERAL DISCUSSION

A tolerance region is a random region that lies in the space of the possible values for an observation from the univariate or multivariate population sampled. The exact shape, size, etc. of a tolerance region depend on the sample values.

The probability results presented are concerned with the coverage properties of tolerance regions. Here coverage can refer to the amount of the population probability that falls within a region, which is the value of $\int_R dF$, where R is the region and F is the population distribution function; this is called population coverage. Also coverage can refer to the number of values of an independent second sample (from the same population) that fall within a region determined by a first sample; this is called sample coverage. Usually, the probability that the amount of coverage belongs to a specified set of values is of primary interest (e.g., that the coverage is at least a specified amount). However, the expected amount of coverage can also be of interest.

For the situations considered, the exact and approximate coverage probability properties stated for tolerance regions are of a distribution-free character. That is, these properties are valid if the sampling is from any population of the rather general class that is being specified for the presentation being considered.

A tolerance region can consist of two or more parts such that the amount of population coverage is controlled separately for each part (in a probability sense). That is, in the probability expression considered, each part satisfies a specified coverage relation.

A special situation considered is that where the multivariate population sampled has a random variable whose coordinates are independent in known groups. For this situation, the population coverage properties are individually controlled for each of these groups of coordinates. More explicitly, a separate "tolerance region" (called a subregion) is determined for each of the independent groups. The methods for obtaining tolerance regions for the general situation can be applied in determining each subregion, and the resulting tolerance region is the combination of these subregions. That is, a point is contained in the over-all tolerance region if and only if, for each of the groups, its coordinate values are contained in the corresponding subregion.

PRACTICAL USES OF TOLERANCE REGIONS

Discussion

From a practical viewpoint, tolerance regions have two principal types of direct applications. One use is to furnish information about the probability concentration in the population sampled. The other use is to predict the concentration of the values of an independent second sample from the same population. Descriptions of these two types of uses are given in this section.

Tolerance regions also have some indirect applications. One use is in testing distribution functions (see Chapter 10). Another use is for the two-sample problem (see page 274). For both of these applications, use of tolerance regions has the advantage that the results are applicable for multivariate situations. Also supplementary information about the population, or populations, sampled can be incorporated into the construction method used to obtain the tolerance region.

Population Coverage Application

For this type of application, location of the probability concentration in the population sampled is of primary interest. As an example, let F be the population distribution function and suppose that the tolerance region R has a probability of .95 of covering at least 96 per cent of the population probability; that is,

$$P\left\{\int_R dF \geqslant .96\right\} = .95.$$

Then the random region R furnishes a strong indication of the location of the probability concentration for this population, especially if R is bounded and of a suitable size and shape. As a second example, suppose that R' is an expected value estimate for a region that covers 99 per cent of the population; that is,

$$E\left\{\int_{R'} dF\right\} = .99.$$

Then R' also furnishes a reasonable indication of the probability concentration for the population sampled.

As indicated, the random variable used for investigating the probability concentration in a population is the population coverage of a tolerance region (i.e., $\int_R dF$ for the region R). Although the amount of population coverage attained by a tolerance region is not an observable random variable, the distribution function of this coverage can be exactly or approximately determined for the situations considered. Exact knowledge of the distribution function for the population coverage of a tolerance region represents the maximum amount of information that is available for locating the population probability concentration on the basis of this region.

Statistical Prediction Application

This type of application is concerned with the sample coverage of a tolerance region. Here a tolerance region has been determined on the basis of a previous sample and the problem is to make a prediction with respect to the number of values of an independent new sample (of specified size and from the same population) that will fall within this region. Predictions of this nature are useful for situations where the major interest is in the outcome for a second sample from the same population rather than in the properties of the underlying population.

The prediction of the coverage of a new sample is made in a probability sense. The distribution function of the number of sample values falling in the given tolerance region represents the maximum amount of information that is available for prediction purposes on the basis of that tolerance region and a new sample of the specified size. However, this distribution depends on the characteristics of the tolerance region used and on the size of the new sample. Consequently, it can be controlled to some extent through the choices affecting these quantities (including the size of the sample used to determine the tolerance region).

Remarks

The population coverage application for tolerance regions can be interpreted as a special case of the statistical prediction application. Namely, it is the case of a new sample of infinite size.

To obtain useful information, a tolerance region used for either type of application should be of a suitable form. Otherwise there may be little interest in the coverage of this region. Ordinarily, the procedure is to decide on a desirable form for a tolerance region on the basis of intuitive considerations. Then a method is devised for constructing a tolerance region that is at least roughly of this form.

Nearly all of the remainder of this chapter is concerned with tolerance regions from the viewpoint of population coverage. As mentioned in the Introduction, all the statistical prediction results are presented in a single section, which is the last presentation section of the chapter.

CONSIDERATIONS IN THE CONSTRUCTION OF TOLERANCE REGIONS

Introduction

This section contains a discussion of tolerance region construction. First, the concept of "statistical blocks" is introduced and the use of such blocks in forming a tolerance region is described. Then, for illustration purposes, a version of the construction process for determining a tolerance region is outlined. On the basis of this illustration, the use of supplementary information, the freedom available in obtaining a region of a desired form, and sources of bias in the construction process are discussed. Finally, some remarks are made concerning more general versions of the construction process.

Role of Statistical Blocks

The concept of statistically equivalent blocks (hereafter shortened to "statistical blocks") is fundamental in the construction of distribution-free tolerance regions. Every tolerance region considered either consists of a specified number of statistical blocks or is determined from regions that consist of specified numbers of statistical blocks. If the sample size is m, statistical blocks are obtained by dividing the space of possible values for an observation into $m+1$ regions; that is, there are $m+1$ statistical blocks when the sample size is m. Any such set of $m+1$ blocks is said to be a basic set of statistical blocks.

Except for approximate situations involving interpolation, a tolerance region can be considered to consist of an integral number of from 1 to m statistical blocks. In the construction of this region, the individual statistical blocks need not be determined. Construction of a tolerance region can be carried out as a sequence of steps. At each step, one or more statistical blocks are removed from consideration. The blocks remaining at the conclusion of this removal process constitute the desired tolerance region. The number of blocks contained in this region equals $m+1$ minus the number of blocks that were removed.

As emphasized in the remainder of this section, the experimenter has a moderate amount of control over the shapes and sizes of the statistical blocks. However, these blocks also depend on the sample values; consequently, their exact sizes and shapes are of a random character.

A Construction Procedure for the Continuous Case

The construction process presented for illustration purposes starts with consideration of any supplementary information that may be available about the population sampled (based on experience with situations of a similar nature, on technical considerations, etc.). However, no knowledge should be available about the sample values that are eligible for use in the construction. A real-valued function is chosen on the basis of the supplementary information and of the form desired for the tolerance region that is being constructed. The function chosen is such that if a random variable (of the dimensionality considered) has a continuous distribution, then this function of that random variable has a continuous distribution.

The first sample value used is that which is largest according to the ordering determined by the function; i.e., the sample value which yields the maximum function value. A statistical block, consisting of all points for which the function exceeds its value for the observation used, is removed; also this sample value is eliminated from the set of the observations that are used (for other than information purposes) in the remaining construction steps. To be certain of avoiding bias, the sample value which maximizes the function should become the only observation that is known to the experimenter at the end of this first step of the process. Moreover, knowledge of the value of this observation and of the fact that it maximizes the function should be all the information that becomes available. Then, on the basis of the supplementary information, the statistical block removed, the sample value eliminated, and the form desired for the tolerance region, a second function (of the specified type) is chosen for ordering the sample values that remain.

The second sample value used is that, of the remaining sample values, which maximizes the second function. Then, in the same manner, a second statistical block is removed (from the remaining region) on the basis of this maximum function value; also the second sample value used is eliminated. At this second step, to be sure of avoiding bias, only the sample value that is used should become known to the experimenter.

This stepwise procedure is continued until a prescribed number of statistical blocks have been removed. Then the remaining set of points is the tolerance region obtained by this version of the construction method. Here the number of blocks to be removed should be specified independently of the sample values.

Use of Supplementary Information

The probability properties for coverage are of a conditional nature when supplementary information is used in the construction of a tolerance region. That is, the supplementary information is considered to be fixed as far as the coverage probability properties of the tolerance region are concerned. However, the imposition of this condition on the probability model has no discernible adverse effects on the practical utility of tolerance regions determined through the use of supplementary information that is independent of the sample values.

One helpful type of supplementary information is knowledge (perhaps rather rough) concerning the location of the central part of the population; e.g., knowledge about the population mean can be very useful. Then, for the case of an n-variate population ($n \geqslant 1$), an n-dimensional "sphere" centered at this location often represents a desirable choice for the first function. When the situation is multivariate, approximate knowledge of relative values of the variances for the coordinates of the random variable can be useful. If rough knowledge of the population mean is also available, an "ellipsoid" centered at the approximate mean value and with axes whose lengths are in ratios determined from the approximate relative values for the coordinate variances often represents a desirable choice for the first function. Various other kinds of supplementary information can also be useful. Supplementary information tends to be most useful when the number of statistical blocks to be removed is quite small (say, one or two).

Freedom in Establishing Form of Region

The construction process allows the experimenter a great amount of freedom in determining the forms of the statistical blocks to be removed. This freedom arises from several sources. First, at each step the function used for determining the next block to be removed can be of a rather general type. Second, at each step additional information is available for use in selecting this region; namely, the forms of the regions already removed and the sample values removed. Third, supplementary information that is independent of the sample values can be used. By judicious exploitation of this freedom, a tolerance region can frequently be obtained that is at least roughly of the desired form. For the case of a bounded tolerance region, this implies that the shape is of the desired type and that the region is small enough to be useful.

Sources of Bias

At any given step, the principal source of bias in the construction procedure arises from the use of sample value information that should not have been available at that step. This unwarranted additional information may have an important influence on the selection of the function to be used at that step. Also bias can enter if the number of blocks to be removed in the construction is specified on the basis of sample value information. If a substantial amount of bias enters in the construction of a tolerance region, the actual probability distribution of the coverage for this region can differ appreciably from the distribution that applies when the construction is not biased.

Number of Blocks Removed at a Step

In the construction process that was considered for illustration purposes, a single statistical block is removed at each step. However, as mentioned previously, more than one block can be removed at a step. Also the decision as to the number of blocks to be removed at a given step can be based on sample information that became available from previous steps, although the total number of blocks to be removed should be specified without knowledge about the sample values.

The procedure of removing a single block per step is appropriate when only a few blocks are to be removed. Then maximum control is maintained over the form of the tolerance region. When the number of blocks to be removed is large, the amount of effort involved in the construction can be appreciably reduced, without much loss in control over the form of the region, by removing more than one block at some or all of the steps.

Another Type of Available Information

At each step of the construction, another type of information can become available. Namely, without knowledge about their values, the observations could be indexed in any desired fashion. The index values of the observations that have not been removed can be known to the experimenter at the end of each step (see ref. 272). This kind of information is not very helpful in obtaining desired forms for tolerance regions but can be useful in situations where alternatives to the condition of a random sample are considered. Information of this type is not considered any further in this chapter.

Remarks on Construction Methods Presented

The construction methods given in this handbook are based on the removal of statistical blocks, with the region sought being the set of points remaining after the prescribed number of blocks have been removed. This presentation approach is used because it allows direct control over the general form of the tolerance region without much loss of generality with respect to the types of tolerance regions that can be obtained. Also, by use of the procedure of removing one block at a time, a basic set of statistical blocks can be obtained; these statistical blocks can then be grouped in any desired (unbiased) fashion to form regions. However, other less restricted approaches to the construction of tolerance regions could be used. General results of this nature are given in ref. 182, 183, 188, 272, 524, 525.

RANDOMIZED AND INTERPOLATED REGIONS

Discussion

Here consideration is limited to the case of sampling from a continuous population and to tolerance regions (or subregions) whose population coverage is controlled as a unit. Then a tolerance region can be considered to consist of a specified number of statistical blocks. When the sample size is m, the possible numbers of blocks for a nontrivial region are

$1, 2, \ldots, m$. For this type of situation, the probability distribution of the population coverage for a tolerance region can be shown to depend only on m and the number of blocks used for the region. That is, the method used to construct the statistical blocks has no influence on the probability properties of the population coverage for a region formed from these blocks. This implies that, from the viewpoint of the distribution for population coverage, only m different types of tolerance regions are available for the type of situation considered.

This limitation on types of tolerance regions, with respect to probability distribution, can cause difficulties in obtaining desired values for expressions that are based on probability considerations. For example, consider

$$E\left\{\int_R dF\right\} \quad \text{and} \quad P\left\{\int_R dF \epsilon A\right\},$$

where R is a tolerance region of the type considered and A is a fixed subset of the interval $[0, 1]$. Each of these expressions is limited to m different nontrivial values (different from 0 and 1), one for each of the m nontrivial types of tolerance regions. In some cases, none of the possible values for a specified expression may be sufficiently close to the desired value. Then some procedure is needed for obtaining a tolerance region such that the specified expression has the desired value (either exactly or approximately). This section presents a randomized-exact scheme for exactly obtaining a desired value and an interpolation method for approximately obtaining a desired value.

Randomized-Exact Method

Let the expression considered be denoted by $p[R]$, where R is the tolerance region used. Two possibilities for $p[R]$ are $E\{\int_R dF\}$ and $P\{\int_R dF \epsilon A\}$. Also let $R(u)$ be any tolerance region that consists of u statistical blocks $(u = 1, \ldots, m)$ while γ is the value desired for $p[R]$. The situation considered is such that there exists an integer U for which γ lies between the values of $p[R(U)]$ and $p[R(U+1)]$, where $1 \leqslant U \leqslant m-1$. For this situation, the values of $p[R(U)]$ and $p[R(U+1)]$ can be exactly determined. The problem is, on the basis of a randomized-exact scheme, to obtain a region $R(U, \gamma)$ with the property that $p[R(U, \gamma)] = \gamma$.

Any randomized region $R(U, \gamma)$ that consists of U specified statistical blocks (chosen independently of the sample values) with probability

$$p(U, \gamma) = \{p[R(U+1)] - \gamma\} / \{p[R(U+1)] - p[R(U)]\},$$

and contains a specified additional block with probability $1 - p(U, \gamma)$, has the property that $p[R(U, \gamma)] = \gamma$. Here an independent probability process is used in determining $R(U, \gamma)$. This procedure for obtaining randomized tolerance regions is not the most general available but is easy to apply and seems to be satisfactory for many purposes.

A randomized-exact method has the advantage of yielding exact values for the expressions considered but the disadvantage that the set of available tolerance regions has not been extended to include more than $R(1), \ldots, R(m)$. That is, the tolerance region yielded by this randomized-exact scheme always equals one of $R(1), \ldots, R(m)$.

Interpolation Method

This scheme has the disadvantage of not being exact but the advantage of extending the set of tolerance regions. When an interpolated region is used, the value of the expression considered is approximately determined and lies between two known bounds.

Let U and γ be the same as for the randomized-exact case. Also let U statistical blocks and an additional block be specified (independently of the sample values), where the additional block is bounded. Then an interpolated region $R'(U, \gamma)$ is furnished by the U blocks plus $100[1-p(U, \gamma)]$ per cent of the additional block; here the part of the additional block used is that which is nearest (in some given sense) to the U blocks. This interpolated region has the properties that $p[R'(U, \gamma)] \doteq \gamma$ and that the true value lies between $p[R(U)]$ and $p[R(U+1)]$ in all cases.

Remark

In a similar fashion, randomized and interpolated results can be obtained for situations where a tolerance region (or subregion) consists of two or more parts such that the amount of population coverage is controlled separately for each part. Then, ordinarily, randomizing or interpolation is applied to only one of the separately controlled parts of a region.

THE CONTINUOUS, PARTIALLY CONTINUOUS, AND DISCONTINUOUS CASES

Consider a population with a random variable that may be multivariate. The continuous case occurs when the population is continuous; this implies that each coordinate of the random variable has a continuous distribution. The partially continuous case occurs if at least one coordinate of the random variable has a continuous distribution (conditionally continuous for all possible values of the other coordinates). If the population is univariate, the continuous and the partially continuous cases are the same. The discontinuous case occurs if, simultaneously, the random variable can be discontinuous in every coordinate; that is, equality of sample values can occur with nonzero probability.

The method used to construct tolerance regions for the partially continuous case is of the same type as that presented for the discontinuous case. However, the coverage probability properties for the regions obtained are the same as those which occur for the continuous case. This mixed construction and probability property situation happens because, although some of the entries can have certain values with nonzero probability, the probability that any of the sample values will be equal is zero. The construction method eliminates all "ties" for which the observations are unequal. With this ambiguity removed, the tolerance regions have the coverage probability properties that exist for the continuous case.

EXPRESSIONS FOR PROBABILITY DISTRIBUTIONS

Consideration is limited to exact nonrandomized results for the continuous and partially continuous cases. The sample size is m and only population coverage situations are examined. Then a tolerance region (or subregion) can be considered to consist of a specified number of statistical blocks, which may be divided into groups such that the population coverage for each group is controlled separately. Here a tolerance region consists of at least one block but of not more than m blocks.

From a complication viewpoint, the most general situation is that where the tolerance region consists of m blocks and the population coverage is controlled separately for each block. Let c_u denote the random population coverage for the uth block ($u=1, \ldots, m$). Then, irrespective of the details of the construction method used to obtain the blocks and of which block is represented by c_u ($u=1, \ldots, m$), the joint frequency function of the c_u is

$$f(c_1, \ldots, c_m)=m!,$$

where $c_u \geqslant 0$ and $\sum_{u=1}^{m} c_u \leqslant 1$. Thus, for specified sets A_u in [0, 1],

$$P(c_1 \epsilon A_1, \ldots, c_m \epsilon A_m)=m! \int_{A'_m} \ldots \int_{A'_1} dc_1 \ldots dc_m,$$

where $A'_u=A'_u(c_{u+1}, \ldots, c_m)$ is the set of points such that $c_u \epsilon A_u$ and $c_u \leqslant 1-\sum_{v=u+1}^{m} c_v$, ($u=1, \ldots, m-1$); also $A'_m=A_m$.

The appropriate frequency function for any given situation can be obtained directly from the joint frequency function $f(c_1, \ldots, c_m)$. For example, consider the situation where the region consists of $r+s$ blocks ($r \geqslant 1$, $s \geqslant 1$, $r+s \leqslant m$) which are divided into sets of r and s blocks with the population coverage being separately controlled for each of the two sets. Let V represent the coverage for the set of r blocks and W the coverage for the set of s blocks. Then, by making the change of variable

$$V=c_1+\ldots+c_r, \quad W=c_{r+1}+\ldots+c_{r+s}, \quad c_2=c_2, \ldots, c_{r+s-1}=c_{r+s-1}$$

and integrating out all the variables except V and W, the joint frequency function of V and W is found to be

$$f(V, W) = \frac{m!}{(r-1)!(s-1)!(m-r-s)!} V^{r-1}W^{s-1}(1-V-W)^{m-r-s},$$

where $V \geqslant 0$, $W \geqslant 0$, and $V+W \leqslant 1$. Thus, for specified sets B_1, B_2 in $[0, 1]$,

$$P(V \epsilon B_1, W \epsilon B_2) = \int_{B'_2} \int_{B'_1} f(V, W) dV dW,$$

where $B'_1 = B'_1(W)$ is the set of points such that $V \epsilon B_1$ and $V \leqslant 1-W$; also $B'_2 = B_2$.

If a region consists of t blocks $(1 \leqslant t \leqslant m)$ and its population coverage is controlled as a unit, then the frequency function of its coverage T is

$$f(T) = \frac{m!}{(t-1)!(m-t)!} T^{t-1}(1-T)^{m-t},$$

where $0 \leqslant T \leqslant 1$. Thus, for a specified set A in $[0, 1]$,

$$P(T \epsilon A) = \int_A f(T) dT.$$

If, as is often the case, the set A is an interval $[a, b]$,

$$P(a \leqslant T \leqslant b) = \int_a^b f(T) dT = I_b(t, m+1-t) - I_a(t, m+1-t),$$

where

$$I_p(t, m+1-t) = \sum_{i=t}^{m} \binom{m}{i} p^i (1-p)^{m-i},$$

is the Pearson incomplete beta function. Thus, for given a, b, m, and t, $P(a \leqslant T \leqslant b)$ can be evaluated by use of tables of the incomplete beta function, tables of the binomial distribution, or approximations to the binomial distribution (see binomial distribution section of Chapter 7). The problem of determining m for given values of a, b, t, and $P(a \leqslant T \leqslant b)$ is considered on pages 245–51.

The special case where the population sampled is multivariate and such that the coordinates of the random variable are independent in known groups can be handled in terms of the probability expressions presented. Namely, then the frequency function for a tolerance region equals the product of the frequency functions for the subregions of this tolerance region.

DISCONTINUOUS SITUATIONS

Most of the probability material presented in this chapter is for the continuous and partially continuous situations. Strictly speaking, however, only the discontinuous case occurs in practice, due to limitations in measurement accuracy. Consequently, distribution-free tolerance region results that are applicable for discontinuous situations are of practical interest.

In the presentations, tolerance regions for the discontinuous case are only considered from the viewpoint of population coverage. These regions are approximate in the sense that their coverage probability properties are bounded rather than precisely determined. Upper and lower bounds, one of which is conditional with respect to the ties among the sample values, are obtained for the values of the probability expressions considered. These bounds tend to be moderately close together when the random variable, which is discontinuous in all its coordinates, is only mildly discontinuous with respect to at least one coordinate.

For the types of probability relations considered, each bound can be stated in terms of the probability expressions that occur for the continuous and partially continuous cases. That is, the bound values for discontinuous situations can be determined on the basis of the coverage probability distribution results that occur for the continuous and partially continuous cases.

CONVERSION OF DISCONTINUOUS CASE TO PARTIALLY CONTINUOUS CASE

An independent probability process can be introduced to convert the discontinuous case to the partially continuous case. However, then the coverage investigated is for the joint population consisting of the population sampled and the population used for the conversion. One way of accomplishing this conversion consists in using a random variable of the form (w, y), where w is a random value from the discontinuous population and y is an independent random value from the uniform distribution $[0, 1]$. Then the coverage of a tolerance region is with respect to the population with random variable (w, y). Although pertaining to (w, y), the results obtained on the basis of the conversion have implications about the coverage of the discontinuous population by the part of the region that is concerned with the value of w (see ref. 183, 184).

Another way is along the lines of that outlined in Chapter 4. Namely, an infinitesimally small value from a continuous population is added to at least one coordinate (all coordinates, if continuous data desired) of each observation (which may be univariate). Since the observations are a random sample, the random sample property is preserved if the infinitesimally small values are a sample and are added to the same coordinate (or coordinates) for each observation. Using this method, a sample is obtained that is from a population which is at least partially continuous and which differs very slightly from the original population. For the tolerance region results considered, the only use made of at least partial continuity is to establish an ordering among the values within one or more specified sets of observations or functions of observations. Consequently, the data are converted to a form that can be considered at least partially continuous, but from a different population, if randomization is used to break ties that are not resolved by the method used in constructing a tolerance region.

Randomization can also be used to break ties for situations where the population sampled is not considered to be converted to a form that is at least partially continuous. Then the population remains discontinuous and the probabilities of the coverage relations considered are bounded rather than exact. This use of randomization is for avoiding bias in the selection of the observations to be discarded at the various construction steps rather than to change the population to a form where exact probability results are obtained.

GENERALITY OF APPLICATION AREAS

The distribution-free character of the statistical procedures considered in this chapter has implications concerning the generality of the areas in which these results are applicable. As an example, for a random variable of given dimensionality, there is an extensive class of functions (real-valued and vector-valued) such that each of these functions preserves distribution continuity. That is, for any function of the class, this function of the random variable has a continuous distribution if the random variable has a continuous distribution. As another example, suppose that the sample size is even and that the sample values have been paired in some fashion that is independent of their values. Then a new sample can be formed by replacing each pair of observations by a suitable function of their values (the same function for each pair); here too this function could be multidimensional and, of course, the sample values can be multivariate. The function used might be the difference of the values for a pair, the arithmetic average of the values for a pair, etc.

Thus, by suitable combinations and change of variable, a set of transformed sample values can be obtained such that the underlying population is concerned with a property that is of interest. Then the probability concentration in this transformed population can be investigated through the use of tolerance regions that are based on the modified sample values.

REMARKS ON PERMISSIBLE FORMS FOR REGIONS

Necessary and sufficient conditions for a tolerance region to be distribution-free with an exactly determined probability distribution for its population coverage are given in ref. 186 and 187 for the continuous case. However, these conditions are not very useful in identifying the allowable forms for the tolerance regions except for the univariate situation and one-sided tolerance intervals. Then (also see ref. 184, 432) the variable endpoint of the tolerance interval must be one of the sample order statistics; i.e., one of $X[i]$, $(i=0, \ldots, n+1)$, where n is the sample size. For the nonrandomized case, this limit is a specified one of $X[1], \ldots, X[n]$. For a general method of obtaining randomized one-sided intervals, one of the $X[i]$, $(i=0, \ldots, n+1)$, is chosen for this limit by use of an independent probability process with the property that each of the $X[i]$ has a specified probability of being used.

Although the variable limit for a one-sided tolerance interval must be a single one of the $X[i]$, this is not the case for the limits of two-sided tolerance intervals. For example, the two-sided interval with limits $x_0 \pm \max \{|X[n]-x_0|, |x_0-X[1]|\}$, where x_0 is arbitrary but specified (independently of the sample values), is distribution-free.

DISCUSSION OF SEQUENTIAL CASE

No presentations are given for sequential determination of tolerance regions. A sequential procedure for determining tolerance intervals has been developed by Jiřina (see ref. 261). However, this procedure is equivalent to using a specified probability distribution for the possible sample sizes, choosing a sample size n at random from this known distribution, and then using the appropriate interval of the form $(X[i_1], X[i_2])$, $0 \leqslant i_1 < i_2 \leqslant n+1$ (the handbook author is indebted to W. Hoeffding for this alternate interpretation of Jiřina's sequential results).

EFFICIENCY DETERMINATION

Introduction

When the population sampled is known to belong to a specified class of parametric populations, efficiency is virtually always lost by using a distribution-free tolerance region rather than a corresponding region that fully exploits this information. Knowledge of the amount of efficiency lost can be valuable in deciding whether to use a distribution-free tolerance region for a given situation. This section contains a discussion of the problem of determining efficiencies for distribution-free tolerance regions. Here tolerance regions are considered from the viewpoint of population coverage and have exact probability properties for coverage.

Required Inputs

Suppose that the population sampled is known to belong to a specified parametric class. Then, to determine the efficiency of given distribution-free tolerance region, two kinds of input information are needed. First, knowledge of the coverage probability properties for the corresponding most desirable type of region must be available. Second, a suitable method should be available for determining the relative efficiency of the distribution-free region with respect to the most desirable region.

The problem of determining the coverage probability properties of the corresponding most desirable tolerance region is not considered here. However, this can sometimes be accomplished, in a feasible manner, by the method presented in ref. 186 and 187. This determination has been made for the cases where efficiency values are given in this chapter.

The features of a suitable procedure for determining relative efficiencies with respect to the most desirable tolerance region are considered in this section. A general method is outlined and several ways of applying this method are discussed.

Assumptions

In developing a general method of determining efficiencies for a parametric class of populations, two assumptions are made about the situation considered. First, for each sample size of interest, a most desirable tolerance region exists which has the same general form and satisfies the same purpose as the distribution-free tolerance region whose efficiency is being determined. Second, the distribution-free region and each of the most desirable regions has a population coverage distribution that is fixed for all populations of the parametric class. These assumptions are satisfied for all the efficiency results (with respect to parametric classes of populations) that are given in the statistical procedure presentations.

One purpose for a tolerance region is expected value estimation of a specified amount of population coverage. Another purpose is, with a given probability of success, to cover at least a specified amount of the population.

Outline of General Method

Since the coverage probability distribution for a tolerance region is the same for all populations of the parametric class, efficiency values can be determined on the basis of a specified population of the class. Then no unknown parameters are involved and all probabilities can be obtained directly. Consequently, the general method for obtaining efficiencies is stated in terms of the case of a given population that is completely specified.

Let us consider the general approach followed in evaluating the efficiency of a distribution-free region for the case of a given population. The procedure is to determine the sample size for that most desirable region which is equivalent to the distribution-free region in a specified sense. Here two regions are considered to be equivalent if they have the same general form, satisfy the same purpose, and have coverage probability distributions that are equivalent in some stated manner. Given the sample size for the equivalent most desirable region, the ratio of this value divided by that for the distribution-free region is the efficiency of the distribution-free region. Here the sample size for the equivalent most desirable region can be fractional (obtained by interpolation).

Actually, the specified purpose of a tolerance region, as considered in this handbook, represents a population coverage probability property. Consequently, equivalence of coverage probability distributions can be considered to imply that the tolerance regions have the same purpose. However, due to some advantages with regard to presentation of material, the purpose of a tolerance region is considered as a separate property.

Interpretations of Distribution Equivalence

If the purpose is expected value estimation of a specified amount of population coverage, equality of mean square errors for the coverage distributions of the distribution-free region and the most desirable region (same general form and purpose) seems to furnish a reasonable interpretation of coverage distribution equivalence. This also appears to be the case if the purpose is, with a given probability of success, to cover at least a specified amount of the population, especially if the coverage distributions are of at least roughly the same shape. However, for some situations, more refined measures of coverage distribution equivalence may be desirable.

The method of determining efficiencies in which the expected values and the mean square errors of the coverage distributions are required to be the same, respectively, has the advantage that it is frequently easy to apply. That is, the sample size for the distribution-free region is usually large and the situation is often such that reasonably accurate asymptotic approximations can be obtained for the mean and mean square error of the coverage distributions considered; for large sample sizes, the mean square error of an estimate is usually about equal to its variance. Another advantage is that results can frequently be obtained which, at least for large sample sizes, are valid for broad classes of populations. Strictly speaking, the efficiency values obtained by this method are only applicable when the purpose is expected value estimation. However, in nearly all cases these efficiencies should furnish at least a rough indication of the corresponding values for the situation where the purpose is, with a given probability, to cover at least a specified amount of the population.

DETERMINATION OF REQUIRED SAMPLE SIZES

Introduction

The results presented in this section are concerned with population coverage and are obtained for the continuous and partially continuous cases. For the general situation, the tolerance regions considered are of a nonrandomized nature and such that the population coverage is controlled as a unit; also these regions have exact coverage probability properties. Then a tolerance region can be considered to consist of a number of statistical blocks equal to $m+1$ minus the number of blocks removed in the construction of this region, where m is the sample size. If, as is the case for this section, the number of blocks to be removed is fixed, the required sample size is determined by the purpose to be satisfied.

Similar remarks apply to the special situation where the population sampled is multivariate with a random variable whose coordinates are independent in known groups (then a tolerance region is a combination of individually controlled subregions). Namely, the situation considered is that where the population coverage for each subregion is controlled as a unit and where the number of blocks removed in its construction is specified for each subregion. Then the purpose of the tolerance region determines the sample size.

In presenting the results, a tolerance region is considered to consist of a specified number of subregions. The general situation is represented by the case of one subregion and the special situation is the case of two or more subregions. The relation of required sample sizes to adequate sample sizes is discussed in Chapter 4.

Two types of purposes are considered. One purpose is expected value estimation of a specified amount of population coverage. The other type of purpose is, with a given probability of success, to cover at least a specified amount of the population.

If the tolerance region consists of three or more subregions, cut-and-try seems to be as good a method as any for determining the required sample size when a specified purpose is to be satisfied. When only one or two subregions are involved, specialized methods are available for determining required sample sizes.

Sample Sizes for Expected Value Estimates

Suppose that there are s independent groups of coordinates and that r_k blocks are removed in determining the subregion for the kth group ($k=1, \ldots, s$; $s \geqslant 1$). Then the expected coverage for the tolerance region is the product of the expected coverages for the subregions. If the purpose for the tolerance region specifies that the expected coverage has the value γ, then the value of m is determined from

$$\prod_{k=1}^{s} [1-r_k/(m+1)]=\gamma,$$

subject to integer restrictions. For $s \geqslant 3$, m is evaluated by some appropriate cut-and-try procedure.

When $s=1$, m is the smallest integer with a value at least equal to $-1+r_1/(1-\gamma)$. For $s=2$, the value of m can be determined by solving a quadratic equation.

Sample Sizes for Minimum Coverage Purpose

Again suppose that there are s independent groups and that r_k blocks are removed in obtaining the subregion for the kth group; also let $C_k=C(r_k, m)$ represent the random coverage for the kth subregion. Then the purpose of the tolerance region is to satisfy the relation

$$P[C_k \geqslant a(k);\ k=1, \ldots, s]=\prod_{k=1}^{s} P[C_k \geqslant a(k)]=\beta,$$

where the $a(k)$ and β are specified. The problem is, subject to integer restrictions, to determine the value of m that satisfies this equation. In terms of the Pearson incomplete beta function, or the binomial distribution,

$$\prod_{k=1}^{s} I_{1-a(k)}(m+1-r_k, r_k)=\prod_{k=1}^{s}\left\{\sum_{j=m+1-r_k}^{m}\binom{m}{j}[1-a(k)]^j a(k)^{m-j}\right\}=\beta$$

is the equation to be solved for m, subject to integer restrictions. For $s \geqslant 3$, the value of m is determined by some appropriate cut-and-try procedure.

When $s=1$, the value of m can often be obtained through use of the graphs given in Fig. 9.1 for $\beta=.90, .95, .99$. Here $a=a(1)$ is graphed as a function of m for various values of $r=r_1$. If $r=2$, the graph given in Fig. 9.2 can frequently be used (also see ref. 463). For general r, inverse use of tables for the incomplete beta function or for the binomial distribution will furnish the value for m in many cases. An approximate method, which is easily applied, consists in using the smallest integer with a value at least equal to

$$\tfrac{1}{4}[(1+a)/(1-a)]\chi^2_{1-\beta}(2r)+(r-1)/2$$

for m. This method is presented in ref. 460.

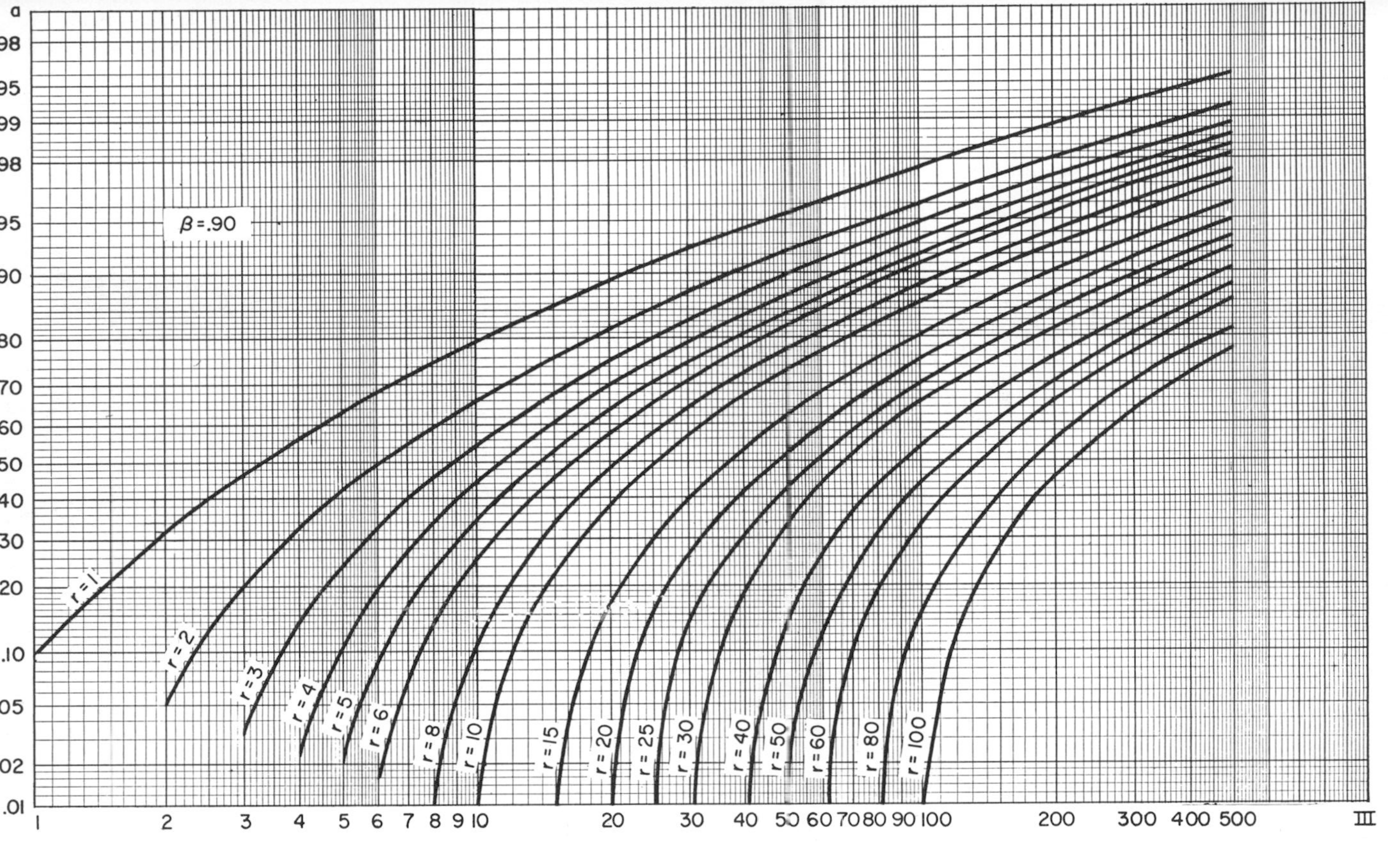

FIG. 9-1. Graphs of Population Coverage for the Tolerance Level .90. Based on ref. 370: Non-parametric tolerance limits, R. B. Murphy, *Annals of Mathematical Statistics*, Vol. 19, 1948, pages 581–89. Used with the kind permission of the author, R. B. Murphy, and of the Editor of the *Annals of Mathematical Statistics*.

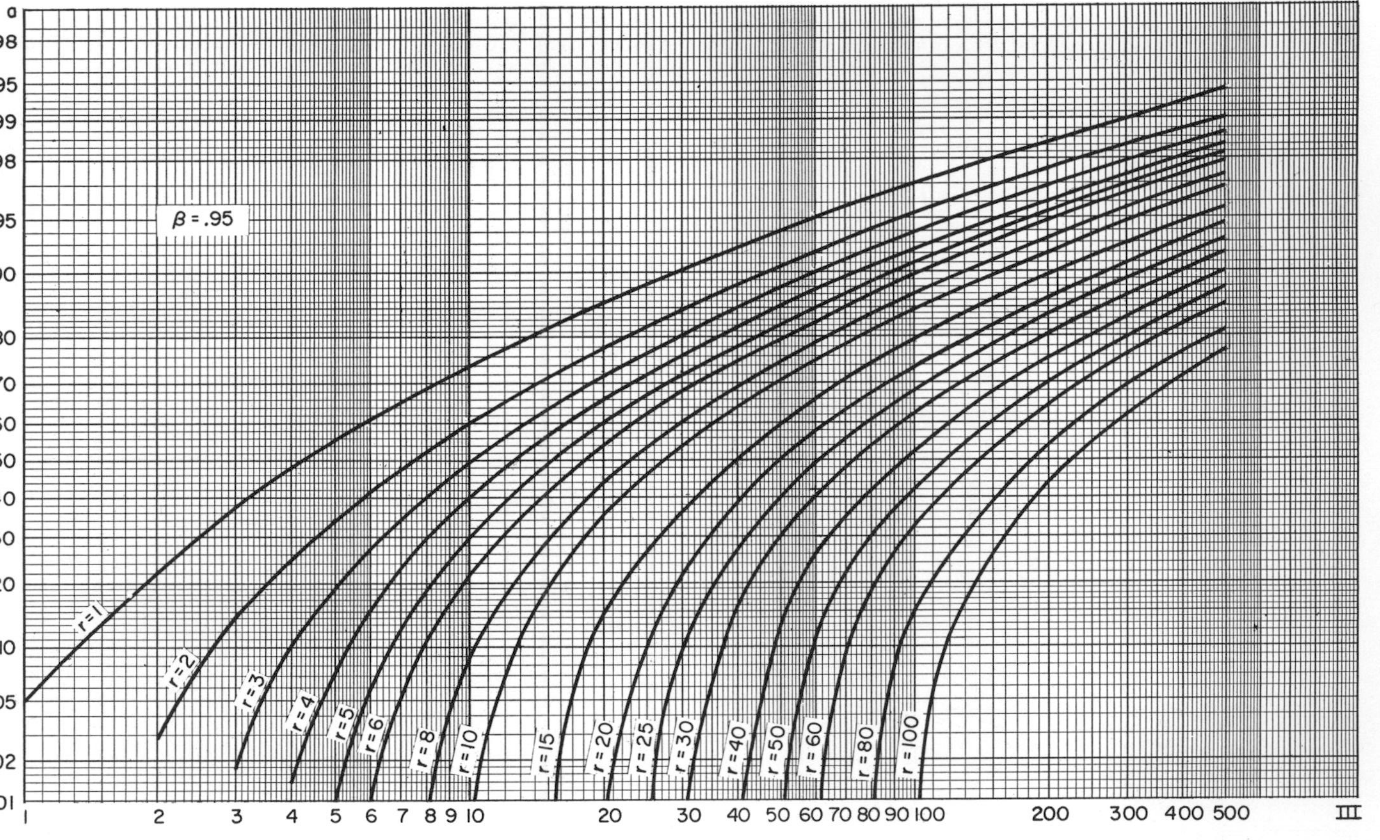

FIG. 9-1. Graphs of Population Coverage for the Tolerance Level .95. Based on ref. 370: Non-parametric tolerance limits, R. B. Murphy, *Annals of Mathematical Statistics*, Vol. 19, 1948, pages 581–89. Used with the kind permission of the author, R. B. Murphy, and of the Editor of the *Annals of Mathematical Statistics*.

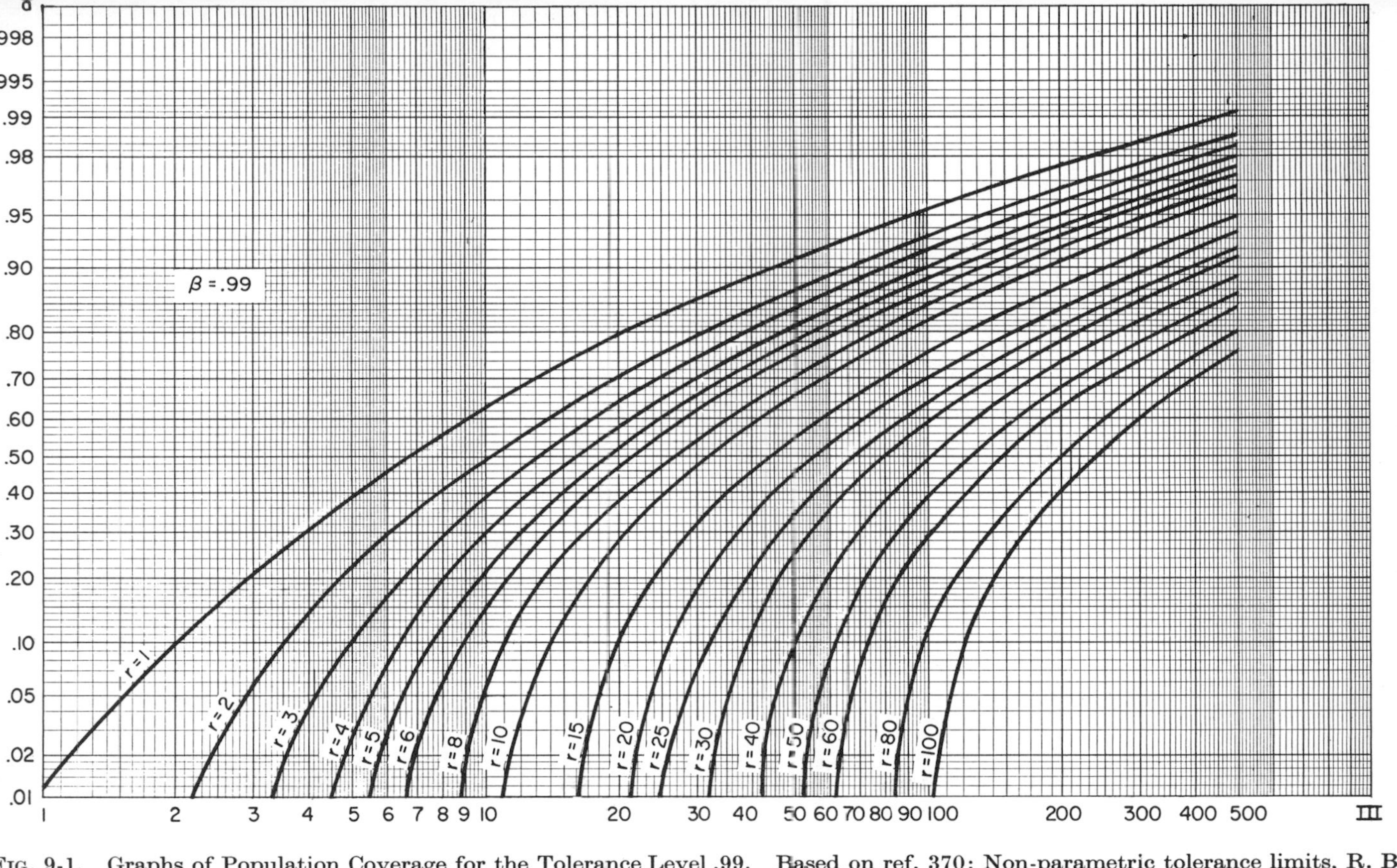

Fig. 9-1. Graphs of Population Coverage for the Tolerance Level .99. Based on ref. 370: Non-parametric tolerance limits, R. B. Murphy, *Annals of Mathematical Statistics*, Vol. 19, 1948, pages 581–89. Used with the kind permission of the author, R. B. Murphy, and of the Editor of the *Annals of Mathematical Statistics*.

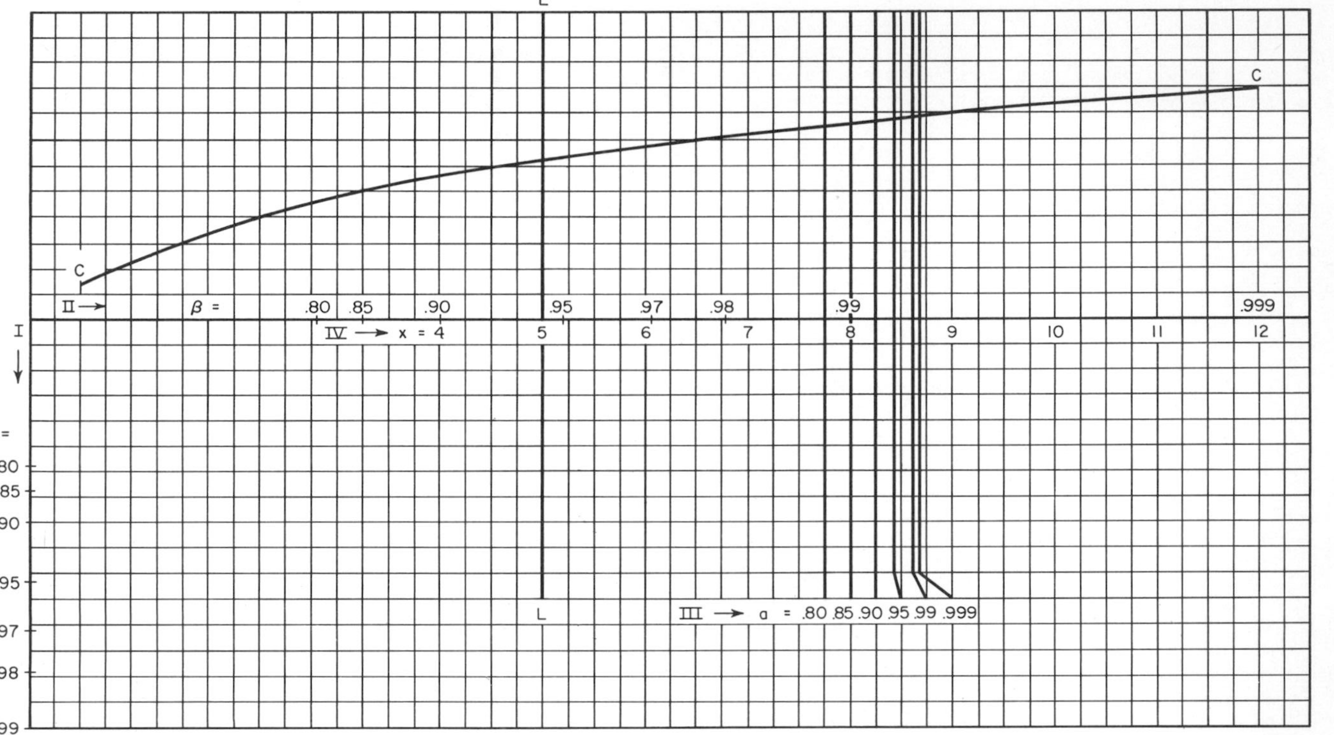

FIG. 9.2. Graph for Determining m (in Four Steps) When $r=2$. (1) Connect β on Scale I and β on Scale II with a straight line; this line cuts vertical line marked a on Scale III at point P, (2) locate on line L the point with the ordinate of P; call this point Q, (3) connect β on Scale I with Q; the connecting line cuts curve C at a point which has abscissa x on Scale IV; read off x, (4) Compute $m=x\,\frac{a}{1-a}$.

Based on ref. 62: A graphical determination of sample size for Wilks' tolerance limits, Z. W. Birnbaum and H. S. Zuckerman, *Annals of Mathematical Statistics*, Vol. 20, 1949, pages 313–16. Used with the kind permission of the authors, Z. W. Birnbaum and H. S. Zuckerman, and of the Editor of the *Annals of Mathematical Statistics*.

When $s=2$, a cut-and-try procedure of the type used for $s \geqslant 3$ could be employed. An alternate method is to determine $\beta(1)$ so that $\beta < \beta(1) < 1$ and also the relation

$$\{[1+a(1)]/[1-a(1)]\}\chi^2_{1-\beta(1)}(2r_1)+2(r_1-1) = \{[1+a(2)]/[1-a(2)]\}\chi^2_{1-\beta/\beta(1)}(2r_2)+2(r_2-1)$$

is satisfied. Then the smallest integer with a value at least equal to

$$\tfrac{1}{4}\{[1+a(1)]/[1-a(1)]\}\chi^2_{1-\beta(1)}(2r_1)+(r_1-1)/2$$

is used for m.

OUTLINE OF STATISTICAL PROCEDURE PRESENTATIONS

The first of the sections that present statistical procedures is concerned with point estimation of a region that has a specified amount of population coverage. Expected value and median estimation (with respect to the amount of population coverage) are considered. The second section containing statistical procedures presents population coverage results for the case of sampling from a univariate population. The third section contains population coverage results for the case of sampling from a multivariate population. The fourth and final section containing statistical procedures is concerned with statistical prediction. Here an expression is given for the distribution function of the number values of an independent second sample that are contained in a tolerance region determined from a first sample. This expression furnishes the basis for various types of statistical predictions.

POINT ESTIMATION OF REGION WITH SPECIFIED POPULATION COVERAGE

Introduction

Expected value and median point estimation are considered from the viewpoint of population coverage. The exact nonrandomized results that are stated apply to the continuous and partially continuous cases. Randomized and interpolated estimates are presented for the continuous case. In every situation examined, the coverage of the tolerance region used for estimation can be considered to be controlled as a unit. Also, none of the observation coordinates are considered to be independent in known groups. That is, in situations where the observation coordinates are independent in known groups, the estimates presented are for subregions. Suitable selection and combination of the estimates for its subregions can be used to furnish a satisfactory estimate for the entire tolerance region (see the discussion of the use of subregions that is given on page 265.

Quantity Estimated

Although the probability properties of the estimates are expressed in terms of population coverage, an estimate is actually a region of the space of possible values for an observation and the quantity estimated is also a region of this space. Namely, the quantity estimated is a region that covers a specified amount of the population sampled; it is identified by this requirement and the requirement of having a specified general form. Here the general form of the region estimated is determined by the general form of the tolerance region used for the estimation.

The form of a tolerance region is chosen on the basis of that part of the population for which coverage is of primary interest. As an example, if the central part of the population is of major interest, the statistical blocks discarded are in the sample tails; etc. A more detailed discussion of the considerations in the choice of the form for a tolerance region is given in the following two presentation sections (Univariate Case, Multivariate Case).

Estimation Methods

All estimation probability properties are concerned with population coverage. A tolerance region is an expected value estimate of a region with a specified amount of coverage if the expected coverage of the tolerance region equals the specified amount. Likewise, a tolerance region is a median estimate if the specified amount of coverage for the region estimated is a median of the coverage probability distribution for the tolerance region.

For the situation considered, an exact nonrandomized tolerance region consists of a given number of statistical blocks. Thus, for a fixed sample size m, only m nontrivial values are available for the expected coverage of a region of this type. However, for the continuous case, if tolerance regions with intermediate expected coverages are desired, they can be exactly obtained by use of randomization and approximately obtained through interpolation. Likewise, for a given sample size, a nonrandomized tolerance region that is an exact median estimate exists for only m values for the specified amount of coverage. If regions are desired which are median estimates where the specified coverage has other (intermediate) values, these regions can be exactly obtained by randomization and approximately obtained by interpolation, for the continuous case.

The procedures for obtaining randomized and interpolated tolerance regions have already been described in sufficient detail for application purposes. However, to illustrate the use of these methods, randomized and interpolated tolerance regions are considered in the presentations of expected value and median estimates. Results are given for the continuous univariate, the continuous multivariate, and the partially continuous multivariate cases.

Efficiency Evaluation

For the situations of this section, the relative desirability of an estimate can be measured in terms of the expected variation of its population coverage about the amount of coverage being estimated, as furnished by the mean square error. Expressions for this expected variation are stated for the estimation cases considered.

When the tolerance region is obtained by interpolation, the expected variation of its coverage about the quantity estimated is approximated by a method that is similar to the interpolation procedure: First, the mean square error values are determined for the two exact situations on which the interpolation that yielded the region is based. Then the mean square error value for the interpolated region is approximated by the weighted sum of the mean square errors for the exact situations; here the weights are the same as were used in determining the interpolated region.

Efficiency values are given only for large samples from a univariate normal population. Then distribution-free tolerance intervals for which the same number of statistical blocks were removed from each tail are compared with $M(i) \pm KS(i)$ tolerance intervals; also one-sided distribution-free intervals are compared with one-sided intervals whose variable endpoints are of the form $M(i)+KS(i)$ or of the form $M(i)-KS(i)$.

Outline of Presentations

Only two presentations are given for point estimates. In both presentations, exact nonrandomized regions are considered for the continuous and partially continuous cases while randomized and interpolated regions are considered for the continuous case. The first presentation is concerned with expected value estimation; the other presentation is devoted to median estimation.

Fixed Material for Section

Data 1 Univariate or multivariate. Case (I): Continuous; Case (II): Partially continuous **2** Construct tolerance region so that it has desired general form **3** $\{X(i)_j\}_m$ **4** m = sample size; $n_1 = \ldots = n_m \geqslant 1$ **Assumptions 1** Random sample **2** Case (I): Continuous population. Case (II): Partially continuous pop. **3** None **Results 1** $R(u)$ is region consisting of u specified statistical blocks ($1 \leqslant u \leqslant m$); $R_u(1)$ is specified additional block and $R(u+1) = R(u) + R_u(1)$ **4** Methods for constructing the $R(u)$ given in Univariate Case and Multivariate Case sects. **Characteristics 1** Low, unless m excessive or region difficult to construct **2** For sample from univariate normal population, two-sided tolerance interval with same no. blocks removed from each tail has asymptotic efficiency $t^2_{(1-\gamma)/2}(m-1)$ $[\pi\gamma(1-\gamma)]^{-1}\exp[-t^2_{(1-\gamma)/2}(m-1)]$, where γ expected pop. coverage of two-sided interval; when $\gamma=.99$, asympt. efficiency is 28 per cent. For normality and one-sided tolerance interval, asymptotic efficiency is $[2+t^2_{(1-\delta)/2}(m-1)][\pi(1-\delta^2)]^{-1}\exp[-t^2_{(1-\delta)/2}(m-1)]$, where $(1+\delta)/2$ is expected pop. coverage of one-sided interval; when $\delta=.99$, asympt. efficiency is 18 per cent **3** Used symmetrically **4** Only mildly sensitive to Case (I) assumption if Case (II) holds. Sample condition must be satisfied to reasonable approx. Moderately sensitive to continuity requirements for Case (II) **5** Not difficult to decide on sample and continuity assumptions **6** None **Bibliography** Ref. 184, 186, 588.

Expected Value Estimates

Description 1 Exact (nonrandomized), randomized, and interpolated expected value estimates (with respect to pop. coverage) **2** Tolerance region R such that $E\{\int_R dF\}$ has specified value γ (exactly or approximately) **Results 1** $1/(m+1)\leqslant\gamma\leqslant m/(m+1)$. U is the integer such that $U/(m+1)\leqslant\gamma<(U+1)/(m+1)$. $R(U,\gamma)$ is region that equals $R(U)$ with prob. $U+1-(m+1)\gamma$ and equals $R(U+1)$ with prob. $(m+1)\gamma-U$, where independent prob. process used. For $R_U(1)$ bounded, $R'(U,\gamma)=R(U)$ plus that $100[(m+1)\gamma-U]$ per cent of $R_U(1)$ which is nearest to $R(U)$ in some specified sense (e.g., min Euclidean distance) **2** *Estimates. Exact*: For Cases (I) and (II), $E\{\int_{R(u)}dF\}=u/(m+1)$. *Randomized*: For Case (I), $E\{\int_{R(U,\gamma)}dF\}=\gamma$. *Interpolated*: For Case (I), $E\{\int_{R'(U,\gamma)}dF\}\doteq\gamma$ and $U/(m+1)\leqslant E\{\int_{R'(U,\gamma)}dF\}\leqslant(U+1)/(m+1)$ **3** None **Characteristics 2** For Cases (I) and (II), $\sigma^2\{\int_{R(u)}dF\}=u(m+1-u)/(m+1)^2(m+2)$. For Case (I), $\sigma^2\{\int_{R(U,\gamma)}dF\}\doteq[U+1-(m+1)\gamma]E\{\int_{R(U)}dF-\gamma\}^2+[(m+1)\gamma-U]E\{\int_{R(U+1)}dF-\gamma\}^2=[U+1-(m+1)\gamma][U(U+1)/(m+1)(m+2)-2\gamma U/(m+1)+\gamma^2]+[(m+1)\gamma-U][(U+1)(U+2)/(m+1)(m+2)-2\gamma(U+1)/(m+1)+\gamma^2]$. For Case (I), $\sigma^2\{\int_{R'(U,\gamma)}dF\}\doteq[U+1-(m+1)\gamma]\sigma^2\{\int_{R(U)}dF\}+[(m+1)\gamma-U]\sigma^2\{\int_{R(U+1)}dF\}$.

Median Estimates

Description 1 Median estimates (of exact, randomized, and interpolated types) **2** Tolerance region R such that $P\{\int_R dF\geqslant a\}=\frac{1}{2}$ (exactly or approximately) **Results 1** $1-(1/2)^{1/m}\leqslant a\leqslant(1/2)^{1/m}$. $a(t)$ is solution of $I_{1-a(t)}(m+1-t,t)=\sum_{i=0}^{t-1}\binom{m}{i}a(t)^i[1-a(t)]^{m-i}=\frac{1}{2}$, $(t=1,\ldots,m)$; for specified value of $a(t)$, required value for m can be obtained by methods given in Determination of Required Sample Sizes sect. T is the integer such that $I_{1-a}(m+1-T,T)\leqslant\frac{1}{2}\leqslant I_{1-a}(m-T,T+1)$. $r(T)$ is region that equals $R(T)$ with prob. $p(T)=[I_{1-a}(m-T, T+1)-\frac{1}{2}]/[I_{1-a}(m-T,T+1) - I_{1-a}(m+1-T, T)]$ and equals $R(T+1)$ with prob. $1-p(T)$. For $R_T(1)$ bounded, $r'(T)=R(T)$ plus that $100[1-p(T)]$ per cent of $R_T(1)$ which is nearest to $R(T)$ in some specified sense (e.g., min Euclidean distance) **2** *Estimates.* *Exact*: For Cases (I) and (II), $P\{\int_{R(t)} dF \geqslant a(t)\}=\frac{1}{2}$. *Randomized*: For Case (I), $P\{\int_{r(T)} dF \geqslant a\}=\frac{1}{2}$. *Interpolated*: For Case (I), $P\{\int_{r'(T)} dF \geqslant a\} \doteq \frac{1}{2}$ and $I_{1-a}(m+1-T, T) \leqslant P\{\int_{r'(T)} dF \geqslant a\} \leqslant I_{1-a}(m-T, T+1)$ **3** See binomial dist. sect. of Chapter 7 for methods of evaluating incomplete beta expressions **Characteristics 2** For Cases (I) and (II), $E\{\int_{R(t)} dF - a(t)\}^2 = t(t+1)/(m+1)(m+2) - 2ta(t)/(m+1) + a(t)^2$. For Case (I), $E\{\int_{r(T)} dF - a\}^2 \doteq p(T)E\{\int_{R(T)} dF - a\}^2 + [1-p(T)]E\{\int_{R(T+1)} dF - a\}^2$. For Case (I), $E\{\int_{r'(T)} dF - a\}^2 \doteq p(T)E\{\int_{R(T)} dF - a(T)\}^2 + [1-p(T)] E\{\int_{R(T+1)} dF - a(T+1)\}^2$.

UNIVARIATE CASE—GENERAL RESULTS

Introduction

This section is concerned with the construction and properties of tolerance regions when the population sampled is univariate. Both the continuous and the discontinuous cases are considered. For continuous cases, the probability properties for population coverage can be obtained on the basis of material that is given in preceding sections of this chapter and are not stated in the presentations. However, some of the probability properties with respect to population coverage are stated when the population sampled is discontinuous. Several suitable two-sided tolerance tolerance intervals are specified for exact situations where 1, 2, 3, or 4 statistical blocks are to be removed.

Types of Regions Considered

In all cases, the tolerance regions considered are closed sets. This limitation was motivated by the ease with which probability properties can be specified for the discontinuous case when the tolerance region used is closed.

From a practical viewpoint, the most important types of tolerance regions for the univariate case are the one-sided and two-sided tolerance intervals. A one-sided tolerance interval consists of the set of all values that are to one side of a specified function of the sample values; e.g., $\{x|x \leqslant X[n]\}$ and $\{x|x \geqslant X[1]\}$ are one-sided tolerance intervals for the case of a sample of size n. A two-sided tolerance interval consists of the set of all values that are between two specified functions of the sample values; e.g., $\{x|x[2] \leqslant x \leqslant x[n]\}$ is a two-sided tolerance interval.

The only one-sided tolerance intervals considered are $\{x|x \leqslant X[i]\}$ and $\{x|x \geqslant X[i]\}$, $(i=1, \ldots, n)$, where the value of i is specified without knowledge of the sample values. As mentioned previously, one-sided intervals where the random endpoint is a sample order statistic are the only one-sided tolerance intervals that are exactly distribution-free for the continuous case.

A moderate amount of freedom is available in obtaining two-sided tolerance intervals. Usually the problem is to construct a suitable two-sided interval by removal of a small number of statistical blocks (nonrandomized exact case). For most purposes of practical interest, the required sample size increases substantially with the number of blocks removed. If appropriate supplementary information is available, a suitable region can often be obtained when only one block is removed. Some suggestions for obtaining two-sided tolerance intervals by removal of one, two, three, or four statistical blocks are given next.

Some Two-Sided Intervals

When a single statistical block is to be removed, one type of two-sided tolerance interval which seems to be suitable for many situations is that with limits $x_0 \pm \max\{|X[n]-x_0|, |x_0-X[1]|\}$, where x_0 is specified without knowledge of the sample values. If enough supplementary information is available, a value that lies somewhere in the central part of the population sampled can be used for x_0. Then, since the central part of the population is emphasized, the interval should tend to have a reasonably small width. In other cases, the value of x_0 may be determined by the fact that the population coverage of an interval centered at a given value is of interest.

When two statistical blocks are to be removed, the tolerance interval $\{x|X[1] \leqslant x \leqslant X[n]\}$ is often satisfactory. If an interval centered at a given value x_0 is desired, the limits $x_0 \pm$ the number in the second position of the sequence where the values of $|X[n]-x_0|$, $|X[n-1]-x_0|$, $|x_0-X[1]|$, $|x_0-X[2]|$ are arranged according to decreasing size furnish a tolerance interval with this property.

When three blocks are to be removed, the tolerance interval with limits $(X[n]+X[1])/2 \pm \max\{|X[n-1]-(X[n]+X[1])/2|, |(X[n]+X[1])/2-X[2]|\}$ is usually satisfactory (note that $X[n]$ and $X[1]$ can be determined in the removal of the first two blocks). If an interval centered at a given value x_0 is desired, the tolerance interval with limits $x_0 \pm$ the number in the third position of the sequence where the values of $|X[n]-x_0|$, $|X[n-1]-x_0|$, $|X[n-2]-x_0|$, $|x_0-X[1]|$, $|x_0-X[2]|$, $|x_0-X[3]|$ are arranged according to decreasing size can be used. The tolerance intervals

$\{x|X[1]\leqslant x\leqslant X[n-1]\}$ and $\{x|X[2]\leqslant x\leqslant X[n]\}$ are also sometimes useful when three blocks are to be removed.

When four blocks are to be removed, the tolerance interval $\{x|X[2]\leqslant x\leqslant X[n-1]\}$ is sometimes useful. However, the tolerance interval with limits $(X[n]+X[1])/2\pm$ the number in the second position of the sequence where the values of $|X[n-1]-(X[n]+X[1])/2|$, $|X[n-2]-(X[n]+X[1])/2|$, $|(X[n]+X[1])/2-X[2]|$, $|(X[n]+X[1])/2-X[3]|$ are arranged according to decreasing size also seems to be useful. If an interval centered at a given value x_0 is desired, the tolerance interval with limits $x_0\pm$ the number in the fourth position of the sequence where the values of $|X[n]-x_0|$, $|X[n-1]-x_0|$, $|X[n-2]-x_0|$, $|X[n-3]-x_0|$, $|x_0-X[1]|$, $|x_0-X[2]|$, $|x_0-X[3]|$, $|x_0-X[4]|$ are arranged according to decreasing size can be used. The tolerance intervals $\{x|X[1]\leqslant x\leqslant X[n-2]\}$ and $\{x|X[3]\leqslant x\leqslant X[n]\}$ are also sometimes useful when four blocks are to be removed.

A construction method can be used such that a specified $u-1$ of the order statistics for the two tails have known values at the step where the uth block is to be removed. As an example, when the fourth block is to be removed, the set $X[1], X[2], X[3]$, the set $X[1], X[2], X[n]$, the set $X[1], X[n-1], X[n]$, or the set $X[n-2], X[n-1], X[n]$ can have known values. Sample value information of this nature can be helpful in the construction of two-sided tolerance intervals that have desired forms, since it furnishes an indication of the probability concentration in the population.

In the above examples, positive and negative deviations from a given point receive the same relative emphasis. Construction methods can be used where this is not the case and where the relative emphasis can change as a function of the distance from the point considered.

Censored Data Applications

To a moderate extent, the results of this section are applicable for censored samples. All of the one-sided tolerance interval results can be used with respect to some types of censoring. Two-sided tolerance intervals of the form $\{x|X[i_1]\leqslant x\leqslant X[i_2]\}$, and randomized or interpolated two-sided intervals based on intervals of this form, can be applied in some cases. In general, any tolerance region that is based on order statistics whose values are available can be used. This implies that two or more statistical blocks are removed for at least the first step of the construction procedure. However, once the statistical blocks that contain the unknown order statistics are removed, the remaining steps of the construction can proceed in any permissible fashion.

Separate Control of Coverage for Parts of Region

The construction methods given for two-sided tolerance intervals and for general tolerance regions are based on the removal of statistical blocks. By removing one block at a time and continuing the process until n blocks have been removed, a basic set of $n+1$ statistical blocks is obtained. These blocks can be combined in any desired fashion (the grouping used should be chosen without any unwarranted knowledge about the sample values). In particular, tolerance regions can be obtained which consist of parts such that the population coverage for each part is controlled separately. E.g., the region could be the two one-sided intervals excluded in the construction of a two-sided tolerance interval; then, by separate control of the coverage for each of these one-sided intervals, the complement of this region is a two-sided interval with the property that the amount of coverage excluded is individually controlled for each tail. As another example, a one-sided or two-sided interval could consist of several parts with the coverage for each part controlled separately.

Randomized and Interpolated Regions

The general methods given for obtaining randomized and interpolated tolerance regions are directly applicable to the univariate case. In particular, these methods can be used to obtain randomized and interpolated tolerance intervals. Since the applications of these methods are straightforward, randomized and interpolated tolerance regions are not explicitly considered in this section; that is, none of the tolerance regions presented is of a randomized or interpolated nature.

Discontinuous Case—General Remarks

The material presented for the discontinuous case falls under two headings, namely the construction of tolerance regions and the probability properties of these regions with respect to population coverage. Under the first heading, a general construction method is given which yields regions that are not necessarily intervals. Due to the importance of intervals for the univariate case, the construction of tolerance intervals is considered separately and in more detail.

Under the second heading, probability properties for population coverage are stated for the regions that are constructed. The properties considered are the probabilities of relations which assert that the population coverage of a specified tolerance region is at least as great as a given value. Upper and lower bounds are obtained for the values of these probability expressions. The value of an upper bound is of a conditional nature; that is, this bound depends on the ties that occurred among the sample values. Probability bounds are stated for regions obtained by the general construction method and, separately, for tolerance intervals.

The construction method presented has the property of separating any two observations. This is accomplished by using their status as order statistics to assign an ordering to observations which yield the same value (are "tied") for the function used at that step of the construction. Randomization is used to determine the order statistic status of observations with the same values.

Outline of Presentations

Two presentations of statistical procedures are given. Tolerance intervals are considered first, for both the continuous and discontinuous cases. The other presentation contains a general method constructing univariate tolerance regions for the continuous and the discontinuous cases.

Fixed Material for Section

Data 1 Univariate; Case (I): Continuous. Case (II): Discontinuous **3** $X(i)$ **4** $m=1$; value of sample size n for given prob. requirement obtained by methods in Determination of Required Sample Sizes sect. **Assumptions 1** Random sample **2** Case (I): Continuous population. Case (II): Discontinuous population **3** None **Results 3** See material beginning on page 238 **Characteristics 1** Low to medium unless sample size excessive or construction method lengthy or complicated **3** Used symmetrically **4** Sample condition must hold to reasonable approx. For Case (I), can be very sensitive to continuity condition; results for Case (II) furnish conditional bounds for sensitivity under Case (I) **5** Not difficult to decide on sample and continuity assumptions.

Tolerance Intervals

Data 2 Construct tolerance interval to have desired general properties **Description 1** Methods for constructing one-sided and two-sided tolerance intervals; also, for Case (II), bounds for some prob. expressions involving these intervals **2** Prob. expressions considered for Case (II) of form $P\{F(U)-F(L-)\geqslant a\}= \quad P\{\int_{[L,U]} dF(x)\geqslant a\}$, where L lower tolerance limit and U upper tolerance limit (one limit can be infinite); here $F(x-)=P[X(i)<x]$ **Results 1** In case of ties, assignment of the corresponding order statistics to the observations performed by independent random process such that all possible assignments equally likely. $h_t(x)$ is fct. used at tth step of construction ($t=1,\ldots,T$), where T is total no. of steps and can depend on sample values determined in construction. These fcts. such that $\bigcap_{t=1}^{T}\{x|h_t(x)\leqslant h_t[x_0^{(t)}]\}$ is a closed two-sided interval for

all sets $x_0^{(1)}, \ldots, x_0^{(T)}$; also $h_t[X(i)]$ has continuous dist. for Case (I). r_t = no. statistical blocks removed at tth step = no. observations removed from consideration at tth step. Arrange the values of $h_t(x)$ for order statistics not removed prior to tth step in a sequence according to decreasing value and, within tied sets, on the basis of decreasing values of the subscripts of the order statistics yielding the values. Let $X(i_t)$ be the observation which corresponds to r_t position in this sequence, where the largest value of $h_t(x)$ occurs for $r_t=1$. Then the observations, among the $n-r_1-\ldots-r_{t-1}$ observations remaining at end of step $t-1$, which occupy positions $1, \ldots, r_t$ in this sequence are removed from further direct use at end of tth step. $h_t(x)$ and r_t can depend on the values of the observations which were removed from direct use by end of step $t-1$ and on any supplementary information that is independent of sample values; however, the total number of blocks to be removed, $r=\sum_{t=1}^{T} r_t$, specified without knowledge about sample values **2** *One-sided intervals with r blocks removed*: $\{x|x \leqslant X[n+1-r]\}$ and $\{x|x \geqslant X[r]\}$. *For Case (I)*, pop. coverage probabilities obtainable from material beginning on page 238. *For Case* (II), suppose that $X[n+1-r]=\ldots=X[n-r+s_1]<X[n+1-r+s_1]$ and that $X[r-s_2]>X[r-s_2+1]=\ldots=X[r]$, where s_1, s_2 integers and $1 \leqslant s_1, s_2 \leqslant r$. Then $I_{1-a}(n+1-r, r) \leqslant P\{\int_{-\infty}^{X[n+1-r]} dF \geqslant a\} \leqslant I_{1-a}(n+1-r-s_1, r+s_1)$, where the upper bound is of a conditional nature. Also $I_{1-a}(n+1-r, r) \leqslant P\{\int_{X[r]}^{\infty} dF \geqslant a\} = P\{1-F(X[r]-) \geqslant a\} \leqslant I_{1-a}(n+1-r-s_2, r+s_2)$, where the upper bound is conditional. *Two-sided intervals with r blocks removed*: $\{x|L \leqslant x \leqslant U\} \equiv \bigcap_{t=1}^{T} \{x|h_t(x) \leqslant h_t[X(i_t)]\}$. *For Case* (I), pop. coverage probabilities obtainable from material starting on page 238. *For Case* (II), let s_3 be the no. of observations that have values equal to L or U but which were removed in the construction $(1 \leqslant s_3 \leqslant r)$; then $I_{1-a}(n+1-r, r) \leqslant P\{\int_{[L,U]} dF \geqslant a\} \leqslant I_{1-a}(n+1-r-s_3, r+s_3)$, where the upper bound is of a conditional nature **4** Corresponding Case (II) results for tolerance intervals that are open sets obtainable on basis of ref. 182. By letting $T=n$ (i.e., $r_t=1$ for all t), x axis divided into basic set of stat. blocks for Case (I); by grouping of blocks, intervals can be obtained which consist of two or more parts and with pop. coverage of each part controlled separately. One of the possible basic sets of blocks for Case (I) is $\{x|X[u-1]<x \leqslant X[u]\}$, $u=1, \ldots, n+1$. Some two-sided intervals for $r \leqslant 4$ stated on page 256. If desired, the $h_t(x)$ can be random choices from specified sets of fcts. **Characteristics 2** For sample from normal population, two-sided interval with same no. blocks removed from each tail has asymptotic efficiency $t^2_{(1-\gamma)/2}(n-1)$ $[\pi\gamma(1-\gamma)]^{-1} \exp[-t^2_{(1-\gamma)/2}(n-1)]$, where γ expected pop. coverage of two-sided interval; when $\gamma=.99$, asympt. efficiency is 28 per cent. For normality and one-sided interval, asymptotic efficiency is $[2+t^2_{(1-\delta)/2}($

$n-1)][\pi(1-\delta^2)]^{-1}\exp\ [-t^2_{(1-\delta)/2}(n-1)]$, where $(1+\delta)/2$ is expected pop. coverage of one-sided interval; when $\delta = .99$, asympt. efficiency is 18 per cent. For Case (I), the coverage of each of the one-sided and two-sided intervals presented has variance $r(n+1-r)/(n+1)^2(n+2)$ and the expected value of the square of its deviation from a is $(n+1-r)(n+2-r)/(n+1)(n+2)-2(n+1-r)a/(n+1)+a^2$ **6** Condition that $h_t[X(i)]$ has continuous dist. for Case (I) can be weakened; however, situation considered that of major practical interest **Bibliography** Ref. 182, 183, 186, 188, 272, 389, 461, 524, 525, 588, 591.

General Univariate Tolerance Regions

Data 2 Construct tolerance region to have desired general form **Description 1** Methods for constructing general nature tolerance regions; also, for Case (II), bounds for some prob. expressions involving these regions **2** General nature prob. expressions can be considered for Case (I) but only prob. expressions of form $P\{\int_R dF \geqslant a\}$ are considered for Case (II), where R tolerance region considered **Results 1** In case of ties, assignment of the corresponding order statistics to the observations performed by independent random process such that all assignments equally likely. $H_t(x)$ is function used at tth step of construction ($t=1, \ldots, T$), where T is total no. of steps and can depend on sample values determined in the construction. These fcts. such that $\bigcap_{t=1}^{T} \{x|H_t(x) \leqslant H_t[x^{(t)}]\}$ contains all its limit pts. that are finite for all sets $x^{(1)}, \ldots, x^{(T)}$; also $H_t[X(i)]$ has continuous dist. for Case (I). r_t = no. stat. blocks removed at tth step = no. observations removed from consideration at tth step. Arrange the values of $H_t(x)$ for order statistics not removed prior to tth step in a sequence according to decreasing value and, within tied sets, on the basis of decreasing values of the subscripts of the order statistics yielding the values. Let $X(u_t)$ be the observation corresponding to r_t position in this sequence, where largest value of $H_t(x)$ occurs for $r_t = 1$. Then the observations, among the $n - r_1 - \ldots - r_{t-1}$ observations remaining at end of step $t-1$, which occupy positions $1, \ldots, r_t$ in this sequence are removed from further direct use at end of tth step. $H_t(x)$ and r_t can depend on the values of the observations which were removed from direct use by end of step $t-1$ and on any supplementary information that is independent of sample values; however, the total no. of blocks removed, $r = \sum_{t=1}^{T} r_t$, specified without knowledge about sample values **2** *Tolerance region with r blocks removed is*: $R = \bigcap_{t=1}^{T} \{x|H_t(x) \leqslant H_t[X(u_t)]\}$. *For Case (I)*, pop. coverage probabilities obtainable from material starting on page 238. *For Case (II)*, suppose that s is no. of observations which have values that are contained in R but which were removed in the construction $(1 \leqslant s \leqslant r)$; then $I_{1-a}(n+1-r, r) \leqslant P\{\int_R dF \geqslant a\} \leqslant I_{1-a}(n+1-r-s, r+s)$, where the upper bound is of a conditional nature **4** By letting $T = n$ (i.e., $r_t = 1$ for all t), x axis divided into basic set of stat. blocks for Case (I); by grouping of blocks, regions can be obtained which consist of two or more parts and with pop. coverage of each part controlled separately. One of the possible basic sets of blocks for Case (I) is $\{x|X[u-1] < x \leqslant X[u]\}$, $u = 1, \ldots, n+1$. If desired, the $H_t(x)$ can be random choices from specified sets of fcts. **Characteristics 2** For Case (I), $\sigma^2\{\int_R dF\} = r(n+1-r)/(n+1)^2(n+2)$ and $E\{\int_R dF - a\}^2 = (n+1-r)(n+2-r)/(n+1)(n+2) - 2(n+1-r)a/(n+1) + a^2$ **6** Condition that $H_t[X(i)]$ has continuous dist. for Case (I) can be weakened; however, situation considered that of major practical interest **Bibliography** Ref. 182, 183, 186, 188, 272, 461, 524, 525, 588, 591.

MULTIVARIATE CASE—GENERAL RESULTS

Introduction

For the multivariate case, construction of tolerance regions is more complicated than for the univariate case but the same general approach is used. The principal complications arise for the partially continuous and discontinuous situations, where various types of "ties" can occur. However, complications also arise in constructing regions which satisfy specified purposes, have desired general forms, and are practical for use (e.g., do not require excessive sample sizes). Only one statistical procedure presentation is required for stating the pertinent results. For the continuous and partially continuous cases, the probability properties for population coverage can be obtained from material given in preceding sections of this chapter and are not stated in the presentation. However, some population coverage probability properties are stated for the discontinuous case.

Obtaining Desired General Forms for Regions

If the number of statistical blocks to be removed in the construction of a tolerance region is not small, obtaining a region with a desired general form (of a reasonable nature) ordinarily is not very difficult. When a very few blocks are to be removed, however, obtaining a tolerance region with a specified general form is not an easy problem. Here supplementary information (e.g., rough knowledge about the location of the central part of the population sampled) can be very helpful. Following are some suggestions for constructing bounded regions when one, two, or three blocks are to be removed and information is desired about the probability concentration in the central part of the population. Here the data are the multivariate sample values $\{X(i)_j\}_m$, where $n_1 = \ldots = n_m = n$; i.e., the sample size is m and the population sampled is n-variate. Strictly speaking, the constructions described are for the continuous case; however, they can be modified so as to be applicable to the partially continuous and the discontinuous cases.

Suppose that one statistical block is to be removed and that the only available information (perhaps only a rough guess) indicates that the central part of the population is in the vicinity of $(x_1^{(0)}, \ldots, x_n^{(0)})$. Let

$$h_1(x_1, \ldots, x_n) = (x_1 - x_1^{(0)})^2 + \ldots + (x_n - x_n^{(0)})^2$$

and define $j(1)$ by the requirement that $h_1[X(1)_j, \ldots, X(n)_j]$ is maximum for $j=j(1)$. Then the block removed is $\{(x_1, \ldots, x_n) | h_1(x_1, \ldots, x_n) > h_1[X(1)_{j(1)}, \ldots, X(n)_{j(1)}]\}$. That is, the tolerance region consists of the surface and interior of the n-dimensional "sphere" that is centered at $(x_1^{(0)}, \ldots, x_n^{(0)})$ and has radius $\{[x_1^{(0)} - X(1)_{j(1)}]^2 + \ldots + [x_n^{(0)} - X(n)_{j(1)}]^2\}^{1/2}$. If the ratios of the variances for the coordinates of the random variable are also at least roughly known, the function

$$(x_1 - x_1^{(0)})^2 + [\sigma^2(2)_j/\sigma^2(1)_j](x_2 - x_2^{(0)})^2 + \ldots + [\sigma^2(n)_j/\sigma^2(1)_j](x_n - x_n^{(0)})^2$$

could be used in place of $h_1(x_1, \ldots, x_n)$ and the same procedure followed. Then the tolerance region consists of the surface and interior of an n-dimensional ellipsoid that is centered at $(x_1^{(0)}, \ldots, x_n^{(0)})$.

Suppose that two blocks are to be removed and that $(x_1^{(0)}, \ldots, x_n^{(0)})$ represents the best guess (may be greatly in error) concerning the location of the central part of the population sampled, also that no further supplementary information is available. Then the first block removed is that specified for the case of removing only one block, leaving the second block to be removed from the points consisting of the interior of an n-dimensional "sphere." If there is not very strong reason to believe that $(x_1^{(0)}, \ldots, x_n^{(0)})$ actually lies in the central part of the population, the second block can be removed on the basis of the function

$$h_2(x_1, \ldots, x_n) = [x_1 - X(1)_{j(1)}]^2 + \ldots + [x_n - X(n)_{j(1)}]^2.$$

That is, define $j(2)$ by the requirement that, among the values of j not equal to $j(1)$, $h_2[X(1)_j, \ldots, X(n)_j]$ is maximum when $j=j(2)$. Then the second block removed is $\{(x_1, \ldots, x_n) | h_1(x_1, \ldots, x_n) \leqslant h_1[X(1)_{j(1)}, \ldots, X(n)_{j(1)}], h_2(x_1, \ldots, x_n) > h_2[X(1)_{j(2)}, \ldots, X(n)_{j(2)}]\}$. If there is moderately strong reason to believe that $(x_1^{(0)}, \ldots, x_n^{(0)})$ is in the central part of the population, the function

$$\{x_1 - [x_1^{(0)} + X(1)_{j(1)}]/2\}^2 + \ldots + \{x_n - [x_n^{(0)} + X(n)_{j(1)}]/2\}^2$$

can be used to remove the second block. If there is very strong reason to believe that $(x_1^{(0)}, \ldots, x_n^{(0)})$ is near the middle of the population (say, near the mean), the function

$$\{x_1 - [9x_1^{(0)} + X(1)_{j(1)}]/10\}^2 + \ldots + \{x_n - [9x_n^{(0)} + X(n)_{j(1)}]/10\}^2$$

can be used to remove the second block. If the ratios of the variances for the observation coordinates are also at least roughly known, the functions used to remove the two blocks are modified accordingly. For example,

$$[x_1 - X(1)_{j(1)}]^2 + [\sigma^2(2)_j/\sigma^2(1)_j][x_2 - X(2)_{j(1)}]^2 + \dots + [\sigma^2(n)_j/\sigma^2(1)_j][x_n - X(n)_{j(1)}]^2$$

can be used to replace $h_2(x_1, \dots, x_n)$; etc.

If three blocks are to be removed and there is not very strong reason to believe that $(x_1^{(0)}, \dots, x_n^{(0)})$ lies in the central part of the population, the first two blocks can be removed by the use of $h_1(x_1, \dots, x_n)$ and $h_2(x_1, \dots, x_n)$ with the third block removed from the remaining region by the use of

$$h_3(x_1, \dots, x_n) = \{x_1 - [\bar{x}_1 + X(1)_{j(1)} + X(1)_{j(2)}]/3\}^2 + \dots + \{x_n - [\bar{x}_n + X(n)_{j(1)} + X(n)_{j(2)}]/3\}^2,$$

where $(\bar{x}_1, \dots, \bar{x}_n)$ is the center of the region remaining after the first two blocks are removed. That is, define $j(3)$ by the requirement that, among the values of j not equal to $j(1)$ or $j(2)$, $h_3[X(1)_j, \dots, X(n)_j]$ is maximum when $j = j(3)$. Then the third block removed is

$$\{(x_1, \dots, x_n) | h_1(x_1, \dots, x_n) \leqslant h_1[X(1)_{j(1)}, \dots, X(n)_{j(1)}], \\ h_2(x_1, \dots, x_n) \leqslant h_2[X(1)_{j(2)}, \dots, X(n)_{j(2)}], \\ h_3(x_1, \dots, x_n) > h_3[X(1)_{j(3)}, \dots, X(n)_{j(3)}]\}.$$

If there is moderately strong reason to believe that $(x_1^{(0)}, \dots, x_n^{(0)})$ is in the central part of the population, the first two blocks can be removed by the procedure stated for this situation in the two-blocks-removed case and the third block can be removed by use of the function

$$\{x_1 - [2x_1^{(0)} + \bar{x}_1 + X(1)_{j(1)} + X(1)_{j(2)}]/5\}^2 + \dots + \{x_n - [2x_n^{(0)} + \bar{x}_n + X(n)_{j(1)} + X(n)_{j(2)}]/5\}^2.$$

If there is strong reason to believe that $(x_1^{(0)}, \dots, x_n^{(0)})$ is near the middle of the population, the first two blocks can be removed by the procedure stated for this situation in the two-blocks-removed case and the function

$$\{x_1 - [17x_1^{(0)} + \bar{x}_1 + X(1)_{j(1)} + X(1)_{j(2)}]/20\}^2 + \dots + \{x_n - [17x_n^{(0)} + \bar{x}_n + X(n)_{j(1)} + X(n)_{j(2)}]/20\}^2$$

can be used to remove the third block. If the ratios of the variances for the observation coordinates are also at least roughly known, the functions used to remove the three blocks are modified accordingly. In particular,

$$\{x_1 - [\bar{x}_1 + X(1)_{j(1)} + X(1)_{j(2)}]/3\}^2 \\ + [\sigma^2(2)_j/\sigma^2(1)_j]\{x_2 - [\bar{x}_2 + X(2)_{j(1)} + X(2)_{j(2)}]/3\}^2 + \dots \\ + [\sigma^2(n)_j/\sigma^2(1)_j]\{x_n - [x_n + X(n)_{j(1)} + X(n)_{j(2)}]/3\}^2$$

can be used to replace $h_3(x_1, \dots, x_n)$; etc.

This type of approach for constructing bounded tolerance regions can be extended to situations where four or more blocks are to be removed. For these situations, however, other methods often yield satisfactory regions with much less effort, especially if the number of blocks to be removed is much greater than four. For example, the region could be unbounded up to the removal of the last block; then if suitable sample values have been determined, a highly satisfactory bounded region can be obtained when the last block is removed. That is, if more than a few blocks are to be removed, all but the last few of these blocks can be used for determining the values of appropriate observations. Then, on the basis of these known sample values, the last few blocks can be removed so that a region of the desired form is obtained.

In the above examples, positive and negative deviations from a given point receive the same emphasis for each coordinate. Construction methods can be used where this is not the case and where the relative emphasis can change as a function of the distance from the point considered.

Separate Coverage Control for Parts of Region

As for all cases, the construction methods given for multivariate tolerance regions are based on the removal of statistical blocks. If one block is removed at each step and the process continued until m blocks have been removed, a basic set of $m+1$ statistical blocks is obtained for the continuous and partially continuous cases (in general, for this section, the data are m n-variate sample values). By suitable grouping of these statistical blocks, tolerance regions can be obtained which consist of parts such that the population coverage is controlled separately for each part.

Randomized and Interpolated Regions

The general methods given in the first part of the chapter for obtaining randomized and interpolated tolerance regions are directly applicable to the continuous multivariate case. Since the use of these methods is straightforward, randomized and interpolated tolerance regions are not explicitly considered in this section.

Observation Coordinates Independent in Known Groups

This situation, which only occurs for the multivariate case, is that where the population sampled has a random variable whose coordinates are independent in known groups. Then a tolerance region consists of a combination of subregions, where each subregion is itself a "tolerance region" for one of the groups. A multivariate value lies in this tolerance region if and only if, for each group, its value for this group of coordinates lies in the corresponding subregion. Thus, from a construction viewpoint, the problem is to separately determine the subregion for each of the groups, where a group can consist of one or more coordinates. For populations that are at least partially continuous with regard to each of the independent groups of coordinates, the probability aspects of this type of tolerance region, with respect to population coverage, can be determined on the basis of the material starting on page 238 and on page 245. When the coordinates of an independent group have a discontinuous distribution, this group can be combined with another independent group whose coordinates have at least a partially continuous distribution. Then exact probabilities are obtained for tolerance regions based on the resulting independent groups.

Use of the additional knowledge that the observation coordinates are independent in known groups tends to yield a more efficient type of tolerance region, since more of the data can be ultilized in the construction. That is, the removal of a group of coordinates for an observation, in the construction of the subregion for that group, does not remove this observation from use in constructing other subregions.

Partially Continuous and Discontinuous Cases

If the situation is either partially continuous or discontinuous, some of the coordinates of the random variable have a discontinuous joint distribution. Then, functions that depend only on these coordinates also have discontinuous distributions. Thus, if functions involving only coordinates with discontinuous distributions occur in the construction of a tolerance region, at some of the steps there can be a nonzero probability that an ambiguity arises concerning which observation is to be removed. That is, two or more sample values can be tied in the sense that they have the same value for the function used to order the observations. "Ties" with respect to the observation to be removed cause difficulties in the construction of a tolerance region since, at each step, the construction is based on a determination of a sequence ordering among the sample values that have not yet been removed.

One method for combating ambiguities in ordering of the observations is to use only functions which involve all the coordinates and, as functions of the observations, have continuous distributions if the observations are of any continuous or partially continuous nature. However, this method noticeably restricts the freedom in constructing regions of desired general forms. A more general method is, at each step, to introduce additional functions for breaking "ties" that occur with respect to the observation to be removed. Explicitly, a second function is used to help break "ties" that occur with respect to the first function; a third function is used to help break "ties" that occur with respect to the first two functions; etc. At each step, a finite sequence of functions can be specified such that "ties" are broken between any two observations that are unequal. For example, the sequence for which each function is a different coordinate of the random variable has this property; here the number of functions equals the dimensionality of the random variable. More generally, consider an arbitrary but specified change of coordinate system; then each of the new coordinates is a specified function of the original coordinates. Use of this set of functions, in any order, breaks "ties" between any two functions that are unequal.

In the presentation, each sequence of functions used for a construction step is required to have the property that "ties" are necessarily broken between any two unequal observations. This implies that, at each step, the ordering is such that the probability of "ties" is zero when the population sampled is at least partially continuous. This property can be shown to imply that the probability distribution of the population coverage for a region with a specified number of blocks removed is the same for the continuous and partially continuous cases. Thus, by use of appropriate sequences of functions, the probability distribution difficulties arising from "ties" are eliminated for the partially continuous case.

Unfortunately, for the discontinuous case, probability difficulties due to "ties" can not be eliminated by the use of "tie-breaking" functions. The reason is that the probability of equality for two or more sample values is nonzero. Ties of this nature can be broken by randomization (see page 240). Two viewpoints can be associated with the use of randomization. In one case, the population is considered to be converted to a form that is at least partially continuous. This involves changing some of the characteristics of the population sampled; although only small changes are made, these can be important for some situations. For the other viewpoint, the population is not considered to be changed and randomization is only used to avoid bias in deciding which observations are to be discarded at each construction step. Then the situation remains discontinuous and exact probability properties are not obtained. Instead bounds are obtained for the probabilities of the population coverage expressions that are considered. Here the lower bound is the value for the case where the population is at least partially continuous while the upper bound is conditional and depends on the ties that actually occur for the sample that is used.

Description of the Presentation

The pertinent results for the continuous, partially continuous, and discontinuous cases are given in a single presentation. Although a sequence of functions is specified for each step of the construction procedure for a tolerance region, only the first function of each sequence would need to be used for the continuous case. From the viewpoint of probability properties, two cases are considered; these are the case where the population sampled is at least partially continuous and the case where this population is discontinuous. Since only one presentation occurs, the Fixed Material for Section part is not used.

Multivariate Tolerance Regions

Data 1 Multivariate. Case (I): At least partially continuous. Case (II): Discontinuous **2** Construct tolerance region to have desired general form **3** $\{X(i)_j\}_m$ **4** Value of sample size m for given prob. requirement obtainable by methods in Determination of Required Sample Sizes sect.; $n_1 = \ldots = n_m = n$ (pop. sampled n-variate) **Description 1** Methods for constructing general nature tolerance regions; also, for Case (II), bounds furnished for some prob. expressions involving these regions **2** General nature prob. expressions can be considered for Case (I) but only prob. expressions of form $P\{\int_R dF \geqslant a\}$ are considered for Case (II), where R tolerance region considered **Assumptions 1** Random sample **2** Case (I): Population continuous or partially continuous. Case (II): Population discontinuous **3** None **Results 1** $H_t^{(u)}(x_1, \ldots, x_n)$ is finite sequence of fcts. used at tth step of construction ($u = 1, \ldots, U_t$; $t = 1, \ldots, T$), where U_t no. of fcts. in sequence for tth step and T total no. of steps (can depend on sample values determined in the construction). These fcts. such that $H_t^{(u)}(x_1, \ldots, x_n) = H_t^{(u)}(x_1^{(0)}, \ldots, x_n^{(0)})$ for $u = 1, \ldots, U_t$ if and only if $(x_1, \ldots, x_n) = (x_1^{(0)}, \ldots, x_n^{(0)})$. $H_t^{(1)}(x_1, \ldots, x_n)$ such that $H_t^{(1)}[X(1)_j, \ldots, X(n)_j]$ has continuous dist. if population sampled continuous. By def., relation $H_t(x_1, \ldots, x_n) < H_t(x_1^{(0)}, \ldots, x_n^{(0)})$ holds if and only if $H_t^{(u)}(x_1, \ldots, x_n) = H_t^{(u)}(x_1^{(0)}, \ldots, x_n^{(0)})$ for $u < u' \leqslant U_t$ and $H_t^{(u')}(x_1, \ldots, x_n) < H_t^{(u')}(x_1^{(0)}, \ldots, x_n^{(0)})$; $H_t(x_1, \ldots, x_n) = H_t(x_1^{(0)}, \ldots, x_n^{(0)})$ if and only if $(x_1, \ldots, x_n) = (x_1^{(0)}, \ldots, x_n^{(0)})$; $H_t(x_1, \ldots, x_n) > H_t(x_1^{(0)}, \ldots, x_n^{(0)})$ if and only if $H_t^{(u)}(x_1, \ldots, x_n) = H_t^{(u)}(x_1^{(0)}, \ldots, x_n^{(0)})$ for $u < u'' \leqslant U_t$ and $H_t^{(u'')}(x_1, \ldots, x_n) > H_t^{(u'')}(x_1^{(0)}, \ldots, x_n^{(0)})$. For all $(x_1^{(t)}, \ldots, x_n^{(t)})$, the sequences of fcts. are such that $\bigcap_{t=1}^{T} \{(x_1, \ldots, x_n) | H_t(x_1, \ldots, x_n) \leqslant H_t(x_1^{(t)}, \ldots, x_n^{(t)})\}$ contains all its limit pts. that are finite. $r_t =$ no. statistical blocks removed at tth step $=$ no. observations removed from consideration at tth step. Use $H_t(x_1, \ldots, x_n)$, combined with randomization for sets of equal observations, to place the sample values in a sequence according to decreasing values of $H_t^{(1)}(x_1, \ldots, x_n)$, where the other functions and the randomization used to break ties. Let $\{X(i)_{j[t]}\}_m$ be the observation in the r_t position of this sequence, where the largest value of $H_t^{(1)}(x_1, \ldots, x_n)$ occurs for $r_t = 1$. Then the observations, among $m - r_1 -$

$\ldots - r_{t-1}$ observations remaining at end of step $t-1$, which occupy positions $1, \ldots, r_t$ in this sequence are removed from further direct use at end of tth step. The U_t, $H_t^{(u)}(x_1, \ldots, x_n)$, and r_t can depend on the observations removed prior to tth step, on $r_1, \ldots, r_{t-1}$, and on any supplementary information that is independent of sample values; however, total no. blocks removed, $r = \sum_{t=1}^{T} r_t$, specified without knowledge about sample values **2** *Tolerance region with r blocks removed is*: $R = \bigcap_{t=1}^{T}\{(x_1, \ldots, x_n) | H_t(x_1, \ldots, x_n) \leqslant H_t[X(1)_{j[t]}, \ldots, X(n)_{j[t]}]\}$. *For Case (I)*, pop. coverage probabilities obtainable from material starting on page 238. *For Case (II)*, suppose that s is no. of observations which have values that are contained in R but which were removed in the construction $(1 \leqslant s \leqslant r)$; then $I_{1-a}(m+1-r, r) \leqslant P\{\int_R dF \geqslant a\} \leqslant I_{1-a}(m+1-r-s, r+s)$, where the upper bound is of a conditional nature **3** See material beginning on page 238 **4** By letting $T = m$ (i.e., $r_t = 1$ for all t), sample space divided into basic set of statistical blocks for Case (I); by grouping of blocks, regions can be obtained which consist of two or more parts and with pop. coverage of each part controlled separately. If desired, the $H_t^{(u)}(x_1, \ldots, x_n)$ can be random choices from specified sets of fcts. **Characteristics 1** Low to lower-medium unless sample size excessive, n large, or region removed of complicated nature **2** For Case (I), $\sigma^2\{\int_R dF\} = r(m+1-r)/(m+1)^2(m+2)$ and $E\{\int_R dF - a\}^2 = (m+1-r)(m+2-r)/(m+2) - 2(m+1-r)a/(m+1) + a^2$ **3** Used symmetrically **4** Sample condition must hold to reasonable approx. Can be very sensitive to continuity required by Case (I); results for Case (II) furnish conditional bounds for sensitivity under Case (I) **5** Not difficult to decide on sample and continuity assumptions **6** Conditions imposed on $H_t^{(1)}(x_1, \ldots, x_n)$ for continuity and partial continuity can be weakened; however, situation considered that of major practical interest **Bibliography** Ref. 182, 183, 186, 188, 272, 524, 525, 536, 591.

STATISTICAL PREDICTION FROM TOLERANCE REGIONS

Introduction

All the material that pertains to the sample coverage of tolerance regions is presented in this section. That is, a distribution-free tolerance region is available and the problem is to predict the number of values of an independent new sample, of given size and from the same population, that will lie in this region. The number of "exceedances" problem furnishes an example of this situation for the univariate case. For the situations considered, the population sampled is at least partially continuous; also the tolerance regions are exact and nonrandomized. Expressions are stated for the expected value of the number of values of the new sample that fall in a given tolerance region and for the distribution function of this number of values.

Type of Tolerance Regions Considered

The tolerance regions considered are those of the type presented in the Univariate Case and the Multivariate Case sections. Thus, for the general situation, a tolerance region consists of a specified number of statistical blocks. For the special multivariate situation where the coordinates are independent in known groups, each subregion consists of a given number of statistical blocks (with respect to the coordinates for the corresponding group). In presenting the results, a tolerance region is considered to be a combination of a stated number of subregions. Then the case where there is only one subregion represents the general situation while the case of two or more subregions represents the special situation of coordinates that are independent in known groups.

Control of Probability Properties

Several quantities affect the probability distribution for statistical coverage. These are the size of the sample on which the tolerance region is based, the number of blocks removed in obtaining each subregion, and the size of the new sample. The probability distribution for the number of values of the new sample that will fall in the tolerance region can be controlled, to some extent, by the choice of the values for these quantities.

Number of Exceedances Problem

Here, for the upper tail case, an initial sample (of given size) and an independent new sample (of given size) are drawn from the same continuous univariate population. The item of interest is the number of the values of the new sample that exceed a specified order statistic of the initial sample. Let N be the size of the initial sample and let $X[r]$ denote the rth order statistic of this sample. Then a stated number of the values of the new sample exceed $X[r]$ if and only if this stated number of sample values fall in the one-sided tolerance interval that has lower endpoint $X[r]$; that is, fall in a tolerance region that consists of $N+1-r$ statistical blocks. Similar considerations apply to the lower tail case where the number of sample values below a given order statistic is of interest; also to the two tail case where the number of sample values not falling between two order statistics is considered. Thus the number of exceedances problem is a special case of the statistical prediction problem.

Probability results and tables that have been developed for the number of exceedances problem are directly applicable to the general situation (univariate or multivariate) where the tolerance region consists of one subregion. Namely, for this situation, the probability distribution for the number of the values of a new sample falling in a tolerance region depends only on the size of the initial sample, the number of blocks in the tolerance region, and the size of the new sample. The details of the method used to obtain the tolerance region and the dimensionality of the observations have no influence on this probability distribution if the population sampled is at least partially continuous.

Applications to Two-Sample Problem

The statistical coverage results presented in this section have direct application to the two-sample problem, for both the univariate and the multivariate cases. Namely, one sample is used to determine a tolerance region that is appropriate with respect to the alternative hypotheses that are of interest. Then the null hypothesis is tested on the basis of how many of the values of the second sample fall in this random region. Here a tolerance region will often consist of two or more disjoint parts, which emphasize the locations where disagreement between the two populations is considered to be most important.

This use of tolerance regions for the two-sample problem has the advantage that it is applicable for multivariate situations where the data are at least partially continuous. Also supplementary information about the populations being sampled can be incorporated into the construction method used in obtaining the tolerance region from one of the samples.

Outline of the Presentation

The results for statistical prediction are given in a single presentation. Tolerance regions of the type considered to be used can be obtained on basis of the presentations for the Univariate Case and the Multivariate Case sections. For the tolerance regions considered, population coverage is controlled as a unit. The random variable is the number of the values of the new sample that fall within a given tolerance region. An easily computed expression is stated for the expected value of this random variable; a somewhat complicated expression is given for the distribution function of this random variable. Since only one presentation occurs, the Fixed Material for Section part is not considered.

Probability Properties for Statistical Coverage of Tolerance Regions

Data 1 At least partially continuous; univariate or multivariate **2** Construct tolerance region to have desired general form **3** $\{X(i)_j\}_m$ **4** $m=$ sample size; $n_1 = \ldots = n_m = n \geqslant 1$ (pop. n-variate) **Description 1** Prob. properties for no. values of new sample falling in tolerance region determined on basis of independent previous sample from same pop. Useful for predicting sample coverage outcome with respect to a region of desired general form **2** Expressions given for EY and the dist. fct. $G(y)$ of Y, where $Y=$no. values of new sample falling in given tolerance region; results unconditional in that pop. coverage prob. dist. of tolerance region

TABLE 9.1. VALUES OF $G(y; r)$ FOR $r-1 \leqslant y \leqslant m-r-1$, $1 \leqslant r \leqslant m/2$, AND $m=N=2(1)15(5)20$*

m	r	$y=0$	1	2	3	4	5	6	7	8	9	10	11	12	13
2	1	.1667													
3	1	.0500	.2000												
4	1	.0143	.0714	.2143											
	2		.2429												
5	1	$.0^{2}397$	.0238	.0833	.2222										
	2		.1032	.2619											
6	1	$.0^{2}108$	$.0^{2}758$	.0303	.0909	.2273									
	2		.0400	.1212	.2727										
	3			.2835											
7	1	$.0^{3}291$	$.0^{2}233$	.0105	.0350	.0962	.2308								
	2		.0146	.0513	.1329	.2797									
	3			.1431	.2960										
8	1	$.0^{4}777$	$.0^{3}699$	$.0^{2}350$	.0128	.0385	.1000	.2333							
	2		$.0^{2}505$	.0203	.0594	.1410	.2846								
	3			.0660	.1573	.3042									
	4				.3096										
9	1	$.0^{4}206$	$.0^{3}206$	$.0^{2}113$	$.0^{2}452$	.0147	.0412	.1029	.2353						
	2		$.0^{2}169$	$.0^{2}761$	.0249	.0656	.1471	.2882							
	3			.0283	.0767	.1674	.3100								
	4				.1735	.3186									
10	1	$.0^{5}541$	$.0^{4}595$	$.0^{3}357$	$.0^{2}155$	$.0^{2}542$	.0163	.0433	.1053	.2368					
	2		$.0^{3}547$	$.0^{2}274$	$.0^{2}988$	.0286	.0704	.1517	.2910						
	3			.0115	.0349	.0849	.1749	.3142							
	4				.0894	.1849	.3250								
	5					.3281									

11	1	$.0^{5}142$	$.0^{4}170$	$.0^{3}111$	$.0^{3}516$	$.0^{2}193$	$.0^{2}619$	.0175	.0451	.1071	.2381				
	2		$.0^{3}173$	$.0^{3}953$	$.0^{2}376$	.0119	.0317	.0743	.1554	.2932					
	3			$.0^{2}446$	.0150	.0402	.0913	.1807	.3176						
	4				.0431	.0992	.1935	.3297							
	5					.1974	.3350								
12	1	$.0^{6}370$	$.0^{5}481$	$.0^{4}337$	$.0^{3}168$	$.0^{3}673$	$.0^{2}229$	$.0^{2}686$	.0186	.0466	.1087	.2391			
	2		$.0^{4}536$	$.0^{3}322$	$.0^{2}138$	$.0^{2}471$	.0136	.0343	.0775	.1584	.2950				
	3			$.0^{2}166$	$.0^{2}614$	.0180	.0447	.0965	.1854	.3202					
	4				.0196	.0498	.1069	.2002	.3334						
	5					.1102	.2068	.3401							
	6						.3421								
13	1	$.0^{7}961$	$.0^{5}135$	$.0^{4}101$	$.0^{4}538$	$.0^{3}229$	$.0^{3}824$	$.0^{2}261$	$.0^{2}745$	.0196	.0478	.1100	.2400		
	2		$.0^{4}163$	$.0^{3}106$	$.0^{3}491$	$.0^{2}180$	$.0^{2}558$	.0151	.0365	.0801	.1609	.2965			
	3			$.0^{3}601$	$.0^{2}242$	$.0^{2}771$	.0207	.0484	.1008	.1891	.3224				
	4				$.0^{2}847$	.0236	.0554	.1131	.2055	.3364					
	5					.0576	.1189	.2142	.3441						
	6						.2169	.3475							
14	1	$.0^{7}249$	$.0^{6}374$	$.0^{5}299$	$.0^{4}170$	$.0^{4}763$	$.0^{3}290$	$.0^{3}966$	$.0^{2}290$	$.0^{2}797$	.0204	.0489	.1111	.2407	
	2		$.0^{5}491$	$.0^{4}344$	$.0^{3}171$	$.0^{3}670$	$.0^{2}221$	$.0^{2}638$	.0164	.0384	.0824	.1630	.2978		
	3			$0.^{3}211$	$.0^{3}919$	$.0^{2}316$	$.0^{2}915$	.0230	.0516	.1043	.1923	.3242			
	4				$.0^{2}351$	.0107	.0271	.0601	.1182	.2099	.3388				
	5					.0285	.0642	.1259	.2200	.3473					
	6						.1284	.2247	.3518						
	7							.3532							
15	1	$.0^{8}645$	$.0^{6}103$	$.0^{6}887$	$.0^{5}526$	$.0^{4}250$	$.0^{3}100$	$.0^{3}350$	$.0^{2}110$	$.0^{2}316$	$.0^{2}843$	.0211	.0498	.1121	.2414
	2		$.0^{5}146$	$.0^{4}109$	$.0^{4}579$	$.0^{3}242$	$.0^{3}850$	$.0^{2}260$	$.0^{2}710$	.0176	.0400	.0843	.1648	.2989	
	3			$.0^{4}725$	$.0^{3}339$	$.0^{2}125$	$.0^{2}389$	.0105	.0251	.0543	.1074	.1949	.3257		
	4				$.0^{2}141$	$.0^{2}461$	.0127	.0302	.0641	.1225	.2135	.3408			
	5					.0134	.0328	.0697	.1318	.2249	.3499				
	6						.0716	.1362	.2311	.3552					
	7							.2331	.3576						

* Taken from ref. 163: Table for the distribution of the number of exceedances, B. Epstein, *Annals of Mathematical Statistics*, Vol. 25, 1954, pages 762–68. Used with the kind permission of the author, Benjamin Epstein, and of the Editor of the *Annals of Mathematical Statistics*.

TABLE 9.1. VALUES OF $G(y; r)$ FOR $r-1 \leq y \leq m-r-1$, $1 \leq r \leq m/2$, AND $m=N=2(1)15(5)20$*—*continued*

m	r	$y=0$	1	2	3	4	5	6	7	8	9
20	1	$.0^{11}725$	$.0^{9}152$	$.0^{8}168$	$.0^{7}128$	$.0^{7}771$	$.0^{6}385$	$.0^{5}167$	$.0^{5}644$	$.0^{4}225$	$.0^{4}727$
	2		$.0^{8}291$	$.0^{7}291$	$.0^{6}203$	$.0^{5}110$	$.0^{5}501$	$.0^{4}197$	$.0^{4}685$	$.0^{3}216$	$.0^{3}624$
	3			$.0^{6}265$	$.0^{5}168$	$.0^{5}832$	$.0^{4}343$	$.0^{3}122$	$.0^{3}386$	$.0^{2}110$	$.0^{2}287$
	4				$.0^{5}969$	$.0^{4}438$	$.0^{3}164$	$.0^{3}532$	$.0^{2}153$	$.0^{2}396$	$.0^{2}935$
	5					$.0^{3}180$	$.0^{3}616$	$.0^{2}182$	$.0^{2}477$	.0112	.0242
	6						$.0^{2}192$	$.0^{2}519$	.0124	.0268	.0527
	7							.0128	.0281	.0555	.1001
	8								.0564	.1025	.1703
	9									.1715	.2636
	10										.3762
		$y=10$	11	12	13	14	15	16	17	18	
20	1	$.0^{3}218$	$.0^{3}614$	$.0^{2}164$	$.0^{2}416$	.0101	.0236	.0530	.1154	.2436	
	2	$.0^{2}167$	$.0^{2}418$	$.0^{2}983$	.0218	.0457	.0909	.1708	.3025		
	3	$.0^{2}691$	.0155	.0324	.0637	.1176	.2037	.3307			
	4	.0204	.0412	.0776	.1367	.2253	.3474				
	5	.0479	.0880	.1504	.2401	.3582					
	6	.0954	.1601	.2503	.3655						
	7	.1666	.2572	.3705							
	8	.2616	.3738								
	9	.3756									
	10										

* Taken from ref. 163: Table for the distribution of the number of exceedances, B. Epstein, *Annals of Mathematical Statistics*, Vol. 25, 1954, pages 762–68. Used with the kind permission of the author, Benjamin Epstein, and of the Editor of the *Annals of Mathematical Statistics*.

taken into consideration **Assumptions 1** Random sample that is independent of random sample used to determine tolerance region **2** Population continuous or partially continuous **3** None **Results 1** Tolerance region of the exact nonrandomized type presented in Univariate Case and Multivariate Case sects. N = size of sample used to determine tolerance region; s = no. of subregions; r_k = no. of stat. blocks removed in obtaining kth subregion ($k = 1, \ldots, s$), where $r_1 = r$ for $s = 1$ **2** *Relations. Estimate*: $EY = m\prod_{k=1}^{s}[1 - r_k/(N+1)]$. *Distributions*: For $s \geqslant 1$, $G(y) = \sum_{u=0}^{y}\sum_{v=0}^{m-u} \binom{m}{u}\binom{m-u}{v}(-1)^v \prod_{k=1}^{s}\left\{\frac{N!(N-r_k+u+v)!}{(N-r_k)!(N+u+v)!}\right\}$; for $s = 1$, $G(y) = G(y; r) = \sum_{u=0}^{y} r\binom{N}{r}\binom{m}{u}\Big/(N+m)\binom{N+m-1}{r+u-1}$ **3** Table 9.1 contains values of $G(y; r)$ for $r-1 \leqslant y \leqslant m-r-1$, $1 \leqslant r \leqslant m/2$, $N = m = 2(1)15(5)20$; for these values of N and m but other values of y and r, $G(y; r)$ can be determined through use of Table 9.1 and the relations $G(m-r; r) = \frac{1}{2}$, $G(y; r) = G(r-1; y+1) = 1 - G(m-y-1; m-r+1)$. Ref. 589 contains some values of $G(y; r)$ for $r = 1, 2$ and N not necessarily equal to m; ref. 440 contains values of y such that $G(y; 2)$ near .95 and .99 for $N, m = 1, \ldots, 50$ **4** EY and $P(Y \geqslant y) = 1 - G(y-1)$ ordinarily of principal interest **Characteristics 1** Low to medium, depending on N, m, n, form of region, etc. **2** $\sigma^2 Y$ can be determined from $G(y)$; for $s = 1$, $\sigma^2 Y = rm(N-r+1)(N+m+1)/(N+1)^2(N+2)$ **3** Used symmetrically (also used symmetrically for sample on which tolerance region based) **4** Sample conditions must hold to reasonable approx. Moderately sensitive to independence between samples and to continuity condition **5** Not difficult to decide on sample, independence, and continuity assumptions **6** Useful for studying exceedances, such as in floods, droughts, extreme temperatures, etc. **Bibliography** Ref. 163, 218, 231, 440, 589.

Chapter 10

NONSEQUENTIAL RESULTS FOR DISTRIBUTIONS FROM UNGROUPED DATA

INTRODUCTION

In this chapter, exact and approximate procedures are presented for investigating the values of distribution functions and of frequency functions for the nonsequential case. Point estimates, confidence regions, and significance tests are given for the values of probability distributions at identified points and for their values over specified regions. In all cases the observations are a random sample from the population whose distribution is being investigated. Most of the procedures are based on continuous univariate data. Additional results based on sequential samples and on categorical type data are given in Chapter 11. Also, some statistical decision theory results for distributions are given in Chapter 11.

USEFULNESS OF INFORMATION ABOUT DISTRIBUTIONS

From the viewpoint of mathematical statistics, complete knowledge of the probability distribution for a statistic represents the maximum amount of information that is attainable about that statistic. Thus statistical procedures for investigating the values of probability distributions can have practical importance.

One method of using statistical information consists in obtaining a point estimate of the population distribution and deriving probability results under the assumption that the estimate represents the true distribution. This method has the attractive feature of yielding a definite answer to any probability question that might be posed. However, it is not very satisfactory unless the estimate has at least a moderately high probability of being reasonably accurate. Ordinarily this probability is not very high unless the sample size is quite large.

A less general use consists in estimating the population distribution at an identified point or over a specified region (which does not include all possible population values). Estimates of this restricted type have many worthwhile applications. However, here too the probability of an estimate being reasonably accurate is ordinarily not very high unless the sample size is quite large.

An important problem is that of deciding when the sample size is sufficiently large to assure that a given estimate has at least a moderately high probability of being reasonably accurate. This requires interpretations for what are meant by a "moderately high probability" and by "reasonably accurate." Some criteria for making decisions of this nature are outlined and discussed in the section on point estimation.

Confidence regions and significance tests are also useful. They can be used for investigating a population distribution at an identified point or over a specified region. Confidence regions furnish bounds for the values of a probability distribution. Tests, perhaps obtained from confidence regions, can be used to decide whether a distribution has a specified form. The problem of deciding when the sample size is adequate also exists for confidence regions and tests, and can be satisfactorily solved in some cases. Many of the confidence regions and tests presented can serve as criteria for deciding when a point estimate is based on a sufficiently large sample.

Ordinarily, the population distribution function is investigated when the values of probability expressions are of principal interest. The population frequency function is considered when information is desired about the shape of the distribution.

RELATION TO THE PERCENTILE AND TOLERANCE REGION PRESENTATIONS

For the univariate case, there is a close relationship among the percentiles of a population, the probability concentration in this population (investigated by tolerance regions), and the values of the probability distribution for this population. The extent of this relationship is appraised by examining what is involved in evaluating each of these population properties and by considering some circumstances in which they are equivalent.

First let us consider what is to be evaluated in the determination of population percentiles, of regions containing a given amount of population probability, and of values for probability distributions. A population percentile is a point at which the population distribution function has a specified value; i.e., the value of the distribution function is given and the percentile is to be determined. For measuring population probability concentrations, the amount of probability to be covered is specified and any region with this probability content is eligible for use; i.e., except for restricted situations, no unique region can be determined. For the probability distribution case, a point or a region is specified and the distribution is to be evaluated for all points considered; i.e., the points are given and the corresponding distribution values are to be determined.

Although the quantity to be evaluated differs for these three types of population properties, there are important situations where these properties are equivalent. As noted in Chapter 9, if population probability concentration is measured in terms of one-sided intervals, knowledge of the population coverages of these intervals is equivalent to knowledge of the population percentiles. Since knowledge of the population percentiles is equivalent to knowledge of the population distribution function, the three types of properties are equivalent for this situation. This equivalence also holds for any region that is defined in terms of values of the population distribution function; i.e., the distribution function value is known for each boundary point of the region.

For the procedures involving distribution functions, every region considered is such that the three types of population properties are equivalent. However, this does not imply that the statistical procedures presented for investigating percentiles or the tolerance interval procedures usually furnish satisfactory methods for investigating distribution functions. Except for point estimation situations and for tests based on tolerance regions, the material presented in Chapters 8 and 9 is not very useful for this purpose. Moreover, the point estimates obtainable from consideration of percentile estimates or of tolerance intervals do not seem to be as satisfactory as those determined directly for the purpose of estimating distribution functions. Although there is a direct correspondence between population percentiles and distribution function values, a confidence region for a percentile does not necessarily yield a suitable confidence region for a distribution function value; likewise for tests. Also, the confidence regions and tests given for percentiles apply only to values at single points. The use of tolerance regions to obtain tests is discussed on pages 284–85.

For the multivariate case, there is a close relationship between regions used to measure the probability concentration in a population and the values of the probability distribution for this population. In fact, knowledge of the population coverages of the regions that are one-sided in every coordinate is equivalent to knowledge of the population distribution function. However, except for the case of tests, none of the procedures based on the material given in Chapter 9 seems to be as desirable as procedures that are directly determined for the purpose of investigating a multivariate distribution function.

CHARACTERISTICS OF THE INVESTIGATION PROCEDURES

Several types of point estimates are considered. These include expected value, median, and minimax estimation. Except for the minimax case, the basic problem is to estimate the value of the probability distribution at an identified point; estimation of the values over a region is accomplished by obtaining an estimate for each point of this region. For the minimax situations that occur, the estimate is to be used over the entire space of points and all of these points are simultaneously considered in the determination of the estimate. Estimates are obtained for distribution functions and for frequency functions. In the case of frequency functions, most of the estimates are for the value at an identified point; here the value of the point can be completely specified, or the point can be identified as a given population percentile (whose value is unknown).

The confidence regions presented can also be divided into two classes, depending on whether the probability distribution is investigated for its value at a point or for its values over a set of points. When the investigation pertains to the distribution values over a set of points, a confidence region includes the distribution if and only if, for each point of the set, the distribution value is included among the values allowed by the confidence region. Significance tests can be obtained from these confidence regions in the usual manner.

Nearly all of the tests presented are for the situation where the probability distribution is investigated over a set of points. For most cases, the distribution is completely specified by the null hypothesis (i.e., the null hypothesis is simple). In some cases, however, the null hypothesis can be composite. For all situations considered, the class of allowable distributions for the null hypothesis is of a rather general nature.

A few results are obtained for the situation where all that is known about the population sampled is that it can be arbitrary. For example, some of the exact confidence regions that can be determined for distribution functions in the continuous case can be modified to furnish tests with bounded significance levels for the case of an arbitrary population.

All the procedures presented for directly investigating frequency functions require the population sampled to be continuous. Some of these procedures (univariate and multivariate cases) are based on categorical data that are obtained by grouping observations. These results are given in Chapter 10, rather than Chapter 11, because of their specialized application to cases where the populations have continuous frequency functions.

Almost all of the statistical procedures presented are of either an exact or a theoretical-approximate nature. Many of the theoretical-approximate results are based on the first few terms of large sample expansions for probability expressions. Sometimes only the first term of the expansion is used (the asymptotic case).

NONPARAMETRIC NATURE OF TESTS

As mentioned in Chapter 4, nonparametric tests for probability distributions are of a somewhat different nature than other nonparametric procedures. Namely, the hypotheses tested are of the type that is encountered for the parametric case. That is, for the tests presented, the hypothetical probability distributions are either completely specified or are specified except for the values of parameters. The nonparametric character of these tests is evidenced by their ability to handle null hypotheses of a rather general nature. That is, although each null hypothesis tested can be considered to be of a parametric form, the totality of possible null hypotheses for a test is of a nonparametric nature.

ADDITIONAL RESULTS OF CHAPTER 11

Procedures that are sequential, are directly based on statistical decision theory, or are of a general nature and based on categorical data are given in Chapter 11. These results are applicable for both univariate and multivariate populations. Also, in many cases they can be used for populations that are arbitrary or that can be discrete as well as continuous.

Sequential methods are useful in estimating, testing, and reaching decisions concerning probability distributions. Estimates, tests, and decision procedures are obtained for distribution functions. Situations where the distribution function can be arbitrary and where it must be continuous are both considered. Only tests and decision procedures are considered for frequency functions. In many cases, for both distribution functions and frequency functions, the hypotheses considered can be simple or composite.

One of the principal features of statistical decision theory is that the decision reached can depend on supplementary information in a direct fashion. For the results presented, two or more probability distributions are specified as the possible distributions that could have yielded the sample values. On the basis of sample values, supplementary information, and a specified risk function, a decision is made as to which of these distributions applies to the population from which these sample values were drawn. The decision procedures considered can be based on fixed sample sizes, sequential sampling with a specified limit on the number of observations, and unlimited sequential sampling.

A few results with the data converted to a categorical form are given in Chapter 10. However, these are for specialized situations. The general procedures for testing probability distributions on the basis of data that have been converted to a categorical form (perhaps obtained by grouping observation values) are given in Chapter 11; also, some decision procedures which are based on categorical data are given there. Although some of the sequential results can be considered to use categorical data, the bulk of the categorical data results presented in Chapter 11 are for the case of fixed sample sizes.

CONVERSION TO CONTINUOUS CASE

Virtually every discontinuous population of practical interest can be approximated as closely as desired by continuous populations. For many purposes, investigation of the distribution function of the discontinuous population is virtually equivalent to investigation of the distribution function of any closely approximating continuous population.

The data can be converted to a sample from a continuous population which very closely approximates the discontinuous population actually sampled by use of procedures of the type mentioned in Chapters 4 and 8. Explicitly, to illustrate the conversion method, let the population sampled be n-variate ($n \geqslant 1$) while the sample is of size m. Using nonoverlapping sets of ten random decimal digits from a random digit table, determine a set of mn approximately random sample values from the rectangular (uniform) distribution with range $-\frac{1}{2}$ to $\frac{1}{2}$. Multiply each of these values by 10^{-100} and add it to a coordinate of one of the n-variate sample values, with one value being added to each of the n coordinates of each of the m observations. In practice, much less than mn of the extremely small sample values would ordinarily be needed. Ordinarily only those combinations of observations and coordinates which are involved in ties (that would not have occurred for a continuous population) need to use the extremely small sample values.

Of course, there are cases where the distinction between a discontinuous distribution function and a continuous distribution function is important, irrespective of closeness of the approximation. The conversion method outlined here is not appropriate for these cases.

MODIFIED COMPOSITE HYPOTHESES

Some of the tests, mainly those for frequency functions, involve the testing of a simple null hypothesis against a simple alternative hypothesis. These procedures can also be used to test some modified types of hypotheses. Let a probability distribution be represented by g, with g_ξ representing the eligible simple hypothesis distributions. Here the univariate or the multivariate case could be considered. A modified composite hypothesis consists of a weighted "average" of the g_ξ such that this "average" is itself a distribution. Here the weights are completely specified and are chosen so that the simple hypotheses of principal interest are emphasized.

Two kinds of modified composite hypotheses are considered in this chapter. In one case, the simple hypothesis which represents the modified composite hypothesis is

$$g^{(1)} = \int_{\text{all } \xi} w(\xi) g_\xi \, d\xi,$$

where integration takes the form of summation when the values for ξ are a discrete set or when the non-negative relative weighting function $w(\xi)$ has zero values except for a discrete set of ξ values. Here $w(\xi)$ is such that

$$\int_{\text{all } \xi} w(\xi) d\xi = 1.$$

The interpretation for this kind of modified composite hypothesis is that, separately for each sample value, the relative probability is $w(\xi)$ that this value is taken from the distribution g_ξ. Hypotheses of this type are referred to as random-selection modified composite hypotheses.

The other kind of modified composite hypothesis is only concerned with a finite number of simple hypotheses out of the totality of the g_ξ. Let $g_{\xi(1)}, \ldots, g_{\xi(R)}$ denote these simple hypotheses. Then the simple hypothesis which represents the modified composite hypothesis is

$$g^{(2)} = \prod_{r=1}^{R} g_{\xi(r)}^{w[\xi(r)]},$$

where the relative weights are such that $g^{(2)}$ is a distribution. This modified composite hypothesis represents a weighted geometric-mean type average of the simple hypotheses that are of major interest for the null or alternative hypothesis situation being considered.

With suitable selection of the values of the weights, both types seem to furnish reasonable representations of combinations of simple hypotheses. In many cases, the first kind of modified composite hypothesis is much easier to apply than the second kind. Since a modified composite hypothesis has the form of a simple hypothesis, one or both of the null and alternative hypotheses of a test with simple hypotheses can be replaced by a modified composite hypothesis.

OBTAINING TESTS FROM CONFIDENCE BANDS

A confidence band is a confidence region for the value of a univariate probability distribution over a set of points (e.g., the entire x axis). A distribution is contained in a confidence band if and only if its value lies within the band for all points of the set considered. Thus a probability distribution is not contained in a confidence band if and only if its value falls outside the band for at least one point of the set. For the cases considered in this chapter, only intervals of points are considered so that the region boundary is a band in the usual sense.

Only simple null hypotheses are considered in the conversion of confidence bands to significance tests; i.e., the probability distribution is completely specified by the null hypothesis. However, a simple null hypothesis can be replaced by a modified composite hypothesis. The null hypothesis is rejected if the hypothetical distribution is not contained in the confidence band on which the test is based. Thus the significance level of the test equals unity minus the confidence coefficient value for the band.

OBTAINING TESTS OVER RESTRICTED SETS OF POINTS

For the continuous case, only a few of the tests considered are constructed for investigating probability distributions over restricted sets of points (having nonzero probability under the null hypothesis). However, many tests are given for investigating a continuous distribution over all points, and these results furnish a basis for testing the distribution over any specified set of points with nonzero measure. The resulting tests do not have fixed sample sizes; these are the only statistical procedures considered in this chapter for which the sample size is not fixed. No presentations are given for tests of this type. However, a method that can be used to develop these tests is outlined here. This method is applicable for distribution functions and for frequency functions; also it can be applied to univariate and multivariate cases.

Let the univariate or multivariate population sampled be continuous and suppose that the problem is to test a probability distribution over a specified set of points s having nonzero probability. Let sample values be drawn until n observations are obtained with values in s. Then these observations are a random sample of size n from the continuous population with distribution function

$$F(x;s) = \int_{z \leqslant x,\, z \epsilon s} dF(z) \Big/ \int_{z \epsilon s} dF(z), \qquad (x \epsilon s)$$

and, if $f(x)$ exists, with frequency function

$$f(x;s) = f(x) \Big/ \int_{z \epsilon s} f(z)dz, \qquad (x \epsilon s)$$

where these distributions are such that a value not belonging to s has zero probability of occurring.

If the set s has zero probability for the population actually sampled, it will be impossible to obtain n observations with values in s. Moreover, if s has a nonzero but small probability, the expected number of sample values required for obtaining n observations with values in s may be very large, even though this would not be the case if the null hypothesis were true. Fortunately, application difficulties of this nature can be protected against by considering only null hypotheses where the null expectation of the number of sample values required is not overly large and by adjoining a categorical data test to the noncategorical data test considered.

Let the noncategorical test based on n observations be denoted by T_N and have significance level α_N. The categorical test, denoted by T_C, has significance level α_C and rejects the null hypothesis H_0 if more than $n(\alpha_C, H_0, s)$ sample values are needed to obtain n observations with values in s. The combined test rejects the null hypothesis if either T_N or T_C is significant. The significance level of this combined test is

$$P(T_N \text{ rejects } | H_0 \text{ and that } T_C \text{ does not reject}) \cdot P(T_C \text{ does not reject } | H_0) + P(T_C \text{ rejects } | H_0) = \alpha_N(1-\alpha_C)+\alpha_C.$$

The relative emphasis to be placed on T_N and T_C is determined by the values used for α_N and α_C. Here T_C protects against large expected sample sizes but ordinarily is not as sensitive a test of the null hypothesis as T_N. One way of choosing values for α_N and α_C would be to first determine α_C by specifying the desired expected sample size. Then α_N is determined from the value of α_C and the desired significance level for the combined test.

The same type of procedure can be used for the case of the sequential tests given in Chapter 11. Then the categorical data test should also be sequential. Since the categorical data test is of a binomial nature, the sequential tests for the binomial parameter that are presented in Chapter 7 can be used directly to obtain the sequential categorical data test.

In general, a probability distribution can be tested over any specified set of points that has nonzero probability under the null hypothesis by converting the data to a categorical form. Chapter 11 contains some tests that are based on categorical data and can be used for this purpose.

OBTAINING TESTS FROM TOLERANCE REGIONS

The tolerance region results of Chapter 9 are directly applicable for testing simple null hypotheses where the probability distribution is specified over all points. Namely, let R be the tolerance region and F the distribution function, with the null hypothesis being $F=F_0$. Then, for example,

$$P\left\{\int_R dF_0 \epsilon A\right\},$$

where A is a specified set of nonzero measure in [0, 1], has a value that is either exactly or approximately determined when the null hypothesis holds. Since $\int_R dF_0$ can be evaluated directly, whether $\int_R dF_0$ has a value in A can be determined on the basis of R. Choice of A and of the characteristics of R determine the significance level of a test and which alternative hypotheses are emphasized.

The more general situation where the population coverage is controlled separately for several parts of a tolerance region can also be used in furnishing tests. Then, the test relation is of the form which requires that simultaneously

$$\int_{R_1} dF \epsilon A_1, \ldots, \int_{R_s} dF \epsilon A_s$$

where $R_1, \ldots, R_s$ are mutually exclusive parts of the tolerance region and $A_1, \ldots, A_s$ are specified sets in [0, 1] which are not necessarily mutually exclusive. Also tests can be obtained on the basis of the $\int_{r(j)} dF$, where the $r(j)$ are a set of basic statistical blocks.

One advantage of the use of tolerance regions is that tests can be obtained for the multivariate case and for arbitrary populations. Another strong advantage is that, for both the univariate and multivariate cases, a very wide variety of possibilities are available for constructing tests. Here the distribution function being tested is known, since it is completely specified by the null hypothesis. Also the deviations from this distribution function that are of principal interest can usually be specified. Thus, by exploiting the large amount of freedom available in the construction process, it should nearly always be possible to obtain a tolerance region (whose coverage might be controlled in parts) that is sensitive to the alternative hypotheses which are of principal interest.

OBTAINING TESTS OF SIMPLE HYPOTHESES

For a simple hypothesis, the probability distribution is completely specified. Thus, in principle, the distribution of any specified function of the sample values can be determined, although the amount of effort required would often be prohibitive. For the continuous univariate case, a transformation of variable can be determined which will convert the observations into a sample from the standard normal distribution and the results that have been developed for normality can be applied. Alternatively, observations from a continuous univariate population can be converted to a sample from the rectangular distribution [0, 1], a method that is used in developing some of the tests presented in this chapter.

For approximate results, moments can be determined for a specified statistic and its distribution approximated by the first few terms of the

Edgeworth series, by the Pearson curves, etc. Since the distribution yielding the data is completely known, reasonably accurate determination of moments should not be overly difficult, even for complicated statistics. This approach is applicable for univariate and multivariate situations. Here the statistic should have a distribution that is at least roughly continuous; however, the population sampled need not be continuous.

These procedures can be used for both null and alternative hypotheses. Here the simple null hypothesis is used to determine the significance level and the simple alternative determines a power function value for the test considered.

Although some of these methods for testing simple hypotheses are used for the material presented, there are many other possibilities, such as converting continuous univariate data to a sample from the standard normal distribution, which are not used in the presentations. In many cases, some of these other possibilities may be more suitable for the alternatives of interest than the tests obtained from the material presented in this chapter. Of course, at least a moderate amount of effort is usually required to develop one of these special methods. As an example, the distribution specified by a simple null hypothesis ordinarily must be tabulated as the first step in converting the univariate data to a sample from a specified standard distribution. However, since the standard distribution is usually already tabulated, the remainder of the conversion is easily accomplished. Namely, each sample value represents some specified percentage point of the null hypothesis distribution and the transformed value of this observation is the value of this percentage point for the standard distribution.

ONE-SIDED TESTS FROM TESTS OF SIMPLE HYPOTHESES

Consider a situation where each null hypothesis and alternative hypothesis of interest can be represented by a probability distribution $g(x; \xi)$, which is a univariate or multivariate distribution function or frequency function. Here the one-dimensional parameter ξ ranges over a specified set of values ω_0 for the null hypotheses of interest and over a specified set ω_1 for the alternatives of interest. The test is one-sided if all the values in ω_1 either exceed all the values in ω_0 or are less than all the values in ω_0. For many important functions $g(x; \xi)$, the probability that the test rejects the null hypothesis for a given value of ξ is a monotonic function of ξ. Then tests for simple null and alternative hypotheses yield tests for one-sided composite null and alternative hypotheses. For example, let the null hypothesis assert that $\xi = \xi_0$ while the alternative asserts that $\xi = \xi_1$, where $\xi_0 < \xi_1$, ξ_0 is the largest value in ω_0, and ξ_1 is the smallest value in ω_1; also $g(x; \xi)$ is such that the probability of rejecting the null hypothesis increases as ξ increases. Then, if α is the significance level and β is the power at ξ_1, the probability of rejecting $\xi=\xi_0$ is at most α for $\xi \leqslant \xi_0$, and thus is $\leqslant \alpha$ for $\xi \epsilon \omega_0$; when ω_0 is not the single point ξ_0, this implies that the test has generalized significance level α. Also the power is at least β for $\xi \geqslant \xi_1$, and thus is $\geqslant \beta$ for $\xi \epsilon \omega_1$. The same considerations hold for the other type of test for one-sided composite hypotheses. For this other case, $\xi_0 > \xi_1$, ξ_0 is the smallest value in ω_0, ξ_1 is the largest value in ω_1, and $g(x; \xi)$ is such that the probability of rejecting $\xi=\xi_0$ decreases as ξ increases.

TESTS FOR GENERAL COMPOSITE HYPOTHESES

In principle, an "optimum" test can always be developed for testing a specified composite null hypothesis against a specified composite alternative hypothesis for the case of frequency functions. The method for obtaining such a test is outlined on pages 200–07 of ref. 67. The resulting tests, which are of a randomized form, are applicable for both the continuous and the discrete cases. These tests are optimum in the sense that they have specified maximum values for the probabilities of type I and type II errors over the simple hypotheses that constitute the composite hypotheses. Unfortunately, constructing the test for a specified situation virtually always requires an appreciable amount of effort. Consequently, this method is not presented in Chapter 10.

TESTS EMPHASIZING SPECIAL PROPERTIES

Tests of simple null hypotheses about probability distributions can be devised so as to emphasize special population properties that are one-dimensional. For the univariate case, the property of interest might be the population mean, the population variance, a specified population percentage point, a given function of specified population percentage points, etc. For the multivariate case, the one-dimensional population property might be a stated weighted average of the expected values of the observation coordinates, a stated weighted average of the correlations among the coordinates, etc.

Development of a test is usually not very difficult when the property of interest equals, or very nearly equals, the expected value of a suitable statistic of the sample values (for all populations such that the expected value of this statistic exists). Then this statistic can be used as the test statistic and its expected value compared with the value that is specified by the null hypothesis. The null distribution of the test statistic, and its expected value, can be approximated by determining the first few moments of the statistic under the null hypothesis and using the first few terms of the Edgeworth series expansion, etc. Ordinarily, use of the first four moments and the first four terms of the Edgeworth series furnishes an acceptable approximation for situations where the sample size is not small.

TESTS OF COMPOSITE HYPOTHESES BY VARIABLE TRANSFORMATION

The viewpoint ordinarily adopted when a completely specified univariate distribution function $F_0(x)$ is furnished by the null hypothesis is that $F_0(x)$ is the null distribution of the sample values, so that any completely specified transformation of variable yields sample values for which the null distribution is determined. The requirement of a completely determined null distribution for a specified transformation of variable can be weakened; then the null hypothesis is composite rather than simple. This more general viewpoint, combined with suitable transformations of variable, can be used to obtain tests of composite hypotheses on the basis of already developed parametric results. The function $F_0(x)$ is selected so that it is representative of the simple null hypotheses of principal interest or so that it is the best guess as to the actual distribution.

Specifically, for sampling from a continuous population, a transformation of variable is made which converts the completely specified distribution function $F_0(x)$ into a standard univariate distribution such as the rectangular (uniform) distribution $[0, 1]$, the standardized normal distribution, the exponential distribution with frequency function e^{-x} $(0 \leqslant x < \infty)$; etc. However, under the null hypothesis, the continuous population obtained by this transformation is only considered to be of a parametric type for which the standard population into which $F_0(x)$ is transformed represents a special case. For the rectangular distribution situation, this might be considered to imply that the distribution is rectangular $[a, b]$ where one or both of a, b are unknown constants such that $0 \leqslant a < b \leqslant 1$. For the normal case, this could be considered to imply that the sample values are normally distributed with zero mean but unknown variance, or with unknown mean and unit variance, or with a specified population percentile (establishes a relation between the population mean and variance), or with unknown mean and unknown variance. For the exponential case, the composite null hypothesis could be considered to imply that the distribution is exponential with frequency function $ce^{-c(x-d)}$, where $c > 0$, $d \leqslant x < \infty$, and one or both of c and d are unknown.

In addition to having composite null hypotheses, tests obtained by this method can often be chosen so as to be sensitive to specified composite alternatives. However, when standard parametric results are used, the alternatives are nearly always restricted to be of the same general parametric type as the population into which $F_0(x)$ is transformed. As an example, consider the normality situation where the null hypothesis asserts that the population mean is zero but the variance is unknown. Use of the appropriate one-sided t test emphasizes alternatives where the population is normal but with a positive mean. As another example, consider the rectangular case where the null hypothesis asserts that $a+b=1$. Use of an appropriate two-tailed test based on the range-midrange statistic emphasizes all alternatives for which the population is uniform $[a, b]$.

Any hypothesis for a transformed distribution represents a determinable hypothesis for the population actually sampled, since the transformation is completely specified. However, the amount of effort required to identify the composite hypothesis corresponding to a given composite hypothesis for the transformed distribution can be large.

Since continuous univariate data are used, these results are mainly useful for the univariate case. However, they can also be used for tests that emphasize special properties for the multivariate case, since then the data are converted to a univariate form.

RESULTS FOR LIFE-TESTING SITUATIONS

Several of the statistical procedures presented for the univariate case in this chapter are useful for life-testing situations. Let a group of items of the same type be simultaneously life-tested with the random variable being the time to failure for an item. Then the sample consists of the times to failure for these items. Consequently, the first sample value determined is the smallest order statistic of the sample, etc.; moreover, all sample order statistics with values at most equal to x are determined if experimentation is stopped at time x after the simultaneous beginning of the life-testing of the items. Thus estimates and tests which are based exclusively on the sample values that are at most equal to some specified time, or on a specified number of the smallest order statistics of a sample, have potential usefulness for life-testing situations. That is, the experiment can be discontinued prior to the failing of all the items; this can result in a substantial saving in time and/or cost.

First let us consider results for distribution values at identified points. Point estimates, confidence intervals and tests for $F(x)$ at a specified value of x can be obtained such that the experiment can be discontinued at a time which is not much larger than x. Point estimates for $f(x)$ can also be obtained which have this property. Point estimates, confidence intervals, and tests for $f(\theta_p)$ can be obtained with the property that the experiment can be stopped when not much more than $100p$ per cent of the items have failed. The frequency function and some of the distribution function results require the population sampled to be continuous.

Tests based on confidence bands have desirable properties for life-testing situations. Namely, the significance of the test is established at the smallest value of x for which the test statistic falls outside the band. The experiment can be stopped then, with a saving in cost and/or time.

Results of life-testing interest are also available for distributions over restricted intervals. Point estimates, confidence bands, and tests can be obtained for $F(y)$ and $f(y)$ over y intervals such that $y \leqslant x$ on the basis of sample values that are not much larger than x; for the distribution function bands where $F(x) \leqslant A$, the experiment can be stopped when not much more than $100A$ per cent of the items have failed. Here, the population sampled is nearly always required to be continuous.

A transformation of variable can also be used to test a simple null hypothesis $F_0(x)$ or a composite hypothesis where $F_0(x)$ is completely specified (see the preceding section). A method that is often satisfactory for the continuous case consists in transforming $F_0(x)$ to the exponential distribution with frequency function e^{-x} $(0 \leqslant x < \infty)$. Ref. 164 contains some investigation procedures for life-testing situations where the population is of an exponential form.

CENSORED DATA APPLICATIONS

The results that are applicable for life-testing are also applicable for the more general situation where only some specified order statistics of a univariate sample have known values. The stopping of a life-testing experiment when a specified or random number of sample values have been determined is a special case of the censoring of a sample. Since censoring often happens accidentally, it is convenient to have statistical procedures which can be used for censored samples and other situations where only specified sample order statistics are available.

ESTIMATION OF DISCRETE FREQUENCY FUNCTION

A general method is available for estimating a discrete frequency function when the set of possible values for an observation is known and finite. Namely, for a given possible value, an expected value estimate of the frequency function value at this point is furnished by the observed relative frequency for this point. That is, if the sample size is m and m_u of the sample values equal the uth possible value, then m_u/m is an unbiased point estimate of the frequency function value for this point. This estimation method is applicable for both the univariate and the multivariate cases.

SOME APPLICATIONS TO SEVERAL-SAMPLE PROBLEM

Testing whether two or more independent samples have the same completely specified distribution, or a common distribution that is specified except for the values of some parameters, is occasionally of interest. The tests given in Chapter 10 can be directly applied to problems of this nature. Specifically, all the sample values are pooled and a test is applied to investigate whether this combined set of observations is a sample with a distribution that is of the stated form. Here the test is used in a manner that is somewhat different from that for the distribution investigations of Chapter 10; namely, the requirement of the same distribution for each observation is a part of the null hypothesis rather than a part of the assumptions.

For the univariate case results, nearly all the tests of Chapter 10 use the observations in a symmetrical fashion. The tests with this property are independent of the randomness tests of Chapter 5. Thus, a combined test, consisting of one of these tests and a test of Chapter 5, is easily developed. This combined test is obtained by determining the result for each of the two tests and rejecting the null hypothesis if and only if at least one of these tests is significant. Here the null hypothesis asserts that the samples are from the same population and that this population has the specified form. One part of the combined test is for investigating whether the samples are from the same population, where this could be any population. The other part investigates whether the samples are from a common distribution which has the specified form. Combined tests of this type are useful when the interest is in situations where the samples are from the same population and the distribution of this population does not differ hugely from a stated form.

OUTLINE OF PRESENTATIONS

This chapter contains five sections that are devoted to the presentation of statistical procedures. The first four of these sections are concerned with the univariate case while the fifth deals with the multivariate case.

The first procedure presentation section is concerned with point estimation of distribution functions and frequency functions. The second section contains confidence regions for distribution functions. The third section consists of tests and confidence regions for frequency functions. The fourth section is concerned with tests of continuous univariate distribution functions. The fifth and final presentation section contains estimates and tests for multivariate situations.

POINT ESTIMATION FOR UNIVARIATE CASE

Discussion

The material presented is concerned with estimation of the values of univariate distribution functions and frequency functions on the basis of random samples. For distribution function estimation, the case of arbitrary data and the case of continuous data are both considered; only the continuous case occurs in the presentations dealing with frequency functions. The points at which the value of the distribution function is to be estimated are completely specified; this is also the situation for some of the estimates for frequency function values. However, some of the frequency function estimates are for values at points that are identified only in the sense of being specified population percentiles.

Expected value, median, and various types of mimimax estimates are furnished for population distribution functions. The expected value estimates and many of the minimax estimates are exact. The median estimates and the remainder of the minimax estimates are theoretical-approximate. The estimates presented for frequency functions are all theoretical-approximate. Expected value estimation for specified points and minimax expected value estimation over all points are considered for frequency functions. Median estimates are stated for the values of frequency functions at specified population percentiles; also, the reciprocal of the frequency function value at a percentile is estimated on an expected value basis.

Additional Estimation Methods

The estimates furnished by the presentations of this chapter do not represent all of the nonparametric type estimation methods that are available. Following are outlines of several other methods which have some practical value:

Functions that can be used to approximate a probability distribution on the basis of its first few moments are sometimes useful for obtaining estimates of distribution functions and/or frequency functions. The procedure is to estimate the population moments from the sample values; then, the approximation function with the population moments replaced by their sample estimates furnishes an estimate of the probability distribution considered. For the continuous case, distribution functions and frequency functions can be estimated by use of the first few terms of the Gram-Charlier A series expansion for the function considered, the first few terms of the Edgeworth series expansion for this function, the Pearson system of curves, etc. Due to the instability of estimates for higher order moments, approximation functions based on moments of higher than sixth order are seldom used.

An alternative method for estimating a population distribution function consists in estimating several suitably chosen population percentiles and using interpolation and/or extrapolation. That is, points for which the distribution function has specified values are estimated; interpolations and/or extrapolations based on these values can be used to furnish an estimate of the entire distribution function or estimates of the distribution function values between specified percentiles. The results of Chapter 8 can be used directly for this method of estimation.

For the continuous case, a frequency function can be estimated on the basis of a suitably chosen histogram of the sample values. If the sample size is large, the material of ref. 5 indicates that the use of a histogram based on 10 to 20 equal-length class intervals is suitable for many purposes.

Efficiency Considerations

For estimating the value of a probability distribution at an identified point, the expected variation of the estimate about the value estimated, as measured by the mean square error (the variance, for expected value estimation), seems to furnish a reasonable basis for relative efficiency measurement. When the probability distribution is estimated over a set of points, however, a method that furnishes some suitable type of relative weighting for the points of the set is needed. One method consists in using a function of the mean square error at several representative points of the set (e.g., a weighted sum) or a function of the mean square error at all points of the set. However, other possibilities are available; here the consideration of these other possibilities is limited to situations where the suitability of an estimate is determined on the basis of a given risk function and a stated class of populations (e.g., all continuous populations).

If a minimax procedure is used for estimating a distribution function, the resulting estimate has 100 per cent efficiency for the combination of risk function, class of estimates, and class of populations considered. When the supremum of the risk function (over the class of populations) can be determined for the minimax estimate and for the other estimates of interest, one method of evaluating the efficiency for each of these other estimates consists in dividing the mimimum value of this supremum by the value for the estimate considered. A more refined method consists in increasing the sample size for the estimate considered until the supremum of its risk function equals the minimum value for the original sample size; then the efficiency of the estimate equals the original sample size divided by this increased sample size.

In estimating a frequency function over a set of specified points, an approximation to the value that the risk function used attains for the (unknown) population actually sampled can be obtained for the class of estimates considered. Explicitly, an approximate expression is obtained which depends only on the sample size and the value of the second derivative of the frequency function over the set of points. This expression, combined with sample estimation of the second derivative, is used to approximately determine the estimate (of the class considered) that is most efficient. The relative efficiencies for other estimates of this class can be approximately evaluated on the basis of the expression for the risk function and its value for the most efficient estimate.

The estimation of frequency function values at percentiles refers to (or is equivalent to) estimates for the reciprocals of these frequency function values. Here individual percentiles are considered and efficiency properties can be determined on the basis of an approximate expression for the mean square error of the estimate.

Determination of Adequate Sample Sizes

The methods considered here are along the lines of those outlined in Chapter 4. First, let us consider estimation of the value of a probability distribution at an identified point. Then the expected variation of the estimate (about the value estimated) or its coefficient of variation should furnish a satisfactory criterion for determining adequate sample sizes; for the case of distribution functions, the coefficient of variation might also be considered for the estimate of unity-minus-the-distribution-function-value. Here the coefficient of variation for an estimate is considered to equal the square root of the mean square error of the estimate about the quantity estimated divided by the value of the quantity estimated; for the cases considered, this exactly or approximately equals the expression with the mean square error replaced by the variance. An estimate based on a sample size for which its coefficient of variation has a sufficiently small value (say, $\frac{1}{5}$) should be satisfactory for many estimation purposes.

For the case of estimating frequency functions at identified percentiles, the coefficient of variation furnishes a convenient criterion for determining adequate sample sizes. In the cases considered, its value, or an upper bound for its value, can always be approximately represented by an expression in which the sample size is the only undetermined quantity.

When a probability distribution is to be estimated over a set of points, many types of criteria might be used for determining adequate sample sizes. One type consists of functions of the mean square error values or of the coefficient of variation values for the points of the set. As an example, the supremum of the mean square error values or the supremum of the coefficient of variation values sometimes furnishes a suitable criterion for determining adequate sample sizes. As another example, the supremum of a function of the coefficient of variation in which the values in the distribution tails receive less emphasis than those in the central part might yield a satisfactory criterion.

Criteria of another type are sometimes applicable for the situation of minimax estimation. Here the minimum (over the class of estimates considered) of the supremum of the risk function (over the class of populations considered) furnishes a criterion if its value can be determined for the sample sizes of interest. Then the sample size is considered to be adequate when this criterion has a specified value that is sufficiently small.

For some of the cases involving frequency functions, the value of a criterion (mean square error, coefficient of variation, risk function, etc.) may not be completely determined for the most efficient estimate but can be determined for a less efficient estimate. Then a conservatively large value for adequate sample sizes can be obtained by use of the criterion expression for the less efficient estimate.

Often the criterion for determining adequate sample sizes is not completely known but can be estimated. Then use of a two-stage sampling procedure may be appropriate. That is, a first sample of only moderately large size is drawn and the unknown probability constants in the criterion are estimated; then an adequate sample size is determined on the basis of the resulting criterion expression. The additional sample values needed to increase the total sample size to this adequate value are then drawn. For the situations considered in this section, the conditional probability effects from the use of a two-stage sampling procedure should not be important.

For some situations, satisfactory criteria can be obtained that are based on the values of the probabilities for specified relations involving the estimate and the probability distribution estimated. As an example, sometimes a statistic can be developed that furnishes a reasonable measure of the deviation of the estimate from the distribution and whose probability properties can be determined. Then the sample size can be considered adequate if there is a sufficiently high probability that the value of this statistic is less than a specified number which is sufficiently small. Several of the statistical procedures presented in later sections can be used to furnish this type of criterion for the case where the empirical distribution function is used to estimate the population distribution function.

Unbiased-Minimax Estimation of Distribution Function

Let us consider the minimax estimation of a distribution function $G(x)$ that is known to belong to a family $\{F(x)\}$ of distribution functions. The loss that results from using an estimate $h_n(x)$ is denoted by $L[h_n(x), G(x)]$

and the risk function is $E_{G(x)}L[h_n(x), G(x)]$. Then the minimax choice for $h_n(x)$ is any function of the sample values that belongs to the allowable class of estimates and which minimizes

$$\sup_{G(x)\varepsilon\{F(x)\}} \{E_{G(x)}L[h_n(x), G(x)]\}$$

with respect to this class. For this situation, a minimax estimate $h_n(x)$ is unbiased-minimax (see ref. 305) if, for every $G(x)$ and $F(x)$ belonging to the specified family of distribution functions,

$$E_{G(x)}L[h_n(x), F(x)]$$

is minimum when $G(x)=F(x)$. Thus a minimax estimate that is unbiased (in the sense that its expected value equals $F(x)$ for all x) is not necessarily an unbiased-minimax estimate of $F(x)$.

Risk Functions for Distribution Function Estimation

Three classes of risk functions are considered for nonasymptotic estimation of continuous distribution functions. One class consists of risk functions of the form

$$E\int_{-\infty}^{\infty} |h_n(x)-F(x)|^r dF(x),$$

where $r=1, 2, \ldots$ and $h_n(x)$ is an estimate based on a sample of size n. Another class consists of

$$E\int_{-\infty}^{\infty} \{|h_n(x)-F(x)|^r/F(x)[1-F(x)]\}dF(x),$$

for $r=1$ and r any even positive integer. The third class consists of

$$\int_{-\infty}^{\infty}\left\{\int_{F(x)}^{\infty} a(x)[h-F(x)]dH_x(h)+\int_{-\infty}^{F(x)} b(x)[F(x)-h]dH_x(h)\right\} dm(x),$$

where $H_x(h)$ is the distribution function of $h_n(x)$ and $m(x)$ is a specified continuous monotonic measure function [e.g., $m(x)$ might be $F(x)$ or x]. Also

$$a(x)=\begin{cases} a & \text{if } x \text{ such that } F(x)\geqslant \epsilon_1 \\ 0 & \text{otherwise} \end{cases}$$

$$b(x)=\begin{cases} b & \text{if } x \text{ such that } F(x)\leqslant 1-\epsilon_2 \\ 0 & \text{otherwise,} \end{cases}$$

where $\epsilon_1, \epsilon_2 > 0$ are arbitrarily small but fixed ($\epsilon_1 = \epsilon_2 = 10^{-6}$ should be satisfactory for virtually all situations) and the constants a, b are positive.

For the first two classes of risk functions, choice of r determines the relative emphasis to be placed on the various deviations of $h_n(x)$ from $F(x)$; here positive and negative deviations receive the same emphasis. For the third class and the deviations of practical interest, the magnitude of a deviation is multiplied by a specified weighting constant; however, the constant used to weight positive deviations can be different from that used for negative deviations.

Empirical Distribution Function—Discussion

As indicated by the procedure presentation of its properties, the empirical (sample) distribution function is in many respects an ideal estimate of the population distribution function. For any sample size n and an arbitrary population, $F_n(x)$ is an unbiased (expected value) estimate of $F(x)$; for sufficiently large n, it is also an approximate median estimate of $F(x)$ at x values where $F(x)[1-F(x)] \neq 0$. In addition, $F_n(x)$ is an asymptotically minimax estimate of $F(x)$ for the class of all univariate distribution functions and a broad class of risk functions that includes most risk functions of practical interest.

A fundamental problem is the determination of adequate values for n. This can be done on the basis of many criteria if the population is continuous. Then there are several statistics which furnish reasonable measures of the deviation of $F_n(x)$ from $F(x)$ and whose probability properties can be determined. These include

$$\sup_x |F_n(x) - F(x)|, \qquad \sup_{F(x) \geqslant A} |[F_n(x) - F(x)]/F(x)|,$$

and

$$\int_{-\infty}^{\infty} [F_n(x) - F(x)]^2 dF(x).$$

Also, for all n, $F_n(x)$ is a minimax estimate of $F(x)$ over the class of all continuous distribution functions if the risk function used is

$$E \int_{-\infty}^{\infty} \{[h_n(x) - F(x)]^2/F(x)[1-F(x)]\}\, dF(x)$$

and consideration is limited to estimates $h_n(x)$ that have constant values between consecutive sample order statistics. For some situations, adequate values for n can be determined by the requirement that

$$\sup_{F(x)} E \int_{-\infty}^{\infty} \{[F_n(x) - F(x)]^2/F(x)[1-F(x)]\}\, dF(x) = 1/n$$

has a specified value which is sufficiently small.

When the population sampled can be arbitrary, criteria based on the mean square error of $F_n(x)$ or on the coefficient of variation of $F_n(x)$ and/or $1-F_n(x)$ are perhaps most suitable for determining adequate values for n. The mean square error equals the variance for expected value estimates and approximately equals the variance for the other cases where it is used.

The basic relations, which can be used in an exact sense for expected value estimation, and in an approximate sense otherwise, are

$$\sigma^2 F_n(x) = F(x)[1-F(x)]/n$$

$$\{[1-F(x)]/nF(x)\}^{\frac{1}{2}} = \text{coefficient of variation for } F_n(x)$$

$$\{F(x)/n[1-F(x)]\}^{\frac{1}{2}} = \text{coefficient of variation for } 1-F_n(x).$$

Let the total sample of size n be taken in two stages, where N is the sample size for the first stage. Then

$$F_N(x)[1-F_N(x)]/n = \text{estimate of } \sigma^2 F_n(x)$$

$$\{[1-F_N(x)]/nF_N(x)\}^{\frac{1}{2}} = \text{estimate of coefficient of variation for } F_n(x)$$

$$\{F_N(x)/n[1-F_N(x)]\}^{\frac{1}{2}} = \text{estimate of coefficient of variation for } 1-F_n(x).$$

These estimates can be used directly if adequate values of n are to be determined for specified x. If a set W of x values is considered, one of the criteria

$$\sup_{x\varepsilon W} F_N(x)[1-F_N(x)]/n, \quad \sup_{x\varepsilon W} \{[1-F_N(x)]/nF_N(x)\}^{\frac{1}{2}},$$
$$\sup_{x\varepsilon W} \{F_N(x)/n[1-F_N(x)]\}^{\frac{1}{2}}$$

might be satisfactory, where the values of W are bounded for the two coefficient of variation criteria.

The coefficient of variation criteria can be modified so that they are applicable when the values of W are not necessarily bounded. One way of doing this is to decrease the emphasis that is placed on the tails of the distribution; this can be accomplished by using modified coefficients of variation that are obtained through multiplication by $2\{F(x)[1-F(x)]\}^{\frac{1}{2}}$. In the central part of the distribution, the modified coefficients of variation are approximately equal to the corresponding coefficients of variation. In the tails, however, they have noticeably smaller values. For example, when $F(x) = .01$, a modified coefficient of variation is only 20 per cent as large as the corresponding coefficient of variation. Explicitly,

$$2[1-F(x)]/\sqrt{n} = \text{modified coefficient of variation for } F_n(x)$$

$$2F(x)/\sqrt{n} = \text{modified coefficient of variation for } 1-F_n(x).$$

Then the corresponding criteria based on two-stage sampling are

$$\sup_{x \varepsilon W} 2[1-F_N(x)]/\sqrt{n}, \quad \sup_{x \varepsilon W} 2F_N(x)/\sqrt{n},$$

where W can be any set of x values. If W is unbounded from below for the first criterion, and unbounded from above for the second, each of these criteria has the value $2/\sqrt{n}$. Then a two-stage sampling procedure is not necessary.

When the criterion consists of the equally weighted average of the two modified correlation coefficients, two-stage sampling is not needed for any W that may be considered. That is, values of n can be determined that are adequate for all possible W. This equally weighted average has the value

$$\tfrac{1}{2}\{2[1-F(x)]/\sqrt{n}\}+\tfrac{1}{2}[2F(x)/\sqrt{n}]=1/\sqrt{n},$$

which is independent of $F(x)$.

In addition to its use as a direct estimate of $F(x)$, the empirical distribution function also occurs in many of the other estimates for $F(x)$. That is, many of the other estimates are specific functions of $F_n(x)$; moreover, $F_n(x)$ is the only quantity in one of these estimates that depends on the sample values.

Assumptions Used in Estimation of Continuous Frequency Functions

More stringent assumptions are needed in estimating frequency function values for the continuous case than in estimating distribution function values for this case. In particular, rather large sample sizes are sometimes needed to assure that the approximations used are reasonably accurate for most situations of practical interest. Also, in a way that is specified for each type of situation considered, a frequency function is required to exist and to be "well-behaved." Here "well-behaved" refers to properties that the frequency function must possess with respect to series expansions and, sometimes, to bounds on its values at specified points.

Actually, for practical situations, these more stringent requirements are not overly restrictive. The sample size needed for reasonable accuracy of an approximation is usually not appreciably larger than the smallest sample size that is considered to be adequate for the situation examined. Also, for the continuous case, little practical generality is lost by assuming that the frequency function exists and is well-behaved with respect to series expansions (see page 44).

Frequency Function Estimation for Discrete Case

As already mentioned, procedures for estimating frequency functions are not specifically presented for the discrete cases considered. However, a general estimation method is outlined for the case where the set of possible values for an observation is known and finite. For the univariate case, this method and other methods of estimating the frequency function value at any specified point can be expressed in terms of estimates for the distribution function. Let $h(x)$ be any estimate for the distribution function $F(x)$ and consider estimating the frequency function $f(x)$ at a value x_1 that is a possible value for an observation. Then

$$f(x_1)=F(x_1)-F(x_0),$$

where $x_0<x_1$, x_0 is not a possible value, and there are no possible values between x_0 and x_1. Consequently, $h(x_1)-h(x_0)$ is an estimate of $f(x_1)$. Of course, $f(x_1)=0$ if x_1 is not a possible value for the random variable.

Life-Testing Use of Estimates

All the estimates presented for $F(x)$ have the property that, for specified x, the experimentation can be stopped when all sample values that are at most equal to x have been determined. Thus, for life-testing situations (see the discussion in the introductory part of this chapter), where time to failure is the observed variable, $F(y)$ can be estimated for $y\leqslant x$ if the experiment is discontinued at time x. One of the two types of estimates presented for $f(x)$ has the property that the experimentation can be stopped when a time that does not exceed x by very much is reached. The estimates for $f(\theta_p)$ have the property that the experiment can be discontinued when not much more than $100p$ per cent of the items being life-tested have failed. In many cases, this ability to obtain a desired estimate within a specified time and/or without failing more than a specified percentage of the items can result in a large saving in time and/or cost.

Outline of Presentations

The first presentation is devoted to a statement of properties of the empirical distribution function as an estimate of the population distribution function. The second presentation contains median estimates for distribution function values at specified points. For the first two presentations, the population sampled can be arbitrary. The third presentation is concerned with unbiased-minimax estimation of continuous distribution functions. The fourth presentation furnishes some estimates for a continuous distribution function that are minimax among step-function estimates which have constant values between consecutive sample order statistics. The fifth presentation deals with expected value estimation of continuous frequency functions at specified points and over all points. The sixth presentation is concerned with expected value estimation of the reciprocal of a continuous frequency function at an identified population percentile. The seventh and final presentation contains median estimates for a continuous frequency function, and its reciprocal, at identified percentiles.

Fixed Material for Section

Data 1 Univariate **2** None **4** $m = 1$. Method for determining adequate n outlined in Results **Assumptions 1** Random sample **Characteristics 3** Used symmetrically **4** Sample condition must be satisfied to reasonable approx.

Estimation Properties of Empirical Distribution Function

Data 1 Arbitrary **3** $X(i)$ **Description 1** Exact expected value estimation; theoretical-approximate median and minimax estimation **2** Properties of $F_n(x)$ as estimate of $F(x)$ **Assumptions 2** None **3** None **Results 1** None **2** *Properties*: $EF_n(x) = F(x)$. For each n, x combination such that $n \geqslant 10/F_n(x)[1-F_n(x)]$, $F_n(x)$ is approx. median estimate of $F(x)$. Asymptotically, $F_n(x)$ is minimax estimate of $F(x)$ over class of all univariate dist. fcts. for most risk fcts. of practical interest; when loss fct. is square of difference between $F(x)$ and estimate, $[F_n(x) + 1/2\sqrt{n}]/(1 + 1/\sqrt{n})$ is minimax estimate for all n. Also $F_n(x) \rightarrow F(x)$ at all pts. of continuity for $F(x)$ and the moments of $F_n(x)$ tend to the corresponding moments of $F(x)$ that exist **3** None **4** Methods of determining adequate values for n outlined in preceding discussion about $F_n(x)$ **Characteristics 1** Low **2** Variance of $F_n(x)$ is $F(x)[1-F(x)]/n$, which is estimated by $F_n(x)[1-F_n(x)]/n$. $F_n(x)$ has minimum variance among estimates of $F(x)$ where only knowledge of whether $X(i) \leqslant x$ or not is used. Minimax over class of all continuous dist. fcts. if consideration limited to step-fct. estimates $h_n(x)$ with constant values between consecutive sample order statistics and risk fct. is $E\int_{-\infty}^{\infty} \{[h_n(x) - F(x)]^2/F(x)[1-F(x)]\}dF(x)$; if risk fct. is $E\int_{-\infty}^{\infty} [h_n(x) - F(x)]^2 dF(x)$, value of risk for minimax estimate is $1/6(n+2)$ while max risk using $F_n(x)$ is $1/6n$ **5** Not difficult to decide on sample assumption **6** Estimates presented useful for life-testing and other censored data situations. Method of ref. 492 can be used to obtain simultaneous minimax estimates of $F(x_1^{(1)}) - F(x_2^{(1)}), \ldots, F(x_1^{(s)}) - F(x_2^{(s)})$ for specified values of $(x_1^{(1)}, x_2^{(1)}), \ldots, (x_1^{(s)}, x_2^{(s)})$ and loss fct. equal to square of difference between estimate and quantity estimated **Bibliography** Ref. 1, 129, 157, 245, 387, 492.

Median Estimation of Distribution Function at Specified Point

Data 1 Arbitrary **3** $X(i)$ **Description 1** Theoretical-approximate median estimates **2** $F(x)$ for specified x **Assumptions 2** None **3** $0 < F(x) < 1$

Results 1 $p'[B]$ determined by $p'[n]=1$ and by $\sum_{b=0}^{B}\binom{n}{b}p'[B]^b\{1-p'[B]\}^{n-b}=\frac{1}{2}$ for $B=0, 1, \ldots, n-1$; $p''[B]$ determined by $p''[0]=0$ and by $\sum_{b=B}^{n}\binom{n}{b}p''[B]^b\{1-p''[B]\}^{n-b}=\frac{1}{2}$ for $B=1, \ldots, n$. Explicitly, in terms of F-dist., $p'[B]=(B+1)F_{\frac{1}{2}}[2(B+1), 2(n-B)]/\{n-B+(B+1)F_{\frac{1}{2}}[2(B+1), 2(n-B)]\}$ for $B<n$ and $p''[B]=B/\{B+(n-B+1)F_{\frac{1}{2}}[2(n-B+1), 2B]\}$ for $B>0$ **2** *Estimates*: $p'[nF_n(x)]$ conservatively high median estimate in that $P\{p'[nF_n(x)]>F(x)\}\geqslant\frac{1}{2}$ and equals $\frac{1}{2}$ for at least one value for $F(x)$. $p''[nF_n(x)]$ conservatively low median estimate in that $P\{p''[nF_n(x)<F(x)\}\geqslant\frac{1}{2}$ and equals $\frac{1}{2}$ for at least one value for $F(x)$. $\{p'[nF_n(x)]+p''[nF_n(x)]\}/2$ is compromise median estimate for $F(x)$ **3** Besides their expression in terms of the F-dist., $p'[B]$ and $p''[B]$ can be evaluated from tables for incomplete beta fct., tables for binomial dist., and from approx. to binomial dist. (see Chapter 7) **4** All three estimates approx. equal to $F_n(x)$ for each n, x combination such that $n\geqslant 10/F_n(x)[1-F_n(x)]$. Adequate n can be approx. determined by considering the estimates to have mean square error $F(x)[1-F(x)]/n$ and using two-stage sampling scheme **Characteristics 1** Low (if suitable table or approx. to binomial dist. used) **2** Estimates have approx. same efficiency properties as $F_n(x)$ if $n\geqslant 10/F_n(x)[1-F_n(x)]$. Compromise estimate approx. minimax over class of all continuous dist. fcts. if risk fct. is $\int_{-\infty}^{\infty}\{\int_{F(x)}^{\infty}a(x)[h-F(x)]dH_x(h)+\int_{-\infty}^{F(x)}b(x)[F(x)-h]dH_x(h)\}dm(x)$, where $H_x(h)$ is dist. fct. of estimate $h_n(x)$ and $m(x)$ is specified continuous monotonic measure fct. (e.g., $m(x)$ could be $F(x)$ or x); here $a(x)=a$ (positive) for $F(x)\geqslant 10^{-6}$ and $=0$ otherwise, $b(x)=a$ for $F(x)\leqslant 1-10^{-6}$ and $=0$ otherwise **5** Not difficult to decide on sample assumption **6** Useful for life-testing situations **Bibliography** Ref. 306, 387.

Unbiased-Minimax Estimates for Continuous Distribution Functions (Lehmann)

Data 1 Continuous **3** $X(i)$ **Description 1** Theoretical-approximate unbiased-minimax estimation **2** $F(x)$ over all x on basis of risk fct. of form $\int_{-\infty}^{\infty}\{\int_{F(x)}^{\infty}a(x)[h-F(x)]dH_x(h)+\int_{-\infty}^{F(x)}b(x)[F(x)-h]dH_x(h)\}dm(x)$, where $H_x(h)$ is dist. fct. of estimate $h_n(x)$ and $m(x)$ is specified continuous monotonic measure fct. (e.g., $m(x)$ might be $F(x)$ or x); here $a(x)=a$ (positive) for $F(x)\geqslant 10^{-6}$ and $=0$ otherwise, $b(x)=b$ (positive) for $F(x)\leqslant 1-10^{-6}$ and $=0$ otherwise **Assumptions 2** Population continuous **3** None **Results 1** $p'_{1-\alpha}[B]$ determined by $p'_{1-\alpha}[n]=1$ and by $\sum_{b'=0}^{B}\binom{n}{b'}p''_{\alpha}[B]^{b'}\{1-p''_{\alpha}[B]\}^{n-b'}=1-\alpha=b/(a+b)$ for $B=0,$

$1, \ldots, n-1$; $p''_\alpha[B]$ determined by $p''_\alpha[0]=0$ and by $\sum_{b'=B}^{n} \binom{n}{b'} p''_\alpha[B]^{b'}\{1-p''_\alpha[B]\}^{n-b'}= \alpha = a/(a+b)$ for $B=1, \ldots, n$. Explicitly, in terms of F-dist., $p'_{1-\alpha}[B]= (B+1)F_{1-\alpha}[2(B+1), 2(n-B)]/\{n-B+(B+1)F_{1-\alpha}[2(B+1), 2(n-B)]\}$ for $B<n$ and $p''_\alpha[B]=B/\{B+(n-B+1)F_\alpha[2(n-B+1), 2B]\}$ for $B>0$. If estimate $h_n(x)$ sought were exact, it would satisfy $P[h_n(x)>F(x)]=1-P[h_n(x)<F(x)]=\alpha$ **2** *Estimates*: $p'_{1-\alpha}[nF_n(x)]$ conservatively high estimate in that $P\{p'_{1-\alpha}[nF_n(x)]>F(x)\}\geqslant\alpha$ and equals α for at least one value for $F(x)$. $p''_\alpha[nF_n(x)]$ conservatively low estimate in that $P\{p''_\alpha[nF_n(x)]<F(x)\}\geqslant 1-\alpha$ and equals $1-\alpha$ for at least one value for $F(x)$. $\{p'_{1-\alpha}[nF_n(x)]+p''_\alpha[nF_n(x)]\}/2$ is compromise estimate **3** Besides their expression in terms of the F-dist., $p'_{1-\alpha}[B]$ and $p''_\alpha[B]$ can be determined from tables for incomplete beta fct., tables for binomial dist., and from approx. to binomial dist. (see Chapter 7) **4** All three estimates approx. equal to $F_n(x)-K_\alpha\{F_n(x)[1-F_n(x)]/n\}^{1/2}$ for each n, x, α combination such that $1/n\leqslant\alpha\leqslant 1-1/n$ and $n\geqslant(10+K_\alpha^2)/F_n(x)[1-F_n(x)]$. Adequate n can be determined from risk fct. value for case where $m(x)=F(x)$; here, for $h_n(x)=p'_{1-\alpha}[nF_n(x)]$ or $p''_\alpha[nF_n(x)]$, $H_x(h)$ is discrete and can be expressed in terms of $F(x)$, on basis of fact that estimate monotonic fct. of $nF_n(x)$ which has binomial dist. with success prob. $=F(x)$ and no. trials $=n$; risk fct. value for compromise estimate approximated by average of risk fct. values for other two estimates **Characteristics 1** Low (if suitable table or approx. to binomial dist. used) **2** Compromise estimate approx. minimax for situation considered **4** Minimax properties can be moderately sensitive to continuity requirement; however, statistic may be approx. $100(1-\alpha)$ per cent estimate of $F(x)$ even if continuity condition moderately violated **5** Not difficult to decide on sample and continuity assumptions **6** Useful for life-testing and other censored data situations **Bibliography** Ref. 306, 387.

Minimax Step-Function Estimates for Distribution Functions (*Aggarwal*)

Data 1 Continuous **3** $X(i)$ **Description 1** Minimax estimation where allowable estimates are step-fcts. whose values are constant between consecutive sample order statistics **2** $F(x)$ over all x **Assumptions 2** Population continuous **3** None **Results 1** $R_1(r)=R_1[r; h_n(x), F(x)]=E\int_{-\infty}^{\infty}|h_n(x)-F(x)|^r dF(x)$; $R_2(r)=R_2[r; h_n(x), F(x)]= E\int_{-\infty}^{\infty}\{|h_n(x)-F(x)|^r/F(x)[1-F(x)]\}dF(x)$. Estimates considered are of form $h_n(x)=c_i$ for $X[i]\leqslant x<X[i+1]$, $(i=0, 1, \ldots, n)$. $c_i^{(s)}(r)=c_i^{(s)}(r, n)$ is value of c_i for the minimax estimate obtained on basis of risk fct. $R_s(r)$ and sample size n $(s=1, 2)$. For cases considered, $c_{n-i}^{(s)}(r)=1-c_i^{(s)}(r)$, so that determination of the $c_i^{(s)}(r)$ for $i\leqslant(n+1)/2$ sufficient; also, for $r=1$ and

for r an even integer, $c_i^{(2)}(r, n) = c_{i-1}^{(1)}(r, n-2)$, when $i = 1, \ldots, n-1$ **2** *Estimates. Case of* $r=1$: $c_i^{(1)}(1)$ is solution for c of $I_c(i+1, n+1-i) = \frac{1}{2}$. $c_i^{(2)}(1)$ is sol. for c of $I_c(i, n-i) = \frac{1}{2}$. Explicitly, in terms of F-dist., $c_i^{(1)}(1) = (i+1)/\{i+1+(n-i+1)F_{1/2}[2(n-i+1), 2(i+1)]\}$ and $c_i^{(2)}(1) = i/\{i+(n-i)F_{1/2}[2(n-i), 2i]\}$. *Case of* $r=2$: $c_i^{(1)}(2) = (i+1)/(n+2)$ and $c_i^{(2)}(2) = i/(n+1)$. *Case of r an even positive integer:* $c_i^{(1)}(r)$ is sol. for c of $c^{r-1} + \sum_{v=1}^{r-1} (-1)^v \binom{r-1}{v} c^{r-1-v} \prod_{w=1}^{v} [(i+w)/(n+1+w)] = 0$; $c_i^{(2)}(r)$ is sol. for c of $c^{r-1} + \sum_{v=1}^{r-1} (-1)^v \binom{r-1}{v} c^{r-1-v} \prod_{w=1}^{v} [(i-1+w)/(n-1+w)] = 0$.

Case of r an odd positive integer: $c_i^{(1)}(r)$ is sol. for c of $\sum_{u=0}^{n-i} (-1)^u \binom{n-i}{u}$ $[(r+i+v)!/(r-1)!(i+v)!]c^{r+i+v} - (1/2)[(n+1)!/i!(n-i)!]\{\sum_{v=1}^{r-1}(-1)^v \binom{r-1}{v}$ $c^{r-1-v} \prod_{w=1}^{v} [(i+w)/(n+1+w)]\} = 0$ **3** Besides statement in terms of F-dist., sol. of $I_c(i+1, n+1-i) = \frac{1}{2}$, etc., obtainable by use of tables of incomplete beta fct., tables of binomial dist., or by approx. to binomial dist. (see Chapter 7) **4** Adequate values of n can be determined on basis of risk fct. used. $F_n(x)$ obtained as minimax estimate for $s=2$, $r=2$ case **Characteristics 1** Low for $r=1, 2$; low to high for $r>2$, depending on r and n **2** 100 per cent efficiency in sense of being minimax estimates for situations considered **4** Minimax properties can be moderately sensitive to continuity requirement; however, statistic may furnish approx. estimate of $F(x)$ even if continuity condition moderately violated (especially if $r \leqslant 2$) **5** Not difficult to decide on sample and continuity assumptions **6** Useful for life-testing and other censored data situations **Bibliography** Ref. 1

Expected Value Estimation of Continuous Frequency Functions (*Rosenblatt*)

Data 1 Continuous **3** $X(i)$ **4** Methods for determining adequate n given in Results **Description 1** Theoretical-approximate expected value estimation **2** $f(x)$ at specified x, also over all x **Assumptions 2** Population continuous; $f(x)$ and first three derivatives exist for each x considered **3** None **Results 1** $f_n(x; \delta) = [F_n(x+\delta) - F_n(x-\delta)]/2\delta$, where δ (positive) $\doteq kn^{-\gamma}$, with $k = O(1)$ and $\gamma > 0$, is type of estimate considered; $f'_n(x; \delta) = [f_n(x+\delta; \delta) - f_n(x-\delta; \delta)]/2\delta$; $f''_n(x; \delta) = [f'_n(x+\delta; \delta) - f'_n(x-\delta; \delta)]/2\delta$. $k_1 = k_1[X(i)] = [9f_n(x; n^{-1/5})/2f''_n(x; n^{-1/5})^2]^{1/5}$; $k_2 = k_2[X(i)] = [9/2\int_{-\infty}^{\infty} f''_n(x; n^{-1/5})^2 dx]^{1/5}$ **2** *General results*: For each x, $Ef_n(x; \delta) = f(x) + O(\delta^2)$. *Efficient at specified point*: On basis of $E[f_n(x; \delta) - f(x)]^2$, $f_n(x; k_1 n^{-1/5})$ is approx. most efficient estimate of $f(x)$ for specified x. *Efficient over all points*: On basis of risk fct. $\int_{-\infty}^{\infty} E[f_n(x; \delta) - f(x)]^2 dx$, $f_n(x; k_2 n^{-1/5})$ is approx. most efficient estimate over all x **3** None **4** In general, $E[f_n(x;\delta)-f(x)]^2 = f(x)/2\delta n + \delta^4 f''(x)^2/36 + o(1/\delta n) + o(\delta^4)$ and $\int_{-\infty}^{\infty} E[f_n(x;\delta)-f(x)]^2 dx = 1/2\delta n + (\delta^4/36)\int_{-\infty}^{\infty} f''(x)^2 dx + o(1/\delta n) + o(\delta^4)$. When $\gamma=\frac{1}{5}$, all of $E[f_n(x;\delta)-f(x)]$, $\sigma f_n(x;\delta)$, and $\{\int_{-\infty}^{\infty} E[f_n(x;\delta)-f(x)]^2 dx\}^{1/2}$ are $O(n^{-2/5})$. For estimation over all x, conservatively large value for adequate n can be determined by using $1/4n^{2/3}$ as risk fct. value (corresponds to $k=2$, $\gamma=\frac{1}{3}$); also, for estimation at specified x, conservatively large value for adequate n can be determined by employing two-stage sampling and using $f(\theta_p)/4n^{2/3}$ as expression for variance (i.e., $k=2$ and $\gamma=\frac{1}{3}$). $\int_{-\infty}^{\infty} f''_n(x;n^{-1/5})^2 dx$ evaluated by approx. integration (perhaps graphical) based on values of $f''_n(x;n^{-1/5})$ at a moderate number of suitable x values. In ref. 443, estimation considered for more general class of risk fcts. which includes that used here; however, minimum risk found to be $O(n^{-4/5})$ in all cases **Characteristics 1** Low for specified x; low to medium when k_2 evaluated, depending on no. of x values used in determining $\int_{-\infty}^{\infty} f''(x;n^{-1/5})^2 dx$ **2** Approx. 100 per cent efficient for types of estimates considered. $E[f_n(x;k_1n^{-1/5})-f(x)]^2 = 5f_n(x;n^{-1/5})^{4/5}|f''_n(x;n^{-1/5})/12|^{2/5}/4n^{4/5} + o(n^{-4/5})$. $\int_{-\infty}^{\infty} E[f_n(x;k_2n^{-1/5})-f(x)]^2 dx = 5[(2/9)\int_{-\infty}^{\infty} f''_n(x;n^{-1/5})^2 dx]^{1/5}/8n^{4/5} + o(n^{-4/5})$ **4** Not very sensitive to differentiability requirements if population continuous to reasonable approx. **5** Not difficult to decide on sample and continuity assumptions **6** Exact expected value estimate does not exist for $f(x)$ unless further assumptions imposed (see ref. 443). Efficient estimate at specified pt. useful for life-testing and other censored data situations **Bibliography** Ref. 443.

Expected Value Estimation of Continuous Frequency Functions at Percentiles

Data 1 Continuous **3** $X[i]$ **4** Lower bound for n, also method of determining adequate n, contained in Results **Description 1** Theoretical-approximate expected value estimation **2** $1/f(\theta_p)$ from linear combination of two order statistics **Assumptions 2** $f(x)$ exists **3** $f(x)$ such that expansions of ref. 138 valid (i.e., $f(x)$ analytic, nonzero over range of def., etc.) **Results 1** $X[w]=X[\text{largest integer} \leqslant w+\frac{1}{2}]$. Estimates considered are of form $D\{X[(n+1)p+C(n+1)^{\beta}]-X[(n+1)p-C(n+1)^{\beta}]\}$, with $D,\beta>0$ and $C\geqslant 0$ **2** *Most desirable estimate*: Obtained when $D=\frac{1}{2}\sqrt{n+1}$, $\beta=\frac{4}{5}$, $C=1$. $E(\frac{1}{2}\sqrt{n+1}\{X[(n+1)p+(n+1)^{4/5}]-X[(n+1)p-(n+1)^{4/5}]\}) = 1/f(\theta_p)+O(n^{-2/5})$ and std. dev. is $O(n^{-2/5})$. Considered satisfactory for use when $n^{3/5}\geqslant 3/p(1-p)$ **3** None **4** Approach of ref. 571 used in analyzing class of estimates. Conservatively large value for adequate n obtainable by using $1/2\sqrt{n}f(\theta_p)^2$ as approx. expression for mean square error of estimate (corresponds to $\beta=\frac{1}{2}$, $C=1$), so that coeff. of variation approx.

$n^{-1/4}\sqrt{\frac{1}{2}}$; coeff. of variation usable without prior sampling and variance usable with two-stage sampling **Characteristics 1** Low **2** Approx. 100 per cent efficient for class of estimates considered (in sense that error in expected value of estimate of same order of magnitude, with respect to n, as its std. dev.) **4** Not overly sensitive to existence of $f(x)$ and expansion requirements if population continuous to reasonable approx. and nearly unimodal **5** Not difficult to decide on sample and continuity assumptions. More difficult to verify that $f(x)$ unimodal **6** Useful for life-testing and other censored data situations. Ref. 571 contains some general results for $\beta=\frac{1}{2}$ case **Bibliography** Ref. 571.

Median Estimation of Continuous Frequency Functions at Percentiles

Data 1 Continuous **3** $X[i]$ **4** Upper and lower bounds for n, also method for determining adequate n, given in Results **Description 1** Theoretical-approximate median estimation **2** $f(\theta_p)$ and $1/f(\theta_p)$ for specified p such that $.05 \leqslant p \leqslant .95$ **Assumptions 2** $f(x)$ exists **3** $.294pq/f(\theta_p) \leqslant \theta_{p+.15pq} - \theta_{p-.15pq} \leqslant .306pq/f(\theta_p)$, where $q=1-p$. Also, for $0 \leqslant \epsilon \leqslant .153pq$, $.7f(\theta_{p-\varepsilon}) \leqslant f(\theta_{p+\varepsilon}) \leqslant 1.3f(\theta_{p-\varepsilon})$ **Results 1** $X[Z]=X$[largest integer $\leqslant Z+\frac{1}{2}$]; n and p such that $(p \pm .15pq)n$ both nearly integral; $32/pq \leqslant n \leqslant 2500/pq$ **2** *Estimates*: $\{X[(p+.15pq)n]-X[(p-.15pq)n]\}/.3pq$ approx. median estimate of $1/f(\theta_p)$ and $.3pq/\{X[(p+.15pq)n]-X[(p-.15pq)n]\}$ approx. median estimate of $f(\theta_p)$. In both cases, estimate is endpoint of one-sided confidence interval with confidence coeff. approx. bounded between ξ and η, where $K_\xi=.01(1.12-.2pq)(1+.3pq)\sqrt{npq}$ and $K_\eta=-.01(1.10-.2pq)(1+.3pq)\sqrt{npq}$ **3** None **4** $\sigma\{X[(p+.15pq)n]-X[(p-.15pq)n]\}/.3pq= 1/(.3npq)^{1/2}f(\theta_p)+O(1/n)+O(.15pq/\sqrt{n})$. Coeff. of variation for this estimate $\doteq (.3npq)^{-1/2}$, and can be used to determine adequate n prior to sampling; also, using two-stage sampling, approx. variance expression, which approx. equals mean square error, furnishes basis for determining adequate n **Characteristics 1** Low **2** For smaller sample size N, $\{X[(p+.15pq)N]-X[(p-.15pq)N]\}/\sqrt{n}(.3pq)^{3/2}$ approx. estimate for $\sigma\{X[(p+.15pq)n]-X[(p-.15pq)n]\}/.3pq$ (also see preceding presentation) **4** Not overly sensitive to existence of $f(x)$ and to accuracy of expansions used in derivations if population continuous to reasonable approx. and unimodal or nearly unimodal for $\theta_{.05} \leqslant x \leqslant \theta_{.95}$. Moderately sensitive to violations of equalities **5** Not difficult to decide on sample and continuity assumptions. More difficult to verify that $f(x)$ approx. unimodal for $\theta_{.05} \leqslant x \leqslant \theta_{.95}$. Inequalities should be acceptable for practical situations if populations believed unimodal except in tails; moderately difficult to verify inequalities otherwise **6** Useful for life-testing and other censored data situations. Value for min n allows for about 20 per cent overlap in probability between dists. of two order statistics used in estimate **Bibliography** Ref. 562.

CONFIDENCE REGIONS FOR UNIVARIATE DISTRIBUTION FUNCTIONS

Introduction

This section is concerned with one-sided and two-sided confidence intervals and confidence bands for univariate distribution functions. For all the confidence band presentations, the population sampled is required to be continuous. However, on the basis of the continuous case results, some one-sided and symmetrical two-sided bands with bounded confidence coefficients can be obtained for the general discontinuous case. For some of the confidence band cases, the interval of points over which a confidence band is considered is restricted by imposing specified nontrivial bounds on the distribution function value. The confidence intervals presented are for the distribution function value at a specified point and are valid for an arbitrary population.

Description of Confidence Regions Presented

For one type of situation, one-sided and two-sided confidence intervals are presented for $F(x)$ at a specified value of x; here the population sampled can be arbitrary. For the other type of situation, the confidence regions are bands that extend over intervals of x values; here the population is required to be continuous.

The one-sided and two-sided confidence bands considered are of the three forms

$$F(x) \leqslant h_1(x), \quad F(x) \geqslant h_2(x),$$
$$F(x) \geqslant h_3(x) \text{ and also } F(x) \leqslant h_4(x).$$

For the cases considered, the $h_t(x)$ are monotonically increasing functions of x and $h_3(x) < h_4(x)$.

If the only bounds imposed on $F(x)$ are the trivial limits of 0 and 1, the confidence bands extend over all values of x. For some cases, however, one or both of the bounds imposed on the values considered for $F(x)$ are nontrivial. When the bounds imposed specify that (A_1, A_2 constants)

$$0 \leqslant A_1 \leqslant F(x) \leqslant A_2 \leqslant 1,$$

each $h_t(x)$ may be considered over a different interval of x values. Explicitly, $h_t(x)$ is considered only for those x values such that

$$A_1 \leqslant h_t(x) \leqslant A_2. \qquad (t=1, \ldots, 4)$$

Each $h_t(x)$ is said to extend over all x values when $A_1 = 0$ and $A_2 = 1$.

In some cases, $h_t(t)$ consists of more than one part, each of which has a different functional form. Here the parts are segregated on the basis of intervals of values for $F(x)$. For example, $h_1(x)$ can have one form for $F(x) \leqslant \frac{1}{2}$ and another form for $F(x) > \frac{1}{2}$. The interval of x values for the part of $h_t(x)$ considered is determined by associated limits for $F(x)$. That is, suppose that $h_t(x) = h_t^{(1)}(x)$ for $A_{t1}^{(1)} \leqslant F(x) \leqslant A_{t2}^{(1)}$. Then the interval of x values for $h_t^{(1)}(x)$ is that for which

$$A_{t1}^{(1)} \leqslant h_t^{(1)}(x) \leqslant A_{t2}^{(1)};$$

etc.

The $h_t(x)$ are functions of $F_n(x)$ for all the situations considered. For $h_1(x)$ and $h_4(x)$, each part is of the form

$$\min [1, a_1 + b_1 F_n(x)],$$

and for $h_2(x)$, $h_3(x)$ each part is of the form

$$\max [0, -a_2 + b_2 F_n(x)],$$

where b_1 and b_2 are positive. In many cases $b_1 = b_2 = 1$ and a_1, a_2 are positive.

Bounded Probability Results for Discontinuous Case

For two situations, the confidence band results presented for the continuous case yield bounded confidence coefficient results that are valid for an arbitrary population. Let $P_c[Z]$ represent the probability that the relation Z is true when the population sampled is continuous. Then, for sampling from an arbitrary population,

$$P[-a_1 + F_n(x) \leqslant F(x) \leqslant a_1 + F_n(x);\ -\infty < x < \infty]$$
$$\geqslant P_c[-a_1 + F_n(x) \leqslant F(x) \leqslant a_1 + F_n(x);\ -\infty < x < \infty]$$
$$P[F(x) \leqslant a_1 + b_1 F_n(x);\ A_1 \leqslant F(x) \leqslant A_2]$$
$$\geqslant P_c[F(x) \leqslant a_1 + b_1 F_n(x);\ A_1 \leqslant F(x) \leqslant A_2].$$

The inequality for the symmetrical two-sided bands over all x is given in ref. 287 while the inequality for the one-sided bands is based on an elementary level analysis that was developed by H. T. David. Thus, for these two situations, the confidence coefficient values for the continuous case furnish lower bounds for the confidence coefficient values when the data can be discontinuous.

An alternative way of obtaining confidence bands for the discontinuous case, which is often sufficiently accurate, is to convert to the continuous case by the method outlined on page 281. Then the continuous case results can be used to obtain confidence bands for $F(x)$.

Obtaining Confidence Regions for a Discrete Case

In Chapter 11, significance tests are presented which are based on categorical type data. These tests can be used to obtain confidence regions for the probability distribution of the numbers of sample values falling in the categories. For a discrete population whose possible values are known and of not too large a number, each possible value can be considered as a separate category. Then the confidence regions obtained for the categorical data case furnish confidence regions for the distribution function (or, equivalently, the frequency function) of this discrete population. This procedure is applicable for both the univariate and the multivariate case.

Obtaining Two-Sided Bands from One-Sided Bands

Let e_3 be the event that $F(x) \geqslant h_3(x)$ for $A_1 \leqslant F(x) \leqslant A_2$ while e_4 is the event $F(x) \leqslant h_4(x)$ for $A_1 \leqslant F(x) \leqslant A_2$; also let e'_3 denote that the event e_3 does not occur while e'_4 denotes that e_4 does not occur. Then, in general, for $A_1 \leqslant F(x) \leqslant A_2$,

$$P[h_3(x) \leqslant F(x) \leqslant h_4(x)] = 1 - P(e'_3 + e'_4) = 1 - P(e'_3) - P(e'_4) + P(e'_3e'_4).$$

Asymptotically (see ref. 326),

$$P(e'_3e'_4) \leqslant P(e'_3)P(e'_4) = \{1 - P[F(x) \geqslant h_3(x)]\}\{1 - P[F(x) \leqslant h_4(x)]\}$$

and the much less stringent relation

$$P(e'_3e'_4) \leqslant 2\{1 - P[F(x) \geqslant h_3(x)]\}\{1 - P[F(x) \leqslant h_4(x)]\}$$

should be acceptable even for rather small sample sizes. If the actual confidence coefficient η for the two-sided band is at least .84, and this less stringent relation holds, use of

$$1 - P(e'_3) - P(e'_4) + P(e'_3)P(e'_4) = P[F(x) \geqslant h_3(x)]P[F(x) \leqslant h_4(x)]$$

for the confidence coefficient value will result in an error of at most 5 per cent in the value of $1 - \eta$.

Conversely, one-sided confidence bands can be obtained from symmetrical two-sided bands. For a symmetrical two-sided band, with $A_1 \leqslant F(x) \leqslant A_2$,

$$P[F(x) \geqslant h_3(x)] = P[F(x) \leqslant h_4(x)].$$

Thus each of the one-sided bands $F(x) \geqslant h_3(x)$ and $F(x) \leqslant h_4(x)$ has a confidence coefficient approximately $\sqrt{\eta}$ if η is the confidence coefficient for the symmetrical two-sided band and $\eta \geqslant .84$.

Bands with Restricted Ranges from Bands Over All Points

Let $e(A_1, A_2)$ be the event that a specified symmetrical confidence band holds for $A_1 \leqslant F(x) \leqslant A_2$. In some cases $P[e(0, 1)]$ is tabulated for all n

and also $P[e(0, A)]$ is known for n sufficiently large $(0 < A < 1)$. Then, when $P[e(0, 1)]$ is not too small, the value of $P[e(0, \frac{1}{2})] = P[e(\frac{1}{2}, 1)]$ can be approximately determined for any n and $P[e(A_1, A_2)]$ can be approximately evaluated for sample sizes that are at least moderately large.

Approximate determination of $P[e(0, \frac{1}{2})]$ is considered first. Use $e'(A_1, A_2)$ to denote that the event $e(A_1, A_2)$ does not occur. Then

$$P[e(0, 1)] = 1 - P[e'(0, \tfrac{1}{2}) + e'(\tfrac{1}{2}, 1)] = \epsilon$$
$$= 1 - P[e'(0, \tfrac{1}{2})] - P[e'(\tfrac{1}{2}, 1)] + P[e'(0, \tfrac{1}{2})e'(\tfrac{1}{2}, 1)].$$

Suppose, as should virtually always be the case, that

$$P[e'(0, \tfrac{1}{2})e'(\tfrac{1}{2}, 1)] \leqslant 10P[e'(0, \tfrac{1}{2})]P[e'(\tfrac{1}{2}, 1)] = 10P[e'(0, \tfrac{1}{2})]^2.$$

Evaluation of $P[e'(0, \frac{1}{2})] = P[e'(\frac{1}{2}, 1)]$ by assuming that this upper bound is attained, and evaluation by assuming that the zero lower bound is attained, combined with taking the geometric mean of these two results, yields

$$P[e(0, \tfrac{1}{2})] = P[e(\tfrac{1}{2}, 1)] \doteq 1 - [(1-\epsilon)(1 - \sqrt{10\epsilon - 9})/20]^{1/2},$$

which is applicable for $\epsilon \geqslant .92$. Use of this value for $P[e(0, \frac{1}{2})]$ when $\epsilon \geqslant .94$ results in an error of at most 10 per cent in the value for $1 - P[e(0, \frac{1}{2})]$ when the stated inequality holds.

Let $P_a[e(0, A)]$ denote the asymptotic expression for $P[e(0, A)]$. Then, using linear interpolation based on $P[e(0, A)]/P_a[e(0, A)]$,

$$P[e(0, A)]/P_a[e(0, A)] \doteq$$
$$(2A-1)P[e(0, 1)]/P_a[e(0, 1)] + 2(1-A)P[e(0, \tfrac{1}{2})]/P_a[e(0, \tfrac{1}{2})]$$

for $\frac{1}{2} \leqslant A \leqslant 1$. This interpolation, which approximately determines $P[e(0, A)]$ for $\frac{1}{2} \leqslant A \leqslant 1$, should be reasonably accurate if the sample size is at least twice the square root of the minimum sample size specified for the asymptotic expression.

If $\frac{1}{2} \leqslant A \leqslant 1$, $P[e(0, A)] \geqslant .95$, and, as is nearly always the case,

$$P[e'(0, A)e'(A, 1)] \leqslant 10P[e'(0, A)]P[e'(A, 1)]$$
$$= 10P[e'(0, A)]P[e'(0, 1-A)],$$

a method similar to that used for approximately evaluating $P[e(0, \frac{1}{2})]$ yields

$$P[e(0, 1-A)] \doteq 1 - \{P[e(0, A)] - \epsilon\}/\{10P[e(0, A)] - 9\}^{1/2}.$$

When $P[e(0, A)] \geqslant .981$, use of this expression for $P[e(0, 1-A)]$ results in an error of at most 10 per cent in the value for $1 - P[e(0, 1-A)]$.

In many cases, the values obtained for $P[e(0, A)]$, $0 \leqslant A \leqslant 1$, can be used to determine values for $P[e(A_1, A_2)]$. The relation used is

$$P[e(0, A_2)] = 1 - P[e'(0, A_1) + e'(A_1, A_2)]$$
$$= 1 - P[e'(0, A_1)] - P[e'(A_1, A_2)] + P[e'(0, A_1)e'(A_1, A_2)].$$

If the situation is such that

$$P[e'(0, A_1)e'(A_1, A_2)] \leqslant 10P[e'(0, A_1)]P[e'(A_1, A_2)],$$

$$P[e(A_1, A_2)] \doteq 1-\{P[e(0, A_1)]-P[e(0, A_2)]\}/\{10P[e(0, A_1)]-9\}^{1/2}$$

when $P[e(0, A_1)] \geqslant .95$. Then, if $P[e(0, A_1)] \geqslant .981$, use of this expression results in an error of at most 10 per cent in the value for $1-P[e(A_1, A_2)]$.

One-sided bands can be obtained from the corresponding symmetrical two-sided bands in the manner outlined in the preceding section. That is, if η is the confidence coefficient for the symmetrical two-sided band, each of the corresponding one-sided bands has a confidence coefficient of approximately $\sqrt{\eta}$.

Life-Testing Use of Bands with Restricted Ranges

The confidence bands where $F(x)$ has a nontrivial upper bound have potential use for life-testing situations (see the discussion of life-testing uses in the first part of the chapter). If $F(x) \leqslant A$ for a band, the sampling can ordinarily be stopped for a value of x that is at most equal to the x value for which $F_n(x) \leqslant A$. That is, the life-testing experiment can be discontinued when at most $100A$ per cent of the smallest sample values have been determined.

Interpolations Based on Coefficient of Empirical Distribution Function

The only exact results presented are for the situation where the coefficient of $F_n(x)$ is unity. However, asymptotic confidence bands are obtained for situations where the coefficient of $F_n(x)$ is not necessarily unity but unity is one of the possible values. For some of these asymptotic bands, there are corresponding exact results for the case where the coefficient of $F_n(x)$ is unity. Then, by considering that the ratio of the actual value to the asymptotic value remains nearly fixed for restricted deviations of the coefficient from unity, approximate confidence bands can be obtained which only require moderately large minimum sample sizes. (The same type of approach can also be based on approximate confidence bands for which the minimum sample sizes are small.)

For a situation of the type considered, the coefficient of $F_n(x)$ is of one of the forms $(b>0)$

$$1 \pm (b-c)/\sqrt{n}$$

for each part of the confidence band. Let $\epsilon(b, b-c, n)$ represent the actual value of the confidence coefficient for the band considered while $\epsilon(b, b-c, \infty)$ is the asymptotic value. Then, for $b/2 \leqslant c \leqslant 3b/2$,

$$\epsilon(b, b-c, n) \doteq \epsilon(b, b-c, \infty)\epsilon(b, 0, n)/\epsilon(b, 0, \infty).$$

This approximation to the value of $\epsilon(b, b-c, n)$ should be usable for sample sizes that are at least equal to

$$(2|b-c|/b)N^{2/3}+N^{1/2} \leqslant N^{2/3}+N^{1/2},$$

where N is the minimum sample size for the asymptotic procedure.

Precision Levels of Procedures

The confidence intervals stated for the value of $F(x)$ at a specified point are theoretical-approximate. These results are valid for all sample sizes.

Four general precision levels are considered for confidence bands. These consist of exact results and of three levels of theoretical-approximate results that depend on the minimum sample size required. The theoretical-approximate levels are determined by whether the minimum sample size is small, moderate, or large.

Bands with exact confidence coefficients are obtained for cases where $A_1=0$, $A_2=1$, the $h_t(x)$ do not consist of parts, and $b_1=b_2=1$. Following are discussions of methods that can be used for obtaining theoretical-approximate confidence bands at the three magnitude levels for minimum sample sizes.

Theoretical-Approximate Bands for Small Sample Sizes

As already mentioned, approximate two-sided confidence bands can be obtained from exact one-sided bands. Also approximate one-sided bands can be obtained from exact symmetrical two-sided bands. Since the exact results are applicable for all sample sizes, the theoretical-approximate bands obtained in this fashion are also applicable for all sample sizes.

Bands Requiring Only Moderate Sample Sizes

In some cases, approximate bands that extend over restricted ranges of x values can be obtained on the basis of asymptotic bands that extend over the same points combined with exact bands that extend over all points. These approximate bands have minimum sample sizes that depend on the minimum sample sizes specified for reasonable accuracy of the asymptotic bands. Namely, as already stated, if N is the minimum sample size for the asymptotic band, the approximate band should be reasonably accurate if the sample size is at least equal to $2\sqrt{N}$. Unless N is extremely large, $2\sqrt{N}$ represents a sample size that is only moderately large.

Approximate confidence bands in which the coefficient of $F_n(x)$ is not unity can sometimes be obtained on the basis of the corresponding asymptotic bands combined with exact bands for the situation where the coefficient of $F_n(x)$ is unity. Then, from the preceding discussion for this type of situation, if N is the minimum sample size for the corresponding asymptotic band, the minimum sample size for the approximate band should not exceed $N^{2/3}+N^{1/2}$, which is only moderately large unless N is quite large.

Bands Requiring Large Sample Sizes

Large samples are needed for the bands that are based exclusively on asymptotic considerations. Here a basic problem is to determine minimum sample sizes for asymptotic procedures. For a given procedure, the method followed is to examine the asymptotic expression for the exact procedure which corresponds most closely to this procedure. By comparison of the exact results with the asymptotic results, sample sizes which are considered to be sufficiently large for use of the asymptotic expression are determined. The minimum sample sizes for the case where tabulated exact results exist are (arbitrarily) increased by 20 per cent to obtain the minimum sample sizes for the given procedure. Here it is to be noted that the minimum sample size for an asymptotic confidence band can depend on the value of the confidence coefficient.

Efficiency Discussion—Confidence Bands

A general method for evaluating the efficiency of a confidence region is to convert this region to the corresponding significance test and determine the efficiency of this test (see Chapter 4). This method is utilized for the one-sided and symmetrical two-sided bands that are applicable for all x. The null hypothesis is simple and asserts that $F(x)=F_0(x)$, where $F_0(x)$ is a completely specified continuous distribution function. Also some remarks are made about determining the type of alternatives to which a test obtained from a confidence band is sensitive from the form of the statistic yielding this confidence band.

In the case of one-sided bands, three classes of alternative hypotheses are considered. For one class, the alternative distribution functions are normal. For another class, the random variable $F_0[X(i)]$ has the frequency function

$$\beta e^{\beta x}/(e^{\beta}-1), \qquad 0 \leqslant x \leqslant 1,\ \beta > 0,$$

where the null hypothesis holds when $\beta=0$. For the remaining class, the alternative is stated in terms of the metric

$$\sup_x\,[F_0(x)-F(x)].$$

Only samples of sizes 2, 3, 5, and asymptotically large are considered for the normal alternatives and only a sample of size 5 for the alternatives expressed in terms of β; however, a best test exists for each of these situations so that approximate efficiencies can be determined. For the class of (composite) alternatives based on the stated metric, no best test is specified, so that efficiency values are not given. Here the material presented consists of sharp upper and lower bounds for the power function values that can be obtained for given values of the metric (note that the value of the metric does not completely determine the power function value).

In the case of symmetrical two-sided bands (i.e., $b_3 = b_4 = 1$ and $a_3 = a_4$), two classes of alternative hypotheses are considered. For one class the random variable $F_0[X(i)]$ has the frequency function

$$\beta e^{\beta x}/(e^{\beta} - 1), \qquad 0 \leqslant x \leqslant 1,$$

where β can be positive or negative and the null hypothesis holds when $\beta = 0$. For the other class, the alternative is stated in terms of the metric

$$\sup_x |F_0(x) - F(x)|.$$

Only a sample of size 5 is considered for the alternatives expressed in terms of β; here a best test exists and an approximate efficiency can be determined. For the (composite) alternatives based on the stated metric, no best test is available and efficiency values are not given. The material presented for this case consists of a lower bound for the power function values that can be obtained for given values of the metric (the power function value is not uniquely determined by the metric value).

The form of the statistic used in determining a confidence band furnishes an indication of the type of alternatives to which a test obtained from this band is most sensitive. As an example, a test based on a statistic of the form

$$\sup_{A_1 \leqslant F(x) \leqslant A_2} |F(x) - F_n(x)|$$

should be sensitive to alternatives that are determined by the metric

$$\sup_{A_1 \leqslant F_0(x),\, F(x) \leqslant A_2} |F_0(x) - F(x)|.$$

As another example, a test based on a statistic of the form

$$\sup_{F(x) < A_2} [F_n(x) - F(x)]/F(x)$$

should be sensitive to alternatives that are determined by values of the metric

$$\sup_{F_0(x),\, F(x) \leqslant A_2} [F(x) - F_0(x)]/F_0(x).$$

To emphasize the type of alternatives to which the test based on a given confidence band is sensitive, the statistic used to obtain the confidence band is explicitly stated for situations where its form is not immediately apparent.

Determination of Suitability of Confidence Bands

Efficiency considerations, combined with technical considerations, furnish a basis for deciding on the most desirable type of confidence band (one-sided, two-sided, values of the a_t and b_t, etc.) to use for a given situation. If it is sufficiently extensive, efficiency information can also be used to decide on the over-all suitability of the confidence band selected for use. For the cases considered in this section, however, the efficiency information is not extensive enough to be very useful in deciding on the suitability of confidence bands, even with respect to selecting the most desirable type for a given situation.

Fortunately, another method of moderately general applicability is available for use in determining the suitability of a confidence band. This method is based on the consideration that the a_t and b_t do not depend on the sample values and that the suitability of a confidence band can be controlled to a substantial degree by the choice of the values for these quantities. Here suitability is controlled in two respects that have opposite types of effects. That is, choice of the a_t and b_t so that a narrower confidence band is obtained increases the suitability in the sense that distribution function is more nearly determined from the band. However, in another sense, the suitability of the band is decreased, because a narrowing of the band invariably reduces the probability that the distribution function is contained within the band. Thus, the problem is to choose the a_t and b_t so that a satisfactory compromise is reached. If no satisfactory compromise solution can be determined, a suitable confidence band (of the desired type) can not be obtained without increasing the sample size.

This method is perhaps most easily interpreted for situations where $b_t = 1$. Then, for one-sided cases, the nontrivial boundary of the confidence band lies at most a specified vertical distance (in the x, y plane) from $F_n(x)$. For two-sided cases, the maximum width of the band is specified; also its boundaries lie within specified vertical distances above and below $F_n(x)$.

Adequate Sample Sizes for Confidence Bands

Here adequate sample sizes can be determined on the same basis as that outlined for determining the suitability of confidence bands. First, a decision is made as to whether the band is to be one-sided or two-sided and as to the interval of x values over which the band is to extend. The next selection furnishes a suitable combination, or set of suitable combinations, of values for the a_t, b_t, and the confidence coefficient. For each suitable combination (fixes the a_t and b_t), any sample size yielding a confidence coefficient at least as great as the specified value is considered to be adequate. From an optimization viewpoint, that suitable combination for which the minimum adequate sample size is smallest should be used. In any case, however, the sample size used should be at least as large as the minimum allowable size stated in the presentation for the confidence band considered.

Adequate Sample Sizes for Confidence Intervals

In the case of a confidence interval for $F(x)$ at a specified value of x, precise determination of adequate sample sizes is difficult. However, by use of two-stage sampling, an approximate method can be obtained that should be satisfactory for many situations. This method, which is outlined in Chapter 4, depends on estimation of $F(x)$ from the first stage sample, and the resulting estimate is denoted by $\hat{F}(x)$.

For values of the total sample size n that are not too small, a confidence interval endpoint which has probability γ of being less than $F(x)$ is estimated by

$$\hat{F}(x)+K_\gamma\{\hat{F}(x)[1-\hat{F}(x)]/n\}^{1/2}.$$

Consequently, the endpoint that is obtained on the basis of the total sample should usually be satisfactory if n is such that

$$|K_\gamma|\{\hat{F}(x)[1-\hat{F}(x)]/n\}^{1/2}\leqslant \min\{c_1, c_2\hat{F}(x), c_3[1-\hat{F}(x)]\}$$

is satisfied for suitably chosen values of c_1, c_2, c_3; that is, when n is sufficiently large for the estimated deviation between the endpoint and $F(x)$ to be acceptably small in both an absolute and a relative sense. If the confidence interval is two-sided, an adequate value for n is estimated for each endpoint and the larger of these values is used.

A rough check on the total sample size n obtained in this manner can be carried out on the basis of the entire sample, with, say, $F_n(x)$ used to replace $\hat{F}(x)$ in the inequalities that are to be satisfied. If the inequalities remain at least roughly satisfied, and also

$$n\geqslant(10+K_\gamma{}^2)/2F_n(x)[1-F_n(x)]$$

holds for all the variable endpoints, the value used for n can usually be considered adequate. The conditional effects arising from the relations imposed on the sample values should not have very much effect on the confidence coefficient of the resulting interval.

General Development of Confidence Bands

As pointed out in the efficiency discussion for confidence bands, the form of the statistic used to obtain a confidence band furnishes an indication of the situations where this band is most efficient. Consequently, if the statistic can be suitably chosen, a confidence band can be obtained whose efficiency tends to be high for a specified situation. Here some general results are given which can serve as a basis for developing a broad class of nonparametric confidence bands for the continuous case. By judicious use of these results, a confidence band can be developed which tends to have a high efficiency for any specified situation of a rather general class. However, determination and tabulation of the distribution for a statistic, even only the asymptotic distribution, can require a large amount of effort.

Let the values of $F(x)$ be restricted to a specified set in [0, 1], where this set can be open, closed, etc. Let $H_1[F(x); X(1), \ldots, X(n)]$ be a measurable function. Then, subject to the restrictions imposed on $F(x)$, if

$$H_1[F(x); X(1), \ldots, X(n)] = H_2\{F[X(1)], \ldots, F[X(n)]\}$$

and H_2 is symmetric in its arguments, the distribution of $H_1[F(x); X(1), \ldots, X(n)]$ does not depend on $F(x)$ for the continuous case (see ref. 56, 59). Here it is to be noted that the imposition of restrictions on the values for $F(x)$ causes no difficulties in obtaining a function that is symmetric in the $F[X(i)]$, since these transformed sample values are still treated symmetrically (i.e., have a common distribution and are subject to the same restrictions).

One-sided confidence bands can be obtained if $H_1[F(x); X(1), \ldots, X(n)]$ is also a strictly monotonic function of $F(x)$ for every set of fixed values for the observations. Suppose that this function is increasing with $F(x)$. Then, for all x such that the value of $F(x)$ lies in the specified set,

$$H_1[F(x); X(1), \ldots, X(n)] \lesseqgtr d$$

if and only if

$$F(x) \lesseqgtr H_1^{-1}[d; X(1), \ldots, X(n)],$$

where H_1^{-1} is the inverse (unique) of the function H_1. Thus the one-sided confidence band determined by

$$F(x) \leqslant H_1^{-1}[d; X(1), \ldots, X(n)]$$

and the specified set of values over which $F(x)$ is considered has a confidence coefficient equal to

$$P[H_2\{F[X(1)], \ldots, F[X(n)]\} \leqslant d],$$

where this probability has a unique value that can be determined on the basis of the specified set and the fact that the $F[X(i)]$ are a sample from the rectangular distribution [0, 1]; etc.

Two-sided confidence bands can be obtained if, for every set of fixed values for the observations, $H_1[F(x); X(1), \ldots, X(n)]$ has exactly one value which is a relative minimum or a relative maximum with respect to $F(x)$. Here this relative minimum or maximum value is known, occurs for exactly one value of $F(x)$, and is the same for all possible sets of observation values; also $H_1[F(x); X(1), \ldots, X(n)]$ is a strictly monotonic function of $F(x)$ on each side of its relative minimum or maximum. Thus H_1^{-1} is a two-valued function, with the two values being unequal when H_1 does not equal its relative minimum or maximum value.

Suppose that $H_1[F(x); X(1), \ldots, X(n)]$ satisfies the stated conditions and has a relative minimum. Then, for d at least equal to the relative minimum and all x such that the value of $F(x)$ lies in the specified set,

$$H_1[F(x); X(1), \ldots, X(n)] \leqslant d$$

if and only if

$$\min H_1^{-1}[d; X(1), \ldots, X(n)] \leqslant F(x) \leqslant \max H_1^{-1}[d; X(1), \ldots, X(n)],$$

and furnishes a two-sided confidence band with confidence coefficient equal to

$$P[H_2\{F[X(1)], \ldots, F[X(n)]\} \leqslant d].$$

Here $\min H_1^{-1}$ denotes the smaller of the two values for H_1^{-1} and $\max H_1^{-1}$ denotes the larger.

As an example, if a two-sided confidence band that emphasizes values of $F(x)$ in the distribution tails is desired, a statistic of the form

$$\sup_{A_1 \leqslant F(x) \leqslant A_2} |F(x) - F_n(x)| / \{F(x)[1 - F(x)]\}^{1/2}$$

might be used. Here $h_3(x)$ and $h_4(x)$ can be determined by solving a quadratic equation in $F(x)$. This statistic has been considered for $A_1 = 0$, $A_2 = 1$ (ref. 9) and an expression obtained for its asymptotic distribution; however, no tabulations have been available.

Some rather general methods for obtaining exact confidence bands for continuous distribution functions over all x are given in ref. 543. However, the computational effort required for the use of these methods is large.

Information Furnished About Distribution Tails

None of the confidence bands presented which hold over all points require any knowledge (other than continuity) about the behavior of the distribution function in its tails. As shown in ref. 19, this implies that these confidence bands can not furnish very much information about the tails of the distribution. Although each nontrivial boundary of a confidence band can have the properties of a distribution function in the central part of the population, this is not the case for at least one of the population tails. That is, no meaningful confidence band fits both tails of the distribution function very well.

Outline of Presentations

The first presentation contains confidence intervals for the value of an arbitrary distribution function at a specified point. This is the only statistical procedure presented in this section for which the population sampled is not required to be continuous.

The next three presentations furnish exact confidence bands that hold over all points. The first of these contains one-sided bands of the Smirnov type. The second is concerned with symmetrical two-sided bands of the Kolmogorov type. The last of these three presentations furnishes general two-sided confidence bands for the situation where the coefficient of $F_n(x)$ is unity. These are the only results presented that are of an exact nature.

The final four presentations are of an asymptotic character and are the only results presented for the situation where the coefficient of $F_n(x)$ is not necessarily unity. The first of these contains one-sided bands that consist of two parts and allow the distribution tails to be emphasized. The second consists of two reversed one-sided bands; i.e., the band consists of two parts, one of which is a one-sided band in a given direction while the other is a one-sided band in the other direction. Reversed bands can be used to emphasize population dispersion. The third asymptotic presentation contains one-sided and two-sided bands for the case where $F(x)$ is nontrivially bounded from above and below. The final presentation is concerned with one-sided bands for the case where $F(x)$ is nontrivially bounded from exactly one side.

Fixed Material for Section

Data 1 Univariate **2** None **3** $X(i)$ **4** $m=1$ **Assumptions 1** Random sample **Characteristics 3** Used symmetrically **4** Sample condition must be satisfied to reasonable approx.

Confidence Intervals for Distribution Function at Specified Point

Data 1 Arbitrary **4** Method for determining adequate n outlined on page 316 **Description 1** Theoretical-approximate one-sided and two-sided confidence intervals **2** $F(x)$ for specified x **Assumptions 2** None **3** $0<F(x)<1$ **Results 1** $p'_\alpha[B]$ determined by $p'_\alpha[n]=1$ and by $\sum_{i=0}^{B}\binom{n}{i}p'_\alpha[B]^i\{1-p'_\alpha[B]\}^{n-i}=\alpha$ for $B=0, 1, \ldots, n-1$; $p''_\alpha[B]$ determined by $p''_\alpha[0]=0$ and by $\sum_{i=B}^{n}\binom{n}{i} p''_\alpha[B]^i\{1-p''_\alpha[B]\}^{n-i}=\alpha$ for $B=1,\ldots,n$. Explicitly, in terms of F-dist., $p'_\alpha[B]= (B+1)F_\alpha[2(B+1), 2(n-B)]/\{n-B+(B+1)F_\alpha[2(B+1), 2(n-B)]\}$ for $B<n$ and $p''_\alpha[B]= B/\{B+(n-B+1)F_\alpha[2(n-B+1), 2B]\}$ for $B>0$ **2** *One-sided intervals*: $P\{p'_\alpha[nF_n(x)]\leqslant F(x)\}\leqslant\alpha$ and equals α for at least one value for $F(x)$; thus $P\{p'_\alpha[nF_n(x)]>F(x)\}\geqslant 1-\alpha$ and equals $1-\alpha$ for at least one value for $F(x)$. $P\{p''_\alpha[nF_n(x)]\geqslant F(x)\}\leqslant\alpha$ and equals α for at least one value for $F(x)$; thus $P\{p''_\alpha[nF_n(x)]<F(x)\}\geqslant 1-\alpha$ and equals $1-\alpha$ for at least one value for $F(x)$. *Two-sided intervals*: $P\{p''_{\alpha/2}[nF_n(x)]<F(x)<p'_{\alpha/2}[nF_n(x)]\}\geqslant 1-\alpha$; $P\{p'_{1-\alpha/2}[nF_n(x)]\leqslant F(x)\leqslant p''_{1-\alpha/2}[nF_n(x)]\}\leqslant 1-\alpha$ **3** Besides their expression in terms of the F-dist., $p'_\alpha[B]$ and $p''_\alpha[B]$ can be determined from tables for incomplete beta fct., tables for binomial dist., and from approx. to binomial dist. (see Chapter 7) **4** Based on results given on page 185. Probabilities for the two-sided intervals do not necessarily attain $1-\alpha$ for some value for $F(x)$. Methods referenced in Chapter 7 can be used to obtain modifications such that $1-\alpha$ attained; other types of modifications also mentioned there. If $nF_n(x)[1-F_n(x)]\geqslant 15$ and $1/n\leqslant\alpha\leqslant 1-1/n$, $P\Big[F_n(x)-K_\alpha\{F_n(x)[1-F_n(x)]/n\}^{1/2}\leqslant F(x)\Big] \doteq P\Big[F_n(x)-K_\alpha\{F_n(x)[1-F_n(x)]/n\}^{1/2}<F(x)\Big] \doteq 1-\alpha$ **Characteristics 1** Low (if suitable approx. or table used) **2** Intuitive considerations indicate that efficiency is very high for situations where $F(x)$ can be arbitrary and null hyp. asserts that $F(x)$ has specified value. One-sided tests based on $F_n(x)$ uniformly most powerful, according to Tocher's extension of Neyman-Pearson lemma, when only available information is whether $X(i)\leqslant x$ for each observation. One-sided and equal-tail two-sided tests asymptotically optimum in an information theory sense when $X(i)\leqslant x$ or not is only available information **5** Not difficult to decide on sample assumption **6** Tests are obtainable from these confidence intervals in usual manner. Additional tests obtainable on basis of material in binomial dist. sect. of Chapter 7. Useful for life-testing and other censored data situations. **Bibliography** Ref. 387.

Exact One-Sided Confidence Bands Over All Points (*Smirnov*)

Data 1 Continuous **4** Methods for determining adequate n outlined in Results **Description 1** Exact one-sided confidence bands **2** $F(x)$ over all x **Assumptions 2** Population continuous **3** None **Results 1** $0<d\leqslant 1$. $h_1(x;d,n)=\min[1, F_n(x)+d]$; $h_2(x;d,n)=\max[0, F_n(x)-d]$. $P_n(d)= 1-d\sum_{t=0}^{T}\binom{n}{t}(1-d-t/n)^{n-t}(d+t/n)^{t-1}$, where T largest integer $\leqslant(1-d)n$ **2** *Confidence band relationships*: $P[F(x)\leqslant h_1(x;d,n);\ -\infty<x<\infty]=$

TABLE 10.1. VALUES OF d AND D_α SUCH THAT $P_n(d)$ AND α HAVE SPECIFIED VALUES*

$P_n(d)$	.90	.95	.975	.99	.995
n α		.90	.95	.98	.99
1	.90000	.95000	.97500	.99000	.99500
2	.68377	.77639	.84189	.90000	.92929
3	.56481	.63604	.70760	.78456	.82900
4	.49265	.56522	.62394	.68887	.73424
5	.44698	.50945	.56328	.62718	.66853
6	.41037	.46799	.51926	.57741	.61661
7	.38148	.43607	.48342	.53844	.57581
8	.35831	.40962	.45427	.50654	.54179
9	.33910	.38746	.43001	.47960	.51332
10	.32260	.36866	.40925	.45662	.48893
11	.30829	.35242	.39122	.43670	.46770
12	.29577	.33815	.37543	.41918	.44905
13	.28470	.32549	.36143	.40362	.43247
14	.27481	.31417	.34890	.38970	.41702
15	.26588	.30397	.33760	.37713	.40420
16	.25778	.29472	.32733	.36571	.39201
17	.25039	.28627	.31796	.35528	.38086
18	.24360	.27851	.30936	.34569	.37062
19	.23735	.27136	.30143	.33685	.36117
20	.23156	.26473	.29408	.32866	.35241
21	.22617	.25858	.28724	.32104	.34427
22	.22115	.25283	.28087	.31394	.33666
23	.21645	.24746	.27490	.30728	.32954
24	.21205	.24242	.26931	.30104	.32286
25	.20790	.23768	.26404	.29516	.31657
26	.20399	.23320	.25907	.28962	.31064
27	.20030	.22898	.25438	.28438	.30502
28	.19680	.22497	.24993	.27942	.29971
29	.19348	.22117	.24571	.27471	.29466
30	.19032	.21756	.24170	.27023	.28987
31	.18732	.21412	.23788	.26596	.28530
32	.18445	.21085	.23424	.26189	.28094
33	.18171	.20771	.23076	.25801	.27677
34	.17909	.20472	.22743	.25429	.27279
35	.17659	.20185	.22425	.25073	.26897
36	.17418	.19910	.22119	.24732	.26532
37	.17188	.19646	.21826	.24404	.26180
38	.16966	.19392	.21544	.24089	.25843
39	.16753	.19148	.21273	.23786	.25518
40	.16547	.18913	.21012	.23494	.25205

* Taken from ref. 346: Table of percentage points of Kolmogorov statistics, L. H. Miller, *Journal of the American Statistical Association*, Vol. 51, 1956, pages 11–21. Used with the kind permission of the author, Leslie H. Miller, and of the Editor of the *Journal of the American Statistical Association*.

TABLE 10.1. (*contd.*)

$P_n(d)$	.90	.95	.975	.99	.995
n α		.90	.95	.98	.99
41	.16349	.18687	.20760	.23213	.24904
42	.16158	.18468	.20517	.22941	.24613
43	.15974	.18257	.20283	.22679	.24332
44	.15796	.18053	.20056	.22426	.24060
45	.15623	.17856	.19837	.22181	.23798
46	.15457	.17665	.19625	.21944	.23544
47	.15295	.17481	.19420	.21715	.23298
48	.15139	.17302	.19221	.21493	.23059
49	.14987	.17128	.19028	.21277	.22828
50	.14840	.16959	.18841	.21068	.22604
51	.14697	.16796	.18659	.20864	.22386
52	.14558	.16637	.18482	.20667	.22174
53	.14423	.16483	.18311	.20475	.21968
54	.14292	.16332	.18144	.20289	.21768
55	.14164	.16186	.17981	.20107	.21574
56	.14040	.16044	.17823	.19930	.21384
57	.13919	.15906	.17669	.19758	.21199
58	.13801	.15771	.17519	.19590	.21019
59	.13686	.15639	.17373	.19427	.20844
60	.13573	.15511	.17231	.19267	.20673
61	.13464	.15385	.17091	.19112	.20506
62	.13357	.15263	.16956	.18960	.20343
63	.13253	.15144	.16823	.18812	.20184
64	.13151	.15027	.16693	.18667	.20029
65	.13052	.14913	.16567	.18525	.19877
66	.12954	.14802	.16443	.18387	.19729
67	.12859	.14693	.16322	.18252	.19584
68	.12766	.14587	.16204	.18119	.19442
69	.12675	.14483	.16088	.17990	.19303
70	.12586	.14381	.15975	.17863	.19167
71	.12499	.14281	.15864	.17739	.19034
72	.12413	.14183	.15755	.17618	.18903
73	.12329	.14087	.15649	.17498	.18776
74	.12247	.13993	.15544	.17382	.18650
75	.12167	.13901	.15442	.17268	.18528
76	.12088	.13811	.15342	.17155	.18408
77	.12011	.13723	.15244	.17045	.18290
78	.11935	.13636	.15147	.16938	.18174
79	.11860	.13551	.15052	.16832	.18060
80	.11787	.13467	.14960	.16728	.17949

* Taken from ref. 346: Table of percentage points of Kolmogorov statistics, L. H. Miller, *Journal of the American Statistical Association*, Vol. 51, 1956, pages 11–21. Used with the kind permission of the author, Leslie H. Miller, and of the Editor of the *Journal of the American Statistical Association.*

TABLE 10.1. (*contd.*)

$P_n(d)$	.90	.95	.975	.99	.995
n α		.90	.95	.98	.99
81	.11716	.13385	.14868	.16626	.17840
82	.11645	.13305	.14779	.16526	.17732
83	.11576	.13226	.14691	.16428	.17627
84	.11508	.13148	.14605	.16331	.17523
85	.11442	.13072	.14520	.16236	.17421
86	.11376	.12997	.14437	.16143	.17321
87	.11311	.12923	.14355	.16051	.17223
88	.11248	.12850	.14274	.15961	.17126
89	.11186	.12779	.14195	.15873	.17031
90	.11125	.12709	.14117	.15786	.16938
91	.11064	.12640	.14040	.15700	.16846
92	.11005	.12572	.13965	.15616	.16755
93	.10947	.12506	.13891	.15533	.16666
94	.10889	.12440	.13818	.15451	.16579
95	.10833	.12375	.13746	.15371	.16493
96	.10777	.12312	.13675	.15291	.16408
97	.10722	.12249	.13606	.15214	.16324
98	.10668	.12187	.13537	.15137	.16242
99	.10615	.12126	.13469	.15061	.16161
100	.10563	.12067	.13403	.14987	.16081

* Taken from ref. 346: Table of percentage points of Kolmogorov statistics, L. H. Miller, *Journal of the American Statistical Association*, Vol. 51, 1956, pages 11–21. Used with the kind permission of the author, Leslie H. Miller, and of the Editor of the *Journal of the American Statistical Association*.

$P[F(x) \geqslant h_2(x; d, n);\ -\infty < x < \infty] = \quad P_n(d)$ **3** For $n = 1(1)100$, Table 10.1 contains values of d such that $P_n(d) = .90, .95, .975, .99, .995$. When $n \geqslant 50$ and $5/\sqrt{n} \leqslant \delta \leqslant 1 - 1/2n$, $P_n(d) \doteq \delta$ if $d = \{[-\log_e(1-\delta)]/2n\}^{1/2}$ **4** Asymptotically (n large), $P_n(d) = 1 - e^{-2nd^2}$. Upper confidence bands have bounded confidence coeff. when population arbitrary (see page 308). Adequate n can be determined by specifying d and a lower bound for $P_n(d)$. Adequate n can also be determined by considering the one-sided tests obtained from these confidence bands when simple null hyp. is $F(x) = F_0(x)$, with $F(x), F_0(x)$ both continuous. Test based on nontrivial upper confidence band can use values of $\xi_1(F) = \sup_{-\infty<x<\infty}[F_0(x) - F(x)]$ as altern. hyp.; min. adequate n is that for which prob. of wrong decision does not exceed $\alpha(1)$ if $\xi_1(F) \leqslant 0$ and does not exceed $\alpha(2)$ if $\xi_1(F) \geqslant \xi > 0$, where $\alpha(1) + \alpha(2) < 1$ and $\alpha(2) < \frac{1}{2}$. Test based on nontrivial lower confidence band can use values of $\xi_2(F) = \inf_{-\infty<x<\infty}[F_0(x) - F(x)]$ as altern.; min adequate n that for which prob. of wrong decision does not exceed $\alpha(2)$ if $\xi_2(F) \leqslant -\xi$. For both types of one-sided tests and small ξ, adequate $n \doteq \xi^{-2}\{\frac{1}{2}K_{\alpha(2)} + [-\frac{1}{2}\log_e \alpha(1)]^{1/2}\}^2$ **Characteristics 1** Low **2** Efficiency properties considered are for one-sided test based on upper confidence band and with simple null hyp. $F(x) = F_0(x)$, where $F(x)$ and $F_0(x)$ continuous dist. fcts. For simple altern. $F(x) = F^{(1)}(x)$, where $F^{(1)}(x)$ continuous dist. fct., let $G(x) = F^{(1)}[F_0^{-1}(x)]$ if $0 < x < 1$, $= \lim_{0 < x \to 0} G(x)$ if $x \leqslant 0$, $= \lim_{1 > x \to 1} G(x)$ if $x \geqslant 1$; then power at altern. $= 1 - n! \int_0^{G(d)} \int_{x_1}^{G[d+1/n]} \cdots \int_{x_{i-1}}^{G[d+(i-1)/n]} \cdots \int_{x_{n=1}}^{G[d+(n-1)/n]} dx_n \ldots dx_i \ldots dx_1$. For composite altern. based on values of $\xi_1(F)$, power has lower bound $\inf_{-\infty < x < \infty} \sum_{i=0}^{I(x)} \binom{n}{i} [F_0(x) - \xi_1(F)]^i [1 - F_0(x) + \xi_1(F)]^{n-i}$, where $I(x) =$ largest integer $\leqslant n[F_0(x) - d]$, and is zero if $I(x)$ negative; $1 - P_n[d - \xi_1(F)]$ is sharp upper bound for power. When altern. based on normal population with known variance and shifts in mean, efficiency of one-sided test with signif. level .01 decreases as n increases through 2, 3, 5, and is only approx. 65 per cent for $n = 5$; asymptotically this efficiency is approx. 45 per cent. When altern. such that random variable $F_0[X(i)]$ has freq. fct. $= \beta e^{\beta x}/(e^{\beta} - 1)$ for $0 \leqslant x \leqslant 1$, $= 0$ otherwise, efficiency roughly 90 per cent for $n = 5$ **4** Moderately sensitive to continuity requirement; for upper bands, confidence coeff. for continuous case furnishes lower bound on value for arbitrary population **5** Not difficult to decide on sample and continuity assumptions **6** Useful in obtaining approx. two-sided bands and approx. bands where x range restricted and/or coeff. of $F_n(x)$ not necessarily unity. Generalization of these types of one-sided bands such that band consists of two parts given on page 324 and on page 329. For tests, $\sup_x [F_0(x) - F_n(x)] = \max_i \{F_0 i(X[\,]) - i/n\}$ and $\inf_x [F_0(x) - F_n(x)] = \min_i \{F_0(X[i]) - i/n\}$ **Bibliography** Ref. 24, 56, 57, 60, 71, 129, 152, 153, 170, 210, 250, 287, 292, 346, 462, 480, 533, 543, 545.

Exact Symmetrical Confidence Bands Over All Points (*Kolmogorov*)

Data 1 Continuous **4** Method for determining adequate n outlined in Results **Description 1** Exact symmetrical two-sided confidence bands **2** $F(x)$ over all x **Assumptions 2** Population continuous **3** None **Results 1** $0 < D \leqslant 1$. $h_3(x; D, n) = \max[0, F_n(x) - D]$; $h_4(x; D, n) = \min[1, F_n(x) + D]$ **2** *Confidence band relation*: $P[h_3(x; D_\alpha, n) \leqslant F(x) \leqslant h_4(x; D_\alpha, n); -\infty < x < \infty] = \alpha$ **3** Table 10.1 on page 321 contains values of D_α for $\alpha = .90, .95, .98, .99$ and $n = 1(1)100$. Table 10.2 contains values of α for $\sqrt{n}D_\alpha = 1(1)15$ and $n = 1(1)100$. When $n \geqslant 50$ and $.85 \leqslant \alpha \leqslant 1 - 1/n$, $D_\alpha \doteq \{[-\log_e(\frac{1}{2} - \alpha/2)]/2n\}^{1/2}$ **4** Asymptotically, $P[h_3(x; c/\sqrt{n}, n) \leqslant F(x) \leqslant h_4(x; c/\sqrt{n}, n); -\infty < x < \infty] = 1 - 2\sum_{v=1}^{\infty} (-1)^{v-1} e^{-2v^2c^2}$.

TABLE 10.2. VALUES OF α VERSUS $\sqrt{n}D_\alpha$ FOR $n=1(1)100$*

n	1	2	3	4	5	6	7	8	9	10
$\sqrt{n}D_\alpha$										
1	1.00000	.50000	.22222	.09375	.03840	.01543	.00612	.00240	.00094	.00036
2		1.00000	.92593	.81250	.69120	.57656	.47446	.38659	.31261	.25128
3			1.00000	.99219	.96992	.93441	.88937	.83842	.78442	.72946
4				1.00000	.99936	.99623	.98911	.97741	.96121	.94101
5					1.00000	.99996	.99960	.99849	.99615	.99222
6						1.00000	1.00000	.99996	.99982	.99943
7								1.00000	1.00000	.99998
8										1.00000

n	11	12	13	14	15	16	17	18	19	20
$\sqrt{n}D_\alpha$										
1	.00014	.00005	.00002	.00001	.00000	.00000	.00000	.00000	.00000	.00000
2	.20100	.16014	.12715	.10066	.07950	.06265	.04927	.03869	.03033	.02374
3	.67502	.62209	.57136	.52323	.47795	.43564	.39630	.35991	.32636	.29553
4	.91747	.89126	.86304	.83337	.80275	.77158	.74019	.70887	.67784	.64728
5	.98648	97885	.96935	.95807	.94517	.93081	.91517	.89844	.88079	.86237
6	.99865	.99732	.99530	.99250	.98882	.98425	.97875	.97235	.96500	.95093
7	.99993	.99979	.99953	.99908	.99837	.99736	.99598	.99419	.99195	.98924
8	1.00000	.99999	.99997	.99993	.99984	.99968	.99944	.99907	.99856	.99788
9		1.00000	1.00000	1.00000	.99999	.99997	.99994	.99989	.99980	.99968
10					1.00000	1.00000	1.00000	.99999	.99998	.99996
11								1.00000	1.00000	1.00000

n	21	22	23	24	25	26	27	28	29	30
$\sqrt{n}D_\alpha$										
1	.00000	.00000	.00000	.00000	.00000	.00000	.00000	.00000	.00000	.00000
2	.01857	.01450	.01132	.00882	.00687	.00535	.00416	.00323	.00251	.00195
3	.26729	.24147	.21793	.19650	.17702	.15935	.14334	.12885	.11575	.10392
4	.61733	.58811	.55970	.53216	.50554	.47987	.45517	.43145	.40870	.38693
5	.84335	.82386	.80401	.78392	.76368	.74338	.72309	.70288	.68280	.66290
6	.94802	.93837	.92805	.91712	.90565	.89368	.88128	.86851	.85541	.84203
7	.98605	.98236	.97817	.97349	.96832	.96269	.95661	.95010	.94318	.93588
8	.99700	.99590	.99456	.99296	.99110	.98895	.98651	.98378	.98076	.97745
9	.99949	.99924	.99890	.99846	.99792	.99725	.99645	.99551	.99441	.99315
10	.99993	.99989	.99982	.99973	.99960	.99943	.99921	.99894	.99861	.99821
11	.99999	.99999	.99998	.99996	.99994	.99990	.99985	.99979	.99971	.99960
12	1.00000	1.00000	1.00000	1.00000	.99999	.99999	.99998	.99997	.99995	.99992
13					1.00000	1.00000	1.00000	1.00000	.99999	.99999
14									1.00000	1.00000

* Taken from ref. 55: Numerical tabulation of the distribution of Kolmogorov's statistic for finite sample size, Z. W. Birnbaum, *Journal of the American Statistical Association*, Vol. 47, 1952, pages 425–41. Used with the kind permission of the author, Z. W. Birnbaum, and of the Editor of the *Journal of the American Statistical Association*.

TABLE 10.2. (*contd.*)

n	31	32	33	34	35	36	37	38	39	40
$\sqrt{n}D_\alpha$										
1	.00000	.00000	.00000	.00000	.00000	.00000	.00000	.00000	.00000	.00000
2	.00151	.00117	.00091	.00070	.00054	.00042	.00033	.00025	.00020	.00015
3	.09325	.08363	.07497	.06717	.06016	.05386	.04820	.04312	.03856	.03448
4	.36612	.34624	.32729	.30923	.29205	.27570	.26018	.24544	.23145	.21819
5	.64323	.62382	.60470	.58590	.56744	.54934	.53161	.51427	.49733	.48078
6	.82843	.81463	.80069	.78663	.77250	.75831	.74410	.72990	.71572	.70159
7	.92822	.92022	.91192	.90332	.89447	.88538	.87608	.86658	.85690	.84707
8	.97384	.96995	.96578	.96134	.95664	.95168	.94648	.94104	.93539	.92952
9	.99172	.99012	.98834	.98638	.98423	.98191	.97939	.97670	.97382	.97077
10	.99773	.99717	.99652	.99578	.99494	.99399	.99294	.99178	.99050	.98910
11	.99946	.99930	.99910	.99886	.99857	.99824	.99785	.99741	.99692	.99636
12	.99989	.99985	.99980	.99973	.99965	.99954	.99942	.99928	.99911	.99891
13	.99998	.99997	.99996	.99994	.99992	.99990	.99986	.99982	.99977	.99971
14	1.00000	1.00000	1.00000	.99999	.99999	.99998	.99997	.99996	.99995	.99993
15				1.00000	1.00000	1.00000	.99999	.99999	.99999	.99999

n	41	42	43	44	45	46	47	48	49	50
$\sqrt{n}D_\alpha$										
1	.00000	.00000	.00000	.00000	.00000	.00000	.00000	.00000	.00000	.00000
2	.00012	.00009	.00007	.00005	.00004	.00003	.00002	.00002	.00001	.00001
3	.03081	.02753	.02459	.02196	.01960	.01750	.01561	.01393	.01242	.01108
4	.20562	.19373	.18247	.17181	.16174	.15222	.14323	.13474	.12672	.11916
5	.46464	.44891	.43359	.41868	.40418	.39008	.37639	.36310	.35020	.33769
6	.68752	.67354	.65965	.64588	.63223	.61872	.60536	.59215	.57911	.56623
7	.83711	.82702	.81684	.80657	.79623	.78583	.77539	.76492	.75442	.74392
8	.92345	.91719	.91075	.90415	.89739	.89048	.88344	.87628	.86899	.86160
9	.96754	.96413	.96056	.95682	.95293	.94888	.94467	.94033	.93584	.93122
10	.98759	.98596	.98421	.98233	.98033	.97822	.97598	.97363	.97115	.96856
11	.99573	.99504	.99428	.99344	.99253	.99154	.99047	.98933	.98810	.98679
12	.99868	.99842	.99813	.99779	.99742	.99701	.99655	.99605	.99550	.99490
13	.99963	.99955	.99945	.99933	.99919	.99904	.99886	.99866	.99844	.99820
14	.99991	.99988	.99985	.99982	.99977	.99972	.99966	.99959	.99951	.99941
15	.99998	.99997	.99996	.99995	.99994	.99993	.99991	.99988	.99986	.99983

n	51	52	53	54	55	56	57	58	59	60
$\sqrt{n}D_\alpha$										
1	.00000	.00000	.00000	.00000	.00000	.00000	.00000	.00000	.00000	.00000
2	.00001	.00001	.00001	.00000	.00000	.00000	.00000	.00000	.00000	.00000
3	.00988	.00880	.00785	.00699	.00623	.00555	.00494	.00440	.00392	.00349
4	.11203	.10530	.09896	.09298	.08735	.08205	.07706	.07236	.06793	.06377
5	.32556	.31381	.30242	.29140	.28073	.27041	.26042	.25077	.24144	.23242
6	.55353	.54101	.52868	.51654	.50459	.49283	.48128	.46992	.45876	.44780
7	.73342	.72294	.71247	.70203	.69162	.68126	.67094	.66068	.65049	.64035
8	.85412	.84654	.83889	.83116	.82337	.81552	.80762	.79968	.79171	.78370
9	.92648	.92161	.91662	.91152	.90632	.90102	.89562	.89013	.88455	.87889
10	.96586	.96304	.96011	.95708	.95393	.95069	.94734	.94390	.94036	.93674
11	.98540	.98392	.98237	.98073	.97900	.97720	.97531	.97334	.97129	.96916
12	.99425	.99356	.99280	.99200	.99113	.99022	.98924	.98821	.98712	.98598
13	.99792	.99762	.99729	.99693	.99654	.99611	.99565	.99515	.99462	.99406
14	.99931	.99919	.99906	.99891	.99875	.99857	.99837	.99815	.99791	.99765
15	.99979	.99975	.99970	.99964	.99958	.99951	.99943	.99934	.99925	.99914

* Taken from ref. 55: Numerical tabulation of the distribution of Kolmogorov's statistic for finite sample size, Z. W. Birnbaum, *Journal of the American Statistical Association,*

TABLE 10.2. (*contd.*)

n	61	62	63	64	65	66	67	68	69	70
$\sqrt{n}D_\alpha$										
1	.00000	.00000	.00000	.00000	.00000	.00000	.00000	.00000	.00000	.00000
2	.00000	.00000	.00000	.00000	.00000	.00000	.00000	.00000	.00000	.00000
3	.00310	.00276	.00246	.00219	.00195	.00173	.00154	.00137	.00122	.00108
4	.05986	.05617	.05271	.04946	.04640	.04352	.04082	.03828	.03589	.03365
5	.22371	.21529	.20717	.19933	.19176	.18445	.17741	.17061	.16406	.15774
6	.43705	.42649	.41614	.40599	.39603	.38628	.37672	.36736	.35819	.34921
7	.63029	.62030	.61040	.60057	.59083	.58119	.57163	.56217	.55280	.54354
8	.77567	.76761	.75955	.75148	.74340	.73533	.72726	.71919	.71115	.70311
9	.87316	.86736	.86150	.85557	.84958	.84355	.83746	.83133	.82516	.81895
10	.93302	.92921	.92533	.92136	.91731	.91320	.90901	.90475	.90042	.89604
11	.96695	.96466	.96230	.95986	.95735	.95476	.95211	.94938	.94659	.94373
12	.98477	.98351	.98218	.98080	.97936	.97786	.97630	.97469	.97301	.97128
13	.99345	.99281	.99212	.99140	.99063	.98983	.98898	.98809	.98716	.98619
14	.99737	.99707	.99674	.99639	.99602	.99562	.99519	.99474	.99425	.99374
15	.99902	.99889	.99874	.99858	.99841	.99823	.99803	.99781	.99758	.99733

n	71	72	73	74	75	76	77	78	79	80
$\sqrt{n}D_\alpha$										
1	.00000	.00000	.00000	.00000	.00000	.00000	.00000	.00000	.00000	.00000
2	.00000	.00000	.00000	.00000	.00000	.00000	.00000	.00000	.00000	.00000
3	.00096	.00086	.00076	.00068	.00060	.00053	.00047	.00042	.00037	.00033
4	.03155	.02958	.02772	.02508	.02435	.02282	.02138	.02003	.01877	.01758
5	.15165	.14578	.14013	.13468	.12943	.12438	.11951	.11482	.11031	.10597
6	.34043	.33183	.32342	.31519	.30714	.29928	.29159	.28407	.27672	.26955
7	.53437	.52531	.51635	.50750	.49875	.49011	.48158	.47316	.46485	.45664
8	.69510	.68712	.67916	.67123	.66333	.65546	.64764	.63985	.63211	.62441
9	.81271	.80644	.80014	.79382	.78748	.78112	.77475	.76836	.76197	.75557
10	.89159	.88709	.88253	.87792	.87326	.86856	.86381	.85902	.85419	.84932
11	.94080	.93781	.93476	.93165	.92848	.92525	.92197	.91864	.91525	.91182
12	.96950	.96765	.96576	.96380	.96180	.95974	.95762	.95546	.95324	.95098
13	.98518	.98412	.98302	.98187	.98069	.97946	.97819	.97687	.97552	.97412
14	.99321	.99264	.99204	.99142	.99076	.99008	.98936	.98861	.98783	.98702
15	.99707	.99678	.99648	.99616	.99582	.99546	.99508	.99468	.99426	.99382

n	81	82	83	84	85	86	87	88	89	90
$\sqrt{n}D_\alpha$										
1	.00000	.00000	.00000	.00000	.00000	.00000	.00000	.00000	.00000	.00000
2	.00000	.00000	.00000	.00000	.00000	.00000	.00000	.00000	.00000	.00000
3	.00030	.00026	.00023	.00021	.00018	.00016	.00015	.00013	.00011	.00010
4	.01647	.01542	.01444	.01353	.01267	.01186	.01110	.01040	.00973	.00911
5	.10178	.09776	.09389	.09017	.08659	.08314	.07983	.07664	.07357	.07063
6	.26253	.25569	.24900	.24247	.23609	.22986	.22379	.21786	.21207	.20643
7	.44855	.44056	.43269	.42493	.41727	.40973	.40229	.39497	.38775	.38064
8	.61675	.60914	.60159	.59408	.58662	.57922	.57188	.56459	.55735	.55018
9	.74917	.74276	.73636	.72996	.72356	.71717	.71079	.70442	.69806	.69172
10	.84442	.83949	.83452	.82953	.82451	.81947	.81440	.80932	.80421	.79909
11	.90833	.90480	.90123	.89761	.89395	.89025	.88651	.88273	.87892	.87507
12	.94867	.94630	.94390	.94144	.93894	.93640	.93381	.93118	.92851	.92580
13	.97268	.97119	.96967	.96811	.96650	.96486	.96317	.96145	.95969	.95789
14	.98618	.98531	.98440	.98346	.98249	.98149	.98046	.97939	.97830	.97717
15	.99336	.99287	.99237	.99184	.99129	.99071	.99011	.98949	.98884	.98818

Vol. 47, 1952, pages 425–41. Used with the kind permission of the author, Z. W. Birnbaum, and of the Editor of the *Journal of the American Statistical Association.*

TABLE 10.2. VALUES OF α VERSUS $\sqrt{n}D_\alpha$ FOR $n=1(1)100$*

n / $\sqrt{n}D_\alpha$	91	92	93	94	95	96	97	98	99	100
1	.00000	.00000	.00000	.00000	.00000	.00000	.00000	.00000	.00000	.00000
2	.00000	.00000	.00000	.00000	.00000	.00000	.00000	.00000	.00000	.00000
3	.00009	.00008	.00007	.00006	.00006	.00005	.00004	.00004	.00003	.00003
4	.00853	.00798	.00747	.00699	.00654	.00612	.00573	.00536	.00502	.00469
5	.06779	.06507	.06245	.05994	.05752	.05520	.05297	.05082	.04876	.04678
6	.20092	.19555	.19031	.18520	.18022	.17536	.17062	.16600	.16150	.15712
7	.37364	.36674	.35995	.35327	.34669	.34021	.33384	.32757	.32140	.31533
8	.54306	.53600	.52901	.52207	.51520	.50839	.50164	.49496	.48834	.48178
9	.68539	.67908	.67279	.66651	.66026	.65403	.64783	.64165	.63549	.62937
10	.79395	.78880	.78364	.77847	.77329	.76810	.76291	.75771	.75251	.74731
11	.87119	.86728	.86334	.85937	.85538	.85136	.84731	.84324	.83915	.83504
12	.92305	.92026	.91743	.91457	.91167	.90874	.90578	.90278	.89975	.89670
13	.95605	.95418	.95226	.95032	.94833	.94632	.94426	.94218	.94006	.93791
14	.97601	.97482	.97359	.97234	.97105	.96974	.96839	.96702	.96561	.96417
15	.98748	.98677	.98602	.98526	.98447	.98366	.98282	.98196	.98107	.98016

* Taken from ref, 55: Numerical tabulation of the distribution of Kolmogorov's statistic for finite sample size, Z. W. Birnbaum, *Journal of the American Statistical Association*, Vol. 47, 1952, pages 425–41. Used with the kind permission of the author, Z. W. Birnbaum, and of the Editor of the *Journal of the American Statistical Association.*

Confidence coeff. has lower bound equal to value for continuity when population arbitrary (see ref. 287, 288). Adequate n can be determined by specifying value of D_α and lower bound for α **Characteristics 1** Low **2** Efficiency properties considered here are for the Kolmogorov test (based on the confidence band) with the simple null hyp. $F(x)=F_0(x)$, where $F(x)$ and $F_0(x)$ continuous dist. fcts. For composite altern. based on values of $\xi(F)=\sup_x|F_0(x)-F(x)|$, power has lower bound $1-\Phi\{2\sqrt{n}[\xi(F)+D_\alpha]\}+\Phi\{2\sqrt{n}[\xi(F)-D_\alpha]\}$. For large sample sizes, signif. level $<\frac{1}{2}$, and $\xi(F)$ small, suppose that N observations are needed to guarantee that power of χ^2 goodness of fit test $\geqslant\frac{1}{2}$; then only $O(N^{4/5})$ observations needed for Kolmogorov test to have power $\geqslant\frac{1}{2}$; the superiority of Kolmogorov test over χ^2 goodness of fit test when altern. expressed in terms of $\xi(F)$ also indicated by results of ref. 338. When altern. such that random variable $F_o[X(i)]$ has freq. fct. $=\beta e^{\beta x}/(e^\beta-1)$ for $0\leqslant x\leqslant 1$, $=0$ otherwise, efficiency roughly 90 per cent for $n=5$. Test biased for finite n but consistent for any continuous altern. dist. fct. $F^{(1)}(x)\neq F_0(x)$ **4** Moderately sensitive to continuity requirement, but confidence coeff. for continuous case furnishes lower bound for value when population arbitrary **5** Not difficult to decide on sample and continuity assumptions. **6** Useful in obtaining approx. bands where x range restricted and/or coeff. of $F_n(x)$ not necessarily unity (see preceding parts of sect.). For tests,

$\sup_x |F_0(x)-F_n(x)| = \max_i |F_0(X[i])-i/n|$ **Bibliography** Ref. 9, 24, 55, 56, 71, 100, 129, 152, 153, 170, 210, 266, 267, 287, 288, 292, 293, 306, 336, 337, 338, 346, 462, 543, 545.

Exact Two-Sided Confidence Bands Over All Points (Blackman)

Data 1 Continuous **4** Method for determining adequate n outlined in Results **Description 1** Exact two-sided confidence bands **2** $F(x)$ over all x **Assumptions 2** Population continuous **3** None **Results 1** $0<d, D\leqslant 1$. $h_3(x; d, n) = \max[0, F_n(x)-d]$; $h_4(x; D, n) = \min[1, F_n(x)+D]$. $H_n(a,u) = \sum_{0\leqslant r\leqslant na}[(-1)^r(u-r)^{u-r-1}(na-r)^r/(u-r)!r! - na(u-na)^{u-1}/u!]$; $J_n(a,u) = (u+na)^u/u!$; $N_1(v; d, D, n) = \sum_{u_1+\cdots+u_{v+1}=n} J_n[(d+D)v-d, u_1]H_n(D, u_{v+1})\prod_{w=2}^{v} H_n(d+D, u_w)$; $N_2(v; d, D, n) = \sum_{u_1+\cdots+u_{v+1}=n} J_n[(d+D)v, u_1]\prod_{w=2}^{v+1} H_n(d+D, u_w)$; $N_3(v; d, D, n) = \sum_{u_1+\cdots+u_{v+1}=n} J_n[(d+D)v-D, u_1]H_n(d, u_{v+1})\prod_{w=2}^{v} H_n(d+D, u_w)$; $N_4(v; d, D, n) = \sum_{u_1+\cdots+u_{v+2}=n} J_n[(d+D)v, u_1]H_n(d, u_2)H_n(D, u_{v+2})\prod_{w=3}^{v+1} H_n(d+D, u_w)$; $\epsilon_n(d, D) = 1 - \sum_{v=1}^{\infty}[N_1(v; d, D, n)+N_3(v; d, D, n)-N_2(v; d, D, n)-N_4(v; d, D, n)]$ **2** *Confidence band relation*: $P[h_3(x; d, n)\leqslant F(x)\leqslant h_4(x; D, n); -\infty<x<\infty] = \epsilon_n(d, D)$ **3** For most cases of interest, reasonably accurate values for $\epsilon_n(d, D)$ can be computed on basis of exact results for one-sided bands (see page 309) **4** Adequate n can be determined by specifying d, D, and a lower bound for $\epsilon_n(d, D)$ **Characteristics 1** Low unless $\epsilon_n(d, D)$ is determined from its definition **2** Corresponding results for exact one-sided and exact symmetrical bands furnish indication of efficiency and consistency properties for exact general two-sided bands **4** Moderately sensitive to continuity requirement **5** Not difficult to decide on sample and continuity assumptions **6** Useful in obtaining approx. bands where x range restricted and/or coeff. of $F_n(x)$ not necessarily unity (see page 309 and page 311) **Bibliography** Ref. 64, 65.

Asymptotic One-Sided Bands Over All Points and in Two Parts (Malmquist)

Data 1 Continuous **4** Min allowable n stated in Results **Description 1** Theoretical-approximate one-sided confidence bands in two parts **2** $F(x)$ over all x. One part of band applies for $F(x)\leqslant\frac{1}{2}$ and the other for $F(x)\geqslant\frac{1}{2}$ **Assumptions 2** Population continuous **3** None **Results 1** $a\geqslant 0$ and $b>0$. $h_1^{(1)}(x; a, b, n) = \min\{1, [\sqrt{n}/(\sqrt{n}-a+b)]F_n(x) + b/(\sqrt{n}-a+b)\}$; $h_1^{(2)}(x; a, b, n) = \min\{1, [\sqrt{n}/(\sqrt{n}+a-b)]F_n(x) + a/(\sqrt{n}+a-b)\}$; $h_2^{(1)}(x; a, b, n) = \max\{0, [\sqrt{n}/(\sqrt{n}+a-b)]F_n(x) - b/(\sqrt{n}+a-b)\}$; $h_2^{(2)}(x; a, b, n) = \max\{0, [\sqrt{n}/(\sqrt{n}-a+b)]F_n(x) - a/(\sqrt{n}-a+b)\}$. $h_1(x; a, b, n) = h_1^{(1)}(x; a, b, n)$ for $h_1^{(1)}(x; a, b, n)\leqslant\frac{1}{2}$ and $= h_1^{(2)}(x; a, b, n)$ for $h_1^{(2)}(x; a, b, n)\geqslant\frac{1}{2}$. $h_2(x; a, b, n) = h_2^{(1)}(x; a, b, n)$ for $h_2^{(1)}(x; a, b, n)\leqslant\frac{1}{2}$ and $= h_2^{(2)}(x; a, b, n)$ for $h_2^{(2)}(x; a, b, n)\geqslant\frac{1}{2}$.

$\epsilon(a, b) = \Phi(a+b) - 2e^{-2ab}\Phi(a-b) + e^{4b(a-b)}\Phi(a-3b)$ **2** *Confidence band relations*: $P[F(x) \leqslant h_1(x; a, b, n); -\infty < x < \infty] = P[F(x) \geqslant h_2(x; a, b, n); -\infty < x < \infty] \doteq \epsilon(a, b)$ for n sufficiently large **3** None **4** Min allowable $n \geqslant (1 + |a-b|) \max \{.6/[1-\epsilon(a, b)], 30/\epsilon(a, b)^2, 60\}$; min n also adequate n for most situations of importance. One-sided Smirnov bands obtained for $a = b$; min n expression based on this exact case. Choice of $a > b$ emphasizes tails of $F(x)$. Approx. two-sided bands can be obtained from these one-sided bands by method given on page 309. Confidence coeff. values can be approx. determined for sample sizes much smaller than min n if b not too different from a (see page 311 and page 312). $P[F(x) \leqslant h_1(x; a, b, n); -\infty < x < \infty] = P\{[F(x) - F_n(x)]\sqrt{n} \leqslant (a-b)F(x) + b$ for $0 \leqslant F(x) \leqslant \frac{1}{2}$ and also $[F(x) - F_n(x)]\sqrt{n} \leqslant (b-a)F(x) + a$ for $\frac{1}{2} \leqslant F(x) \leqslant 1\}$; $P[F(x) \geqslant h_2(x; a, b, n); -\infty < x < \infty] = P\{[F_n(x) - F(x)]\sqrt{n} \leqslant (a-b)F(x) + b$ for $0 \leqslant F(x) \leqslant \frac{1}{2}$ and also $[F_n(x) - F(x)]\sqrt{n} \leqslant (b-a)F(x) + a$ for $\frac{1}{2} \leqslant F(x) \leqslant 1\}$ **Characteristics 1** Low **2** For case of normal population with unit variance and altern. of shifts in mean, taking $a > b$ (say, $a = 2b$) tends to increase asymptotic efficiency of test based on confidence band; this efficiency is approx. 45 per cent for $a = b$ **4** Moderately sensitive to continuity requirement **5** Not difficult to decide on sample and continuity assumptions **6** Useful in obtaining approx. bands of same type as these but where x range restricted **Bibliography** Ref. 326.

Asymptotic Reversed One-Sided Bands in Two Parts (*Malmquist*)

Data 1 Continuous **4** Min allowable n stated in Results **Description 1** Theoretical-approx. two-sided confidence bands in two parts, where each part one-sided but in opposite directions **2** $F(x)$ over all x. One part of band applies for $F(x) \leqslant \frac{1}{2}$ and the other for $F(x) \geqslant \frac{1}{2}$ **Assumptions 2** Population continuous **3** None **Results 1** $b > 0$ and $a + b > 0$. $h^{(1)}(x; a, b, n) = \max \{0, [\sqrt{n}/(\sqrt{n} + a - b)]F_n(x) - b/(\sqrt{n} + a - b)\}$; $h^{(2)}(x; a, b, n) = \min \{1, [\sqrt{n}/(\sqrt{n} - a + b)]F_n(x) + b/(\sqrt{n} - a + b)\}$; $h_3(x; a, b, n) = \min [\frac{1}{2}, h^{(1)}(x; a, b, n)]$ and $h_4(x; a, b, n) = \max [\frac{1}{2}, h^{(2)}(x; a, b, n)]$. $\eta(a, b) = 1 - 2\Phi(-a-b) - e^{-2ab}[1 - 2\Phi(-a-3b)] + e^{-8ab}[\Phi(3a-b) - \Phi(a-3b)]$ **2** *Confidence band relation*: $P[h_3(x; a, b, n) \leqslant F(x) \leqslant h_4(x; a, b, n); -\infty < x < \infty] \doteq \eta(a, b)$ for n sufficiently large **3** None **4** Min allowable $n \geqslant (1 + |a-b|) \max \{.7/[1 - \eta(a, b)], 35/\eta(a, b)^2, 70\}$; min n also adequate n for most situations of importance. For $a = b$ two parts of one-sided Smirnov bands obtained, and min n based on this case. Confidence coeff. values can be approx. determined for sample sizes much smaller than min n if b not too different from a (see page 311 and page 312).

$P[h_3(x;a,b,n) \leqslant F(x) \leqslant h_4(x;a,b,n); -\infty < x < \infty] = P\{[F_n(x)-F(x)]\sqrt{n} \leqslant (a-b)F(x)+b$ for $0 \leqslant F(x) \leqslant \frac{1}{2}$ and also $[F_n(x)-F(x)]\sqrt{n} \geqslant -(a-b)F(x)-b$ for $\frac{1}{2} \leqslant F(x) \leqslant 1\}$ **Characteristics 1** Low **2** Unknown; however, band should be useful when population dispersion emphasized **4** Moderately sensitive to continuity requirement **5** Not difficult to decide on sample and continuity assumptions **6** Useful in obtaining approx. bands of same type as these but where x range restricted **Bibliography** Ref. 326.

Asymptotic Bands—$F(x)$ Bounded From Both Sides

Data 1 Continuous **4** Min allowable n stated in Results **Description 1** Theoretical-approximate one-sided and two-sided confidence bands **2** $F(x)$ for $A_1 \leqslant F(x) \leqslant A_2$ and for $1-A_2 \leqslant F(x) \leqslant 1-A_1$ **Assumptions 2** Population continuous **3** None **Results 1** $A \geqslant 0, a \geqslant 0, b > 0$. $h_1(x;d,n) = \min[1, F_n(x)+d]$; $h_2(x;d,n) = \max[0, F_n(x)-d]$. $H_1(x;A,n) = [\sqrt{n}/(\sqrt{n}+A)]F_n(x)$; $H_2(x;A,n) = [\sqrt{n}/(\sqrt{n}+A)]F_n(x) + A/(\sqrt{n}+A)$. $H_3(x;a,b,n) = \max\{0, [\sqrt{n}/(\sqrt{n}+a-b)]F_n(x) - b/(\sqrt{n}+a-b)\}$; $H_4(x;a,b,n) = \min\{1, [\sqrt{n}/(\sqrt{n}-a+b)]F_n(x) + b/(\sqrt{n}-a+b)\}$. $d_1 = \sqrt{n}d/[A_1(1-A_1)]^{1/2}$; $d_2 = \sqrt{n}d/[A_2(1-A_2)]^{1/2}$; $d'_1 = (1-2A_1)\sqrt{n}d/[A_1(1-A_1)]^{1/2}$; $d'_2 = (2A_2-1)\sqrt{n}d/[A_2(1-A_2)]^{1/2}$. $R = [A_1(1-A_2)/A_2(1-A_1)]^{1/2}$. $a_1 = A[A_2/(1-A_2)]^{1/2}$; $a_2 = [A_1(1-A_2)/(A_2-A_1)]^{1/2}$. $v_1 = A_1/(1-A_1)$; $v_2 = A_2/(1-A_2)$; $v'_1 = av_1+b$; $v'_2 = av_2+b$; $V_1^{(1)}(w) = -v'_1/\sqrt{v_1} - 2aw\sqrt{v_1}$; $V_1^{(2)}(w) = v'_1/\sqrt{v_1} - 2aw\sqrt{v_1}$; $V_2^{(1)}(w) = -v'_2/\sqrt{v_2} - 2bw\sqrt{v_2}$; $V_2^{(2)}(w) = v'_2/\sqrt{v_2} - 2bw\sqrt{v_2}$. $\gamma_1(d;A_1,A_2) = [1/(2\pi\sqrt{1-R^2})]\int_{-\infty}^{d_1}\int_{-\infty}^{d_2}\exp\{-\frac{1}{2}[z_1^2 + 2Rz_1z_2 + z_2^2]/(1-R^2)\}dz_2dz_1 - [e^{-nd^2}/(2\pi\sqrt{1-R^2})]\int_{-\infty}^{d'_1}\int_{-\infty}^{d'_2}\exp\{-\frac{1}{2}[z_1^2 - 2Rz_1z_2 + z_2^2]/(1-R^2)\}dz_2dz_1$. $\gamma_2(A;A_1,A_2) = (1/\pi)\int_{-\infty}^{a_1}\{\Phi[a_2(a_1-z)]-\frac{1}{2}\}e^{-z^2/2}dz$. $\gamma_3(a,b;A_1,A_2) = [1/(2\pi\sqrt{1-R^2})]\int_{-v'_1/\sqrt{v_1}}^{v'_1/\sqrt{v_1}}\int_{-v'_2/\sqrt{v_2}}^{v'_2/\sqrt{v_2}}\exp\{-\frac{1}{2}[z_1^2 + 2Rz_1z_2 + z_2^2]/(1-R^2)\} dz_2dz_1 - [1/(\pi\sqrt{1-R^2})]\sum_{w=1}^{\infty}(-1)^{w+1}e^{-2w^2ab}\int_{V_1^{(1)}(w)}^{V_1^{(2)}(w)}\int_{V_2^{(1)}(w)}^{V_2^{(2)}(w)}\exp\{-\frac{1}{2}[z_1^2-2Rz_1z_2+z_2^2]/(1-R^2)\}dz_2dz_1$ **2** *One-sided confidence band relations*: $P\Big[F(x) \geqslant h_2(x;d,n)$; all x such that $A_1 \leqslant h_2(x;d,n) \leqslant A_2\Big] = P\Big[F(x) \leqslant h_1(x;d,n)$; all x such that $1-A_2 \leqslant h_1(x;d,n) \leqslant 1-A_1\Big] \doteq \gamma_1(d;A_1,A_2)$ for n sufficiently large. $P\Big[F(x) \geqslant H_1(x;A,n)$; all x such that $A_1 \leqslant H_1(x;A,n) \leqslant A_2\Big] = P\Big[F(x) \leqslant H_2(x;A,n)$; all x such that $1-A_2 \leqslant H_2(x;A,n) \leqslant 1-A_1\Big] \doteq \gamma_2(A;A_1,A_2)$ for n sufficiently large. *Two-sided confidence band relation*: $P\Big[F(x) \geqslant H_3(x;a,b,n)$ for all x such that $A_1 \leqslant H_3(x;a,b,n)$

$\leqslant A_2$ and also $F(x) \leqslant H_4(x; a, b, n)$ for all x such that $A_1 \leqslant H_4(x; a, b, n) \leqslant A_2\Big] \doteq \gamma_3(a, b; A_1, A_2)$ for n sufficiently large **3** Bivariate normal probabilities can be obtained from the tables of ref. 401. $\gamma_2(A; A_1, A_2) = 2[\Phi(A\sqrt{v_1}) - \frac{1}{2}] - (1/\pi)(1-J) \tan^{-1} a_2$, where $0 \leqslant J \leqslant \exp[-A_2A^2/2(1-A_2)]$ **4** For one-sided bands based on h_1 or h_2, min allowable $n \geqslant (A_2 - A_1)^{-1/2} \max\{.6/[1-\gamma_1(d; A_1, A_2)], 30/\gamma_1(d; A_1, A_2)^2, 60\}$. For the one-sided bands based on H_1, min $n \geqslant \max(1, .1/A_1)(A_2 - A_1)^{-1/2}(1+A) \max\{.7/[1-\gamma_2(A; A_1, A_2)], 35/\gamma_2(A; A_1, A_2)^2, 70\}$. For the one-sided bands based on H_2, min $n \geqslant \max[1, .1/(1-A_2)](A_2 - A_1)^{-1/2}(1+A) \max\{.7/[1-\gamma_2(A; A_1, A_2)], 35/\gamma_2(A; A_1, A_2)^2, 70\}$. Min n for two-sided bands $\geqslant (A_2 - A_1)^{-1/2}(1 + |a-b|) \max\{1.2/[1-\gamma_3(a, b; A_1, A_2)], 30/\gamma_3(a, b; A_1, A_2)^2, 60\}$. Min allowable n should also be adequate n for most situations of importance. When $A_1 = 0$, $A_2 = 1$, one-sided case involving h_1 and h_2 yields Smirnov one-sided bands; Kolmogorov symmetrical bands obtained for two-sided case where $a = b$, $A_1 = 0$, and $A_2 = 1$; min n expressions based on these exact cases. For one-sided cases involving h_1 or h_2, approx. confidence coeff. values can be obtained for sample sizes much smaller than stated min n; likewise for the two-sided cases where b is not too different from a; see first part of sect. for methods. $P\Big[F(x) \geqslant H_1(x; A, n)$; all x such that $A_1 \leqslant H_1(x; A, n) \leqslant A_2\Big] = P\Big\{[F_n(x) - F(x)]/F(x) \leqslant A/\sqrt{n}; A_1 \leqslant F(x) \leqslant A_2\Big\}$. $P\Big[F(x) \leqslant H_2(x; A, n)$; all x such that $1 - A_2 \leqslant H_2(x; A, n) \leqslant 1 - A_1\Big] = P\Big\{[F(x) - F_n(x)]/[1-F(x)] \leqslant A/\sqrt{n}; 1 - A_2 \leqslant F(x) \leqslant 1 - A_1\Big\}$. $P\Big[F(x) \geqslant H_3(x; a, b, n)$ for all x such that $A_1 \leqslant H_3(x; a, b, n) \leqslant A_2$ and also $F(x) \leqslant H_4(x; a, b, n)$ for all x such that $A_1 \leqslant H_4(x; a, b, n) \leqslant A_2\Big] = P\Big[|F(x) - F_n(x)|\sqrt{n} - (a-b)F(x) \leqslant b; A_1 \leqslant F(x) \leqslant A_2\Big]$ **Characteristics 1** Low for one-sided bands based on the h's; low to medium otherwise **2** Consider tests with simple null hyp. $F(x) = F_0(x)$ and $A_1 \leqslant F(x) \leqslant A_2$ or $1 - A_2 \leqslant F(x) \leqslant 1 - A_1$. Test based on h_1 should be sensitive to altern. based on metric $\sup_{1-A_2 \leqslant F_0(x), F(x) \leqslant 1-A_1} [F(x) - F_0(x)]$; test based on h_2 should be sensitive to altern. based on metric $\inf_{A_1 \leqslant F_0(x), F(x) \leqslant A_2}[F(x) - F_0(x)]$. Test based on H_1 should be sensitive to altern. based on metric $\inf_{A_1 \leqslant F_0(x), F(x) \leqslant A_2}[F(x) - F_0(x)]/F_0(x)$; test based on H_2 should be sensitive to altern. based on metric $\sup_{1-A_2 \leqslant F_0(x), F(x) \leqslant 1-A_1}[F_0(x) - F(x)]/[1-F_0(x)]$. Test based on two-sided band should be sensitive to altern. expressed in terms of the metric $\sup_{A_1 \leqslant F_0(x), F(x) \leqslant A_2}\{|F(x) - F_0(x)| - (a-b)F_0(x)/\sqrt{n}\}$ **4** Moderately sensitive to continuity requirement **5** Not difficult to decide on sample and continuity assumptions **6** Approx. two-sided bands of various types can be obtained from the one-sided bands (see page 309). **Bibliography** Ref. 326, 327, 401, 425.

Asymptotic Bands—$F(x)$ Bounded From One Side (Rényi)

Data 1 Continuous **4** Min allowable n stated in Results **Description 1** Theoretical-approximate one-sided and two-sided confidence bands **2** $F(x)$ for $F(x) \geqslant A_1$ and for $F(x) \leqslant 1 - A_1$ **Assumptions 2** Population continuous **3** None **Results 1** $A \geqslant 0, A_1 > 0$. $H_1^{(1)}(x; A, n) = \min\{1, [\sqrt{n}/(\sqrt{n} - A)]F_n(x)\}$; $H_2^{(1)}(x; A, n) = [\sqrt{n}/(\sqrt{n} + A)]F_n(x)$. $H_1^{(2)}(x; A, n) = [\sqrt{n}/(\sqrt{n} + A)]F_n(x) + A/(\sqrt{n} + A)$; $H_2^{(2)}(x; A, n) = \max\{0, [\sqrt{n}/(\sqrt{n} - A)]F_n(x) - A/(\sqrt{n} - A)\}$. $\xi_1(A; A_1) = 2\Phi\{A[A_1/(1 - A_1)]^{1/2}\} - 1$. $\xi_2(A; A_1) = (4/\pi)\sum_{W=0}^{\infty}(-1)^W/(2W+1)\exp[(2W+1)^2\pi^2(1 - A_1)/A_1A^2]$ **2** *One-sided confidence band relations*: $P\Big[F(x) \geqslant H_2^{(1)}(x; A, n)$; all x such that $H_2^{(1)}(x; A, n) \geqslant A_1\Big] = P\Big[F(x) \leqslant H_1^{(2)}(x; A, n)$; all x such that $H_1^{(2)}(x; A, n) \leqslant 1 - A_1\Big] \doteq \xi_1(A; A_1)$ for n sufficiently large. *Two-sided confidence band relations*: $P\Big[F(x) \geqslant H_2^{(1)}(x; A, n)$ for all x such that $H_2^{(1)}(x; A, n) \geqslant A_1$ and also $F(x) \leqslant H_1^{(1)}(x; A, n)$ for all x such that $H_1^{(1)}(x; A, n) \geqslant A_1\Big] \doteq \xi_2(A; A_1)$ for n sufficiently large. $P\Big[F(x) \geqslant H_2^{(2)}(x; A, n)$ for all x such that $H_2^{(2)}(x; A, n) \leqslant 1 - A_1$ and also $F(x) \leqslant H_1^{(2)}(x; A, n)$ for all x such that $H_1^{(2)}(x; A, n) \leqslant 1 - A_1\Big] \doteq \xi_2(A; A_1)$ for n sufficiently large **3** Table 10.3 contains values of $\xi_2(A; A_1)$ for $A = .1$, .5(.5)25(1)30(5)40, 43 and $A_1 = .01(.01).1(.1).5$. When $\xi_1(A; A_1) \geqslant .915$, $\xi_2(A; A_1) \doteq \xi_1(A; A_1)^2$, with an error of at most 5 per cent in $1 - \xi_2(A; A_1)$ **4** For one-sided bands based on $H_2^{(1)}$, min allowable $n \geqslant \max(1, .1/A_1)(1 - A_1)^{-1/2}(1 + A)\max\{.7/[1 - \xi_1(A; A_1)], 35/\xi_1(A; A_1)^2, 70\}$. For one-sided bands based on $H_1^{(2)}$, min $n \geqslant \max[1, .1/(1 - A_1)]A_1^{-1/2}(1 + A)\max\{.7/[1 - \xi_1(A; A_1)], 35/\xi_1(A; A_1)^2, 70\}$. For the two-sided bands based on $H_1^{(1)}$ and $H_2^{(1)}$, min $n \geqslant \max(1, .1/A_1)(1 - A_1)^{-1/2}(1 + A)\max\{1.4/[1 - \xi_2(A; A_1)], 35/\xi_2(A; A_1)^2, 70\}$. For the two-sided bands based on $H_1^{(2)}$ and $H_2^{(2)}$, min $n \geqslant \max[1, .1/(1 - A_1)]A_1^{-1/2}(1 + A)\max\{1.4/[1 - \xi_2(A; A_1)], 35/\xi_2(A; A_1)^2, 70\}$. Min allowable n should also be adequate n for most situations of importance. $P\Big[F(x) \geqslant H_2^{(1)}(x; A, n)$; all x such that $H_2^{(1)}(x; A, n) \geqslant A_1\Big] = P\Big\{[F_n(x) - F(x)]/F(x) \leqslant A/\sqrt{n}; F(x) \geqslant A_1\Big\}$. $P\Big[F(x) \leqslant H_1^{(2)}(x; A, n)$; all x such that $H_1^{(2)}($

TABLE 10.3. VALUES OF $\xi_2(A; A_1)$ FOR VARIOUS VALUES OF A AND A_1*

A \ A_1	.01	.02	.03	.04	.05	.06	.07	.08	.09	.1	.2	.3	.4	.5
.1													.0000	.0000
.5											.0000	.0000	.0008	.0092
1.0						.0000	.0000	.0000	.0000	.0000	.0092	.0716	.2001	.3708
1.5			.0000	.0000	.0000	.0002	.0009	.0023	.0050	.0092	.1420	.3543	.5591	.7328
2.0		.0000	.0001	.0008	.0036	.0101	.0212	.0367	.0563	.0791	.3708	.6193	.7951	.9082
2.5		.0001	.0022	.0112	.0299	.0578	.0925	.1320	.1730	.2155	.5778	.7966	.9714	.9751
3.0	.0000	.0015	.0157	.0474	.0941	.1487	.2061	.2632	.3184	.3708	.7328	.9009	.9915	.9954
3.5	.0001	.0092	.0491	.1135	.1879	.2629	.3341	.3994	.4598	.5140	.8398	.9561	.9978	.9991
4.0	.0006	.0291	.1052	.2001	.2942	.3804	.4570	.5244	.5835	.6353	.9082	.9823	.9995	.9999
4.5	.0031	.0643	.1776	.2950	.4001	.4902	.5665	.6311	.6860	.7328	.9511	.9936	.9999	1.0000
5.0	.0096	.1135	.2582	.3895	.4985	.5873	.6594	.7193	.7683	.8088	.9751	.9979	1.0000	
5.5	.0225	.1726	.3511	.4784	.5863	.6723	.7374	.7903	.8326	.8665	.9887	.9994		
6.0	.0428	.2375	.4204	.5591	.6627	.7409	.8006	.8463	.8817	.9081	.9954	.9999		
6.5	.0707	.3045	.4952	.6310	.7282	.7989	.8509	.8895	.9181	.9395	.9977	1.0000		
7.0	.1053	.3708	.5639	.6939	.7834	.8461	.8904	.9220	.9446	.9607	.9991			
7.5	.1452	.4347	.6193	.7484	.8294	.8839	.9207	.9460	.9633	.9752	.9996			
8.0	.1889	.4959	.6811	.7951	.8671	.9135	.9436	.9634	.9763	.9847	.9999			
8.5	.2348	.5513	.7301	.8345	.8977	.9365	.9606	.9756	.9850	.9908	1.0000			
9.0	.2819	.6032	.7731	.8696	.9221	.9540	.9729	.9849	.9907	.9946				
9.5	.3290	.6510	.8104	.8950	.9410	.9713	.9817	.9898	.9944	.9969				
10.0	.3754	.6938	.8427	.9175	.9564	.9770	.9878	.9936	.9967	.9983				
10.5	.4205	.7328	.8704	.9358	.9680	.9840	.9921	.9961	.9981	.9991				
11.0	.4640	.7678	.8939	.9505	.9768	.9891	.9949	.9976	.9989	.9995				
11.5	.5055	.7992	.9137	.9622	.9833	.9927	.9968	.9986	.9994	.9997				
12.0	.5450	.8271	.9303	.9713	.9882	.9951	.9980	.9992	.9997	.9999				
12.5	.5824	.8517	.9441	.9784	.9917	.9968	.9988	.9995	.9998	.9999				
13.0	.6174	.8734	.9555	.9841	.9943	.9980	.9993	.9997	.9999	1.0000				
13.5	.6509	.8924	.9648	.9883	.9961	.9987	.9996	.9999	1.0000					

14.0	.6812	.9090	.9724	.9915	.9973	.9992	.9998	.9999
14.5	.7099	.9234	.9780	.9938	.9982	.9995	.9999	1.0000
15.0	.7367	.9358	.9833	.9956	.9988	.9997	.9999	
15.5	.7615	.9464	.9872	.9969	.9992	.9998	1.0000	
16.0	.7844	.9555	.9902	.9978	.9995	.9999		
16.5	.8055	.9631	.9927	.9985	.9997	.9999		
17.0	.8249	.9697	.9944	.9990	.9998	1.0000		
17.5	.8428	.9752	.9958	.9993	.9999			
18.0	.8591	.9797	.9969	.9995	.9999			
18.5	.8740	.9836	.9977	.9997	1.0000			
19.0	.8876	.9867	.9983	.9998				
19.5	.9000	.9893	.9988	.9999				
20.0	.9112	.9915	.9991	.9999				
20.5	.9213	.9932	.9994	.9999				
21.0	.9304	.9946	.9996	1.0000				
21.5	.9386	.9957	.9997					
22.0	.9460	.9967	.9998					
22.5	.9526	.9974	.9998					
23.0	.9590	.9980	.9999					
23.5	.9636	.9984	.9999					
24.0	.9696	.9988	1.0000					
24.5	.9724	.9991						
25	.9760	.9993						
26	.9821	.9996						
27	.9867	.9998						
28	.9902	.9999						
29	.9929	.9999						
30	.9949	1.0000						
35	.9991							
40	.9999							
43	1.0000							

* Based on ref. 425: On the theory of order statistics, A. Rényi, *Acta Mathematica Academiae Scientiarum Hungaricae*, Vol. 4, 1953, pages 191–232. Used with the kind permission of the author, Alfréd Rényi.

$x; A, n) \leqslant 1 - A_1\Big] = P\Big\{[F(x) - F_n(x)]/[1 - F(x)] \leqslant A/\sqrt{n};\ F(x) \leqslant 1 - A_1\Big\}$. $P\Big[F(x) \geqslant H_2^{(1)}(x; A, n)$ for all x such that $H_2^{(1)}(x; A, n) \geqslant A_1$ and also $F(x) \leqslant H_1^{(1)}(x; A, n)$ for all x such that $H_1^{(1)}(x; A, n) \geqslant A_1\Big] = P\Big[|F_n(x) - F(x)|/F(x) \leqslant A/\sqrt{n};\ F(x) \geqslant A_1\Big]$. $P\Big[F(x) \geqslant H_2^{(2)}(x; A, n)$ for all x such that $H_2^{(2)}(x; A, n) \leqslant 1 - A_1$ and also $F(x) \leqslant H_1^{(2)}(x; A, n)$ for all x such that $H_1^{(2)}(x; A, n) \leqslant 1 - A_1\Big] = P\Big\{|F_n(x) - F(x)|/[1 - F(x)] \leqslant A/\sqrt{n};\ F(x) \leqslant 1 - A_1\Big\}$. Ref. 90 contains an evaluation of $P[F_n(x)/F(x) \leqslant A/\sqrt{n};\ 0 < F(x) \leqslant A_1]$ **Characteristics 1** Low **2** Tests based $H_1^{(1)}$ and/or $H_2^{(1)}$ have simple null hyp. $F(x) = F_0(x)$ for $F(x) \geqslant A_1$; tests based on $H_2^{(1)}$ and/or $H_2^{(2)}$ have simple null hyp. $F(x) = F_0(x)$ for $F(x) \leqslant 1 - A_1$. Test based on $H_2^{(1)}$ should be sensitive to altern. based on metric $\sup_{F_0(x),\, F(x) \geqslant A_1} [F(x) - F_0(x)]/F_0(x)$. Test based on $H_1^{(2)}$ should be sensitive to altern. based on metric $\sup_{F_0(x),\, F(x) \leqslant 1 - A_1} [F_0(x) - F(x)]/[1 - F_0(x)]$. Two-sided test based on $H_1^{(1)}$ and $H_2^{(1)}$ should be sensitive to altern. based on metric $\sup_{F_0(x),\, F(x) \geqslant A_1} |F(x) - F_0(x)|/F_0(x)$. Two-sided test based on $H_1^{(2)}$ and $H_2^{(2)}$ should be sensitive to altern. based on metric $\sup_{F_0(x),\, F(x) \leqslant 1 - A_1} |F(x) - F_0(x)|/[1 - F_0(x)]$ **4** Moderately sensitive to continuity requirement **5** Not difficult to decide on sample and continuity assumptions **6** Approx. two-sided bands of various types can be obtained from the one-sided bands (see page 309) **Bibliography** Ref. 90, 425.

TESTS AND CONFIDENCE REGIONS FOR UNIVARIATE FREQUENCY FUNCTIONS

Introduction

This section contains confidence regions and significance tests for frequency functions of continuous populations. Theoretical-approximate confidence intervals are obtained for the frequency function value at an identified population percentile. Theoretical-approximate confidence bands, and some related tests, are given for the frequency function value over a specified finite interval. For the case of a simple null hypothesis and a simple alternative hypothesis, some exact tests are presented; these tests are obtained by converting the data to a binomial form or to a multinomial form and the frequency function value is considered over all points. The procedure of converting the data to a multinomial form is also used as a basis for rank sum tests; here the alternative hypothesis can be composite. Also, some nearly optimum approximate tests are given for testing a simple null hypothesis against a simple alternative.

Although no presentation is given, an asymptotic method is outlined for testing composite null hypotheses in which the frequency function is specified (over all points) except for the value of a parameter. In addition, without a presentation, the use of the likelihood ratio method for obtaining tests of composite null and alternative hypotheses is outlined.

Discussion of Confidence Regions and Related Tests

The one-sided and two-sided confidence intervals for the frequency function value at an identified percentile are obtained by first finding confidence intervals for the reciprocal of this frequency function value and then inverting these intervals. For this reason, and convenience of analysis, the properties of the confidence intervals for frequency function values at identified percentiles (e.g., with respect to adequate sample sizes) are determined on the basis of the corresponding confidence intervals for the reciprocal of the frequency function.

The confidence band results presented are one-sided. These bands do not extend over all points. Instead, the allowable points are restricted to a specified finite interval which does not contain all the population probability and in which the frequency function is known to be nonzero. The endpoints of this finite interval are given numbers that are determined on the basis of past experience, technical considerations, etc. These confidence bands are of an asymptotic nature and the minimum sample sizes stated for their use are quite large.

Although corresponding tests can be determined directly from the confidence bands, similar tests that require somewhat smaller minimum sample sizes are available. These one-sided tests are also stated in the presentation that contains the confidence band results.

Discussion of Binomial and Multinomial Tests

Three of the types of tests presented are based on categorical type data obtained by grouping of the observations. They are given here rather than in Chapter 11 because of their specialized application to continuous frequency functions. For these tests, the sample from a continuous population is converted into a sample from a binomial population or a sample from a multinomial population. This conversion is accomplished by dividing the space of possible values for an observation into disjoint sets on the basis of the null hypothesis and the alternative hypothesis. In all cases, the null hypothesis is simple; i.e., the frequency function is completely specified. For the binomial test and one of the multinomial tests, the alternative hypothesis is also simple. For the other type of multinomial test, which is of a rank sum nature with the disjoint sets (categories) given rank numbers, the alternative hypothesis is composite and depends on an unknown parameter.

A special case of the multinomial tests is that with two categories. However, this test based on binomial data is not necessarily the same as the binomial test which is given in a separate presentation. The multinomial tests are subject to the condition that each category (disjoint set) has the same probability under the null hypothesis. For the binomial test, the disjoint sets are chosen so as to obtain the desired significance level and to maximize the power at the alternative. Thus the binomial test is always at least as powerful at the alternative as the multinomial test with two disjoint sets.

Let the null hypothesis specify that the population frequency function is $f_0(x)$. Then, for H a real number that takes values in a given set, the alternative frequency functions for the rank sum test are of the form

$$g(x; H)f_0(x),$$

where, for fixed H, $g(x; H)$ is a continuous monotonic function of x (increasing in the same direction for each H). For fixed x,

$$\int_{-\infty}^{x} g(y; H)f_0(y)dy$$

is monotonic in H (increasing in the same direction for each x); also, under the null hypothesis, the set $\{x|g(x;H)=c\}$ has zero probability for all H in the specified set and all c.

Here $f_0(x)$ is completely specified and $g(x; H)$ can be chosen in any desired fashion, subject to the few general nature restrictions that are imposed. Thus a wide variety of composite alternative hypotheses can be specified for the rank sum test. It would seem that many composite alternatives of interest can be approximated by appropriate choice of $g(x; H)$ and the set of values for H.

Approximately Optimum Tests for Simple Hypotheses

The Neyman-Pearson lemma furnishes a basis for obtaining nearly optimum approximate tests for a simple null hypothesis and a simple alternative hypothesis. Under the null hypothesis, H_0, let the frequency function of the $X(i)$ be $f_0[x]$, while it is $f_1[x]$ for the alternative. Then, the most powerful test is of the product form where rejection of H_0 occurs when

$$\prod_{i=1}^{n} f_1[X(i)] \Big/ \prod_{i=1}^{n} f_0[X(i)] \geqslant A(\alpha),$$

or equivalently, of the summation form where H_0 is rejected when

$$\sum_{i=1}^{n} \log_{10}\{f_1[X(i)]/f_0[X(i)]\} \geqslant B(\alpha).$$

Only the summation form for the test is considered in the discussion that follows. Both the null and the alternative hypothesis are rejected if observed values $X(i_1)$ and $X(i_2)$ occur such that $f_0[X(i_1)]$ and $f_1[X(i_2)]$ are zero.

The null distribution of the test statistic can be approximated by computing its first few moments under the assumption that the distribution is $f_0[x]$. These moments can always be approximately evaluated by numerical integration. Then, since the test statistic should have an almost normal distribution for large n, a reasonable approximation to its null distribution should be furnished, for sample sizes that are not too small, by using these moments and the Edgeworth series, the Gram-Charlier A series, the Pearson curves, etc. The first four moments and use of the Edgeworth series, or the Cornish-Fisher inversion of this series (see Chapter 4), should be satisfactory for most situations. The test obtained using this approximation to the null distribution should be nearly equal to the most powerful test; in fact, it would be most powerful if its null distribution were accurately known. Although stated for the univariate case, this approximate procedure can also be used for multivariate data.

A modification of this test is available for which the power at the alternative may be somewhat smaller but the amount of computation is often substantially reduced. Here the expected value of

$$Y_i = \log_{10} \{f_1[X(i)]/f_0[X(i)]\}$$

is determined under the null hypothesis and, using this mean value, the appropriate one-sided t test based on the Y_i is applied. The null hypothesis properties of the t test, which are determined to terms of order $1/n$, are given in Chapter 7. The minimum allowable sample size for this test is evidently larger than that for the other test. Specifically, the modified test consists in rejecting the null hypothesis if

$$\sum_{i=1}^{n} Y_i \geqslant nE(Y_i|H_0) + \sqrt{n}t_\alpha(n-1)SY_i$$

and has a significance level that approximately equals α. Although stated for univariate data, this modified method can also be applied to the multivariate case.

Tests For Modified Composite Hypotheses

As mentioned on page 281, tests for simple null and alternative hypotheses can also be used to test some types of modified composite hypothesis. Let the hypotheses of principal interest be represented by $f(x;\xi)$ where ξ ranges over a specified set of values, which could be finite or infinite in number. Then the two types of modified composite hypotheses considered in this section are represented by the completely specified frequency functions

$$f^{(1)}(x) = \int_{\text{all } \xi} w_1(\xi) f(x;\xi) d\xi$$

and

$$f^{(2)}(x) = \prod_{r=1}^{R} f[x;\xi(r)]^{w_2[\xi(r)]}$$

where the integral can be a summation and $\xi(1), \ldots, \xi(R)$ are R specified values of ξ. In addition to being chosen so that $f^{(1)}(x)$ and $f^{(2)}(x)$ are frequency functions, the weight functions $w_1(\xi)$, $w_2[\xi]$ and the $\xi(r)$ are selected so that the simple hypotheses of principal interest are emphasized. Although stated in terms of the univariate case, these kinds of modified composite hypotheses are also useful for the multivariate case.

Life-Testing Use of Confidence Regions and Related Tests

The confidence intervals for $f(\theta_p)$, the confidence bands for $f(x)$ over a specified range of x values, and their related tests have potential life-testing uses (see the discussion of life-testing uses at the beginning of the chapter). The confidence intervals for $f(\theta_p)$ are such that experimentation can be stopped when not much more than $100p$ per cent of the smallest sample values have been determined. A band for $f(x)$ can be obtained with the property that the experiment can be discontinued when all observations that are at most equal to a specified value have been determined. Tests based on a band for $f(x)$ have the desirable life-testing property that significance is determined when the statistic first falls outside the band, and that the test can be discontinued at the smallest value of x for which this occurs.

Determination of Adequate Sample Sizes

For two of the types of statistical procedures, the specified minimum sample sizes are very large. These are the procedures involving confidence bands and the related tests. In these two situations, the minimum sample sizes should also be adequate sample sizes for most cases of practical interest.

Mean square error or coefficient of variation (based on mean square error) considerations can be utilized in determining adequate sample sizes for confidence intervals involving the frequency function value at an identified percentile (see Chapter 4). Specifically, each of the mean square error and the coefficient of variation for the reciprocal of the variable endpoint value (considered as a point estimate) seems to furnish a satisfactory criterion for one-sided intervals. When the confidence interval is two-sided, the maximum of the criterion values for the two endpoints might be suitable. The coefficient of variation for the reciprocal of a variable endpoint can be approximately evaluated without any sampling information. A two-stage sampling procedure can be used to estimate the mean square error for the reciprocal of a variable endpoint. Unless the first-stage sample is large compared to the second-stage sample, the conditional probability effects introduced by two-stage sampling should not be very important. In many cases, the minimum sample size stated for the use of one of these confidence intervals is at least as large as the smallest sample sizes that would usually be considered adequate. For the presentations of this section, the mean square error of an estimate is approximately equal to the estimate variance. Consequently, the variance is used in determining adequate sample sizes.

For the two exact presentations which involve a simple null hypothesis and a simple alternative hypothesis, adequate sample sizes can be determined on the basis of power function considerations. That is, let a lower bound be specified for the value that the power function is to have when the alternative hypothesis holds. Then the sample size is considered to be adequate if at least this power is attained. For the case where the sample values are converted to a binomial form, obtaining an exact expression for the power function value at the alternative is not difficult; a large sample approximation is given for the case where the data are converted to a multinomial form.

The method based on the power at a specified simple alternative hypothesis is often also appropriate for determining adequate sample sizes for the rank sum tests for the situation where the observations have been converted to a multinomial form. For example, this is the case if a simple alternative which is representative of the alternatives of principal interest can be specified or if a suitable modified composite hypothesis can be determined.

For the nearly optimum approximate presentation involving simple null and alternative hypotheses, the power for the alternative can be evaluated by determining the first few moments of the test statistic under the alternative hypothesis and using the first few terms of the Edgeworth series, or some other suitable method, for approximating a distribution on the basis of its moments. The power function value depends on the sample size and adequate n can be determined by the requirement that the power at the alternative has at least a specified value.

General Asymptotic Tests For Composite Null Hypotheses

Ref. 382 furnishes a somewhat general asymptotic method for testing composite null hypotheses in which the continuous frequency function is completely specified except for the value of a one-dimensional parameter (population constant). The test statistic depends on the frequency function being tested and on another function which is selected by the experimenter. Let the frequency function be denoted by $f(x;\xi)$ while the function chosen by the experimenter is $c(x;\xi)$. Suppose that $f(x;\xi)$ and $c(x;\xi)$ are reasonably well behaved and let

$$\hat{\xi} = \text{maximum likelihood estimate of } \xi$$

$$f_1(x;\xi) = f'(x;\xi)/f(x;\xi)\sigma\{f'[X(i);\xi]/f[X(i);\xi]\}$$

$$c_1(x;\xi) = \{c(x;\xi) - Ec[X(i);\xi]\}/\sigma\{c[X(i);\xi]\}$$

$$\rho(f_1, c_1;\xi) = \rho\{f_1[X(i);\xi], c_1[X(i);\xi]\}; \quad |\rho(f_1, c_1)| \leqslant \delta < 1$$

$$g(x;\xi) = [c_1(x;\xi) - \rho(f_1, c_1;\xi)f_1(x;\xi)]/\sqrt{1-\rho(f_1, c_1;\xi)^2}$$

$$Z_n = \sum_{i=1}^{n} g[X(i);\hat{\xi}]/\sqrt{n},$$

where the $X(i)$ are the sample values. Then, under the null hypotheses, the large sample distribution of Z_n is standard normal and the null hypothesis can be tested, for example, by an equal-tail procedure.

Due to the great freedom in the selection of $c(x;\xi)$, and the wide range of possibilities for $f(x;\xi)$, specifying sample sizes that are sufficiently large for valid application of tests based on Z_n is exceedingly difficult. However, this specification may not be so difficult for some special cases.

Likelihood Ratio Tests For Composite Hypotheses

For large sample sizes, the likelihood ratio approach can be used to test composite null and alternative hypotheses. Let the null hypothesis assert that the population frequency function is of the form $f\Big[x;\eta(1),\ldots,\eta(r_1),$ $\eta^{(0)}(r_1+1),\ldots,\eta^{(0)}(r_2)\Big]$, with $\eta^{(0)}(r_1+1),\ldots,\eta^{(0)}(r_2)$ being specified numbers and $\eta(1),\ldots,\eta(r_1)$ unknown constants. The alternative hypothesis asserts that the frequency function is of this same form but that $\eta(r_1+1),\ldots,\eta(r_2)$ do not all have the stated values. Here the function $f[x;\eta(1),\ldots,\eta(r_2)]$ is completely specified except for the values $\eta(1),$ $\ldots,\eta(r_2)$ and is such that the large sample likelihood ratio test applies. Let $\eta'(1),\ldots,\eta'(r_1)$ be the maximum likelihood estimates of $\eta(1),\ldots,\eta(r_1)$ when the null hypothesis holds while $\hat{\eta}(1),\ldots,\hat{\eta}(r_2)$ are the maximum likelihood estimates of $\eta(1), \ldots, \eta(r_2)$ when the alternate hypothesis holds. Also let

$$\lambda_n = \frac{\prod_{i=1}^{n} f[X(i); \eta'(1), \ldots, \eta'(r_1), \eta^{(0)}(r_1+1), \ldots, \eta^{(0)}(r_2)]}{\prod_{i=1}^{n} f[X(i); \hat{\eta}(1), \ldots, \hat{\eta}(r_2)]}$$

where $X(1), \ldots, X(n)$ are the sample values used for the test. Then, under the null hypothesis, $-2 \log_e \lambda_n$ has a χ^2 distribution with $r_2 - r_1$ degrees of freedom for n sufficiently great and rejection of the null hypothesis occurs if $-2 \log_e \lambda_n$ is too large.

The likelihood ratio method is of very wide applicability and permits composite null and alternative hypotheses of a very general nature. Also it is applicable for discrete as well as continuous populations and for the univariate and multivariate cases. Due to this great freedom, specifying minimum allowable sample sizes for the general case is extremely difficult.

This difficulty can be partially overcome by using a modification of $-2 \log_e \lambda_n$ (see ref. 304). Specifically, an expression $e[\eta(1), \ldots, \eta(r_1); \eta^{(0)}(r_1+1), \ldots, \eta^{(0)}(r_2)]$ is determined which equals $E(-2 \log_e \lambda_n) + O(n^{-2})$ under the null hypothesis. Then, except for terms that are $O(n^{-3/2})$, the moments of the null distribution of

$$(r_2 - r_1)(-2 \log_e \lambda_n)/e[\eta'(1), \ldots, \eta'(r_1); \eta^{(0)}(r_1+1), \ldots, \eta^{(0)}(r_2)],$$

are the same as the moments of the χ^2 distribution with $r_2 - r_1$ degrees of freedom. Thus, in most cases, tests based on this modification should be reasonably accurate even for values of n that are only moderately large. Unfortunately, determination of $e[\eta(1), \ldots, \eta^{(0)}(r_2)]$ nearly always requires a substantial amount of effort, even when r_1 is as small as 1. Consequently, no presentation is given for this modified method.

Fixed Material for Section

Data 1 Continuous, univariate **2** None **4** $m = 1$ **Assumptions 1** Random sample **2** $f(x)$ exists **Characteristics 3** Used symmetrically.

Confidence Intervals for Value at Identified Percentile

Data 3 $X[i]$ **4** Upper and lower bounds for n, also method for determining adequate n, given in Results **Description 1** Theoretical-approximate one-sided and two-sided confidence intervals **2** $f(\theta_p)$ for specified p such that $.05 \leqslant p \leqslant .95$ **Assumptions 3** $.294pq/f(\theta_p) \leqslant \theta_{p+.15pq} - \theta_{p-.15pq} \leqslant .306pq/f(\theta_p)$, where $q = 1 - p$. Also, for $0 \leqslant \epsilon \leqslant .153pq$, $.7f(\theta_{p-\varepsilon}) \leqslant f(\theta_{p+\varepsilon}) \leqslant 1.3f(\theta_{p-\varepsilon})$ **Results 1** $X[Z] = X$[largest integer $\leqslant Z + \frac{1}{2}$]; $.01 \leqslant \alpha \leqslant .99$; $c_\alpha = .3K_\alpha\sqrt{pq}/(1 + .3pq)$; n, p, α such that $[p \pm (.15pq +$

$c_\alpha/\sqrt{n})]n$ both nearly integral; $[4.9\alpha^{-1/5} - 2K_\alpha/(1+.3pq)]^2/pq \leqslant n \leqslant 2500/pq$; $D_1(\alpha, p, n) = K_\alpha + .01(1+3pq)\sqrt{npq}$ and $D_2(\alpha, p, n) = K_\alpha - .01(1+.3pq)\sqrt{npq}$; ξ defined by $K_\xi = (1.12 - .2pq)D_1(\alpha, p, n)$ for $D_1(\alpha, p, n) \geqslant 0$ and $= (.90+.2pq)D_1(\alpha, p, n)$ for $D_1(\alpha, p, n) < 0$; η defined by $K_\eta = (.88+.2pq)D_2(\alpha, p, n)$ for $D_2(a, p, n) \geqslant 0$ and $= (1.10 - .2pq)D_2(\alpha, p, n)$ for $D_2(\alpha, p, n) < 0$ **2** *Lower one-sided intervals*: $\left(0, .3pq/\{X[(p+.15pq)n + c_\alpha\sqrt{n}] - X[(p-.15pq)n - c_\alpha\sqrt{n}]\}\right)$; confidence coeff. roughly equal to α and approx. bounded between ξ and η. *Upper one-sided confidence intervals*: Obtained as complements of lower one-sided intervals. *Two-sided intervals*: Obtained as nonoverlapping combinations of a lower one-sided interval and an upper one-sided interval; here restrictions for both of the one-sided intervals should be satisfied **3** None **4** Here $\sigma\{X[(p+.15pq)n + c_\alpha\sqrt{n}] - X[(p-.15pq)n - c_\alpha\sqrt{n}]\}/.3pq = 1/(.3npq)^{1/2}f(\theta_p) + O(1/n) + O(.15pq/\sqrt{n})$. Thus coeff. of variation for $\{X[(p+.15pq)n + c_\alpha\sqrt{n}] - X[(p-.15pq)n - c_\alpha\sqrt{n}]\}/.3pq$, considered as estimate, approx. equals $(.3npq)^{-1/2}$ and can be used to determine adequate n prior to sampling; also, using two-stage sampling, approx. variance expression $1/.3npqf(\theta_p)^2$ furnishes basis for determining adequate n (see page 316) **Characteristics 1** Low **2** For smaller sample size N, $\{X[(p+.15pq)N + c_\alpha\sqrt{N}] - X[(p-.15pq)N - c_\alpha\sqrt{N}]\}/\sqrt{n}(.3pq)^{3/2}$ approx. estimate for $\sigma\{X[(p+.15pq)n + c_\alpha\sqrt{n}] - X[(p-.15pq)n - c_\alpha\sqrt{n}]\}/.3pq$ (also see pages 304 and 305) **4** Not overly sensitive to existence of $f(x)$ and to accuracy of expansions used in derivations if population continuous to reasonable approx. and unimodal or nearly unimodal for $\theta_{.05} \leqslant x \leqslant \theta_{.95}$. Moderately sensitive to violations of inequalities **5** Not difficult to decide on sample and continuity assumptions. More difficult to verify that $f(x)$ nearly unimodal except in tails. Inequalities should be acceptable for practical situations if populations believed unimodal except in tails; moderately difficult to verify inequalities otherwise **6** Value for min n allows only about 20 per cent overlap in prob. between dists. of two order statistics used in estimate. Useful for life-testing and other censored data situations **Bibliography** Ref. 562.

One-Sided Confidence Bands and Tests—Finite Interval (*Smirnov*)

Data 3 $X(i)$ **4** Min allowable n (should also be adequate for most situations of interest) stated in Results **Description 1** One-sided confidence bands and tests **2** $f(x)$ for x in given finite interval; $f(x)$ completely specified for tests **Assumptions 2** $f(x)$ is continuous **3** A and B specified finite numbers $(A < B)$ and $f(x) > 0$ for $A \leqslant x \leqslant B$; also $\int_A^B f(x)dx < 1$. For confidence bands, $f''(x)$ exists and is bounded for $A \leqslant x \leqslant B$ **Results 1** s is largest integer such that $s \log_e s \leqslant n^{1/3}$; n is such that $s \geqslant n^{1/4}$. Interval

$[A, B]$ divided into s subintervals $\Delta_1, \ldots, \Delta_s$ of equal length $(B-A)/s$. For $A \leqslant x \leqslant B$, $g_n(x)$ defined by: When $x \epsilon \Delta_k$, $g_n(x) = $[no. of the $X(i)$ in $\Delta_k]s/n(B-A)$, $k=1, \ldots, s$; $g(x)$ defined by: When $x \epsilon \Delta_k$, $g(x) = [s/(B-A)]\int_{\Delta_k} f(x)dx$; $g_n^*(x)$ is the fct. whose graph is the polygonal line joining the pts. $[x_k, g_n(x_k)]$, where x_k is the midpoint of Δ_k. h_s is root of $\Phi(h) = 1 - 1/s$. $\lambda^2 \leqslant h_s^{7/2}$ and $d(\lambda) = (h_s + \lambda/h_s)[s/n(B-A)]^{1/2}$ **2** *Confidence bands*: If $n \geqslant \exp[.4e^{4e^{-\lambda}}(1-e^{-2e^{-\lambda}})^{-2}]$, $P\{f(x) \geqslant \frac{1}{2}[-d(\lambda) + \sqrt{d(\lambda)^2 + 4g_n^*(x)}]; A \leqslant x \leqslant B\} \doteq e^{-2e^{-\lambda}}$. *Tests*: If $n \geqslant \exp[.35e^{4e^{-\lambda}}(1-e^{-2e^{-\lambda}})^{-2}]$, one-sided tests obtainable on basis of $P\{\sup_{A \leqslant x \leqslant B}[g_n(x) - f(x)]g(x)^{-1/2} \leqslant d(\lambda)\} \doteq e^{-2e^{-\lambda}}$ **3** None **4** If s and n only required to satisfy $s \log s = O(n^{1/3})$, $P\{\sup_{A \leqslant x \leqslant B}[g_n(x) - f(x)]g(x)^{-1/2} \leqslant d(\lambda)\} = e^{2e^{-\lambda}} + O[(\log s)^{-1/2}]$; if also $n \log s = o(s^5)$, $\lim_{n \to \infty} P\{\sup_{A \leqslant x \leqslant B}[g_n^*(x) - f(x)] f(x)^{-1/2} \leqslant d(\lambda)\} = e^{-2^{-\lambda}}$ **Characteristics 1** Low to medium **2** Unknown **4** Moderately sensitive to assumptions **5** Not difficult to decide on sample and continuity assumptions. More difficult to choose A, B values so that part 3 of Assumptions satisfied; however, this choice simplified if $f(x)$ believed unimodal for $A \leqslant x \leqslant B$. For usual $f(x)$ for practical situations, $f''(x)$ exists when $f(x)$ exists and is continuous **6** Stated sample size restrictions based on judgment-intuitive considerations. Tests can be discontinued for smallest x such that statistic falls outside band **Bibliography** Ref. 482.

Optimum Binomial Test—Simple Null and Alternative Hypotheses (*J. Roy*)

Data 3 $X(i)$ **4** Method for determining adequate n outlined in Results **Description 1** Exact tests with simple null hyp. and simple alternative hyp.; based on data converted to binomial form **2** $f(x)$ over all x. Null hyp. is $f(x) = f_0(x)$ and alternative is $f(x) = f_1(x)$, where $f_0(x)$ and $f_1(x)$ continuous freq. fcts. such that $\{x | f_1(x)/f_0(x) = t\}$ has zero prob. under null hyp. for all t **Assumptions 2** $f(x)$ is continuous **3** None **Results 1** $\omega(t) = \{x | f_0(x) < tf_1(x)\}$; $p_0(t) = \int_{\omega(t)} f_0(x)dx$ and $p_1(t) = \int_{\omega(t)} f_1(x)dx$. t and integer T determined by requirements that signif. level, $\sum_{k=T}^{n} \binom{n}{k} p_0(t)^k[1 - p_0(t)]^{n-k}$, is α and power at alternative, $\sum_{k=T}^{n} \binom{n}{k} p_1(t)^k[1-p_1(t)]^{n-k}$, is max **2** *Test*: Accept $f(x) = f_1(x)$ if no. of the $X(i)$ with values in $\omega(t)$ is at least T; otherwise accept $f(x) = f_0(x)$ **3** t and T can be determined on cut-and-try basis; using table of incomplete beta fct., table of binomial dist., or approx. given in binomial dist. sect. of Chapter 7 **4** Useful tests obtained only when $p_1(t) > p_0(t)$. Then adequate n determined by additional requirement that $\sum_{k=T}^{n} \binom{n}{k} p_1(t)^k[1-p_1(t)]^{n-k} \geqslant$ specified lower bound value for power of test at alternative. Special case where $f_0(x) = f(x; \theta_0)$ and $f_1(x) = f(x; \theta_1)$ considered in ref. 444. Although hyp. are simple for resulting binomial population, they are actually composite for $f(x)$, since no distinction can be made between this dist. and any other yielding the same prob. for the two categories. **Characteristics 1** Low to medium **2** Most powerful of this binomial type; ordinarily more powerful than binomial form of optimum multinomial test given in next presentation. Unbiased if $p_1(t) > p_0(t)$ **4** Moderately sensitive to assumptions **5** Not difficult to decide on assumptions **6** Useful when a specified simple altern. of principal interest or representative of the altern. of principal interest. Sometimes yields tests for one-sided composite null and/or altern. hyp. (see page 286) **Bibliography** Ref. 444.

Multinomial Tests—Optimum For Simple Alternative; Also Rank Sum (Tsao)

Data 3 $X(i)$ **4** Methods for determining adequate n outlined in Results **Description 1** Exact signif. tests; based on data converted to multinomial form in such a manner that categories have equal prob. under null hyp. Case (I): Optimum test against specified simple altern. Case (II): Rank sum test, where categories given rank values, for composite altern. of specified type **2** $f(x)$ over all x. In both cases, null hyp. (simple) is $f(x) = f_0(x)$. For Case (I), altern. hyp. is $f(x) = f_1(x)$. For Case (II), altern. is of form $f(x) = g(x; H)f_0(x) = f_1(x; H)$, where real no. H takes values in specified set; here $\int_{-\infty}^{x} f_1(y; H)dy$ monotonic in H for fixed x (increasing in same direction for each x value); also $g(x; H)$ continuous and monotonic in x for fixed H (monotonic in same direction for each H). $f_0(x), f_1(x), f_1(x; H)$ are continuous freq. fcts. such that, under the null hyp., $\{x|f_1(x)/f_0(x) = c\}$ and $\{x|f_1(x; H)/f_0(x) = c\}$ have zero prob. for H in specified set and all c **Assumptions 2** $f(x)$ is continuous **3** None **Results 1** Space of values for $X(i)$ divided into U disjoint sets s_u $(u = 1, \ldots, U)$, where $2 \leqslant U \leqslant \max(2, \sqrt{n})$. Case (I): $s_u = \{x|c_{u-1} > f_1(x)/f_0(x) \geqslant c_u\}$, where $\infty = c_0 > c_1 > \ldots > c_{U-1} > c_U = 0$ such that $\int_{s_u} f_0(x)dx = 1/U$, $(u = 1, \ldots, U)$. $p_u = \int_{s_u} f_1(x)dx$; $\mu_0 = n\sum_{u=1}^{U} [\log_{10}(1/p_u)]/U$; $\sigma_0^2 = n\{\sum_{u=1}^{U} [\log_{10}(1/p_u)]^2/U - \mu_0^2/n^2\}$; $\mu_1 = n\sum_{u=1}^{U} p_u[\log_{10}(1/p_u)]$; $\sigma_1^2 = n\{\sum_{u=1}^{U} p_u[\log_{10}(1/p_u)]^2 - \mu_1^2/n^2\}$. Case (II): $s_u = \{x|d_{u-1} < x \leqslant d_u\}$, where $-\infty = d_0 < d_1 < \ldots < d_{U-1} < d_U = \infty$ such that $\int_{d_{u-1}}^{d_u} f_0(x)dx = 1/U$. $p_u(H) = \int_{d_{u-1}}^{d_u} f_1(x; H)dx$; $m_1(H) = n\sum_{u=1}^{U} up_u(H)$; $v_1(H)^2 = n[\sum_{u=1}^{U} u^2 p_u(H) - m_1(H)^2/n^2]$. For both cases, N_u is no. of the $X(i)$ with values in s_u. $X = \sum_{u=1}^{U} N_u \log_{10}(1/p_u)$. $Y = \sum_{u=1}^{U} uN_u$ **2** *Tests. Case (I)*: Accept altern. hyp. if $X \leqslant X_\alpha$. *Case (II)*: Accept altern. hyp. if $Y \leqslant Y_\alpha$ **3** Case (I): $X_\alpha \doteq \mu_0 - K_\alpha\sigma_0$ when $1/2n \leqslant \alpha \leqslant 1 - 1/2n$, $\min_u p_u(1 - p_u) \geqslant 3/nU$,

$n\ \max_u \log_{10}(1/p_u) - \mu_0 \geqslant 5\sigma_0$, and $\mu_0 - n\ \min_u \log_{10}(1/p_u) \geqslant 5\sigma_0$. Otherwise X_α determined from exact null dist. Case (II): For $n \geqslant 12$, $1/4n \leqslant \alpha \leqslant 1 - 1/4n$, $Y_\alpha \doteq -\frac{1}{2} + n(U+1)/2 - \sqrt{n}K_\alpha[(U^2-1)/12]^{1/2}$ for α such that this value integral. In general, when null hyp. holds, Y_α (integral) and allowable α determined from $(1/U)^n \sum_{v=n}^{Y_\alpha} \sum_{i=0}^{n} (-1)^i \binom{n}{i}$ $\binom{v-1-iU}{n-1} = \alpha$, where $\binom{v-1-iU}{n-1} = 0$ for $v-1-iU < n-1$ **4** For Case (I), adequate n determined on basis of power at altern. (see page 341); power fct. $\doteq \Phi[(\mu_0-\mu_1)/\sigma_1 - K_\alpha\sigma_0/\sigma_1]$ for power values in interval $(1/2n, 1-1/2n)$ when $\min_u p_u(1-p_u) \geqslant 3/nU$, $n\ \max_u \log_{10}(1/p_u) - \mu_1 \geqslant 5\sigma_1$, and $\mu_1 - n\ \min_u \log_{10}(1/p_u) \geqslant 5\sigma_1$. For Case (II), adequate n can be determined by choosing value H' that is representative of set of H values and considering power at this altern. (see page 341); power fct. $\doteq \Phi\{[n(U+1)/2 - m_1(H')]/v_1(H') - \sqrt{n}K_\alpha[(U^2-1)/12]^{1/2}/v_1(H')\}$ for power values in the interval $(1/2n, 1-1/2n)$ when $\min_u p_u(H')[1-p_u(H')] \geqslant 3/nU$, $nU - m_1(H') \geqslant 5v_1(H')$, and $m_1(H') - n \geqslant 5v_1(H')$. Although the hyp. are simple for the resulting multinomial population, they are composite for $f(x)$ since no distinction can be made between this dist. and any other yielding the same prob. for the categories **Characteristics** **1** Low when normal approx. used. Otherwise medium to high **2** Case (I): Most powerful of multinomial type considered with respect to altern; when $U=2$, ordinarily not as powerful at altern. as binomial test of preceding presentation. Consistent in choosing between $f_0(x)$ and $f_1(x)$; not consistent in general. Case (II): Most powerful of type considered when $f_1(x; H) = H^{F_0(x)}(\log_e H)/(H-1)$ and $H > 1$, where $F_0(x) = \int_{-\infty}^{x} f_0(y)dy$. For case of one-sided normal altern. (pop. variance known), asymptotic efficiency $\geqslant 90$ per cent when $U \geqslant 6$; ref. 521 contains values of these asymptotic efficiencies for $2 \leqslant U \leqslant 10$. Consistent in choosing between $f_0(x)$ and $f_1(x; H)$ for all allowable $f_1(x; H)$; not consistent against general altern. **4** Moderately sensitive to assumptions **5** Not difficult to decide on assumptions **6** Case (I) useful when a specified simple altern. is of principal interest or is representative of alternatives of principal interest. Sometimes yields tests of one-sided composite null and/or altern. hyp. (see page 286) **Bibliography** Ref. 521.

Approximately Optimum Test—Simple Hypotheses

Data 3 $X(i)$ **4** Methods for determining min n and adequate n given in Results **Description 1** Theoretical-approx. test **2** $f(x)$ over all x. Simple null hyp. H_0 asserts that $f(x) = f_0[x]$; simple altern. H_1 is that $f(x) = f_1[x]$; here $f_0[x]$ and $f_1[x]$ bounded **Assumptions 2** $f(x)$ exists and is continuous

3 None **Results 1** $Y_i = \log_{10}\{f_1[X(i)]/f_0[X(i)]\}$. For $a=0$ and 1 (also 2, if another altern. H_2 considered), $\mu_a = E(Y_i|H_a)$, $\sigma_a = \sqrt{n}\sigma(Y_i|H_a)$, $\alpha_3^{(a)} = n\mu_3(Y_i|H_a)/\sigma_a^3$, $\alpha_4^{(a)} = 3(1-1/n) + n\mu_4(Y_i|H_a)/\sigma_a^4$. $G_a(x) = \Phi[(x-\mu_a)/\sigma_a] - \alpha_3^{(a)}\Phi^{(3)}[(x-\mu_a)/\sigma_a]/3! + (\alpha_4^{(a)}-3)\Phi^{(4)}[(x-\mu_a)/\sigma_a]/4! + 10(\alpha_3^{(a)})^2\Phi^{(6)}[(x-\mu_a)/\sigma_a]/6!$. W_α determined from $G_0(W_\alpha) = 1-\alpha$ **2** *Test*: Accept H_1 if $nMY_i \geqslant W_\alpha$; otherwise accept H_0. Signif. level $= \alpha + O(n^{-3/2})$. Reject both H_0 and H_1 if there are $X(i_1)$ and $X(i_2)$ such that $f_0[X(i_1)]=0$ and $f_1[X(i_2)]=0$ **3** None **4** Required computation less but power at H_1 reduced and min n increased by using t test method outlined on page 339. Min n is smallest value such that $|\alpha - \Phi[(W_\alpha - \mu_0)/\sigma_0]| \leqslant \alpha(1-\alpha)/10$ for this and all larger n. Adequate n determined by requirement that approx. power fct. at H_1, $1-G_1(W_\alpha)$, has specified value; this approx. usable when resulting n such that $|G_1(W_\alpha) - \Phi[(W_\alpha - \mu_1)/\sigma_1]| \leqslant G_1(W_\alpha)[1-G_1(W_\alpha)]/10$. Method also applicable when population discrete with same set of possible values for all H_a **Characteristics 1** Low to medium **2** Approx. power fct. for any simple altern. H_2, which specifies that $f(x) = f_2[x]$, can be obtained as $1-G_2(W_\alpha)$ for n such that $|G_2(W_\alpha) - \Phi[(W_\alpha - \mu_2)/\sigma_2]| \leqslant G_2(W_\alpha)[1-G_2(W_\alpha)]/10$. To neglected terms that are $O(n^{-3/2})$, this test most powerful for H_0 against H_1 **3** Used symmetrically **4** Moderately sensitive to assumptions **5** Not difficult to decide on assumptions **6** Useful when specified simple altern. of principal interest or representative of altern. of principal interest. Sometimes yields tests for one-sided composite null and/or altern. hyp. (see page 286). Statistical decision theory interpretation of test given in Chapter 11. Corresponding decision theory results for truncated sequential situation outlined in ref. 67 **Bibliography** Ref. 67 (pages 263–66), 253 (pages 184–86), 383, 384.

TESTS FOR CONTINUOUS UNIVARIATE DISTRIBUTION FUNCTIONS

Introduction

This section is concerned with testing continuous univariate distribution functions on the basis of ungrouped continuous data. In all but one case, the tests considered have simple null hypotheses; in all cases, classes of alternative hypotheses to which given tests should be sensitive can be at least roughly specified. Most of the results are of an exact nature; however, approximate methods are sometimes used in the application of tests for which exact results could be obtained. All the procedures presented are concerned with the distribution function value over all points. Tests for the distribution function value over a restricted interval can be obtained from the confidence band results of a preceding section. In fact, all the confidence bands for distribution functions can be converted to significance tests with simple null hypotheses. A bibliography of some additional results that have potential usefulness but do not seem to warrant presentation is given near the end of this section.

Null Hypotheses Considered

All but one of the types of tests for which presentations are given in this section have simple null hypotheses. Here a simple null hypothesis asserts that $F(x) = F_0(x)$ for the set of x values considered, where $F(x)$ is the (unknown) distribution function of the population sampled and $F_0(x)$ is a completely specified continuous distribution function.

A procedure for converting a confidence band for a distribution function to a significance test is outlined on page 282. All of the resulting tests for distribution functions have simple (or modified composite) null hypotheses.

Under the null hypothesis, $F_0[X(i)]$ has the rectangular (uniform) distribution [0, 1] when this hypothesis is simple. The only type of composite null hypothesis for which tests are directly presented is that where $F(x)$ is of the form $F_0(x)/L$ for $F_0(x) < L$ and is unity for $F_0(x) \geqslant L$, where L is unknown and $0 < L \leqslant 1$; i.e., $F_0[X(i)]$ has the rectangular distribution $[0, L]$. This situation can occur when the completely specified distribution function $F_0(x)$ has the correct general shape but the distribution of $X(i)$ is such that $P[X(i) > F_0^{-1}(L)] = 0$ for some value of L which can be less than unity.

Ref. 128 outlines some nonparametric tests for composite null hypotheses of the form $F(x) = F_0(x)^a$ or of the form $F(x) = 1 - [1 - F_0(x)]^a$, where a is an unknown positive constant. However, these tests are not yet suitable for application, since none of their probability properties are explicitly stated, even for the asymptotic case.

Discussion of Alternative Hypotheses

For all the tests considered in the presentations, it is possible to specify one or more classes of alternative hypotheses to which a given test should be sensitive. These specifications of classes of alternative hypotheses fall under three general headings. Some of the tests are constructed so that they are optimum, according to a stated criterion, for a specified class of alternative hypotheses. Other of the tests seem, on a heuristic or an intuitive basis, to be sensitive to classes of alternatives that are only specified in vague and somewhat general senses. The tests falling under the remaining heading are based on statistics from which metrics can be developed for identifying the alternatives to which the tests should be sensitive. The development of such metrics in the space of alternative hypotheses is considered on page 314.

Description of Decision Procedure

The final presentation of this section contains a decision procedure, based on a sample, that accepts one of the three decisions

$$F(x) < F_0(x), \quad F(x) = F_0(x), \quad F(x) > F_0(x)$$

for each value of x in a specified bounded interval. For given x, the decision is made on the basis of a significance test. However, the application of this procedure over all the allowable x is not considered to represent a significance test. The decision process presented is unbiased (see ref. 305). The relative desirability of a decision procedure of this nature can be measured in terms of its total risk over all x considered. For the procedure presented, this risk is uniformly minimum, among corresponding unbiased procedures, for a specified class of loss functions. This decision method is presented here, rather than in Chapter 11, because it is based on a significance testing procedure and because no supplementary information is utilized in its application.

Methods For Determining Adequate Sample Sizes

Methods for determining adequate values of n are specified for nearly all of the distribution function confidence bands that are presented in a preceding section. Ordinarily, these values of n can also be considered adequate for the significance tests that are obtained from these confidence bands.

For the presentations of this section, no explicit methods are included for determining adequate values of n. However, a method of the following type, although rather rough, seems to be useful for the tests that have simple null hypotheses and can be expressed in terms of $F_0[X(1)], \ldots, F_0[X(n)]$.

Suppose that a set of k simple alternative hypotheses, denoted by $G_1(x), \ldots, G_k(x)$, can be specified which are representative of the alternatives of principal interest and are such that

$$G_1(x) = H_1[F_0(x)], \ldots, G_k(x) = H_k[F_0(x)],$$

where $H_1[y], \ldots, H_k[y]$ are strictly monotonic increasing functions of y. Consider tests of the form which specify that the null hypothesis is rejected if and only if

$$A\{F_0[X(1)], \ldots, F_0[X(n)]\} \leqslant A_\alpha,$$

where A_α is the 100α per cent point of the test statistic distribution when the null hypothesis holds. Use E_1A to denote the expected value of the test statistic when $F(x) = G_1(x)$ and $\sigma_1{}^2$ to denote its variance; use E_2A

and σ_2^2 to represent the expected value and variance, respectively, when $F(x)=G_2(x)$; etc. Since

$$E_1A=\int_{-\infty}^{\infty}\cdots\int_{-\infty}^{\infty}A\{H_1^{-1}[G_1(x_1)],\ldots,H_1^{-1}[G_1(x_n)]\}dG_1(x_1)\ldots dG_1(x_n)$$

$$=\int_0^1\cdots\int_0^1 A\{H_1^{-1}[y_1],\ldots,H_1^{-1}[y_n]\}dy_1\ldots dy_n,$$

$$\sigma_1^2=\int_{-\infty}^{\infty}\cdots\int_{-\infty}^{\infty}\left[A\{H_1^{-1}[G_1(x_1)],\ldots,H_1^{-1}[G_1(x_n)]\}-EA_1\right]^2 dG_1(x_1)\ldots dG_1(x_n)$$

$$=\int_0^1\cdots\int_0^1\left[A\{H_1^{-1}[y_1],\ldots,H_1^{-1}[y_n]\}-EA_1\right]^2 dy_1\ldots dy_n,$$

etc., these values can be determined. Then n can be considered to be adequate if

$$\min\{(A_\alpha-E_1A)/\sigma_1,\ldots,(A_\alpha-E_kA)/\sigma_k\}\geqslant J,$$

where J is positive and not too small. From the one-sided form of Tchebycheff's inequality, stated (case of $k=1$) on page 90, this relation implies that the power of the test is at least

$$1-1/(1+J^2)$$

for all the alternatives considered. For example, if $J=3$, the power is at least 90 per cent for all these alternatives. Ordinarily, the power should be noticeably greater than the extremely conservative value given by the one-sided form of Tchebycheff's inequality. Closer lower bound approximations to the minimum power for the alternatives considered can be obtained by computing additional moments and using the appropriate Tchebycheff type inequality.

An alternate method, which does not have the lower bound property but should give reasonably accurate results, consists in computing the approximate power at each alternative by determining the first few moments and using the Edgeworth series expansion, etc. to compute power values. Then n is considered to be adequate if the minimum of the power values at the alternatives is at least equal to a specified value.

General Development of Tests

As mentioned in the discussion of alternative hypotheses, the form of the statistic used for a test sometimes furnishes an indication of situations to which this test is sensitive. That is, a class of alternatives to which a test should be sensitive can often be determined by developing a metric in the space of alternative hypotheses on the basis of the statistic used in the test. A moderately general method for obtaining nonparametric tests is stated below for the continuous case and simple null hypotheses; included are situations where the distribution function is only considered over a restricted set of points. By judicious use of this method, and selection of the test statistic on the basis of a specified metric, a test can often be developed that is sensitive to any specified class of a rather extensive set of classes of alternatives. However, a substantial amount of effort may be required for determining and tabulating the null hypothesis distribution of a test, even for the asymptotic case.

Let us consider the general method for obtaining tests. For the test being developed, the values considered for the distribution function are restricted to a specified set of nonzero measure in [0, 1]. Consideration is limited to test statistics that can be expressed in both of the forms $T_1[F_0(x), F_n(x)]$ and $T_2\{F_0[X(1)], \ldots, F_0[X(n)]\}$, where T_2 is symmetric in its arguments. Then, under the null hypothesis, $T_1[F_0(x), F_n(x)]$ has the same probability distribution as $T_2(y_1, \ldots, y_n)$, where the y's are a random sample that is obtained from the rectangular (uniform) distribution [0, 1] by considering only the allowable values for $F_0(x)$ and normalizing the probability of this set to unity.

The metric $T_1[F_0(x), F(x)]$ should nearly always be satisfactory for identifying a class of alternatives to which a test based on $T_1[F_0(x), F_n(x)]$ is at least moderately sensitive. By suitable choice of the test statistic and of the critical region, a test which should be sensitive to a specified class of alternative hypotheses can frequently be constructed. For further discussion of test construction methods of this nature, see Ref. 56 and 59.

Bounded Significance Level Tests for Arbitrary Populations

Some of the tests for the distribution function of a continuous population can be used to obtain corresponding bounded significance level tests for the situation of an arbitrary population. The continuous data tests considered for this purpose are those based on confidence bands for the population distribution function. In some cases, these bands for the continuous case yield bounded confidence level bands (see page 308); in all cases, they can be used to obtain bounded significance level tests.

Let $P_c[Z]$ represent the probability that the relation Z is true when the population sampled is continuous. Then, for sampling from an arbitrary population,

$$P[F(x) \leqslant a_1 + b_1 F_n(x);\ A_1 \leqslant F(x) \leqslant A_2] \geqslant P_c[F(x) \leqslant a_1 + b_1 F_n(x);\ A_1 \leqslant F(x) \leqslant A_2],$$

$$P[F(x-)\geqslant a_2+b_2F_n(x);\ A_1\leqslant F(x-)\leqslant A_2]\geqslant P_c[F(x)\geqslant a_2+b_2F_n(x);\ A_1\leqslant F(x)\leqslant A_2],$$

$$P[F(x-)\geqslant a_3+b_3F_n(x) \text{ and also } F(x)\leqslant a_4+b_4F_n(x);\ A_1\leqslant F(x-),\ F(x)\leqslant A_2]$$

$$\geqslant P_c[F(x)\geqslant a_3+b_3F_n(x) \text{ and also } F(x)\leqslant a_4+b_4F_n(x);\ A_1\leqslant F(x)\leqslant A_2],$$

$$P[|F_n(x)-F(x)|\leqslant a;\ -\infty<x<\infty]\geqslant P_c[|F_n(x)-F(x)|\leqslant a;\ -\infty<x<\infty],$$

where $b_1, \ldots, b_4$, a are positive and $F(x-)=P[X(i)<x]$. All relations but the last, which has already been stated on page 308, are based on an elementary analysis that was developed by H. T. David. Bounded significance level tests with simple null hypotheses (for the specified range of x) can be directly obtained from these probability relations, since the values of both $F_0(x)$ and $F_0(x-)$ are known when the null hypothesis is simple. An alternative method of obtaining approximate tests for arbitrary populations is to convert the population to an approximately equivalent continuous form (see page 281). Also, some of the tests obtained on the basis of tolerance regions are applicable for arbitrary distribution functions.

Tests From Tolerance Regions

As mentioned on page 284, tests of simple hypotheses, where the distribution function is specified over all points, can be obtained by the use of the tolerance region results of Chapter 9. Specifically, let the population coverage of the tolerance region be controlled in parts, where there may be only one part, and let the null hypothesis be $F(x)=F_0(x)$. Then tests of the form

Reject the null hypothesis if any of the relations

$$\int_{R_1} dF_0 \epsilon A_1, \ldots, \int_{R_s} dF_0 \epsilon A_s$$

are not satisfied.

can be obtained. Here $R_1, \ldots, R_s$ are the parts of the tolerance region and $A_1, \ldots, A_s$ are specified sets, of nonzero measure, in [0, 1]. Selection of $s, R_1, \ldots, R_s, A_1, \ldots, A_s$ determines the significance level of the test and the alternative hypotheses that are emphasized.

The $n+1$ differences $\{F(X[i])-F(X[i-1])\}$, $(i=1, \ldots, n+1)$, are population coverages over a basic set of statistical blocks for the continuous case. Consequently, tests that are based on these differences are also applicable when $F_0(X[i+1])-F_0(X[i])$ is replaced by $\int_{r(i)} dF_0(x)$ for all i, where the $r(i)$ are any basic set of univariate statistical blocks. That is, the significance levels of the tests obtained by these replacements are the same as those of the corresponding tests based on the distribution function differences. Of course, the alternative hypotheses emphasized when this replacement is made depend on the forms of the $r(i)$ and are not necessarily the same as those when the differences are used. By suitable construction of the $r(i)$, it should be possible to obtain tests which tend to emphasize specified classes of alternative hypotheses.

The tests based on the distribution function differences at consecutive order statistics can also be modified and applied to testing a simple null hypothesis for the continuous and the partially continuous multivariate case. Here the replacement is by $\int_{r(i)} dF_0$ where F_0 is the null hypothesis multivariate distribution function and the $r(i)$ are any basic set of multivariate statistical blocks for this situation.

Adequate Sample Sizes for Point Estimates

Many of the tests with simple null hypotheses that are presented in this section can be used as a basis for determining adequate sample sizes in the point estimation of $F(x)$ by $F_n(x)$. These are the tests with statistics of the form $T_1[F_0(x), F_n(x)]$. Then at least a few percentage points of the distribution of $T_1[F(x), F_n(x)]$ are available, since this quantity has the same distribution as that of $T_1[F_0(x), F_n(x)]$ under the null hypothesis. If $T_1[F(x), F_n(x)]$ furnishes a reasonable measure of the deviation of $F_n(x)$ from $F(x)$, adequate values of n, with respect to $F_n(x)$ as an estimate of $F(x)$, can be specified on the basis of the probability properties of $T_1[F(x), F_n(x)]$. That is, suppose that increasing values of $T_1[F(x), F_n(x)]$ represent increasing deviations of $F_n(x)$ from $F(x)$ and that the deviation is considered to be sufficiently small when

$$T_1[F(x), F_n(x)] \leqslant T_s,$$

where T_s is a specified constant. Then n can be considered adequate when

$$P\{T_1[F(x), F_n(x)] \leqslant T_s\} \geqslant \gamma,$$

where γ is a specified probability that is sufficiently large. A discussion of the use of methods of this type for determining adequate n is given on page 295.

Tests Obtained From Frequency Function Results

For a simple null hypothesis and the continuous case, the sample values can always be transformed into a sample where each observation has the rectangular distribution [0, 1]. Specifically, under the null hypothesis that $F(x)=F_0(x)$, the observations $Y(i)=F_0[X(i)]$ have this property. Thus, tests can be obtained by considering the $Y(i)$ to be a sample from a population whose frequency function is unity for $0 \leqslant x \leqslant 1$ and is zero otherwise. Alternatively, the transformation could be to the standard normal distribution, etc. Then the confidence regions and tests for frequency functions given in the preceding section can be used to test $F(x)$; in addition, if the transformation is to normality, standard results for the normal population can be used. The population obtained by transformations of variable can also be used as a basis for testing composite null hypotheses; situations of this nature are considered next.

Tests of Composite Hypotheses by Change of Variable

As mentioned in the introductory part of the chapter, tests for special types of composite null and alternative hypotheses can be obtained by suitable changes of variable. Here a completely specified distribution function $F_0(x)$ furnishes the basis for the transformation of variable. However, the transformed sample values are merely considered to have a type of distribution for which the distribution obtained when $F(x) = F_0(x)$ represents a special case. As an example, if the transformed distribution is the standardized normal distribution when $F(x) = F_0(x)$, the composite null hypothesis might assert that the transformed observations are from a normal distribution with zero mean but unknown variance. The composite alternative hypothesis emphasized might assert that the transformed distribution is normal with unknown variance but that the mean has a negative value. By suitable changes of variable, many of the parametric results that have been developed can be used to test composite hypotheses about continuous univariate distribution functions.

Life-Testing Applications

For life-testing situations, a set of the smallest sample order statistics represents the available data; i.e., $X[1], \ldots, X[N]$ are the available observations, where $N < n$. Then any statistical procedure used must be entirely determined on the basis of this data. Four of the types of statistical tests presented in this section can be applied for life-testing situations. One of these tests has a statistic of the form $(N' \leqslant N)$

$$2(N'-1-n)\log_e\{1-F_0(X[N'])\} - 2\sum_{i=1}^{N'}\log_e\{1-F_0(X[i])\}.$$

Another type of test has a statistic that can take the form

$$\sum_{i=i(1),\ldots,i(N')} \{F_0(X[i]) - F_0(X[i-1])\}^Q,$$

where $Q > 0$ and $i(1) < \ldots < i(N') \leqslant N$. A statistic of the form

$$\sum_{i=0}^{N'} F_0(X[i])$$

is used for a third type of test. The other type of test considered for situations where the only available data are $X[1], \ldots, X[N]$ is that based on a statistic of the form $F_0(X[N'])$.

In addition to the tests that are presented, tests that are useful for life-testing situations can be obtained by a suitable transformation of variable that is based on a completely specified distribution function $F_0(x)$. As mentioned on page 288, this method can be used to test the simple null hypothesis $F(x) = F_0(x)$ or a composite null hypothesis. The procedure is to transform $F_0(x)$ into the exponential distribution with frequency function e^{-x} $(0 \leqslant x < \infty)$ and use life-testing results that have been developed for the exponential case (see ref. 164); here the transformation is $y = -\log_e [1 - F_0(x)]$.

The tests that are based on the confidence band results for distribution functions also have advantages for life-testing situations. Namely, the experiment can be stopped at the smallest value of x for which $F_0(x)$ falls outside the band. This will often result in a substantial saving in cost and/or time for the experiment.

Even though they are not useful for life-testing situations, some of the tests presented are useful for censored samples and/or for cases where only specified sample order statistics have known values. For example, only the largest order statistics are available for some tests.

Tests For Nonsample Case

The tests presented in this section are applicable to the more general situation where the observations are not necessarily a random sample. Suppose that the observations are independent and that each observation is from a continuous population. Let the null hypothesis assert that the distribution function of $X(i)$ is $F_0^{(i)}(x)$, $(i = 1, \ldots, n)$, where the $F_0^{(i)}(x)$ are continuous and completely specified. Then, under the null hypothesis, the transformed observations $F_0^{(i)}[X(i)]$ are a sample of size n from a continuous population and the results of this section can be applied to these observations.

Remark on Tests for the Discontinuous Case

For both the continuous and discontinuous cases, tests of simple and composite null hypotheses can be obtained by grouping the observations and using categorical type results (see Chapter 11). Here the range of x values considered can be restricted or unrestricted. Otherwise, there is little available for direct use in discontinuous situations except the bounded significance level results already stated, some of the decision theory and sequential material given in Chapter 11, and the tests obtainable from the confidence regions that are valid for arbitrary univariate populations.

In ref. 462, Schmid obtains the asymptotic distributions, under the simple null hypothesis that $F(x)=F_0(x)$, of the statistics,

$$\sqrt{n} \sup_{-\infty<x<\infty} [F_n(x)-F_0(x)] \quad \text{and} \quad \sqrt{n} \sup_{-\infty<x<\infty} |F_n(x)-F_0(x)|$$

for the case of an arbitrary distribution function. However, application of these results can be very tedious and determination of a minimum allowable value for n, even in a rough sense, seems to be very difficult.

An indirect method of obtaining tests for the discontinuous case that are often sufficiently accurate is to convert to the continuous case by use of the procedure outlined on page 281. Then the tests developed for the continuous case can be used directly.

Tests Emphasizing Special Properties

As mentioned on page 287, when the null hypothesis H_0 is simple, tests can be developed which emphasize population properties that are one-dimensional. Here the special population property considered could be the population mean, the population variance, the population third moment about the mean, the population fourth moment about the mean, given functions of these moments, a specified population percentile, given functions of specified population percentiles, etc. In every case, the property of interest equals, or very nearly equals, the expected value of a suitable statistic of the sample values (for all populations where the expected value of this statistic exists). This statistic is used for testing whether its expected value equals the expected value specified by the null hypothesis. Ordinarily, for sample sizes that are not too small, the null distribution of the test statistic can be reasonably approximated by evaluating its first four moments under H_0 and using the first four terms of the Edgeworth series.

Outline of Presentations

Thirteen presentations are given in this section. Following are some short descriptions of these statistical procedures.

The first presentation contains the λ_n test of K. Pearson and some modifications of this test; these results are exact. In some cases, a class of alternatives for which a given test is most powerful can be identified; for the other cases, alternatives to which a given test should be sensitive are specified on a heuristic or an intuitive basis. One of these types of tests is based on the smallest sample order statistics and is useful for life-testing situations. The second presentation is concerned with the Neyman smooth tests; as applied, are theoretical-approximate. The Neyman smooth tests are locally optimum, according to a given criterion, for specified classes of alternatives.

The third and fourth presentations deal with tests of the Cramér-von Mises type; as applied, these tests are theoretical-approximate. The first of these two presentations contains tests with a somewhat general emphasis with respect to alternatives. Here the class of alternative hypotheses to which a test should be sensitive can be specified in terms of the corresponding metric in the space of alternatives. The other presentation contains a test of a more specialized nature. This test is constructed to emphasis alternatives where the population shape is the same as that specified by the null hypothesis but the population location has been shifted.

The fifth through eighth presentations are concerned with tests that are based on the $n+1$ differences $F_0(X[i])-F_0(X[i-1])$, $(i=1,\ldots,n+1)$. The fifth presentation contains a test that is based on

$$\sum_{i=1}^{n+1} \left|F_0(X[i])-F_0(X[i-1])-1/(n+1)\right|.$$

This test is exact and the alternatives to which it should be sensitive can be roughly identified from intuitive considerations. The sixth presentation deals with tests based on the summation of a stated power of some or all of the $n+1$ differences; as applied, these tests are theoretical-approximate. Some forms of this test are useful for life-testing situations. When the differences are squared and they are all used, a class of alternatives is identified for which the test is most powerful; when the power to which the differences are raised is other than the second, general nature alternatives to which a test should be sensitive can be specified on intuitive grounds.

The seventh presentation is concerned with tests that are based on order statistics of the $n+1$ observed differences of hypothetical distribution function values; these results are of an exact nature. Some of the tests are based on ratios of order statistics of the differences. These tests have a composite null hypothesis. Classes of alternatives to which given tests of these types are sensitive can be roughly identified on an intuitive basis. The eighth presentation contains tests which are based on statistics that are of correlation coefficient forms. Some of these tests are exact while the others are theoretical-approximate. Types of alternatives to which given types of tests should be sensitive are specified on heuristic and intuitive bases.

The ninth through eleventh presentations are based on the value of $F_0(x)$ at stated sample order statistics; all of these tests are exact. The test statistic for the ninth presentation is the sum of the hypothetical distribution values at one or more consecutive sample order statistics. Some forms of this test are useful for life-testing situations. The test based on the sum over all sample order statistics is most powerful for a stated class of alternatives; for the other types of tests, alternatives to which a given test should be sensitive are specified on intuitive grounds. The tenth presentation contains three types of tests that are based on the value of the hypothetical distribution function at one or two order statistics; the tests using a single order statistic can be useful for life-testing situations. For each type of test, a class of alternatives to which a given test should be sensitive is roughly identified on heuristic and intuitive bases. The eleventh presentation contains the only other type of test given in this section for which the null hypothesis is composite. The test statistic is the ratio of the sum of the observations $F_0[X(i)]$ divided by the largest value. Classes of alternatives to which these tests should be sensitive are identified on intuitive grounds.

The twelfth presentation consists of exact tests based on the sum of $F_n[X(i)-]-F_0[X(i)]$ over i such that this quantity is nonnegative. These tests are sensitive to alternatives where the population shape is unchanged but its location is shifted, as compared with the situation specified by the null hypothesis. The thirteenth and final presentation contains an unbiased decision process that allows for three possible decisions at each point of the finite interval of values considered. For a specified class of loss functions, this decision procedure has uniformly minimum over-all risk among unbiased procedures of this nature.

Fixed Material for Section

Data 1 Continuous, univariate **2** None **4** $m=1$ **Assumptions 1** Random sample **3** None **Characteristics 3** Used symmetrically **4** Sample condition must be satisfied to reasonable approx. **5** Not difficult to decide on sample and continuity assumptions.

K. Pearson's λ_n and Related Tests (E. S. Pearson, Malmquist)

Data 3 $X[i]$ **Description 1** Exact sig. tests **2** Simple null hyp.; asserts that $F(x)=F_0(x)$ **Assumptions 2** Continuous population **Results 1** $Q_1=-2\sum_{i=1}^{n}\log_e F_0(X[i])=-2\log_e\lambda_n$; $Q_2=-2\sum_{i=1}^{n}\log_e\{1-F_0(X[i])\}$; $Q_3=-2\sum_{i=1}^{n}\log_e\{1-2|F_0(X[i])-\tfrac{1}{2}|\}$. $Q_4=-2\sum_{i=1}^{n}\log_e Y_i$, where $Y_i=1-5F_0(X[i])$ for $0\leqslant F_0(X[i])\leqslant .2$, $=\{5F_0(X[i])-1\}/3$ for $.2<F_0(X[i])\leqslant .8$, $=5-5F_0(X[i])$ for $.8<F_0(X[i])\leqslant 1$. $Q_5=-2(n-r)\log_e F_0(X[n-r])-2\sum_{i=n-r+1}^{n}\log_e F_0(X[i])$; $Q_6=-2(n-r)\log_e\{1-F_0($

$X[r+1])\}$ $-$ $2\sum_{i=1}^{r} \log_e \{1-F_0(X[i])\}$ **2** *Tests*: For the four tests based on $Q_1, \ldots, Q_4$, respectively, the null hyp. is rejected at signif. level α if $Q_k \geqslant \chi_\alpha^2(2n)$. For the test based on Q_5 and the test based on Q_6, the null hyp. is rejected at signif. level α if $Q_k \geqslant \chi_\alpha^2(2r+2)$ **3** None **4** Test based on Q_5 useful for situations where only $X[n-r], \ldots, X[n]$ available; likewise, test based on Q_6 useful for situations (e.g., life-testing) where only $X[1], \ldots, X[r+1]$ available **Characteristics 1** Low to medium, depending on n and whether $F_0(x)$ already tabulated **2** Test based on Q_1 most powerful when altern. such that dist. fct. of $F_0[X(i)]$ of form x^c, $(c>0, 0 \leqslant x \leqslant 1)$. Test based on Q_2 most powerful when altern. such that dist. fct. of $F_0[X(i)]$ of form $1-(1-x)^c$. Test using Q_5 most powerful based only on $X[n-r], \ldots, X[n]$ when altern. such that dist. fct. of $F_0[X(i)]$ of form x^c. Test using Q_6 most powerful based only on $X[1], \ldots, X[r+1]$ when altern. such that dist. fct. of $F_0[X(i)]$ of form $1-(1-x)^c$. Test based on Q_3 seems to be sensitive, on heuristic basis, when altern. such that dist. fct. of $F_0[X(i)]$ of form $[\Gamma(2c+2)/\Gamma(c+1)^2] \int_0^x y^c(1-y)^c dy$. Test based on Q_4 seems to be sensitive, on a heuristic basis, when altern. is that dist. fct. of $F_0[X(i)]$ approx. of Pearson Type III form with zero mean and unit variance **4** Moderately sensitive to continuity requirement **6** Test based on Q_6 useful for life-testing situations and test based on Q_5 useful when lower tail of sample is censored **Bibliography** Ref. 131, 325, 374, 403, 410, 411.

Neyman Smooth Test

Data 3 $X(i)$ **4** Min allowable n stated in Results **Description 1** Theoretical-approx. sig. tests **2** Simple null hyp.; asserts that $F(x)=F_0(x)$ **Assumptions 2** Continuous population **Results 1** $\pi_1(y)=2\sqrt{3}y$; $\pi_2(y)=\sqrt{5}(6y^2-\frac{1}{2})$; $\pi_3(y)=\sqrt{7}(20y^3-3y)$; $\pi_4(y)=210y^4-45y^2+\frac{9}{8}$; $\pi_{u+1}(y) = 2y[(2u+3)(2u+1)]^{1/2}\pi_u(y)/(u+1) - u[(2u+3)/(2u-1)]^{1/2} \pi_{u-1}(y)/(u+1)$. $\psi_k^2=(1/n)\sum_{u=1}^{k} [\sum_{i=1}^{n}\pi_u\{F_0[X(i)]-\frac{1}{2}\}]^2$; can be expressed in terms of $MF_0[X(i)]$, $M'_2F_0[X(i)], \ldots, M'_kF_0[X(i)]$ **2** *Test*: Reject the null hyp. if $\psi_k^2 \geqslant \chi_\alpha^2(k)$ **3** Table 2 at end of book contains values of $\chi_\alpha^2(k)$ **4** Value of k chosen on basis of altern. emphasized (see part 2 of Characteristics). Min allowable $n \geqslant .15/\min(.01, \alpha)$. Use of $k \leqslant 4$ seems suitable for most applications. Some exact results given in ref. 28 and 29 for $k=1$, 2 and $n \leqslant 20$. Grouped data version of test given in Chapter 11. Adequate n can be determined on basis of asymptotic power fct. **Characteristics 1** Low to upper medium, depending on n, k and whether $F_0(x)$ already tabulated. Computation often noticeably reduced by using grouped data version **2** Investigated for two types of classes of altern. One type, with a class of altern. denoted by $H_s^{(1)}$, asserts that $F_0[X(i)]$ has a freq. fct. of the form $C \exp[\sum_{r=1}^{s} \xi_r\pi_r(x-\frac{1}{2})]$

for $0 \leqslant x \leqslant 1$ (zero otherwise). The other type, with a class of altern. denoted by $H_s^{(2)}$, asserts that freq. fct. of $F_0[X(i)]$ is of form $1+\sum_{r=1}^{s} \xi_r \pi_r(x-\frac{1}{2})$ for $0 \leqslant x \leqslant 1$ (zero otherwise), where the ξ_r are restricted by fact that freq. fct. non-negative. For both $H_s^{(1)}$ and $H_s^{(2)}$, asymptotic distribution of ψ_k^2 is that of a noncentral χ^2 variable with parameter $n\sum_{r=1}^{min(k,s)} \xi_r^2$ and k degrees of freedom (see ref. 179 and 402 for prob. values of noncentral χ^2); thus if altern. (unknown) that actually occurs requires $s>k$, the values of $\xi_1, \ldots, \xi_k$ for this altern. will be tested for large n even though $\xi_{k+1}, \ldots, \xi_s$ are not tested. Preferably k should equal the value of s corresponding to the class of altern. of principal interest. For both $H_s^{(1)}$ and $H_s^{(2)}$, test is locally most powerful unbiased for large n; also is maximum likelihood ratio test for large n. When $n \geqslant .15/\min(.01, \alpha)$, actual power fct. of approx. same form as asymptotic power fcts. for $k=1$ and $H_1^{(2)}$, also for $k=2$ and $H_2^{(2)}$; these results indicate that, for $n \geqslant .15/\min(.01, \alpha)$, adequate n can be determined by use of asymptotic power fct. for all k **4** As indicated by grouped data version, test not very sensitive to moderate violations of continuity requirement **6** Case of composite null hyp. considered in ref. 31. Then test no longer nonparametric since even asymptotic dist. depends on form of dist. fct. specified by null hyp. **Bibliography** Ref. 28, 29, 30, 31, 132, 380, 403.

Cramér-von Mises Type Tests (Smirnov, Anderson-Darling)

Data 3 $X[i]$ **4** Min n for applications furnished in part 3 of Results **Description 1** Theoretical-approx. one-sided sig. tests **2** Simple null hyp.; asserts that $F(x)=F_0(x)$ **Assumptions 2** Continuous population **Results 1** $W_n^{(1)} = 1/12n + \sum_{i=1}^{n} \{F_0(X[i]) - (2i-1)/2n\}^2 = n\int_{-\infty}^{\infty} [F_0(x) - F_n(x)]^2 dF_0(x)$. $W_n^{(2)} = -n - \sum_{i=1}^{n} (2i-1)\{\log_e F_0(X[i]) + \log_e [1 - F_0(X[n+1-i])]\}/n = n\int_{-\infty}^{\infty} [F_0(x) - F_n(x)]^2 \{F_0(x)[1-F_0(x)]\}^{-1} dF_0(x)$ **2** *First test*: Reject null hyp. if $W_n^{(1)} \geqslant W_1(\alpha, n)$. *Second test*: Reject null hyp. if $W_n^{(2)} \geqslant W_2(\alpha, n)$ **3** $W_1(\alpha, n) \doteq W_1(\alpha, \infty) = W_1(\alpha)$ when $\alpha \leqslant \frac{1}{2}$ and $n \geqslant 20/\sqrt{\alpha}$; Table 10.4 contains values of $W_1(\alpha)$ for $\alpha = .001(.001) .01(.01).5$. $W_2(\alpha, n) \doteq W_2(\alpha, \infty)$ when $\alpha \leqslant \frac{1}{2}$ and $n \geqslant 25/\sqrt{\alpha}$; $W_2(.1, \infty) = 1.933$, $W_2(.05, \infty) = 2.492$, $W_2(.01, \infty) = 3.857$ **4** Test based on $W_n^{(2)}$ emphasizes tails of dist. fct. Min n should also be adequate n for most situations of importance. Grouped data version of $W_n^{(1)}$ test given in Chapter 11. **Characteristics 1** Low to medium, depending on n and whether $F_0(x)$ already tabulated. For $W_n^{(1)}$ test, computation often reduced by using grouped data version **2** Both tests consistent for any continuous altern. dist. fct. $F^{(1)}(x) \not\equiv F_0(x)$. Test based on $W_n^{(1)}$ should be sensitive to altern. expressed in terms of metric $n\int_{-\infty}^{\infty} [F_0(x) - F(x)]^2 dF_0(x)$; test based on $W_n^{(2)}$ should be sensitive to altern. based on metric $n\int_{-\infty}^{\infty} [F_0(x) - F(x)]^2 \{F_0(x)[1-F_0(x)]\}^{-1} dF_0(x)$. Let the metric used for

TABLE 10.4. VALUES OF $W_1(\alpha)$ VERSUS α FOR $\alpha = .001(.001).01(.01).5$*

α	$W_1(\alpha)$	α	$W_1(\alpha)$	α	$W_1(\alpha)$
.001	1.168	.12	.318	.32	.1757
.002	1.039	.13	.306	.33	.1716
.003	.963	.14	.295	.34	.1677
.004	.910	.15	.284	.35	.1639
.005	.870	.16	.274	.36	.1602
.006	.836	.17	.265	.37	.1566
.007	.808	.18	.257	.38	.1532
.008	.784	.19	.249	.39	.1499
.009	.763	.20	.241	.40	.1466
.010	.743	.21	.234	.41	.1435
.020	.620	.22	.227	.42	.1405
.030	.549	.23	.221	.43	.1375
.040	.499	.24	.215	.44	.1346
.050	.461	.25	.209	.45	.1318
.060	.431	.26	.204	.46	.1291
.070	.405	.27	.1987	.47	.1265
.080	.383	.28	.1937	.48	.1239
.090	.364	.29	.1889	.49	.1213
.100	.347	.30	.1843	.50	.1189
.110	.332	.31	.1799		

* Based on ref. 9: Asymptotic theory of certain "goodness of fit" criteria based on stochastic processes, T. W. Anderson and D. A. Darling, *Annals of Mathematical Statistics*, Vol. 23, 1952, pages 193–212 and on ref. 281: K-sample analogues of the Kolmogorov-Smirnov and Cramér-v. Mises tests, J. Kiefer, *Annals of Mathematical Statistics*, Vol. 30, 1959, pages 420–47. Used with the kind permission of the authors, T. W. Anderson, D. A. Darling, and J. Kiefer, and of the Editor of the *Annals of Mathematical Statistics*.

$W_n^{(1)}$ test be $\eta(F) = \{\int_{-\infty}^{\infty} [F_0(x) - F(x)]^2 dF_0(x)\}^{1/2}$. For large n, $\alpha < \frac{1}{2}$, and $\eta(F)$ small, suppose that N observations are needed to guarantee that power of χ^2 goodness of fit test $\geqslant \frac{1}{2}$; then ref. 267 implies that only $O(N^{4/5})$ observations needed for $W_n^{(1)}$ test to have power $\geqslant \frac{1}{2}$ **4** Grouped data version of $W_n^{(1)}$ test furnishes indication of sensitivity of tests to violations of continuity requirement **6** An extension of $W_n^{(1)}$ test that is sensitive to population shifts is given in next presentation **Bibliography** Ref. 9, 10, 56, 116, 129, 144, 152, 153, 214, 266, 267, 347, 350, 478, 479.

Cramér-von Mises Type Tests Emphasizing Population Shifts (*Blackman*)

Data 3 $X[i]$ **4** Min allowable n stated in Results **Description 1** Theoretical-approx. sig. test **2** Simple null hyp.; asserts that $F(x) = F_0(x)$ **Assumptions 2** $F(x)$ and $F_0(x)$ such that their first three derivatives exist, are continuous, and are bounded for all x **Results 1** a_n is value of a which minimizes $\int_{-\infty}^{\infty} [F_0(x-a)-F_n(x)]^2 dF_0(x-a) = 1/12n^2 + \sum_{i=1}^{n} \{F_0(X[i]-a)-(2i-1)/2n\}^2/n$. $F_0^{-1}(x) = \sup_y \{y|F_0(y)=x\}$; $A_1 = \int_{-\infty}^{\infty} [F'_0(x)]^2 dF_0(x)$; A_2 = non-negative square root of $\int_0^1 \left\{ \int_0^x F'_0[F_0^{-1}(y)]dy - \int_0^x \left[y^2 \int_0^y zF'_0[F_0^{-1}(z)]dz\right]dy\right\}dx$. $a(\alpha, n) = (A_2 K_{\alpha/2})/A_1\sqrt{n}$ **2** *Test*: Reject null hyp. if $|a_n| \geqslant a(\alpha, n)$ **3** None **4** Min allowable $n \geqslant 30/\sqrt{\alpha}$ for $\alpha \leqslant \frac{1}{2}$. First-order approx. to a_n, which is accurate for large n, is $\left[\sum_{i=1}^{n} \{F_0(X[i]) - i/n\}F'_0(X[i]) + \sum_{i=1}^{n} F'_0(X[i])/2n\right] / \left[\sum_{i=1}^{n} \{F_0(X[i]) - i/n\}F''_0(X[i]) + \sum_{i=1}^{n} \{F'_0(X[i])\}^2 + \sum_{i=1}^{n} F''_0(X[i])/2n\right]$ **Characteristics 1** Upper low to upper medium, depending on n and whether $F_0(x)$ already tabulated **2** Sensitive to altern. of form $F(x) = F_0(x-a)$ **4** Moderately sensitive to continuity requirement but not so sensitive to derivative requirements if population continuous to reasonable approx. **6** None **Bibliography** Ref. 63.

Test Based on Absolute Values of Distribution Function Differences (Sherman)

Data 3 $X[i]$ **Description 1** Exact sig. test **2** Simple null hyp.; asserts that $F(x) = F_0(x)$ **Assumptions 2** Continuous population **Results 1** $\omega_n = \frac{1}{2}\sum_{i=1}^{n+1} |F_0(X[i]) - F_0(X[i-1]) - 1/(n+1)|$. $\omega(\alpha, n)$ = value of ω such that $\sum_{u=0}^{n-R+1} \sum_{v=0}^{u} (-1)^{v-u} \binom{n}{v}\binom{n+1}{u+1}\binom{n+u-v}{n}\left(\frac{n-u}{n+1}\right)^v \left(\frac{n-u}{n+1} - \omega\right)^{n-v} = 1-\alpha$, where, for given ω, R is non-negative integer satisfying $R/(n+1) \leqslant \omega < (R+1)/(n+1)$. $h(\omega_n) = \sqrt{n}[\omega_n - .03679\,(1-1/2n)]/.2431(1-.605/n) - .0995\,\{n[\omega_n - .03679(1-1/2n)]^2/[.2431(1-.605/n)]^2 - 1\}/\sqrt{n}$ **2** *Exact test*: Reject the null hyp. if $\omega_n \geqslant \omega(\alpha, n)$. *Approximation to the exact test*: Reject the null hyp. if $h(\omega_n) \geqslant K_\alpha$; usable when $n \geqslant \max(10, 2/\sqrt{\alpha})$ **3** Table 10.5 contains values of $\omega(\alpha, n)$ for $\alpha = .01, .05, .10$ and $n = 1(1)20$ **4** Approximation to test obtained by fitting Pearson Type I curve to range of variation and first two moments of ω_n **Characteristics 1** Low to upper medium, depending on n, whether $F_0(x)$ already tabulated, and whether α outside range .01 to .10 with approximation not usable **2** Intuitive considerations indicate that this test should be sensitive to alternatives where the freq. fct. of $F_0[X(i)]$ is linear with a slope noticeably different from zero or is of the form $1 + A|x-B|^D \operatorname{sgn}(x-B)$, where A is noticeably different from zero. In fact, the ω_n test should be sensitive to any type of altern. for which $(n+1)E\{F_0(X[i]) - F_0(X[i-1])\}$ tends to be noticeably different from unity for a substantial percentage of the values of i. Test consistent against any altern. $F^{(1)}(x) \not\equiv F_0(x)$ if dist. fcts. considered have first derivative which is continuous except at a finite no. of pts. **4** Moderately sensitive to continuity requirement **6** None **Bibliography** Ref. 23, 127, 469, 470.

TABLE 10.5. VALUES OF $\omega(\alpha, n)$ FOR $\alpha = .90, .95, .99$ AND $n = 1(1)20$*

n \ α	.01	.05	.10	n \ α	.01	.05	.10
1	.495	.475	.450	11	.521	.470	.443
2	.609	.538	.484	12	.516	.466	.440
3	.614	.518	.477	13	.511	.463	.438
4	.589	.510	.469	14	.506	.460	.436
5	.574	.502	.462	15	.502	.458	.435
6	.563	.494	.458	16	.499	.456	.433
7	.551	.488	.454	17	.495	.453	.431
8	.542	.482	.451	18	.492	.451	.430
9	.534	.478	.448	19	.489	.449	.429
10	.527	.473	.445	20	.486	.448	.427

* Taken from ref. 470: Percentiles of the ω_n statistics, B. Sherman, *Annals of Mathematical Statistics*, Vol. 28, 1957, pages 259–61. Used with the kind permission of the author, Bernard Sherman, and of the Editor of the *Annals of Mathematical Statistics*.

Tests Using Sums of Powers of Distribution Function Differences (Kimball, Moran)

Data 3 $X[i]$ **4** Min allowable n stated in Results **Description 1** Theoretical-approx. sig. tests **2** Simple null hyp.; asserts that $F(x) = F_0(x)$ **Assumptions 2** Continuous population **Results 1** $i_1 < \ldots < i_T$ is specified subset of the integers $1, \ldots, n+1$. $Z'_n = Z'_n(i_1, \ldots, i_T; Q) = \sum_{t=1}^{T} \{F_0(X[i_t]) - F_0(X[i_t - 1])\}^Q$, where Q any positive real no. $\neq 1$. $Z_n = (n+1)^Q[Z'_n - T\Gamma(n+1)\Gamma(Q+1)/\Gamma(n+Q+1)\Gamma(2Q+1) - \Gamma(Q+1)^2 - TQ^2\Gamma(Q+1)^2/n]^{1/2}\sqrt{T}$ **2** *Test*: Reject the null hyp. if $Z_n \geqslant K_\alpha$ **3** None **4** Min allowable $n \geqslant 200/(T\sqrt{\alpha} - 40)$, where $T\sqrt{\alpha} > 40$; obtained from requirement $T \geqslant 40(1 + 5/n)/\sqrt{\alpha}$. When $T = n+1$, $Q = 2$, and the null hyp. holds, $EZ'_n = 2/(n+2)$, $\sigma^2 Z'_n = 4n/(n+2)^2(n+3)(n+4)$, $\alpha_3 Z'_n = (10n-4)[(n+3)(n+4)/n]^{1/2}/(n+5)(n+6)$, $\alpha_4 Z'_n = 3 + 6(41n^4 + 241n^3 + 118n^2 - 784n - 48)/n(n+5)(n+6)(n+7)(n+8)$; then the approx. dist. of Z'_n under the null hyp. can be determined by using these four moments and Pearson curves, Edgeworth series expansion, etc.; the resulting test based on Z'_n should be reasonably accurate for $n \geqslant 15/\sqrt{\alpha}$ **Characteristics 1** Low to upper medium, depending on n, Q, and whether $F_0(x)$ already tabulated **2** Test with $T=n+1$ and $Q=2$ most powerful when freq. fct. of $F_0[X(i)]$ of form $1+A(x-\frac{1}{2})$ for $0\leqslant x\leqslant 1$ (zero otherwise). Consider case of large n, $T=n+1$, $Q>1$, and altern. such that freq. fct. $g(x)$ of $F_0[X(i)]$ has a finite no. of dicontinuities and is bounded away from 0 and ∞; let $c_n(\alpha, Q)=\sqrt{n}\Gamma(Q+1)+K_\alpha[\Gamma(2Q+1)-(1+Q^2)\Gamma(Q+1)^2]^{1/2}-\sqrt{n}\Gamma(Q+1)\int_0^1 g(x)^{1-Q}dx$ and let $d(Q)=$positive square root of $[\Gamma(2Q+1)-2Q\Gamma(Q+1)^2]\int_0^1 g(x)^{1-2Q}dx-[(Q-1)\Gamma(Q+1)\int_0^1 g(x)^{1-Q}dx]^2$; then power of test approx. equals $1-\Phi[c_n(\alpha, Q)/d(Q)]$. In general, this test should be sensitive to any type of altern. for which $E\{F_0(X[i_t])-F_0(X[i_t-1])\}^Q\Gamma(n+Q+1)/\Gamma(n+1)\Gamma(Q+1)$ tends to be noticeably different from unity for a substantial percentage of the values of t **4** Moderately sensitive to continuity requirement **6** Useful for life-testing and other censored data situations **Bibliography** Ref. 127, 282, 283, 356, 577, 579.

Tests Using Order Statistics of Distribution Function Differences (Barton, F. N. David)

Data 3 $X[i]$ **Description 1** Exact sig. tests **2** Null hyp. H_0 simple for some tests and composite for others. Simple null hyp. asserts that $F(x)=F_0(x)$. Composite null hyp. asserts that $F(x)=F_0(x)/L$ for $F_0(x)\leqslant L$ and is unity for $F_0(x)\geqslant L$, where L unknown and $0<L\leqslant 1$; i.e., $F_0[X(i)]$ has rectangular dist. $[0, L]$ **Results 1** $Y[i]=i$th order statistic of the $\{F_0(X[i'])-F_0(X[i'-1])\}$, $(i'=1, \ldots, n+1)$. $U_n^{(1)}(B)=\sum_{i=1}^{B} Y[i]$; $U_n^{(2)}(B)=Y[B+1]+Y[B]$; $U_n^{(3)}(B)=Y[B]$; $U_n^{(4)}(B)=Y[B]/Y[n+1]$; $U_n^{(5)}(B)=Y[1]/Y[B]$; $U_n^{(6)}(B_1, B_2)=Y[B_2]-Y[B_1]$, $(B_2>B_1)$; $U_n^{(7)}(B_1, B_2)=\sum_{i=B_1}^{B_2} Y[i]$. $U_1(\alpha; B, n)=$solution for U of $\binom{n+1}{B}(n+1-B)^{-B-1}\sum_{i=1}^{B}\binom{B}{i}(-1)^{i-1}i^B\left(1-\{1-\min[1, (n+1+i-B)U/i]\}^n\right)\Big/(n+1+i-B)=\alpha$. $U_2(\alpha; B, n)=$sol. for U of $\{1-\min[1, (n+1-B)U]\}^n-1+2[(n+1)!/(B-1)!(n-B)!]\sum_{i=0}^{B-1}\binom{B-1}{i}(-1)^{B-i-1}\left(1-\{1-\min[1, (n+1-i)U/2]\}^n\right)\Big/(n+1-i)^2=\alpha$. $U_3(\alpha; B, n)=$sol. for U of $(n+1)\binom{n}{B-1}\sum_{i=0}^{B-1}(-1)^i\binom{B-1}{i}\left(1-\{\min[1, (n-B+i+2)U]\}^n\right)\Big/(n-B+i+2)=\alpha$. $U_4(\alpha; B, n)=$sol. for U of $[(n+1)!U^B/(n+1-B)!]\sum_{i_1=1}^{n+1-B}(-1)^{i_1-1}\binom{n+1-B}{i_1}\prod_{i_2=0}^{B-1}[i_1+(n-B-i_1+i_2+2)U]^{-1}=\alpha$. $U_5(\alpha; B, n)=$sol. for U of $(n+1)nU\binom{n-1}{B-2}\sum_{i=0}^{B-2}(-1)^i\binom{B-2}{i}\Big/(n-B+i+2)[(B-1-i)$

$U+n-B+i+2]=\alpha$. $U_6(\alpha; B_1, B_2, n)=$ sol. for U of $[(n+1-B_1)!/(n+1-B_2)!(B_2-B_1-1)!]\sum_{i=0}^{B_2-B_1-1}(-1)^i\binom{B_2-B_1-1}{i}\Big(1-\{1-\min[1,(n-B_2+i+2)U]\}^n\Big)\Big/(n-B_2+i+2)=\alpha$. $U_7(\alpha; B_1, B_2)=$ sol. for U of $[(n+1)!/(n+1-B_2)!(B_2-B_1)!(B_1-1)!(n+1-B_2)^{B_2-B_1-1}]\sum_{i_1=0}^{B_1-1}\sum_{i_2=0}^{B_2-B_1-1}(-1)^{i_1+i_2}\binom{B_1-1}{i_1}\binom{B_2-B_1}{i_2}(B_2-B_1-i_2)^{B_2-B_1}\Delta(i_1,i_2)/[(i_2+1)(n+1-B_2)-i_1(B_2-B_1-i_2)]=\alpha$, where $\Delta(i_1,i_2)=(B_2-B_1+1)/(n-B_1+i_1+2)-(B_2-B_1-i_2)/(n-B_1-i_2+1)+(B_2-B_1-i_2)\{1-\min[1,(n-B_1-i_2+1)U/(B_2-B_1-i_2)]\}^n/(n-B_1-i_2+1)-(B_2-B_1+1)\{1-\min[1,(n-B_1+i_1+2)U/(B_2-B_1+1)]\}^n/(n-B_1+i_1+2)$. Under the null hyp.: $EU_n^{(1)}(B)=\sum_{i=1}^{B} i/(n+1)(n-B+i+1)$; $EU_n^{(2)}(B)=\Big[\sum_{i_1=1}^{2} i_1/(n-B+i_1+1)+\sum_{i_2=1}^{B-1}2/(n+2-i_2)\Big]\Big/(n+1)$; $EU_n^{(3)}(B)=\sum_{i=1}^{B}1/(n+1)(n-i+2)$; $EU_n^{(4)}(B)=[(n+1)!/(n-B)!(B-1)!]\sum_{i_1=0}^{B-1}\sum_{i_2=0}^{n-B}(-1)^{i_1+i_2}\binom{B-1}{i_1}\binom{n-B}{i_2}(n+1-B+i_1-i_2)^{-1}\{(n+1-B+i_1-i_2)^{-1}\log_e[(n+2-B+i_1)/(i_2+1)]-(n+2-B+i_1)^{-1}\}$; $EU_n^{(5)}(B)=[(n+1)!/(n+1-B)!(B-2)!]\sum_{i=1}^{B-2}\binom{B-2}{i}(-1)^i\{(B-1-i)^{-1}\log_e[(n+1)/(n+2-B+i)]-1/(n+1)\}/(B-1-i)$; $EU_n^{(6)}(B_1,B_2)=\sum_{i=B_1}^{B_2+1}1/(n+1)(n+2-i)$; $EU_n^{(7)}(B_1,B_2)=\Big\{\sum_{i_1=1}^{B_2-B_1-1} i_1/(n+1-B_2+i_1)+\sum_{i_2=1}^{B_1-1}(B_2-B_1+1)/(n+2-i_2)\Big\}\Big/(n+1)$; $\sigma^2U_n^{(1)}(B)=\sum_{i=1}^{B}[i/(n+1-B+i)]^2/(n+1)(n+2)-[EU_n^{(1)}(B)]^2/(n+2)$; $\sigma^2U_n^{(2)}(B)=\Big\{\sum_{i_1=1}^{2}[i_1/(n+1-B+i_1)]^2+\sum_{i_2=1}^{B-1}4/(n+2-i_2)^2\Big\}\Big/(n+1)(n+2)-[EU_n^{(2)}(B)]^2/(n+2)$; $\sigma^2U_n^{(3)}(B)=\sum_{i=1}^{B}[1/(n+2-i)]^2/(n+1)(n+2)-[EU_n^{(3)}(B)]^2/(n+2)$; $\sigma^2U_n^{(6)}(B_1,B_2)=\sum_{i=B_1}^{B_2+1}[1/(n+2-i)^2]/(n+1)(n+2)-[EU_n^{(6)}(B_1,B_2)]^2/(n+2)$; $\sigma^2U_n^{(7)}(B_1,B_2)=\Big\{\sum_{i_1=1}^{B_2-B_1+1}[i_1/(n+1-B_2+i_1)]^2+\sum_{i_2=1}^{B_2-1}[(B_2-B_1+1)/(n+2-i_2)]^2\Big\}\Big/(n+1)(n+2)-[EU_n^{(7)}(B_1,B_2)]^2/(n+2)$ **2** *One-sided tests*, based on $U_n^{(d)}(B)$: Accept $EU_n^{(d)}(B)<E[U_n^{(d)}(B)|H_0]$ if $U_n^{(d)}(B)\leqslant U_d(\alpha; B, n)$, $(d=1,\ldots,5)$. Accept that $EU_n^{(d)}(B)>E[U_n^{(d)}(B)|H_0]$ if $U_n^{(d)}(B)\geqslant U_d(1-\alpha; B, n)$, $(d=1,\ldots,5)$. The tests based on $U_n^{(4)}(B)$ and $U_n^{(5)}(B)$ have composite null hypotheses. *One-sided tests*, based on $U_n^{(d)}(B_1, B_2)$: Accept that $EU_n^{(d)}(B_1,B_2)<E[U_n^{(d)}(B_1,B_2)|H_0]$ if $U_n^{(d)}(B_1,B_2)\leqslant U_d(\alpha; B_1, B_2, n)$, $(d=6, 7)$. Accept that $EU_n^{(d)}(B_1,B_2)>E[U_n^{(d)}(B_1,B_2)|H_0]$ if $U_n^{(d)}($

$B_1, B_2) \geq U_d(1-\alpha; B_1, B_2, n)$, $(d=6, 7)$. *Two-sided tests*, for comparing $EU_n^{(d)}(B)$ with $E[U_n^{(d)}(B)|H_0]$, and $EU_n^{(d)}(B_1, B_2)$ with $E[U_n^{(d)}(B_1, B_2)| H_0]$, obtainable as combinations of corresponding one-sided tests **3** $U_d(\alpha; B, n)$ easily computed for $d=1, 2, 3, 5$ when B small; $U_4(\alpha; B, n)$ only moderately difficult to compute if $n+1-B$ small or B small; $U_6(\alpha; B_1, B_2, n)$ easily computed when B_2-B_1 small; $U_7(\alpha; B_1, B_2, n)$ easily computed when B_1 and B_2 small. Table 10.6 contains values of $U_4(\alpha; 1, n)=U_5(\alpha; n+1, n)$ for $n=2(1)20$ and $\alpha=.01, .05, .1, .9, .95, .99$. When $n \geq \max[25, 6/\sqrt{\alpha(1-\alpha)}]$ and $n/2 \leq B \leq 4n/5$, $U_d(\alpha; B, n) \doteq E[U_n^{(d)}(B)|H_0] - K_\alpha\sigma[U_n^{(d)}(B)|H_0]$ for $d=1, 2, 3$. When $n \geq \max [25, 6/\sqrt{\alpha(1-\alpha)}]$, $1 \leq B_1 \leq 4n/5$, and $\max[B_1, n/2-(B_1-1)/3] \leq B_2 \leq 4n/5+5(B_1-1)(4n/5-B_1)/8n$, $U_d(\alpha; B_1, B_2, n) \doteq E[U_n^{(d)}(B_1, B_2)|H_0] - K_\alpha\sigma[U_n^{(d)}(B_1, B_2)|H_0]$ for $d=6, 7$ **4** Case involving ratio statistic of the more general form $Y[B_1]/Y[B_2]$ considered in ref. 36. Asymptotic dists.

TABLE 10.6. VALUES OF $U_4(\alpha; 1, n)=U_5(\alpha; n+1, n)$ FOR $n=2(1)20$ AND $\alpha=.01, .05, .1, .9, .95, .99$*

n \ α	.01	.05	.10	.90	.95	.99
2	.00224	.0114	.0235	.501	.618	.809
3	.00138	.00701	.0145	.334	.429	.618
4	.000967	.00494	.0102	.241	.317	.479
5	.000735	.00376	.00775	.186	.246	.381
6	.000588	.00300	.00620	.149	.198	.311
7	.000487	.00248	.00513	.124	.165	.262
8	.000412	.00210	.00433	.105	.140	.224
9	.000354	.00182	.00376	.0909	.121	.194
10	.000310	.00159	.00329	.0794	.106	.170
11	.000277	.00141	.00293	.0707	.0943	.150
12	.000250	.00127	.00263	.0634	.0850	.134
13	.000227	.00115	.00237	.0573	.0768	.121
14	.000207	.00105	.00217	.0523	.0698	.104
15	.000191	.000970	.00198	.0481	.0645	.101
16	.000176	.000895	.00185	.0446	.0599	
17	.000164	.000830	.00170	.0414	.0558	
18	.000152	.000775	.00158	.0387	.0522	
19	.000142	.000725	.00149	.0363	.0491	
20	.000134	.000681	.00139	.0341	.0463	

* Taken from ref. 36: Some notes on ordered random intervals, D. E. Barton and F. N. David, *Journal of the Royal Statistical Society, Series B*, Vol. 18, 1956. Used with the kind permission of the authors, D. E. Barton and F. N. David, and of the Royal Statistical Society.

of the $U_n^{(d)}$ considered in ref. 33 and 36 **Characteristics 1** Low to moderately high depending on n, d, α, B, B_1, B_2, whether $F_0(x)$ already tabulated, and whether an approx. used in applying test **2** Altern. of principal interest indicated by form used in stating tests. In general, if the test statistic contains only $Y[i]$ with small values for i, test emphasizes the high prob. concentrations in the dist. of $F_0[X(i)]$; if statistic contains only $Y[i]$ with large values of i (near $n+1$), test emphasizes low prob. concentrations in the dist. of $F_0[X(i)]$, including situation of an extensive upper tail (important for tests with composite null hyp.); if statistic contains only $Y[i]$ for values of i near $n/2$, test tends to emphasize moderate level prob. concentrations in dist. of $F_0[X(i)]$; combinations of emphasis can be obtained from combinations of these three types of situations **4** Moderately sensitive to continuity requirement **6** Tests with composite null hyp. useful when $F_0(x)$ of correct general shape but maybe $F_0(x) < 1$ for all x in the unknown range of nonzero prob. for $X(i)$. Some results are useful for life-testing and other censored data situations **Bibliography** Ref. 33, 36, 197, 342.

Correlation Coefficient Type Tests Based on Distribution Function Differences

Data 3 $X[i]$ **4** Min allowable n stated in Results for approx. tests **Description 1** Exact and theoretical-approx. sig. tests **2** Simple null hyp. H_0; asserts that $F(x)=F_0(x)$ **Assumptions 2** Continuous population **Results 1** $Y[i]=i$th order statistic of the $Y(i')= F_0(X[i'])-F_0(X[i'-1])$, $(i'=1,\ldots,n+1)$; $Y\langle i\rangle$ = rank of $Y(i)$ among the $Y(i')$. $V_n^{(1)}=V_n^{(1)}(\lambda_2,\ldots,\lambda_{n+1}) = \sum_{n=2}^{n+1}\lambda_i Y(i)/(n+1)$, where $0=\lambda_1<\lambda_2<\ldots<\lambda_{n+1}$; $V_n^{(2)}=V_n^{(1)}(1,\ldots,n)+1/(n+1)= \sum_{i=1}^{n+1} iY(i)/(n+1)=$ measure of correlation between the positions of the $Y(i)$ and their sizes. $V_n^{(3)}= V_n^{(3)}(b)=\sum_{i=b}^{n+1} Y\langle i\rangle Y[i]$; proportional to a measure of the correlation between the positions of the $Y[i]$ and their sizes, when some of the smallest $Y[i]$ not considered. $V_n^{(4)}= \sum_{i=1}^{n+1} Y[i]Y(i)/(n+1) =$ measure of correlation between the positions in the $Y(i)$ and the $Y[i]$ sequences. $I(V)$ = largest value of i such that $V>\lambda_i/(n+1)$; $V_1(\alpha)=V_1(\alpha;\lambda_2,\ldots,\lambda_{n+1})$ = solution for V of $\sum_{i=1}^{I(V)}[\lambda_i+(n+1)V]^n/(\lambda_i-\lambda_1)\ldots(\lambda_i-\lambda_{i-1})(\lambda_i-\lambda_{i+1})\ldots(\lambda_i-\lambda_{n+1})= 1-\alpha$. $V_2(\alpha)=V_2(\alpha;n)=V_1(\alpha;1,\ldots,n)+1/(n+1)$. Tests based on $V_n^{(3)}$ and $V_n^{(4)}$ are approx. as applied; $V_3(\alpha)= V_3(\alpha;b,n)$ and $V_4(\alpha)=V_4(\alpha;n)$ defined by $P[V_n^{(3)}\geqslant V_3(\alpha)]=\alpha$ and $P[V_n^{(4)}\geqslant V_4(\alpha)]=\alpha$ under H_0. Under the null hyp., $EV_n^{(1)}= \sum_{i=2}^{n+1}\lambda_i/(n+1)^2$, $\sigma^2 V_n^{(1)}= [\sum_{i=2}^{n+1}\lambda_i^2-(\sum_{i=2}^{n+1}\lambda_i)^2/(n+2)]/(n+1)^3(n+2)$; $EV_n^{(2)}=(n+2)/2(n+1)$, $\sigma^2V_n^{(2)}=(n+3)/12(n+1)^2$; $EV_n^{(3)} \doteq \frac{1}{2}(n+1-b)\{1-\log_e[(n+1-b)/(n+1)]\}$, $\sigma^2 V_n^{(3)} \doteq (n+1-b)\Big(7-3[(n+1-b)/(n+1)] +\{1+4[(n+1-b)/(n+1)]\}\{1-\log_e[(n+1-b)/(n+1)]\}^2\Big)\Big/12$; $EV_n^{(4)}=1$,

$\sigma^2 V_n^{(4)} = (n^2+9n+2)/(n+2)(n+3)(n+4)$, $\alpha_3 V_n^{(4)} = 16(n+2)(n+3)(n+4)$ $(n^3+54n^2-28n-21)^2/(n-3)^2(n+6)^2(n^2+9n+2)^3$, $\alpha_4 V_n^{(4)} = 3(n+2)$ $(n+3)(n+4)(n^5+61n^4+4873n^3-1121n^2+590n+1464)/(n+5)(n+6)(n+7)$ $(n+8)(n^2+9n+2)^2$, $(n \geqslant 4)$ **2** *One-sided tests*: Accept that $EV_n^{(d)} < E[V_n^{(d)}|H_0]$ if $V_n^{(d)} \leqslant V_d(\alpha)$, $(d=1, \ldots, 4)$. Accept that $EV_n^{(d)} > E[V_n^{(d)}|H_0]$ if $V_n^{(d)} \geqslant V_d(1-\alpha)$. *Two-sided tests*, for comparing $EV_n^{(d)}$ with $E[V_n^{(d)}|H_0]$, obtained as combinations of corresponding one-sided tests **3** When $n \geqslant \max\{20, 5\sqrt{n}\sigma[V_n^{(1)}|H_0]/E[V_n^{(1)}|H_0]\sqrt{3\alpha(1-\alpha)}\}$, $V_1(\alpha) \doteq E[V_n^{(1)}|H_0] - K_\alpha \sigma[V_n^{(1)}|H_0]$. When $n \geqslant \max[20, 5/\sqrt{\alpha(1-\alpha)}]$, $V_2(\alpha) \doteq (n+2)/2(n+1) - K_\alpha(n+1)^{-1}\sqrt{(n+3)/12}$. When $n \geqslant \max[25, 7/\sqrt{(n+1)\alpha(1-\alpha)/(n+1-b)}]$, $V_3(\alpha) \doteq E[V_n^{(3)}|H_0] - K_\alpha \sigma[V_n^{(3)}|H_0]$. Approx. value of $V_4(\alpha)$ determined by using first four moments of $V_n^{(4)}$ and Pearson curves, Edgeworth series, etc.; should be reasonably accurate for $n \geqslant \max[15, 4/\sqrt{\alpha(1-\alpha)}]$ **4** Other correlation type tests obtainable by suitable choice of $\lambda_2, \ldots, \lambda_{n+1}$; e.g., use of $\lambda_i = (i-1)^2$ correlates the $Y(i)$ with the squares of their positions (starting with position 0) **Characteristics 1** Low to moderately high, depending on n, d, α, b, whether $F_0(x)$ already tabulated, and whether an approx. used **2** Tests based on $V_n^{(1)}$, $V_n^{(2)}$, and $V_n^{(3)}$ sensitive to trends in the freq. fct. for $F_0[X(i)]$. Tests based on $V_n^{(4)}$ sensitive to situations where the $Y(i)$ become too regular (test of $EV_n^{(4)} > E[V_n^{(4)}|H_0]$) or where they become too irregular (test of $EV_n^{(4)} < E[V_n^{(4)}|H_0]$) **4** Moderately sensitive to continuity requirement **6** The $Y\langle i \rangle$ could be replaced by random ranks in $V_n^{(3)}$ (see Chapter 4) **Bibliography** Ref. 34, 197.

Tests Using Sums of Distribution Function Values at Order Statistics (Barton, F. N. David)

Data 3 $X[i]$ **Description 1** Exact one-sided and two-sided sig. tests **2** Simple null hyp.; asserts that $F(x) = F_0(x)$ **Assumptions 2** Continuous population **Results 1** $Y_n^{(1)}(b) = (1/b)\sum_{i=1}^{b} F_0(X[i])$; $Y_n^{(2)}(b) = (1/b)\sum_{i=n+1-b}^{n} F_0(X[i])$. Under null hyp., $EY_n^{(1)}(b) = (b+1)/2(n+1)$ and $EY_n^{(2)}(b) = (2n+1-b)/2(n+1)$. $Y(\alpha; b, n) =$ solution for y of $(1/b!)$ $\sum_{i=1}^{b}(-i)^{b+1}\binom{b}{i}\left\{1-[1-\min(1, yb/i)]^{n+1}\right\} = \alpha$ **2** *One-sided tests*, based on $Y_n^{(1)}(b)$: Accept $EY_n^{(1)}(b) > (b+1)/2(n+1)$ if $Y_n^{(1)}(b) \geqslant Y(1-\alpha; b, n)$. Accept $EY_n^{(1)}(b) < (b+1)/2(n+1)$ if $Y_n^{(1)}(b) \leqslant Y(\alpha; b, n)$. *One-sided tests*, based on $Y_n^{(2)}(b)$: Accept $EY_n^{(2)}(b) > (2n+1-b)/2(n+1)$ if $Y_n^{(2)}(b) \geqslant 1 - Y(\alpha; b, n)$. Accept $EY_n^{(2)}(b) < (2n+1-b)/2(n+1)$ if $Y_n^{(2)}(b) \leqslant 1 - Y(1-\alpha; b, n)$. *Equal-tail test*, based on $Y_n^{(1)}(b)$: Accept $EY_n^{(1)}(b) \neq (b+1)/2(n+1)$ if $Y_n^{(1)}(b) \leqslant Y(\alpha/2; b, n)$ or $Y_n^{(1)}(b) \geqslant Y(1-\alpha/2; b, n)$. *Equal-tail test*, based on $Y_n^{(2)}(b)$: Accept $EY_n^{(2)}(b) \neq$

$(2n+1-b)/2(n+1)$ if $Y_n^{(2)}(b) \leqslant 1 - Y(1-\alpha/2; b, n)$ or $Y_n^{(2)}(b) \geqslant 1 - Y(\alpha/2; b, n)$. Other two-sided tests can be obtained as nonoverlapping combinations of one-sided tests **3** When $1/n \leqslant \alpha \leqslant 1 - 1/n$ and $b \geqslant \max(15, n/3)$, $Y(\alpha; b, n) \doteq (b+1)/2(n+1) - K_\alpha\{(b+1)[2(n+1)(2b+1) - 3b(b+1)]/12(n+1)^2(n+2)\}^{1/2}$. When $1/4n \leqslant \alpha \leqslant 1 - 1/4n$ and $b \geqslant \max(10, n/5)$, $Y(\alpha; b, n)$ can be approx. determined from Pearson Type I curve with first four moments equal to null hyp. moments of $Y_n^{(1)}(b)$ **4** Under null hyp., $\sigma^2 Y_n^{(1)}(b) = (b+1)[2(n+1)(2b+1) - 3b(b+1)]/12b(n+1)^2(n+2)$; $\mu_3 Y_n^{(1)}(b) = (b+1)^2(n-b+1)(n-b)/2b(n+1)^3(n+2)(n+3)$; $\mu_4 Y_n^{(1)}(b) = 3[\sigma^2 Y_n^{(1)}(b)]^2 + (b+1)\{24(n+1)^3(2b+1)(3b^2+3b-1) - 40(n+1)^2b(b+1)(13b^2+13b+1) + 300(n+1)b^2(b+1)^2(2b+1) - 225b^3(b+1)^3 - 5(n+2)^{-1}b(b+1)[2(n+1)(2b+1) - 3b(b+1)]^2\}/120b^3(n+1)^4(n+2)(n+3)(n+4)$. If $n \to \infty$ so that b/n tends to a positive value, null dist. of $Y_n^{(1)}(b)$ and of $Y_n^{(2)}(b)$ tend to normality. More general case of statistic of form $\sum_{i=b_1}^{b_2} F_0(X[i])$ considered in ref. 33 **Characteristics 1** Low to lower high, depending on n, α, b, whether $F_0(x)$ already tabulated, and whether an approx. is used in applying test **2** Tests based on $Y_n^{(1)}(b)$ optimum when freq. fct. $g_0(x)$ of $F_0[X(i)]$ is of form $\beta e^{\beta x}/(e^\beta - 1)$, $0 \leqslant x \leqslant 1$, where $\beta = 0$ denotes null hyp. situation of $g_0(x) = 1$ and suitable class of altern. considered for each test; likewise, tests based on $Y_n^{(2)}(b)$ optimum when freq. fct. of $1 - F_0[X(i)]$ of this form. For this type of altern., $n \geqslant 15\sqrt{1+\beta^2}$, and $1/n \leqslant \xi \leqslant 1 - 1/n$, $P[Y_n^{(1)}(b) > \mu_\beta + K_\xi \sigma_\beta] \doteq \xi$, where $\mu_\beta = (\beta e^\beta - e^\beta + 1)/\beta(e^\beta - 1)$ and $\sigma_\beta^2 = [1/\beta^2 - e^\beta/(e^\beta - 1)^2]/n$; also $P[Y_n^{(2)}(b) > 1 - \mu_\beta + K_\xi \sigma_\beta] \doteq \xi$. Some power fct. values for one-sided and equal-tail tests based on $Y_n^{(1)}(b)$ given in ref. 24 for $\alpha = .05$ and $n = 5$. Tests based on $Y_n^{(1)}(b)$ emphasize deviations of $g_0(x)$ from 1 that occur for $0 \leqslant x \leqslant b/(n+1)$; tests based on $Y_n^{(2)}(b)$ emphasize deviations of $g_0(x)$ from 1 that occur for $1 - b/(n+1) \leqslant x \leqslant 1$ **4** Tests very sensitive to continuity requirement if b small compared to n; otherwise only moderately sensitive to this requirement **6** Tests based on $Y_n^{(1)}(b)$ useful for life-testing situations; tests based on $Y_n^{(2)}(b)$ useful when lower tail of sample is censored **Bibliography** Ref. 24, 33, 138.

Tests Based on One or Two Sample Order Statistics

Data 3 $X[i]$ **Description 1** Exact one-sided and two-sided signif. tests. **2** Simple null hyp.; asserts that $F(x) = F_0(x)$ **Assumptions 2** Continuous population **Results 1** $\theta_p^{(0)} = 100p$ per cent pt. for dist. of $F_0[X(i)]$; under null hyp., $\theta_p^{(0)} = p$. $b(g) = b(g; n, p) = \sum_{i=g}^{n} \binom{n}{i} p^i (1-p)^{n-i}$. $y_\alpha^{(1)} = y_\alpha^{(1)}(n) = (2\alpha)^{1/n}$ for $\alpha \leqslant \frac{1}{2}$ and $= 2 - [2(1-\alpha)]^{1/n}$ for $\alpha > \frac{1}{2}$. $y_\alpha^{(2)} = y_\alpha^{(2)}(n) =$ solution for y of $y^{n-1}[n - (n-1)y] = \alpha$. Under the null hyp. $E\{F_0(X[n]) - F_0(X[1])\} = (n-1)/(n+1)$ **2** *One-sided tests*, based on

$F_0(X[g])$: Accept that $\theta_p^{(0)} < p$ if $F_0(X[g]) \leqslant p$. Accept that $\theta_p^{(0)} > p$ if $F_0(X[n+1-g]) \geqslant p$. Both tests have signif. level $b(g)$. *One-sided tests,* based on $F_0(X[n]) + F_0(X[1])$: Accept that $\theta_{1/2}^{(0)} < \frac{1}{2}$ if $F_0(X[n]) + F_0(X[1]) \leqslant y_\alpha^{(1)}$. Accept that $\theta_{1/2}^{(0)} > \frac{1}{2}$ if $F_0(X[n]) + F_0(X[1]) \geqslant y_{1-\alpha}^{(1)}$. *One-sided tests,* based on $F_0(X[n]) - F_0(X[1])$: Accept that $E\{F_0(X[n]) - F_0(X[1])\} < (n-1)/(n+1)$ if $F_0(X[n]) - F_0(X[1]) \leqslant y_\alpha^{(2)}$. Accept that $E\{F_0(X[n]) - F_0(X[1])\} > (n-1)/(n+1)$ if $F_0(X[n]) - F_0(X[1]) \geqslant y_{1-\alpha}^{(2)}$. In all cases, two-sided tests can be obtained as combinations of corresponding one-sided tests **3** $b(g)$ can be evaluated by methods in binomial dist. sect. of Chapter 7. For some values of n and α, $y_\alpha^{(2)}$ can be evaluated by use of Fig. 9.2 (page 250) **4** These tests elementary consequences of fact that $F_0[X(i)]$ has rectangular dist. [0, 1] under null hyp. Randomized-exact and interpolated tests based on $F_0(X[g])$ can also be obtained (see page 205 and page 206) **Characteristics 1** Low to medium, depending on n the type of test, the sig. level, and whether $F_0(x)$ already tabulated **2** Altern. of principal interest indicated by form used in stating tests. For n at least moderately large, tests based on $F_0(X[n]) + F_0(X[1])$ should be much more sensitive than those based on $F_0(X[(n+1)/2])$, since, under the null hyp., $\sigma^2\{F_0(X[n]) + F_0(X[1])\} = 2/(n+1)(n+2)$ but $\sigma^2 F_0\{X[(n+1)/2]\}$ is only $1/4(n+2) + O(n^{-2})$. Under the null hyp., $\sigma^2\{F_0(X[n]) - F_0(X[1])\} = 2(n-1)/(n+1)^2(n+2)$; thus, for n at least moderately large, the test of $E\{F_0(X[n]) - F_0(X[1])\} < (n-1)/(n+1)$ should be sensitive to altern. where freq. fct. of $F_0[X(i)]$ has an extensive upper and/or lower tail **4** Tests based on central order statistics only moderately sensitive to continuity requirement but those based on extreme order statistics very sensitive to this requirement **6** Some of tests based on single order statistic can be useful in life-testing and other censored data situations **Bibliography** Ref. 438.

Tests Based on Extreme Values—Composite Null Hypothesis (*Darling*)

Data 3 $X[i]$ **Description 1** Exact one-sided and two-sided sig. tests **2** Composite null hyp. in terms of $F_0(x)$ and an unknown constant, where $F_0(x)$ completely specified continuous dist. fct. Null hyp. asserts that $F(x) = F_0(x)/L$ for $F_0(x) \leqslant L$ and is unity for $F_0(x) > L$, where L unknown and $0 < L \leqslant 1$; i.e., $F_0[X(i)]$ has rectangular dist. $[0, L]$ **Assumptions 2** Continuous population **Results 1** $D_n = \sum_{i=1}^{n} F_0[X(i)]/F_0(X[n])$; $P(D_n \geqslant 1) = 1$. $D' =$ largest integer $\leqslant D-1$; $D_n(\alpha) =$ solution for D of $\sum_{d=0}^{D'} \binom{n-1}{d}(-1)^d(D-1-d)^{n-1}/(n-1)! = \alpha$. Under null hyp., $ED_n = (n+1)/2$ and $\sigma^2 D_n = (n-1)/12$ **2** *One-sided tests:* Accept $ED_n < (n+1)/2$ if $D_n \leqslant D_n(\alpha)$. Accept $ED_n > (n+1)/2$ if $D_n \geqslant D_n(1-\alpha)$. *Two-sided tests* obtained as combinations of one-sided tests **3** When $n \geqslant 15$ and $1/2n \leqslant$

$\alpha \leqslant 1-1/2n$, $D_n(\alpha) \doteq (n+1)/2 - K_\alpha[(n-1)/12]^{1/2}$ **4** D_n has same dist. as $1+$sum of sample of size $n-1$ from rectangular dist. [0, 1] under the null hyp. **Characteristics 1** Low to medium, depending on n and whether $F_0(x)$ already tabulated **2** Test of $ED_n > (n+1)/2$ sensitive to situations where freq. fct. of $F_0[X(i)]$ has extensive upper tail. Test of $ED_n < (n+1)/2$ sensitive to situations where substantial amount of population prob. for variable $F_0[X(i)]$ concentrated near L **4** Very sensitive to continuity requirement **6** Useful when $F_0(x)$ of correct general shape but maybe $F_0(x) < 1$ in the unknown range of nonzero prob. for $X(i)$ **Bibliography** Ref. 126.

Tests Based on Sum of Excesses of $F_n(x-)$ over $F_0(x)$, (Gnedenko-Mihalevič)

Data 3 $X(i)$ **Description 1** Exact one-sided and two-sided sig. tests **2** Simple null hyp.; asserts that $F(x)=F_0(x)$ **Assumptions 2** Continuous population **Results 1** $\delta(z)=1$ if $z \geqslant 0$, $=0$ otherwise. $\Delta_n = \sum_{i=1}^{n} \{F_n[X(i)-] - F_0[X(i)]\}\delta\{F_n[X(i)-] - F_0[X(i)]\}$. Under null hyp., $E\Delta_n = \frac{1}{2}$ **2** *One-sided tests*: Accept $E\Delta_n < \frac{1}{2}$ if $\Delta_n \leqslant \alpha$. Accept that $E\Delta_n > \frac{1}{2}$ if $\Delta_n \geqslant 1-\alpha$. *Two-sided tests*, obtained as combinations of one-sided tests **3** None **4** None **Characteristics 1** Low to medium depending on n and whether $F_0(x)$ already tabulated **2** One-sided test of $E\Delta_n < \frac{1}{2}$ sensitive to shift situations where $F(x)=F_0(x-a)$, $a>0$; test of $E\Delta_n > \frac{1}{2}$ sensitive to situations where $F(x)=F_0(x+a)$ **4** Moderately sensitive to continuity requirement **6** None **Bibliography** Ref. 129, 207, 266.

Unbiased Decision Process With Three Possible Decisions at Each Point (Lehmann)

Data 3 $X(i)$ **Description 1** Randomized-exact unbiased decision process **2** Decision process accepts one of $F(x) < F_0(x)$, $F(x)=F_0(x)$, $F(x) > F_0(x)$ for each value of x in interval determined by $1-(1-\alpha/2)^{1/n} < F_0(x) < (1-\alpha/2)^{1/n}$, where α sig. level of test used in making decision for given x **Assumptions 2** Population continuous. $F(x)$ and $F_0(x)$ are strictly monotonic fcts. in x interval considered; also the set of x for which $F(x) > F_0(x)$ in this interval is union of intervals that are open on the right **Results 1** $A[x; I] = \sum_{i=0}^{I} \binom{n}{i} F_0(x)^i [1-F_0(x)]^{n-i}$. $I_1(\alpha; x)=$ largest value of I such that $A[x, I] \leqslant \alpha/2$; $I_2(\alpha; x)=$ smallest value of I such that $A[x, I-1] \geqslant 1-\alpha/2$. $a_1(\alpha, x) = I_1(\alpha, x) + \{1-\alpha/2 - A[x, I_1(\alpha; x)-1]\}/\{A[x, I_1(\alpha; x)-1] - [A[x, I_1(\alpha, x)-2]\}$; $a_2(\alpha, x) = I_2(\alpha, x) + 1 + \{\alpha/2 - A[x, I_2(\alpha; x)]\}/\{A[x, I_2(\alpha; x)+1] - A[x, I_2(\alpha; x)]\}$. $Z=$independent value from rectangular dist. [0, 1]; used for randomization purposes **2** *Unbiased decision procedure*: For each x of interval considered, accept $F(x) < F_0(x)$ if $nF_n(x) + Z \leqslant a_1(\alpha, x)$, accept $F(x) > F_0(x)$ if

$nF_n(x)+Z \geqslant a_2(\alpha, x)$; otherwise accept $F(x)=F_0(x)$ **3** $A[x, I]$ can be evaluated by methods in binomial dist. sect. of Chapter 7 **4** For given x, the decision process consists of an unbiased randomized-exact equal-tail sign test. Decision that $F(x)=F_0(x)$ for all x in interval accepted when $a_1[x, X(i)]-Z<nF_n[X(i)]<a_2[\alpha, X(i)]-Z$ for all i such that $1-(1-\alpha/2)^{1/n}<F_0[X(i)]<(1-\alpha/2)^{1/n}$. Decision can be reached for entire intervals of x values on basis of situations at $x=X(i)$ **Characteristics** **1** Low to medium, depending on n, whether $F_0(x)$ already tabulated, etc. **2** For given x, let loss from false rejection of $F(x) \leqslant F_0(x)$ equal loss from false rejection of $F(x) \geqslant F_0(x)$ equal $L_1(x)$, and let loss from false acceptance of $F(x) \leqslant F_0(x)$ equal loss from false acceptance of $F(x) \geqslant F_0(x)$ equal $L_2(x)$. Decision procedure, considered over all allowable x, is unbiased (see ref. 305 for definition) and has uniformly minimum risk among corresponding unbiased procedures if $L_2(x)/[L_1(x)+L_2(x)]=\alpha/2$ for all x considered **4** Moderately sensitive to continuity requirement for x values where discontinuities occur for $F(x)$. Not very sensitive to requirements of strict monotonicity and of intervals where $F(x)>F_0(x)$ being open on right **6** Ref. 306 outlines a somewhat general class of nonparametric unbiased decision processes with three possible decisions at each pt.; many of these decision procedures applicable for $-\infty<x<\infty$ **Bibliography** Ref. 305, 306.

Additional Bibliography of Potentially Useful Results

For the continuous case, $F_0[X(i)]$ has the rectangular (uniform) distribution [0, 1] when the simple null hypothesis $F(x)=F_0(x)$ holds. Thus, results based on a sample from the rectangular distribution [0, 1] can be useful in testing the distribution functions of continuous populations. Ref. 111, 320, 325, 371, 428, 429, 532 contain some material of this nature. Ref. 480 contains some asymptotic results pertaining to the crossings of $F_n(x)$ and $F(x)$. Ref. 578, 580 contain some partial results for testing composite null hypotheses of the form $F(x)=F_0(Ax+B)$, where A and B are unknown constants. The following short bibliography is not intended to be a comprehensive coverage of the additional results that have potential usefulness in testing continuous distribution functions: Ref. 111, 320, 325, 371, 428, 429, 480, 532, 578, 580.

ESTIMATES AND TESTS FOR MULTIVARIATE CASE

Introduction

This section contains point estimates, confidence intervals, and significance tests for probability distributions of bivariate and higher dimensional random variables. Here, as for all multivariate sampling situations,

m represents the sample size while n represents the dimensionality of the random variable. The point estimates and confidence intervals considered are for the distribution function value at a specified point; the expected value estimates are exact while the median estimates and the confidence intervals are theoretical-approximate. All the point estimates and confidence intervals presented are valid for arbitrary populations. With one exception (involving a bivariate population), tests are presented for the values of probability distributions over all points. Also a transformation of variable is outlined which, under the null hypothesis, yields a sample of size mn from the rectangular (uniform) distribution [0, 1]. Of the types of tests considered, only the type which is obtained on the basis of this variable change exploits an increase in the dimensionality of a random variable. All but one of the tests presented have simple (or modified composite) null hypotheses and are of an exact nature; also they require a continuous population and, with one exception, this population must also have a frequency function. Two of the exact tests are for frequency functions and have simple alternative hypotheses. These are of a categorical data type. They were stated here, rather than in Chapter 11, because of their specialized application to continuous frequency functions. Also, a nearly optimum approximate test is presented for the case of simple null and alternative hypotheses.

Other tests with composite null hypotheses and/or restricted to specified sets of points can be obtained by converting the data to a categorical form and using the categorical data results that are given in Chapter 11. Also a broad class of tests can be obtained by use of the tolerance region results of Chapter 9.

Difficulties for Multivariate Case

For the continuous univariate case, important statistical results are obtained by considering the deviations of the empirical distribution function from the population distribution function over sets of points of nonzero probability. Any function of these deviations (e.g., the maxima or the minima) has a probability distribution that is independent of the continuous population sampled. Unfortunately, direct analogs of this situation, even for special functions of the deviations such as the maxima or the minima, are not available for the continuous multivariate case; moreover, the additional requirement that the populations have frequency functions does not change this situation. For example, the maximum deviation between the empirical and the population distribution function is not distribution-free for the absolutely continuous bivariate case (see ref. 196 and 477). Thus one of the most valuable statistical procedures for the continuous univariate case, which yields confidence regions for a distribution function over sets of points, does not carry over to the continuous multivariate case.

This lack of availability of nonparametric confidence regions over sets of points is directly related to the fact that a transformation of variable situation which holds for the continuous univariate case needs to be modified for the continuous multivariate case. A useful property for the univariate case is that $F(X)$ has the rectangular distribution [0, 1] if the random variable X has the continuous distribution function $F(x)$; i.e., the distribution of $F(X)$ is independent of the continuous function F. In general, this convenient situation does not occur for the continuous bivariate or any higher dimensional continuous multivariate case, even when the population has a frequency function. That is, let $F(x_1, \ldots, x_n)$ be the distribution function for $\{X(1), \ldots, X(n)\}$; then the distribution of $F[X(1), \ldots, X(n)]$ is not necessarily independent of F. However, a modified transformation of variable, based on conditional probability considerations, is available for constructing significance tests for the continuous multivariate case where the population frequency function exists. Also, for the bivariate case, tests are obtained by letting one coordinate be a specified function of the other coordinate, which reduces the problem to a univariate form.

In addition to difficulties arising because methods for the continuous univariate case do not extend to the continuous multivariate case in a direct fashion, there are application difficulties due to the more complicated nature of multivariate observations. As an example, determining multidimensional regions with stated properties is ordinarily much more difficult than determining the corresponding one-dimensional regions. As another example, tabulations of specified multivariate distributions can require large amounts of effort. For tests, these application difficulties can often be substantially lessened by grouping the data into a categorical form and using a procedure based on categorical data. However, the level of effort required to apply a test may be at least medium even when the data are grouped.

Transformation of Variable for Obtaining Tests

Let us restrict consideration to situations where a simple null hypothesis is to be tested on the basis of a sample of size m from a continuous n-variate population with frequency function $f(x_1, \ldots, x_n)$. Then, for each n-variate sample value, a transformation of variable is available which, under the null hypothesis, yields n observations that are a sample from the rectangular distribution [0, 1]. Thus use of this transformation of variable for all m of the multivariate sample values yields mn observations which, under the null hypothesis, are a sample from the rectangular distribution [0, 1]. The null hypothesis can be tested by the use of these mn observations and the results of the preceding section (Tests for Continuous Univariate Distribution Functions). Tests obtained on this basis are the only results considered in this chapter which directly exploit the extra information obtained from an increase in the dimensionality of a random variable.

Suppose that the null hypothesis asserts that $f(x_1, \ldots, x_n)$ equals $f_0(x_1, \ldots, x_n)$ for all points $(x_1, \ldots, x_n)$, where $f(x_1, \ldots, x_n)$ is the joint frequency function for $\{X(1), \ldots, X(n)\}$. For $k < n$, let

$$f_0(x_1, \ldots, x_k) = \int_{-\infty}^{\infty} \cdots \int_{-\infty}^{\infty} f_0(x_1, \ldots, x_n) dx_{k+1} \ldots dx_n.$$

Then the transformed observations

$$Z(1) = \int_{-\infty}^{X(1)} f_0(x_1) dx_1,$$

$$Z(k) = \int_{-\infty}^{X(k)} \{f_0[X(1), \ldots, X(k-1), x_k]/f_0[X(1), \ldots, X(k-1)]\} dx_k, \qquad (k = 2, \ldots, n)$$

are a random sample of size n from the rectangular distribution [0, 1]. Here it is to be noted that $f_0[X(1), \ldots, X(k-1)] = 0$ for any k automatically implies that the null hypothesis is not satisfied.

This transformation is given in ref. 441. For the transformation stated, the coordinates of an observation are considered in the natural order $1, \ldots, n$. They could also be considered in any order determined by a permutation of the integers $1, \ldots, n$ and corresponding transformed observations obtained. In using transformations of this type, the order in which the observation coordinates are to be considered should, for each multivariate sample value, be specified independently of the value obtained for that observation or any of the other sample values. The major practical difficulty encountered for this transformation is that a large amount of tabulation may be required to determine the required frequency function values.

In applying this transformation of variable, using test statistics which are the same for every possible order in which the coordinates of an observation could be considered seems desirable. A statistic with this property is examined in ref. 442 and its asymptotic distribution is identified. However, this test is not yet in a form that is suitable for application, since none of its probability properties are explicitly stated, even for the asymptotic case.

Tests Obtained From Tolerance Regions

As stated in the introductory part of this chapter, the tolerance region material of Chapter 9 can be used to obtain tests of simple null hypotheses over all points. In fact, for ungrouped data, the most general class of available nonparametric tests for the multivariate case seems to be that obtained on the basis of distribution-free tolerance regions.

Let the population coverage of the tolerance region be controlled in parts, where these mutually exclusive parts are $R_1, \ldots, R_s$ $(s \geqslant 1)$. The null hypothesis is $F(x_1, \ldots, x_n) = F_0(x_1, \ldots, x_n)$ and the tests obtained are of the form

Reject the null hypothesis if any of the relations

$$\int_{R_1} dF_0 \epsilon A_1, \ldots, \int_{R_s} dF_0 \epsilon A_s$$

are not satisfied.

Here $A_1, \ldots, A_s$ are specified sets of nonzero measure, not necessarily mutually exclusive, which lie in $[0, 1]$. The choice of s, $R_1, \ldots, R_s$, $A_1, \ldots, A_s$ determines the significance level and the alternative hypotheses which are emphasized.

As mentioned on page 353, the tests presented there that are based on differences of distribution functions at consecutive order statistics can be modified and applied to the continuous and the partially continuous multivariate case. Let the sample size be m and let $r(1), \ldots, r(m+1)$ be any basic set of statistical blocks for the multivariate situation considered. Then the test statistic is obtained by replacing $F_0(X[j]) - F_0(X[j-1])$ by $\int_{r(j)} dF_0(x_1, \ldots, x_n)$ for $j = 1, \ldots, m$. Under the null hypothesis that $F(x_1, \ldots, x_n) = F_0(x_1, \ldots, x_n)$, the modified test statistic has the same distribution as that based on the univariate distribution function differences. The alternative hypotheses emphasized depend on the properties of the $r(j)$.

Remark on Determining Adequate Sample Sizes

All the procedures for which presentations are given in this section either reduce to a univariate situation or have direct univariate analogs. The methods for determining adequate sample sizes for these procedures are very similar to those used for the corresponding univariate procedures. Consequently, referral to the corresponding univariate results should be sufficient with respect to determining adequate sample sizes for most of the procedures that are presented.

Optimum Tests for Simple Hypotheses

As pointed out in the section that contains tests of univariate frequency functions, for the continuous case the Neyman-Pearson lemma furnishes a basis for obtaining nearly optimum tests for simple hypotheses. Under the simple null hypothesis, let the frequency function of the $\{X(i)_j\}_m$ be $f_0[x_1, \ldots, x_n]$ while it is $f_1[x_1, \ldots, x_n]$ for the simple alternative. Let

$$Y_j = \log_{10} \{f_1[X(1)_j, \ldots, X(n)_j]/f_0[X(1)_j, \ldots, X(n)_j]\}.$$

Then the most powerful test with significance level α consists in rejecting the null hypothesis when

$$\sum_{j=1}^{m} Y_j \geqslant B(\alpha),$$

where the constant $B(\alpha)$ is determined on the basis of the null distribution for $\sum Y_j$. Both the null and the alternative hypothesis are rejected if observed values $\{X(i)_{j(1)}\}$ and $\{X(i)_{j(2)}\}$ occur such that $f_0[X(1)_{j(1)}, \ldots, X(n)_{j(1)}]$ and $f_1[X(1)_{j(2)}, \ldots, X(n)_{j(2)}]$ are zero.

The null distribution of $\sum Y_j$ can be approximated by evaluating its first few moments under the assumption that the null hypothesis holds and using the first few terms of the Edgeworth series, etc. Ordinarily, use of the first four moments and the first four terms of the Edgeworth series should furnish a reasonable approximation to the null distribution of the test statistic for sample sizes that are not too small. The resulting test would be most powerful if its null distribution were exactly known.

As also mentioned in the section dealing with continuous univariate frequency functions, a modification of this test is available which uses some of the approximate results presented for the t statistic in Chapter 7. Here only $E(Y_j|H_0)$ is evaluated and the null hypothesis H_0 is rejected if

$$\sum_{j=1}^{m} Y_j \geqslant E(Y_j|H_0) + \sqrt{m}t_\alpha(m-1)SY_j.$$

This test has a significance level that approximately equals α when m is not too small. The power of this test at the alternative may be somewhat smaller, and the minimum allowable sample size is evidently larger, than that for the test based on the Edgeworth series. However, the modified test has the advantage that the amount of computation required is often substantially reduced.

Tests Emphasizing Special Properties

As mentioned on page 287, it is sometimes desirable to test a distribution in such a manner that some special population property (one-dimensional) of interest is emphasized. That is, for a specified simple null hypothesis H_0, a one-dimensional property such as a stated weighted average of the means of the coordinates, of the coordinate standard deviations, of the correlations among the coordinates, etc. is emphasized. Then the procedure is to test the one-dimensional population property considered on the basis of a corresponding statistic of the sample values whose expected value equals, or very nearly equals, the property considered for all populations such that this expected value exists. The null distribution of the statistic can be approximated by evaluating its first few moments under H_0 and using the first few terms of the Edgeworth series, etc. Ordinarily use of the first four moments and the first four terms of the Edgeworth series should furnish a reasonable approximation when the sample size is not small. Then this statistic is tested to decide on whether its expected value equals the value specified by H_0.

Extensions of Results Presented

Methods of extending the procedures given in the presentations, and of developing other results, have been outlined in the introductory material for the chapter and in the two sections that present tests for univariate frequency functions and for univariate distribution functions. Some of these methods are also applicable for the multivariate case and are mentioned here. However, since the univariate applications are very nearly the same as the multivariate applications, and the descriptions in the introductory part of the chapter are reasonably complete, not very much detail is given.

First, the method mentioned on page 283 can be used to obtain tests over restricted sets of points from tests over all points. The sample size is not fixed for this method.

For tests of simple null hypotheses, the methods outlined on page 285 that are not specifically for the univariate case can be used for the multivariate case. The results for the univariate case are also applicable if the variable transformation described earlier in this section is used. In general, the concept of modified composite hypotheses is applicable for the multivariate case and can be used in tests with simple null hypotheses and/or simple alternative hypotheses.

The large sample likelihood ratio method for testing a composite null hypothesis against a composite alternative that was given in the section on univariate frequency functions is also applicable for multivariate frequency functions. However, the application difficulties, which are substantial for the univariate case, are even more severe for the multivariate case.

Also, as mentioned in the first part of the chapter, additional material for distribution functions and frequency functions is given in Chapter 11. This next chapter contains sequential analysis and statistical decision theory results; also general nature tests are presented for the situation where the data are converted to a categorical form.

Outline of Presentations

Seven presentations of statistical procedures are given in this section. The first of these furnishes exact expected value and minimax estimates for the value of a distribution function at a specified point. The second presentation contains theoretical-approximate median estimates for the distribution function value at a specified point. The third presentation is concerned with theoretical-approximate confidence intervals for the distribution function value at a specified point. The results given in these three presentations are valid for arbitrary populations.

The fourth presentation is concerned with a continuous bivariate population. Exact tests are given for the value of the distribution function over all points in one coordinate and for a specified function of these values in the other coordinate.

The fifth and sixth presentations contain exact tests for the frequency function of a continuous population; these tests are based on categorical type data. For the fifth presentation, the tests are obtained by converting the data to a binomial form; they are optimum, among tests based on this type of data, against specified simple alternative hypotheses. The tests for the sixth presentation are obtained by converting the data to a multinomial form such that, under the null hypothesis, each category has the same probability. These tests are optimum, among those based on multinomial data of this type, against specified simple alternative hypotheses. The seventh and final presentation contains approximately optimum tests of frequency functions for the case of a simple null hypothesis, a simple alternative hypothesis, and continuous data.

Fixed Material for Section

Data 3 $\{X(i)_j\}_m$ **Assumptions 1** Random sample **Characteristics 3** Used symmetrically **4** Sample condition should be satisfied to reasonable approx.

Expected Value and Minimax Estimation of Distribution Function

Data 1 Arbitrary, multivariate **4** $n_1 = \ldots = n_m = n \geqslant 2$ **Description 1** Exact expected value and minimax estimation **2** $F(x_1, \ldots, x_n)$ for any specified value of $(x_1, \ldots, x_n)$ **Assumptions 2** None **3** None **Results 1**

Risk fct. is $E[F_m(x_1, \ldots, x_n) - h_m]^2$ for minimax estimation, where h_m is estimate **2** *Estimates*: $F_m(x_1, \ldots, x_n)$ is expected value estimate. $[F_m(x_1, \ldots, x_n) - 1/2\sqrt{m}]/(1 + 1\sqrt{m})$ is minimax estimate **3** None **4** Adequate values of m can be determined by methods given for corresponding univariate case (i.e., use of empirical dist. fct. as estimate) in Point Estimation for Univariate Case sect. If $0 < F(x_1, \ldots, x_n) < 1$, asymptotic dist. of $F_m(x_1, \ldots, x_m)$ is normal. Using risk fct. considered, value of risk for minimax estimate is $1/6(m+2)$ while max risk for $F_m(x_1, \ldots, x_n)$ is $1/6m$ **Characteristics 1** Low **2** $F_m(x_1, \ldots, x_n)$ consistent estimate with variance $F(x_1, \ldots, x_n)[1 - F(x_1, \ldots, x_n)]/m$, which is estimated by $F_m(x_1, \ldots, x_m)[1 - F_m(x_1, \ldots, x_m)]/m$; $F_m(x_1, \ldots, x_n)$ has min variance among unbiased estimates of $F(x_1, \ldots, x_n)$ where only knowledge of whether $\{X(1)_j, \ldots, X(n)_j\} \leqslant (x_1, \ldots, x_n)$ or not is used; also minimax estimate has 100 per cent efficiency for this case **5** Not difficult to decide on sample assumption **6** Method of ref. 492 can be used to obtain simultaneous minimax estimates of $F(x_{11}^{(1)}, \ldots, x_{n1}^{(1)}) - F(x_{12}^{(1)}, \ldots, x_{n2}^{(1)}), \ldots, F(x_{11}^{(s)}, \ldots, x_{n1}^{(s)}) - F(x_{12}^{(s)}, \ldots, x_{n2}^{(s)})$ for specified values of $(x_{11}, \ldots, x_{n1})$, $(x_{12}, \ldots, x_{n2})$ and loss fct. equal to square of difference between estimate and quantity estimated **Bibliography** Ref. 129, 492.

Median Estimation of Distribution Function at Specified Point

Data 1 Arbitrary, multivariate **4** $n_1 = \ldots = n_m = n \geqslant 2$ **Description 1** Theoretical-approx. median estimation **2** $F(x_1, \ldots, x_n)$ for any specified value of $(x_1, \ldots, x_n)$ **Assumptions 2** None **3** $0 < F(x_1, \ldots, x_n) < 1$ **Results 1** $p'[B]$ determined by $p'[m] = 1$ and by $\sum_{b=0}^{B} \binom{m}{b} p'[B]^b \{1 - p'[B]\}^{m-b} = \frac{1}{2}$ for $B = 0, 1, \ldots, m-1$; $p''[B]$ determined by $p''[0] = 0$ and by $\sum_{b=B}^{m} \binom{m}{b} p''[B]^b \{1 - p''[B]\}^{m-b} = \frac{1}{2}$ for $B = 1, \ldots, m$. Explicitly, in terms of F-dist., $p'[B] = (B+1)F_{1/2}[2(B+1), 2(m-B)]/\{m - B + (B+1)F_{1/2}[2(B+1), 2(m-B)]\}$ for $B < m$ and $p''[B] = B/\{B + (m - B + 1) F_{1/2}[2(m - B + 1), 2B]\}$ for $B > 0$ **2** *Estimates*: $p'[mF_m(x_1, \ldots, x_n)]$ conservatively high median estimate in that $P\{p'[mF_m(x_1, \ldots, x_n)] > F(x_1, \ldots, x_n)]\} \geqslant \frac{1}{2}$ and equals $\frac{1}{2}$ for at least one value for $F(x_1, \ldots, x_n)$. $p''[mF_m(x_1, \ldots, x_n)]$ conservatively low median estimate in that $P\{p''[mF_m(x_1 m, \ldots, x_n)] < F(x_1, \ldots, x_n)\} \geqslant \frac{1}{2}$ and equals $\frac{1}{2}$ for at least one value for $F(x_1, \ldots, x_n)$. $\{p'[mF_m(x_1, \ldots, x_n)] + p''[mF_m(x_1, \ldots, x_n)]\}/2$ is compromise median estimate for $F(x_1, \ldots, x_n)$ **3** Besides their expression in terms of the F-dist., $p'[B]$ and $p''[B]$ can be evaluated from tables for incomplete beta fct., tables for binomial dist., and from approx. to binomial dist. (see Chapter 7) **4** All three estimates approx. equal to

$F_m(x_1, \ldots, x_n)$ for each m, $(x_1, \ldots, x_n)$ combination such that $m \geqslant 10/F_m(x_1, \ldots, x_n)[1-F_m(x_1, \ldots, x_n)]$. Adequate m can be approx. determined by considering the estimates to have mean square error $F(x_1, \ldots, x_n)[1-F(x_1, \ldots, x_n)]/m$ and using a two-stage sampling scheme (also see Point Estimation for Univariate Case sect.) **Characteristics** **1** Low (if suitable table or approx. to binomial dist. used) **2** Estimates have approx. same efficiency properties as $F_m(x_1, \ldots, x_n)$ if $m \geqslant 10/F_m(x_1, \ldots, x_n)[1-F_m(x_1, \ldots, x_n)]$ **5** Not difficult to decide on sample assumption **6** None **Bibliography** Ref. 387.

Confidence Intervals for Distribution Function at Specified Point

Data **1** Arbitrary, multivariate **4** $n_1 = \ldots = n_m = n \geqslant 2$ **Description** **1** Theoretical-approx. one-sided and two-sided confidence intervals **2** $F(x_1, \ldots, x_n)$ for specified $(x_1, \ldots, x_n)$ **Assumptions** **2** None **3** $0 < F(x_1, \ldots, x_n) < 1$ **Results** **1** $p'_\alpha[B]$ determined by $p'_\alpha[m] = 1$ and by $\sum_{b=0}^{B} \binom{m}{b} p'_\alpha[B]^b\{1-p'_\alpha[B]\}^{m-b} = \alpha$ for $B = 0, 1, \ldots, m-1$; $p''_\alpha[B]$ determined by $p''_\alpha[0] = 0$ and by $\sum_{b=B}^{m} \binom{m}{b} p''_\alpha[B]^b\{1-p''_\alpha[B]\}^{m-b} = \alpha$ for $B = 1, \ldots, m$. Explicitly, in terms of F-dist., $p'_\alpha[B] = (B+1)F_\alpha[2(B+1), 2(m-B)]/\{m-b+(B+1)F_\alpha[2(B+1), 2(m-B)]\}$ for $B < m$ and $p''_\alpha[B] = B/\{B+(m-B+1)F_\alpha[2(m-B+1), 2B]\}$ for $B > 0$ **2** *Confidence Interval Relations*: $P\{p'_\alpha[mF_m(x_1, \ldots, x_n)] \leqslant F(x_1, \ldots, x_n)\} \leqslant \alpha$ and equals α for at least one value for $F(x_1, \ldots, x_n)$; thus $P\{p'_\alpha[mF_m(x_1, \ldots, x_n)] > F(x_1, \ldots, x_n)\} \geqslant 1-\alpha$ and equals $1-\alpha$ for at least one value for $F(x_1, \ldots, x_n)$. $P\{p''_\alpha[mF_m(x_1, \ldots, x_n)] \geqslant F(x_1, \ldots, x_n)\} \leqslant \alpha$ and equals α for at least one value for $F(x_1, \ldots, x_n)$; thus $P\{p''_\alpha[mF_m(x_1, \ldots, x_n)] < F(x_1, \ldots, x_n)\} \geqslant 1-\alpha$ and equals $1-\alpha$ for at least one value for $F(x_1, \ldots, x_n)$. $P\{p''_{\alpha/2}[mF_m(x_1, \ldots, x_n)] < F(x_1, \ldots, x_n) < p'_{\alpha/2}[mF_m(x_1, \ldots, x_n)]\} \geqslant 1-\alpha$; $P\{p'_{1-\alpha/2}[mF_m(x_1, \ldots, x_n)] \leqslant F(x_1, \ldots, x_n) \leqslant p''_{1-\alpha/2}[mF_m(x_1, \ldots, x_n)]\} \leqslant 1-\alpha$ **3** Besides their expression in terms of F-dist., $p'_\alpha[B]$ and $p''_\alpha[B]$ can be determined from tables for incomplete beta fct., tables for binomial dist., and from approx. to binomial dist. (see Chapter 7) **4** Based on results given on page 185. Probabilities for the two-sided intervals do not necessarily attain $1-\alpha$ for some value for $F(x_1, \ldots, x_n)$. Methods referenced in presentation starting on page 185 can be used to obtain modifications such that $1-\alpha$ attained; other types of modifications also mentioned there. If $mF_m(x_1, \ldots, x_n)[1-F_m(x_1, \ldots, x_n)] \geqslant 15$ and $1/m \leqslant \alpha \leqslant 1-1/m$, $P\Big[F_m(x_1, \ldots, x_n) - K_\alpha\{F_m(x_1, \ldots, x_n)[1-F_m(x_1, \ldots, x_n)]/m\}^{1/2} \leqslant F(x_1, \ldots, x_n)\Big] \doteq P\Big[F_m(x_1, \ldots, x_n)$

$-K_\alpha\{F_m(x_1, \ldots, x_n)[1-F_m(x_1, \ldots, x_n)]/m\}^{1/2} < F(x_1, \ldots, x_n)\Big] \doteq 1-\alpha.$ Adequate values of m can be determined by methods given for corresponding univariate case on page 319 **Characteristics 1** Low (if suitable table or approx. to binomial dist. used) **2** Intuitive considerations indicate that efficiency is very high for situations where $F(x_1, \ldots, x_n)$ can be arbitrary and null hyp. asserts that it has a specified value. One-sided tests uniformly most powerful, according to Tocher's extension of Neyman-Pearson lemma, when only available information is whether $\{X(1), \ldots, X(n)\} \leqslant (x_1, \ldots, x_n)$ or not for each observation. One-sided and equal-tail two-sided tests asymptotically optimum in an information theory sense when $\{X(1), \ldots, X(n)\} \leqslant (x_1, \ldots, x_n)$ or not is only available information **5** Not difficult to decide on sample assumption **6** Tests obtainable from these confidence intervals in usual manner. Additional tests obtainable from binomial dist. part of Chapter 7 **Bibliography** Ref. 387.

Tests for a Continuous Bivariate Distribution Function (*Simpson*)

Data 1 Continuous, bivariate **4** $n_1 = \ldots = n_m = 2$ **Description 1** Exact two-sided sig. tests **2** $F[x_1, h(x_1)]$ over all x_1, where $h(x_1)$ is a specified continuous strictly increasing fct. Null hyp. (simple) asserts that $F[x_1, h(x_1)] = F_0[x_1, h(x_1)]$ **Assumptions 2** Population continuous **3** None **Results 1** If $X(2)_j \geqslant h[X(1)_j]$, let $u_j = h^{-1}[X(2)_j]$ and $v_j = X(2)_j$; if $X(2)_j < h[X(1)_j]$, let $u_j = X(1)_j$ and $v_j = h^{-1}[X(1)_j]$; this yields the bivariate observations (u_j, v_j), $(j=1, \ldots, m)$. The $u[j]$ are the order statistics of the u_j and $v[j]$ is the second coordinate of the bivariate observation for which $u[j]$ is the first coordinate. $D = \max\{\max_j |F_m(u[j], v[j]) - j/m|, \max_j |F_m(u[j], v[j]) - (j+1)/m|\}$. D_α = value such that $P[\sup_x |F_m(x) - F(x)| \leqslant D_\alpha] = \alpha$ for case of sample of size m from a continuous univariate population **2** *Test:* Accept that $F[x_1, h(x_1)] \neq F_0[x_1, h(x_1)]$ if $D \geqslant D_\alpha$; signif. level is $1-\alpha$ **3** Table 10.1 on page 321 contains values of D_α for $\alpha = .90, .95, .98, .99$ and sample size = 1(1)100. Additional values of D_α furnished by Table 10.2 on page 325. When $m \geqslant 50$ and $.85 \leqslant \alpha \leqslant 1 - 1/m$, $D_\alpha \doteq \{[-\log_e(\frac{1}{2} - \alpha/2)]/2m\}^{1/2}$ **4** Function $h(x)$ chosen so as to emphasize situation of interest. Adequate m determined by specifying value of D_α and lower bound for α (i.e., upper bound for signif. level). Obvious modification yields test for $F[h(x_2), x_2]$ **Characteristics 1** Upper low to medium, depending on m and $h(x)$ **2** Efficiency and consistency properties very similar to those for testing continuous $F(x)$ on basis of magnitude of its max deviation from empirical dist. fct. over all x (see Confidence Regions for Univariate Distribution Functions sect.) **4** Moderately sensitive to continuity requirement **5** Not difficult to decide on sample and continuity assumptions **6** Useful when investigation of $F(x_1, x_2)$ over a specified surface is of principal interest **Bibliography** Ref. 477.

Optimum Binomial Test for Simple Hypotheses (*J. Roy*)

Data 1 Continuous, multivariate **4** $n_1 = \ldots = n_m = n \geqslant 2$. Method for determining adequate m given in Results **Description 1** Exact tests with simple null hyp. and simple altern. hyp.; based on data converted to binomial form **2** $f(x_1, \ldots, x_n)$ over all $(x_1, \ldots, x_n)$. Null hyp. is $f(x_1, \ldots, x_n) = f_0(x_1, \ldots, x_n)$ and altern. is $f(x_1, \ldots, x_n) = f_1(x_1, \ldots, x_n)$, where $f_0(x_1, \ldots, x_n)$ and $f_1(x_1, \ldots, x_n)$ are continuous freq. fcts. such that $\{(x_1, \ldots, x_n) | f_1(x_1, \ldots, x_n)/f_0(x_1, \ldots, x_n) = t\}$ has zero prob. under null hyp. for all t **Assumptions 2** $f(x_1, \ldots, x_n)$ is continuous **3** None **Results 1** $\omega(t) = \{(x_1, \ldots, x_n) | f_0(x_1, \ldots, x_n) < tf_1(x_1, \ldots, x_n)\}$. $p_0(t) = \int_{\omega(t)} \cdots \int f_0(x_1, \ldots, x_n) dx_1 \ldots dx_n$ and $p_1(t) = \int_{\omega(t)} \cdots \int f_1(x_1, \ldots, x_n) dx_1 \ldots dx_n$. t and integer T determined by requirements that sig. level, $\sum_{k=T}^{m} \binom{m}{k} p_0(t)^k [1 - p_0(t)]^{m-k}$, is α and power at altern., $\sum_{k=T}^{m} \binom{m}{k} p_1(t)^k [1 - p_1(t)]^{m-k}$, is max **2** *Test*: Accept $f(x_1, \ldots, x_n) = f_1(x_1, \ldots, x_n)$ if no. of the $\{X(1)_j, \ldots, X(n)_j\}$ with values in $\omega(t)$ is at least T; otherwise accept $f(x_1, \ldots, x_n) = f_0(x_1, \ldots, x_n)$ **3** t and T can be determined on cut-and-try basis, using table of incomplete beta fct., table of binomial dist., or approx. given in binomial dist. sect. of Chapter 7 **4** Useful tests obtained only when $p_1(t) > p_0(t)$. Then adequate m determined by additional requirement that $\sum_{k=T}^{m} \binom{m}{k} p_1(t)^k [1 - p_1(t)]^{m-k} \geqslant$ specified lower bound value for power of test at altern. Although hyp. are simple for the resulting binomial population, they are composite for $f(x_1, \ldots, x_n)$, since no distinction can be made between this dist. and any other yielding the same prob. for the categories **Characteristics 1** Upper low to upper medium, depending on m, n, and method used to determine t and T **2** Most powerful of this binomial type; ordinarily more powerful than binomial form of optimum multinomial test given in next presentation. Unbiased if $p_1(t) > p_0(t)$ **4** Not very sensitive to existence and continuity of freq. fct. if population continuous to reasonable approx. **5** Not overly difficult to decide on sample and continuity assumptions **6** Useful when a specified simple altern. of principal interest or representative of altern. of principal interest. Sometimes yields tests for one-sided composite null and/or altern. hyp. (see page 286) **Bibliography** Ref. 444.

Optimum Multinomial Test for Simple Hypotheses (*Tsao*)

Data 1 Continuous, multivariate **4** $n_1 = \ldots = n_m = n \geqslant 2$ **Description 1** Exact tests with simple null hyp. and simple altern. hyp.; based on data converted to multinomial form in such a manner that categories have equal prob. under null hyp. **2** $f(x_1, \ldots, x_n)$ over all $(x_1, \ldots, x_n)$. Null hyp. is $f(x_1, \ldots, x_n) = f_0(x_1, \ldots, x_n)$ and altern. is $f(x_1, \ldots, x_n) = f_1(x_1, \ldots, x_n)$, where $f_0(x_1, \ldots, x_n)$ and $f_1(x_1, \ldots, x_n)$ are continuous freq. fcts. such that $\{(x_1, \ldots, x_n) | f_1(x_1, \ldots, x_n)/f_0(x_1, \ldots, x_n) = c\}$ has zero prob. under null hyp. for all c **Assumptions 2** $f(x_1, \ldots, x_n)$ is continuous **3** None **Results 1** n-space divided into U disjoint sets s_u $(u = 1, \ldots, U)$, where $2 \leqslant U \leqslant \max(2, \sqrt{m})$; $s_u = \{(x_1, \ldots, x_n) | c_{u-1} > f_1(x_1, \ldots, x_n)/f_0(x_1, \ldots, x_n) \geqslant c_u\}$, where $\infty = c_0 > c_1 > \ldots > c_{u-1} > c_u = 0$ are such that $\int_{s_u} \cdots \int f_0(x_1, \ldots, x_n) dx_1 \ldots dx_n = 1/U$, $(u = 1, \ldots, U)$. $p_u = \int_{s_u} \cdots \int f_1(x_1, \ldots, x_n) dx_1 \ldots dx_n$; $\mu_0 = m \sum_{u=1}^{U} [\log_{10}(1/p_u)]/U$; $\sigma_0^2 = m\{\sum_{u=1}^{U} [\log_{10}(1/p_u)]^2/U - \mu_0^2/m^2\}$; $\mu_1 = m \sum_{u=1}^{U} [\log_{10}(1/p_u)] p_u$; $\sigma_1^2 = m\{\sum_{u=1}^{U} [\log_{10}(1/p_u)]^2 p_u - \mu_1^2/m^2\}$. N_u = no. of the $\{X(1)_j, \ldots, X(n)_j\}$ with values in s_u; $Y = \sum_{u=1}^{U} N_u \log_{10}(1/p_u)$ **2** *Test*: Accept $f(x_1, \ldots, x_n) = f_1(x_1, \ldots, x_n)$ if $Y \leqslant Y_\alpha$; otherwise accept $f(x_1, \ldots, x_n) = f_0(x_1, \ldots, x_n)$ **3** $Y_\alpha \doteq \mu_0 - K_\alpha \sigma_0$ when $1/2m \leqslant \alpha \leqslant 1 - 1/2m$, $\min_u p_u(1 - p_u) \geqslant 3/mU$, $m \max_u \log_{10}(1/p_u) - \mu_0 \geqslant 5\sigma_0$, and $\mu_0 - m \min_u \log_{10}(1/p_u) \geqslant 5\sigma_0$. Otherwise Y_α determined from exact null dist. **4** Adequate m determined on basis of desired power at altern. (see method outlined on page 341). Although hyp. are simple for resulting multinomial population, they are composite for $f(x_1, \ldots, x_n)$, since no distinction can be made between this dist. and any other yielding the same prob. for the categories **Characteristics 1** Upper low to high, depending on m, n, the difficulty in determining the s_u, and whether the normal approx. to Y_α used **2** Most powerful of multinomial type considered with respect to specified altern; when $U = 2$, ordinarily not as powerful at altern. as binomial test of preceding presentation; consistent in choosing between $f_0(x_1, \ldots, x_n)$ and $f_1(x_1, \ldots, x_n)$; not consistent in general **4** Not very sensitive to existence and continuity of freq. fct. if population continuous to reasonable approx. **5** Not overly difficult to decide on sample and continuity assumptions **6** Useful when a specified simple altern. of principal interest or is representative of altern. of principal interest. Sometimes yields tests of one-sided composite null and/or altern. hyp. (see page 286) **Bibliography** Ref. 521.

Approximately Optimum Test for Simple Hypotheses

Data 1 Continuous, multivariate **4** $n_1 = \ldots = n_m = n \geqslant 2$. Methods for determining min m and adequate m given in Results **Description 1** $f(x_1, \ldots, x_n)$ over all $(x_1, \ldots, x_n)$. **2** Simple null hyp. H_0 is $f(x_1, \ldots, x_n) = f_0[x_1, \ldots, x_n]$; simple altern. H_1 is that $f(x_1, \ldots, x_n) = f_1[x_1, \ldots, x_n]$; here $f_0[x_1, \ldots, x_n]$ and $f_1[x_1, \ldots, x_n]$ bounded **Assumptions 2** $f(x_1, \ldots, x_n)$ exists and is continuous **3** None **Results 1** $Y_j = \log_{10}\{f_1[X(1)_j, \ldots, X(n)_j]/$

$f_0[X(1)_j, \ldots, X(n)_j]\}$. For $a=0, 1$ (also 3, if extra altern. H_3 considered), $\mu_a = E(Y_j|H_a)$, $\sigma_a = \sqrt{m}\sigma(Y_j|H_a)$, $\alpha_3^{(a)} = m\mu_3(Y_j|H_a)/\sigma_a^3$, $\alpha_4^{(a)} = 3(1-1/m) + m\mu_4(Y_j|H_a)/\sigma_a^4$. $G_a(x) = \Phi[(x-\mu_a)/\sigma_a] - \alpha_3^{(a)}\Phi^{(3)}[(x-\mu_a)/\sigma_a]/3! + (\alpha_4^{(a)}-3)\Phi^{(4)}[(x-\mu_a)/\sigma_a]/4! + 10(\alpha_3^{(a)})^2\Phi^{(6)}[(x-\mu_a)/\sigma_a)]/6!$. W_α determined from $G_0(W_\alpha) = 1-\alpha$ **2** *Test*: Accept H_1 if $mMY_j \geqslant W_\alpha$; otherwise accept H_0. Signif. level $= \alpha + O(m^{-3/2})$. Reject both H_0 and H_1 if observations occur for which both of corresponding frequency fcts. are zero **3** None **4** Required computation less but power at H_1 reduced and min m increased by using t test method outlined on page 378. Min m is smallest value such that $|\alpha - \Phi[(W_\alpha - \mu_0)/\sigma_0]| \leqslant \alpha(1-\alpha)/10$ for this and all larger m. Adequate m determined by requirement that approx. power fct. at H_1, $1-G_1(W_\alpha)$, has specified value; this approx. usable when resulting m such that $|G_1(W_\alpha) - \Phi[(W_\alpha - \mu_1)/\sigma_1]| \leqslant G_1(W_\alpha)[1-G_1(W_\alpha)]/10$ **Characteristics 1** Low to upper medium **2** Approx. power fct. for any simple altern. H_3, specifying that $f(x_1, \ldots, x_n) = f_3[x_1, \ldots, x_n]$, can be obtained as $1-G_3(W_\alpha)$ for m such that $|G_3(W_\alpha) - \Phi[(W_\alpha - \mu_3)/\sigma_3]| \leqslant G_3(W_\alpha)[1-G_3(W_\alpha)]/10$. To neglected terms that are $O(m^{-3/2})$, test most powerful for H_0 against H_1 **3** Used symmetrically **4** Moderately sensitive to assumptions **5** Not overly difficult to decide on sample and continuity assumptions **6** Useful when specified simple altern. of principal interest or representative of altern. of principal interest. Sometimes yields tests for one-sided composite null and/or altern. hyp. (see page 286) **Bibliography** Ref. 383, 384.

Chapter 11

SEQUENTIAL, DECISION, AND CATEGORICAL DATA RESULTS FOR DISTRIBUTIONS

INTRODUCTION

This chapter, like Chapter 10, is devoted to procedures for investigating the properties of distribution functions and frequency functions. Sequential point estimates, confidence intervals, and tests are presented for distribution functions and sequential tests are presented for frequency functions. For distribution functions, statistical decision theory methods are presented for point estimation and for selecting one of several eligible hypotheses; only the selection of an hypothesis is considered for frequency functions. Finally, some tests are presented for situations where the data have been converted to a categorical form. Many of the results for distribution functions are valid for arbitrary populations while many of the frequency function procedures are valid for both continuous and discrete populations. Also many of the results are applicable for both the univariate and multivariate cases. To cover the most general situation, the material given in this chapter is expressed in terms of multivariate distributions, with m representing the sample size and the population sampled being n-variate ($n \geqslant 1$).

OUTLINE OF MATERIAL COVERED

The first presentation section contains sequential results. Most of the material of this section is concerned with tests, and various types of composite hypotheses are considered. Some of the sequential tests are for situations where the data have been converted to a categorical form.

The second presentation section contains results based on statistical decision theory. Most of these results make strong use of supplementary information about the properties of the population sampled. Some of the procedures for selecting one of two or more eligible hypotheses are sequential. Also some of the procedures are for the situation of categorical data.

The final two presentation sections contain tests and a decision procedure that use categorical data. The first of these sections consists of

K. Pearson's chi-square test for goodness of fit and related tests. The other section contains a grouped data version of the Neyman smooth test, a grouped data version of the Cramér-von Mises-Smirnov test, results based on Matusita's distance definition, and some additional tests based on combinatorial considerations.

As mentioned in the above outlines, there is overlap among the presentation sections with respect to the type of material considered. That is, categorical data results are presented in the sequential section, sequential results are presented in the decision theory section, decision theory results are given in one of the categorical data sections, etc. This overlap is due to the fact that some of the procedures can fall under either one of two headings. Since these procedures are only presented in one of the places where they could belong (to avoid repetition), some procedures of a given type may be overlooked if all the available sequential procedures are considered to occur in the sequential section, etc.

NONPARAMETRIC NATURE OF TESTS AND DECISIONS

As mentioned in Chapter 4, "nonparametric" has a special interpretation for tests and decision theory results which involve the selection of an hypothesis about a probability distribution. That is, the hypotheses considered are of the type that occurs for the parametric case, with the probability distribution being either completely specified or specified except for the values of one or more parameters. The nonparametric character of the tests and decision theory results considered is evidenced by their generality of application. That is, although the eligible hypotheses are stated in a parametric form, the over-all class of hypotheses that can be handled by the test or decision procedure is of a nonparametric nature.

GENERALITY OF RESULTS PRESENTED

As mentioned in the Introduction, much of the material given in this chapter is valid under rather general conditions. In many cases, the population sampled can be univariate or multivariate. For distribution functions, the population can often be of an arbitrary nature; in particular, this is the case for nearly all of the categorical data procedures. Many of the results for frequency functions are applicable for any continuous or discrete population. Also, for the categorical data procedures, distribution functions can be investigated over any specified nontrivial region.

USE OF TRANSFORMATIONS OF VARIABLE

Several of the tests and decision procedures involving the selection of an hypothesis are obtained by the use of a change of variable. A generally applicable type of transformation is that where the data are converted to a categorical form in an arbitrary but specified manner. Another type is that where data are converted to a categorical form on the basis of specified simple null and alternative hypotheses for the frequency function of a continuous population. These transformations to categorical data are applicable for univariate and multivariate cases.

More specialized kinds of transformations are used for the continuous univariate case. Here a completely determined distribution function is used in the transformation of the sample values. If the observations were actually from a population with this distribution function, the transformed sample values would be from a completely specified standard distribution, such as the uniform (rectangular) distribution [0, 1] or the standardized normal distribution. Each of the hypotheses considered for the transformed observations asserts that the true distribution is of a form (completely specified or specified except for the values of some parameters) which is of the same type as the standard distribution. As an example when the standard distribution is standardized normal, one hypothesis might state that the distribution is normal with unit variance and positive mean, a second hypothesis might assert that the distribution is normal with unit variance and negative mean, while the other hypothesis states that the distribution is standardized normal. The same type of situation can occur where the variance is the same but unknown for the three hypotheses.

Use of these specialized kinds of transformations has the advantage that results which have been developed in the parametric field of statistics can be used directly. Their principal disadvantage is that consideration is limited to a class of hypotheses that may not include hypotheses which are reasonably close approximations to some of the hypotheses of major interest.

RELATION BETWEEN TESTS AND DECISIONS

A significance test is a procedure that is used to make a decision as to whether the null hypothesis is accepted or is rejected. The null hypothesis considered can be either simple or composite. When the null hypothesis is rejected, some alternative hypothesis is accepted which may be either simple or composite. In some cases, the alternative hypothesis may consist of all simple hypotheses that are not included in the null hypothesis. Also, for some situations, one of two or more alternative hypotheses may be selected when the null hypothesis is rejected. Thus a test can be interpreted as a decision procedure for selecting one of two or more eligible hypotheses.

Although tests are used for making decisions, they ordinarily are not directly based on the use of a specified loss function; also they often have no direct method of incorporating supplementary information about the population sampled. In this handbook, significance tests are distinguished from statistical decision procedures by the fact that they do not make direct use of a specified loss function. When a test is interpreted in terms of a loss function, it is considered to be a statistical decision procedure with regard to this interpretation. A characteristic of many of the decision theory results is that supplementary information can be directly incorporated into a procedure. Usually, incorporation of supplementary information involves specifying (subjectively) an *a priori* distribution for the relative probabilities of the eligible hypotheses; this is referred to as a Bayes approach.

DESCRIPTION OF SEQUENTIAL MATERIAL

The material given in the section on sequential procedures is concerned with arbitrary univariate or multivariate distribution functions at specified points or over specified nontrivial sets of points, with continuous univariate distribution functions over all points, and with continuous or discrete univariate and multivariate frequency functions over all points. Point estimates, confidence intervals, and tests are given for the value of a distribution function at a stated point. Conversion of the data to a categorical form and use of the corresponding multinomial distribution furnishes tests for distribution functions over specified nontrivial sets of points, including the set of all points. For the case of continuous univariate distribution functions, specialized transformations are used to convert the data to a form where available parametric methods can be used. Sequential methods for life-testing situations can be obtained through the use of one type of transformation. Some of the tests for frequency functions are for simple hypotheses, or for modified composite hypotheses that can be represented by simple hypotheses. Other of the tests for frequency functions permit somewhat general types of composite hypotheses but their general operating characteristic properties and their average sample numbers are not determined in advance. The data are converted to a categorical form with three categories for one of the tests for frequency functions.

STATISTICAL DECISION THEORY MATERIAL

The material given in the section on statistical decision theory procedures is concerned with arbitrary univariate or multivariate distribution functions at specified points and over all points, with continuous univariate distribution functions over all points, and with univariate or multivariate frequency functions (from discrete or absolutely continuous populations) over all points. Bayes estimates are presented for the value of a distribution function at a given point. Conversion of the data to a categorical form can be used to investigate arbitrary distribution functions over all points. For the situation of continuous univariate distribution functions, special transformations are utilized to convert the observations to a sample from a specified type of parametric population and results for this population are applied. Some sequential decision procedures of a non-Bayes character are given for selecting an hypothesis for the case of frequency functions; here the hypotheses can be composite. Finally, some nonsequential Bayes procedures are given for selecting one of two or more simple hypotheses (or modified composite hypotheses).

RESULTS BASED ON CATEGORICAL DATA

The material given in the sections devoted to results based on categorical data is, with one exception, concerned with tests for nonsequential situations. The exception consists of a nonsequential decision procedure that is based on Matusita's distance definition. One section contains the well-known chi-square test of fit, the likelihood ratio test, the chi-square "smooth" test, and a modification of the chi-square test in which specified material deviations from the null hypothesis are considered. The other presentation section contains the Neyman smooth test for grouped data, a Cramér-von Mises type test for grouped data, tests based on the number of empty categories, tests based on combinatorial functions of the data, a test based on the maximum of the numbers for the categories, and tests and decision procedures based on Matusita's distance definition. By suitable choice of the categories, these results can often be used to simultaneously test the value of an arbitrary distribution function at several specified points.

RELATION TO RESULTS OF CHAPTER 10

The material of this chapter is concerned with the same general problem as is considered in Chapter 10; namely, with the investigation of properties of distribution functions and frequency functions. However, no sequential results and very few decision theory and categorical data results are given in Chapter 10. Also, the bulk of the material of Chapter 10 is devoted to the situation of continuous univariate populations. On the whole, the amount of material given in Chapter 11 for investigating arbitrary distribution functions and for investigating discrete frequency functions is larger than the amount of corresponding material given in Chapter 10.

SOME APPLICATIONS TO SEVERAL-SAMPLE PROBLEM

As mentioned in Chapter 10, testing whether two or more independent samples are from the same completely specified population, or are from a common population whose distribution is specified except for the values of some parameters, is sometimes of interest. The nonsequential tests given in Chapter 11 are directly applicable to problems of this type. Specifically, the procedure is to pool all the sample values and test whether this combined set of observations is a sample from a population with a distribution of the specified form. Here it is to be noted that the requirement of the same distribution for each observation is a part of the null hypothesis rather than a part of the assumptions.

Some useful joint tests can be easily developed for the univariate case. If a test procedure of Chapter 11 uses the univariate observations on which it is based in a symmetrical fashion, it is independent of the randomness tests of Chapter 5 and can be easily combined with a test of Chapter 5. One part of the resulting combined test is for investigating whether the samples are from the same population, where this could be any population. The other part investigates whether the samples are from a common population whose distribution has the specified form. The combined test consists in determining the result for each of the two tests and rejecting the null hypothesis if and only if one or both of these tests are significant. Combined tests of this nature are useful when the interest is in situations where the samples are from the same population and the population distribution does not differ hugely from a specified form. Then the significance level used for the Chapter 5 test is much larger (relatively) than the significance level for the Chapter 11 test.

Decision theory procedures can also be developed for the several-sample problem by direct use of the decision results in Chapter 11. In fact, with suitable interpretation, decision theory procedures that are combinations of the tests of Chapter 5 and the decision theory material of Chapter 11 can be developed.

INVESTIGATION OF MODE BY STOCHASTIC PROCESSES—BIBLIOGRAPHY

Stochastic processes with the observations determined sequentially and of a response, no-response type (similar to those presented in Chapter 8) can be used to investigate the mode of the frequency function for a continuous population. Also, the difference between the maximum of the frequency function and its value at the estimate of the mode can be investigated by use of these stochastic processes. Specifically, point estimates and confidence regions (of an asymptotic nature) can be obtained for the value of the population mode and for the difference between the frequency function value at the population mode and at the estimate of this mode. Determination of minimum numbers of observations for use of these procedures is not easy and no presentations are given. However, useful information about procedures for investigating these properties can be found in ref. 80, 81, 145.

SEQUENTIAL ESTIMATES AND TESTS

Introduction

This section contains nearly all of the sequential results that are stated for investigating probability distributions. In addition to the material that occurs in the presentations, several methods of modifying this material for other uses are outlined. Also, a moderate amount of introductory material is given concerning types of procedures, types of hypotheses, categorical data tests, use of transformations of variable, truncated tests, and properties of tests.

Discussion of Sequential Methods

Sequential point estimates, confidence intervals, and significance tests are considered. In most cases, these results are valid under rather general conditions. That is, they can be used for both univariate and multivariate populations which are not necessarily continuous. Also various types of composite hypotheses can be tested. In addition, the tests presented seem to possess the usual sequential advantage; namely, for specified operating characteristics, they have expected sample sizes which are substantially smaller than the sample sizes required by corresponding nonsequential tests. In fact, the probability-ratio sequential tests have the minimum possible expected sample sizes for given significance level and probability of type II error when simple hypotheses concerning frequency functions are tested. For some situations, no corresponding tests with fixed sample sizes are available.

Basis for Tests

Several different approaches are used to obtain tests. The method applied for testing the value of an arbitrary distribution function at a specified point is based on the binomial distribution results given in Chapter 7. Namely, with a suitable interpretation of what represents a success, the value of the distribution function at the specified point equals the success probability for a binomial distribution. The method for testing an arbitrary distribution function over a specified nontrivial set of points (nonzero null probability) is based on the conversion of the data to a categorical form and use of the corresponding multinomial distribution.

Tests of a continuous univariate distribution function over all points are determined by use of transformations of variable. In one case, the transformation is to a generalization of the uniform distribution [0, 1]. In another case, the transformation is to normality. For the remaining case, the application is for life-testing situations and the transformation is to an exponential form.

The probability-ratio method is used to obtain frequency function tests for simple hypotheses and for composite hypotheses of various kinds. A categorical data approach is used to obtain tests for continuous frequency functions and simple hypotheses; here the three categories used are determined from the hypotheses being tested.

Tests When Sample Values Obtained in Groups

The tests which can be applied to multivariate populations can be directly used for situations where the sample values (univariate or multivariate) are obtained in groups of equal size. Specifically, each group of observations represents an independent sample value from the same multivariate distribution and tests that are applicable for multivariate populations can be used to test this distribution, which is identified in terms of the distribution for each of the ungrouped sample values.

Obtaining sample values in groups can have advantages on the basis of cost and/or time considerations. In some cases, allowing each group to have a possibly different size is desirable. Tests for this situation can be obtained on the basis of the material in ref. 539.

Point Estimation

The only point estimates presented are for the value of an arbitrary univariate or multivariate distribution function at a specified point. These estimates are based on the binomial distribution results of Chapter 7. Separate use of this unbiased sequential estimation procedure is not recommended. However, it can be profitably used in conjunction with tests for the value of the distribution function at this specified point.

Confidence Regions

The only confidence region results presented are two-sided intervals for the value of an arbitrary univariate or multivariate distribution function at a specified point. These confidence intervals are also based on the binomial distribution results of Chapter 7. An advantage of the two-sided intervals presented is that their endpoints satisfy a specified relation, where this can be any specified one of a broad class of relations. In particular, the maximum width of the confidence interval can be specified. A disadvantage is that the expected sample sizes for these procedures cannot be predetermined.

Types of Hypotheses Considered

A number of different kinds of null and alternative hypotheses are considered in this section. These include simple hypotheses (where the probability distribution is completely specified), modified composite hypotheses which are geometric-mean type weighted averages of completely specified distributions, one-sided composite hypotheses, and hypotheses where the distribution is specified except for the values of one or more parameters. About the only combination of null and alternative hypotheses not directly considered is that where the null hypothesis is composite and the alternative hypothesis (or hypotheses) is simple. In one continuous univariate case, where the population is transformed to a normal form, a null hypothesis and two separate alternative hypotheses are simultaneously considered.

Types of Tests Considered

For testing an arbitrary distribution function at a specified point, one-sided tests and two kinds of two-sided tests are presented. Here the null hypothesis is simple; however, for the one-sided tests, the null hypothesis can be considered to be one-sided. The tests presented for the case of a continuous univariate distribution function are of a parametric nature. Only simple hypotheses and modified composite hypotheses based on the geometric-mean method are tested when the transformation is to a generalized uniform distribution. Several tests that have been developed for the normal case are stated for use when the population is transformed to a normal form. A test that is applicable for life-testing situations is presented for the case where the population is transformed to an exponential form.

A generally applicable test is presented for general situations where the data have been converted to a categorical form. Only simple hypotheses (for a multinomial population) are considered for this test.

Some tests involving simple hypotheses, or modified composite hypotheses, are presented for frequency functions. Tests having hypotheses involving one or more unknown parameters are also given for frequency functions. However, many of the properties of these tests are determined from sample information and are therefore not known to any reasonable accuracy until at least a moderate number of sample values have been obtained. Some simplified frequency function tests of simple (or modified composite) hypotheses are developed by converting the data to a categorical form, with three categories, on the basis of the hypotheses. In essence, these are tests of composite hypotheses, since the categories test a class of simple hypotheses which include the hypotheses that are explicitly considered.

One-Sided Tests From Tests of Simple Hypotheses

If the hypotheses of interest can be expressed in terms of a distribution which depends on a single one-dimensional parameter ξ, then a test of a simple null hypothesis against a simple alternative hypothesis can frequently be interpreted as a test of a one-sided null hypothesis against a one-sided alternative hypothesis. Explicitly, let the null hypothesis assert that $\xi=\xi_0$ while the alternative asserts that $\xi=\xi_1$, where $\xi_0<\xi_1$; also let α be the significance level and β the probability of type II error when $\xi=\xi_1$ for the resulting test. Suppose that the test is such that its significance level is $\leqslant\alpha$ for all $\xi\leqslant\xi_0$ (when individually considered as simple null hypotheses) and its probability of type II error is $\leqslant\beta$ for $\xi\geqslant\xi_1$. Then this test can be interpreted as having the one-sided composite null hypothesis $\xi\leqslant\xi_0$, the one-sided composite alternative $\xi\geqslant\xi_1$, generalized significance level α, and maximum probability of type II error β for the alternative. Similar considerations apply to the case where $\xi_1<\xi_0$.

Tests of Modified Composite Hypotheses

Analogous to Chapter 10, modified composite hypotheses consist of weighted "averages" of completely specified distributions (perhaps joint distributions) with the weights completely specified and chosen so that a distribution is obtained at each step of the sequential procedure and so that the simple hypotheses of principal interest are emphasized. Since, with suitable changes in the sequential test, a modified composite hypothesis can nearly always be used instead of a simple hypothesis, tests developed to handle simple hypotheses can be applied with a simple or a modified composite null hypothesis and a simple or a modified composite alternative hypothesis. In all cases the population sampled can be univariate or multivariate.

Three kinds of modified composite hypotheses are considered. Let g_ξ represent the eligible simple hypothesis distributions from which the modified composite hypothesis is to be developed. That is, the simple hypotheses are the g_ξ for each permissible value of ξ. In one case, the simple hypothesis which represents the modified composite hypothesis is

$$g^{(1)}=\int_{\text{all }\xi} w(\xi)g_\xi d\xi,$$

where $w(\xi)$ is a non-negative relative weighting function such that

$$\int_{\text{all }\xi} w(\xi)d\xi=1.$$

Here the integrations take the form of summations when the set of values for ξ is discrete or when $w(\xi)$ is zero except for a discrete set of values for ξ. The interpretation for this kind of modified composite hypothesis is that, separately for each sample value, the relative probability is $w(\xi)$ that this sample value is taken from the distribution g_ξ. As in Chapter 10, hypotheses of this type are referred to as random-selection modified composite hypotheses.

The second kind of modified composite hypothesis considered is ordinarily only concerned with a finite number of simple hypotheses out of the totality of the g_ξ. Let these simple hypotheses be $g_{\xi(1)}, \ldots, g_{\xi(R)}$. Then the simple hypothesis which represents the modified composite hypothesis is

$$g^{(2)} = \prod_{r=1}^{R} g_{\xi(r)}^{w[\xi(r)]},$$

where the relative weights $w[\xi(1)], \ldots, w[\xi(R)]$ are such that $g^{(2)}$ is a distribution. This modified composite hypothesis represents a weighted geometric-mean type average of the simple hypotheses that are of principal interest for the null or alternative hypothesis situation being considered.

The other kind of modified composite hypothesis considered in this section is that proposed in ref. 539. Here all the sample values are taken from the same simple hypothesis distribution g_ξ. However, all the g_ξ are eligible for use and the weighting function $w(\xi)$ furnishes the relative probability that g_ξ is used. Thus, the modified composite hypothesis for the first m sample values is represented by (x_j is n-dimensional)

$$g^{(3)}(x_1, \ldots, x_m) = \int_{\text{all } \xi} w(\xi) \prod_{j=1}^{m} g_\xi(x_j) d\xi,$$

where this becomes a summation in some cases. This third kind of modified composite hypothesis differs from the first two in the sense that the joint distribution is not a product of distributions for individual observations.

Of the three kinds of modified composite hypotheses considered, the last seems to have the most desirable properties in some respects. However, with suitable selection of the weighting functions, all three types seem to furnish satisfactory representations of combinations of simple hypotheses. In many cases, one or both of the first two kinds are much easier to apply and also less difficulty is involved in evaluating their properties.

Obtaining Tests for General Composite Hypotheses

The wide applicability of the probability-ratio sequential method (see ref. 539) allows tests to be obtained for a moderately general class of composite hypotheses involving frequency functions. Explicitly, let the eligible class of hypotheses be represented by $f(x_1, \ldots, x_n; \xi_1, \ldots, \xi_r; \eta_1, \ldots, \eta_s)$ for an n-variate population, where the null hypothesis specifies the values for $\xi_1, \ldots, \xi_r$ and the alternative hypothesis specifies values for zero or more of the ξ's. The η's, which may not occur in some cases, are nuisance parameters for both the null and the alternative hypotheses.

If the null hypothesis is tested against every possible alternative, no conditions are imposed on the $\xi_1, \ldots, \xi_r$ except that the null hypothesis values do not exactly occur. At the other extreme, the values of all the ξ's can be specified by the alternative hypothesis. Then, a simple null hypothesis is tested against a simple alternative in the presence of nuisance parameters. Any situation between these two extremes can occur for alternative hypotheses.

At the start of a test, guesses based on the available supplementary information are used for the parameters whose values are not specified. For further steps in the sequential procedure, the initial guesses are combined with estimates of the parameters that are based on the observation values that have become available. Here the estimates based on the data are maximum likelihood estimates computed under the assumption that the available observations are a random sample. Actually, since some conditions must be satisfied in order for a prior decision not to be reached from the test, the available observations are only an approximate random sample. However, the resulting estimates should be satisfactory for most situations of interest. Supplementary information is incorporated into these tests only through the initial guesses about parameter values. The influence of this supplementary information steadily decreases as the experiment continues.

For each sequential step, the test statistic form is such that the numerator consists of the joint frequency function specified by the alternative and the denominator consists of the null hypothesis joint frequency function. Then, the parameter estimates used in the numerator are determined under the assumption that the alternative holds while the parameter estimates for the denominator are determined on the basis of the null hypothesis.

The major advantage of these tests is their capability to handle rather general kinds of composite hypotheses. In fact, in many cases these are the only available tests, sequential or nonsequential, for handling such hypotheses. Their principal disadvantage is that substantial computational effort can be required in their application and that their expected sample sizes are not determined in advance. The computational effort can be reduced by only determining new parameter estimates every five observations, every ten observations, etc. Successive estimates of the average sample number can be obtained as observations become available.

General Tests for Distribution Functions

As already mentioned, the development of tests for the values of arbitrary distribution functions at specified points is based on recognition of the fact that the value of a distribution at a specified point represents the success probability for a given binomial distribution. Thus, the situation is converted to one that is concerned with a frequency function; namely, the frequency function for this binomial distribution. Then the tests are obtained by using the probability-ratio test for this frequency function. The tests presented are direct applications of the sequential binomial tests given in Chapter 7. The two-sided hypotheses for these tests represent elementary modified composite hypotheses of the first two kinds considered in this chapter. Other modified composite hypotheses can also be developed and used through strict interpretation of the one-sided tests as tests with a simple null hypothesis and a simple alternative; then, in general, modified composite hypotheses can be substituted for one or both of these simple hypotheses.

A general class of tests for arbitrary distribution functions can be obtained by converting the data to a categorical form. As already mentioned, simultaneous testing of the distribution function value at several specified points can often be accomplished by suitable choice of the categories. A discussion of the sequential tests based on categorical data is given on page 400. Also, composite hypotheses of a rather general nature can be tested by converting the data to a categorical form and using the tests for general composite hypotheses that are presented for frequency functions (see pages 397 and 422).

General Tests for Frequency Functions

As already mentioned, three types of tests are presented which are directly concerned with the properties of the frequency function of the population sampled. These are tests for simple (or modified composite) hypotheses, tests for a rather general class of composite hypotheses, and categorical data (three categories) tests for simple hypotheses (or modified composite hypotheses). The categorical data test requires a continuous population but the other two kinds of tests are applicable for both continuous and discrete populations. All of these tests are applicable for the univariate case and the multivariate case. Due to the application generality of the sequential probability-ratio approach, which is the basis for these tests, many types of simple and/or composite hypotheses concerning frequency functions can be compared.

Tests Based on Categorical Data

As has already been mentioned, a general class of tests for arbitrary distribution functions and a test for frequency functions of continuous populations can be obtained by converting the data to a categorical form. The nature of these tests, some special uses of the distribution function tests, and extensions of the frequency function test are discussed here.

Converting of the data to a categorical form has the effect of converting the population sampled to a multinomial population. Thus, the presentation of general sequential tests for categorical data also furnishes general sequential tests for a multinomial population.

A special application of the general categorical data results is to test simple (or modified composite) hypotheses, or to test composite hypotheses of a special type, concerning the values of an arbitrary distribution function at several specified points. This special type of composite hypothesis occurs when the distribution function is tested over a nontrivial subregion and, ordinarily, when the population is univariate. Specifically, for the univariate case, the distribution function can be tested over the interval from the smallest specified point to the largest specified point. Then the categories consist of the intervals between consecutive specified points and of the region that remains. The hypotheses are composite in the sense that the probabilities for the categories are given but that the distribution function values at the specified points are not given. The tests of simple hypotheses, where the distribution function value is specified for several given points, are not primarily restricted to univariate situations. These tests have the property that categories and their probabilities are determined by the specified points and the distribution function values at these points. If the dimensionality of the random variable is small and the number of specified points is not too large, tests with this property can usually be developed without great difficulty by use of the general categorical data results.

The three categories for the categorical data test of continuous frequency functions are determined by the simple (or modified composite) null and alternative hypotheses. One category represents strong preference for the null hypothesis, another category represents strong preference for the alternative, and the remaining category represents no strong preference for either the null or the alternative hypothesis. If f_1 represents the alternative and f_0 the null hypothesis, the three regions which define the categories are based on f_1/f_0. One region consists of all points for which $f_1/f_0 \leqslant A$; another region consists of all points for which $f_1/f_0 \geqslant B > A$; and the indifference region consists of the remaining points. This test can be extended to situations with less coarse preference gradations by determining more categories on the basis of f_1/f_0 and using the general test for categorical data. This extension has the advantage of being more sensitive to differences between f_0 and f_1 but the disadvantage that the determination of its properties is not as thorough as that which has been made for the trinomial case; also the computational effort is increased.

Special Tests for Univariate Case

When the population sampled is continuous and univariate, specialized transformations of variable can be used to convert the data to a form where available parametric statistical procedures are applicable. The type of transformation used and the interpretation of the hypotheses for the transformed data are described here. Also, an outline is given which furnishes a description of the parametric tests considered for handling this type of transformed data.

In all cases, the transformation is based on a completely specified continuous distribution function $F_0(x)$, which is representative of the simple null hypotheses of principal interest or is the best guess as to the actual distribution function. However, the properties claimed for the probability distribution resulting from this transformation of variable can vary over a wide range. At one extreme, the null hypothesis asserts that the transformed observations have a completely determined distribution; e.g., if X is the random variable and $F_0(X)$ is the transformed variable, the null hypothesis might assert that the distribution of the transformed variable is uniform (rectangular) with range [0, 1]. At the other extreme, the only assertion might be that the observations are a random sample from a specified type of parametric population; here both the null and alternative hypotheses could be composite and complicated. For all situations considered, the null and alternative hypotheses are based on the viewpoint that the transformed observations are a sample from some well-known parametric population, which is identified by $F_0(x)$ and the other characteristics of the special transformation that is used. Each transformation is determined by the requirement that a specified standard distribution, which is a particular case of the parametric class considered, is obtained for the situation where $F_0(x)$ is the distribution function of the population sampled. The three standard distributions considered in this section are the uniform distribution [0, 1], the standardized normal distribution, and the exponential distribution with frequency function e^{-x} $(0 \leqslant x < \infty)$.

The transformation $y = F_0(x)$ is used for the generalized uniform distribution case. For the transformed population, the simple hypotheses considered for its frequency function are of the form $\exp(A + By + Cy^2)$, where $0 \leqslant y \leqslant 1$; these include the uniform distribution [0, 1] as a special case. When the null hypothesis is simple, it usually asserts that the uniform distribution [0, 1] occurs. A modified composite hypothesis based on a weighted geometric-mean type average of simple hypotheses of the form $\exp(A+By+Cy^2)$ can also be used for the null hypothesis. The alternative hypotheses considered are simple or are weighted geometric-mean type averages of simple alternatives.

For the normality case, sequential tests based on the transformed observations are presented for several situations. One of these situations consists in testing a simple or modified composite null hypothesis against a simple or modified composite alternative; here the modified composite hypotheses which are easiest to use are weighted geometric-mean type averages of simple hypotheses. Tests of the population mean are given for the case where the population variance is known; one of these tests has two separate alternatives, so that one of three hypotheses will be selected on the basis of the test. Also, tests of the population mean are given for the case where the variance is unknown. Tests are given for the population variance for the case where population mean is known and for the case where this mean is unknown. Finally, tests are given for population percentage points where neither the mean nor the variance is known. The other tests where the mean and/or the variance is known can be modified so as to yield tests of percentage points.

The material given for the case of transformation to an exponential distribution is oriented toward life-testing situations; that is, these results are for situations where a large number of similar items are simultaneously life-tested with time to failure being the observed value for each item. Two situations are considered: In one case only the initial items are life-tested; in the other case, each failed item is immediately replaced by a new item in the life-testing. Precisely speaking, the significance tests for the case of no replacement are of a truncated sequential nature, since a fixed number of items are life-tested. However, they can be treated as non-truncated sequential without much loss of accuracy if the number of items is sufficiently large. Here the transformed sample values are considered to be from a population with a frequency function of the form $\xi e^{-\xi y}$ $(0 \leqslant y < \infty$ and $\xi > 0)$.

Since the transformation is completely specified, any hypothesis for a transformed distribution represents a determinable hypothesis for the population sampled. However, the amount of effort required to identify the composite hypothesis that corresponds to a given composite hypothesis for the transformed distribution can be substantial.

Special Composite Hypotheses—Univariate Case

For the case of transformation to a generalized uniform distribution, the simple hypotheses for the frequency function of the transformed population are of the form exp $(A+By+Cy^2)$, where $0 \leqslant y \leqslant 1$. They are of this same form, with $C<0$ and $-\infty<y<\infty$ when the transformation is to a normal distribution, and of this form with $C=0$, $B<0$, $0 \leqslant y<\infty$ for the transformation to the exponential distribution. Simple hypotheses of this form are very convenient from two viewpoints. First, modified composite hypotheses of the same form as these simple hypotheses are easily obtained by use of the weighted geometric-mean method of averaging simple hypotheses. Second, the value of the operating characteristic function is easily determined for any simple hypothesis of this form. Thus, the operating characteristics are not difficult to determine for this kind of modified composite hypotheses. This implies that determination of suitable values for the weights is not overly difficult when the number of simple hypotheses is small. For example, let two simple hypotheses be used for a modified composite alternative hypothesis. Then the values of the two weights can be determined without great difficulty by the requirements that a frequency function is obtained and that the maximum of the probabilities of type II error at the two simple hypotheses is minimum. For a modified composite null hypothesis, the second requirement could be that the maximum of the probabilities of type I error at the two simple hypotheses is minimum.

Transformation of Univariate Variables

The principal effort involved in transforming univariate data for the uniform, normal, and exponential distribution cases lies in obtaining a suitable tabulation for $F_0(x)$. The functions K_α and $\log_e \alpha$ are also used for the normality and exponential cases, respectively, but tables of these functions are readily available.

Evaluation of Operating Characteristics

The operating characteristic function for a test represents the probability that the null hypothesis will be accepted when it is false, and depends on the alternative hypothesis that is considered to be true. That is, for any alternative hypothesis, the operating characteristic function equals unity minus the power function. For the case of simple hypotheses (or modified composite hypotheses), an approximation to the operating characteristic function can be obtained that should have acceptable accuracy for nearly all practical situations where $\alpha, \beta<\frac{1}{2}$. Here the test has significance level α and the probability of type II error is β for the simple alternative used in determining the test.

Let the simple null hypothesis assert that $f(x_1, \ldots, x_n)=f_0(x_1, \ldots, x_n)$ while the simple alternative asserts that $f(x_1, \ldots, x_n)=f_1(x_1, \ldots, x_n)$; the value of the operating characteristic function is to be determined for a simple hypothesis $f_2(x_1, \ldots, x_n)$, which could be the null or the alternative hypothesis. First, a value $h \neq 0$ is determined by

$$\underset{\text{all } (x_1, \ldots, x_n)}{\int \cdots \int} [f_1(x_1, \ldots, x_n)/f_0(x_1, \ldots, x_n)]^h f_2(x_1, \ldots, x_n) dx_1 \ldots dx_n = 1,$$

where the integration becomes a summation for the discrete case. This equation has a unique nonzero solution for nearly all frequency functions of practical interest (page 158 of ref. 539 contains conditions for a unique solution). Using the resulting value of h, the value of the operating characteristic function is approximately

$$\{[(1-\beta)/\alpha]^h - 1\}/\{[(1-\beta)/\alpha]^h - [\beta/(1-\alpha)]^h\}$$

for the hypothesis $f(x_1, \ldots, x_n) = f_2(x_1, \ldots, x_n)$ and the kinds of tests considered.

For all the presentations of tests, including those with composite hypotheses, a test can be considered to be based on the ratio of two frequency functions and, with suitable interpretation, can be considered to have simple hypotheses; in some cases, these hypotheses depend on supplementary information (including sample values that have become available). When the hypotheses depend on the sample values that have become available, they are only approximately determined and change as additional sample values are obtained; then the operating characteristics determined at any given stage of the experiment are statistical estimates of the true operating characteristics.

Thus, in principle, the method given for determining values of the operating characteristic function is applicable to all of the tests that are presented. Rather than continually repeat the statement of this method, only reference to it, and suggestions for its use, are given in the presentations. The suggestions include special ways of evaluating h; the evaluation of h is relatively easy for cases where transformations to the uniform, normal, and exponential distributions are used. When an explicit expression for the operating characteristic function is available and not too complicated, it is usually stated in the presentations.

In cases where the simple hypotheses are expressed in terms of a one-dimensional parameter ξ, with ξ_0 being the null hypothesis and ξ_1 the alternative, approximate values of the operating characteristic function for ξ between ξ_0 and ξ_1 can be determined on the basis of three points and interpolation. Explicitly, the operating characteristic function has the value $1-\alpha$ for $\xi = \xi_0$, the value β for $\xi = \xi_1$, and the value

$$\{\log_{10}[(1-\beta)/\alpha]\}/\{\log_{10}[(1-\beta)/\alpha] + |\log_{10}[\beta/(1-\alpha)]|\}$$

for $\xi=\xi'$, where ξ' is such that

$$E \log_{10} \{f[X(1), \ldots, X(n); \xi_1]/f[X(1), \ldots, X(n); \xi_0]\}=0$$

when ξ' is the value of ξ; here, for nearly all situations of practical interest, ξ' is unique and lies between ξ_0 and ξ_1.

Average Sample Numbers

The average sample number is the expected number of sample values required to reach a decision for a sequential test and is denoted by Em. The value of Em depends on the population actually sampled, the value of α, the value of β, the frequency function representing the null hypothesis, the frequency function representing the alternative, and sometimes on additional quantities.

Suppose that the simple hypotheses which are possibilities can be represented by $f(x_1, \ldots, x_n; \xi)$, where ξ is a one-dimensional parameter. Let ξ_0 be the simple null hypothesis considered and ξ_1 the simple alternative. Then the value $E_\xi m$ of the average sample number when ξ is the parameter value for the population sampled is approximately given by

$$\{B(\xi) \log_{10} [\beta/(1-\alpha)]+[1-B(\xi)] \log_{10} [(1-\beta)/\alpha]\}/E_\xi Z, \text{ when } E_\xi Z \neq 0$$
$$\{\log_{10} [(1-\alpha)/\beta]\}\{\log_{10}[(1-\beta)/\alpha]\}/\sigma_\xi{}^2 Z, \text{ when } E_\xi Z=0,$$

where $B(\xi)$ is the value of the operating characteristic function for parameter value ξ [the notation $L(\xi)$ is also sometimes used for the *OC* function at ξ],

$$Z=\log_{10} \{f[X(1), \ldots, X(n); \xi_1]/f[X(1), \ldots, X(n); \xi_0]\},$$

$E_\xi Z$ is the expected value of Z and $\sigma_\xi{}^2 Z$ is the variance of Z when the parameter value is ξ. Since, for given ξ, $f(x_1, \ldots, x_n; \xi)$ is a completely specified frequency function, $E_\xi Z$ and $\sigma_\xi{}^2 Z$ can always be directly determined. These expressions for $E_\xi m$ should be reasonably accurate when $\alpha, \beta<\frac{1}{2}$.

As mentioned when discussing operating characteristics, the sequential tests presented can be considered to be based on the ratio of two frequency functions and, with suitable interpretation, can be considered to have simple hypotheses. Thus, in principle, these approximations to the value of $E_\xi m$ are applicable to all the tests considered. Except when explicit expressions of not too complicated a nature are available, the presentations will not contain values for $E_\xi m$. Instead, reference will be made to the material given here.

When the possible forms for the population sampled are satisfactorily represented by the frequency functions $f(x_1, \ldots, x_n; \xi)$, the largest possible average sample number equals $\sup_\xi E_\xi m$. Frequently, the maximum value of $E_\xi m$ is approximately equal to $E_{\xi'} m$, where ξ' is such that $E_{\xi'} Z = 0$.

In addition to an approximate evaluation of $E_\xi m$, it is often useful to have information about $P_\xi(m \leqslant m_0)$, the probability that the sample size required to reach a decision is at most m_0 when the parameter value is ξ. If m_0 is not too small, to a reasonable approximation

$$P_\xi(m \leqslant m_0) \geqslant 1 - \Phi[a(\xi, m_0)] + \Phi[b(\xi, m_0)],$$

where

$$a(\xi, m_0) = \{\log_{10} [(1-\beta)/\alpha] - m_0 E_\xi Z\}/\sqrt{m_0}\sigma_\xi Z,$$

$$b(\xi, m_0) = \{\log_{10} [\beta/(1-\alpha)] - m_0 E_\xi Z\}/\sqrt{m_0}\sigma \xi Z,$$

and $E_\xi Z$, $\sigma_\xi Z$ are the expected values and standard deviation, respectively, of Z when the parameter value is ξ. To avoid repetition, this relation is referred to but not explicitly stated in the presentations.

Truncated Tests and Their Properties

It is frequently desirable to place an upper limit on the number of sample values that are used for a sequential test. Also, it would seem inefficient to continue taking sample values after a stage is reached where, by use of a suitable termination procedure, a test can be obtained with very nearly the same operating characteristics as the nontruncated sequential test. Here three possible termination procedures are considered for probability-ratio tests with simple hypotheses. Ordinarily, a test can be truncated without much effect on its operating characteristics when the sample size is three times the average sample number for the test. However, a more quantitative method of determining the effect of truncation at a given sample size is furnished by upper bounds for the significance level and probability of type II error (at the alternative) for the resulting test. Rough upper bounds for these quantities are determined for each of the three termination procedures that are considered. These bounds are applicable for all the tests with simple hypotheses presented except those for life-testing situations where the data are transformed to an exponential form.

One termination procedure consists in accepting the null hypothesis if the test statistic is at most zero and accepting the alternative otherwise. Another termination procedure consists in accepting the null hypothesis if the test statistic is at least as near the lower boundary as the upper boundary, and in accepting the alternative otherwise. The remaining termination procedure consists in accepting the null hypothesis if the test statistic is at most equal to a specially determined value and in accepting the alternative otherwise. Here the value is determined so that the percentage increase in the significance level upper bound is the same as the percentage increase in the upper bound for the probability of type II error, as compared to the values (α and β) that would occur if the test were not truncated. Of course, a termination procedure is only used when no prior decision has been reached.

The first termination procedure is similar to that advocated in ref. 539. Let $\alpha(m)$ and $\beta(m)$ be the significance level and probability of type II error, respectively, that result when the sequential test with simple null hypothesis $f(x_1, \ldots, x_n) = f_0(x_1, \ldots, x_n)$ and simple alternative $f(x_1, \ldots, x_n) = f_1(x_1, \ldots, x_n)$ is truncated at sample size m. Then, if the first termination procedure is used,

$$\alpha(m) \leqslant \alpha + (1-\alpha)\Big\{\Phi\Big[(\sqrt{m}\sigma_0 Z)^{-1} \log_{10} [(1-\beta)/\alpha] - \sqrt{m}(E_0 Z)/\sigma_0 Z\Big] - \Phi[-\sqrt{m}(E_0 Z)/\sigma_0 Z]\Big\},$$

$$\beta(m) \leqslant \beta + (\beta-1)\Big\{\Phi\Big[(\sqrt{m}\sigma_1 Z)^{-1} \log_{10} [\beta/(1-\alpha)] - \sqrt{m}(E_1 Z)/\sigma_1 Z\Big] - \Phi[-\sqrt{m}(E_1 Z)/\sigma_1 Z]\Big\},$$

where

$$Z = \log_{10} \{f_1[X(1), \ldots, X(n)]/f_0[X(1), \ldots, X(n)]\};$$

here $E_0 Z$, $\sigma_0 Z$ and $E_1 Z$, $\sigma_1 Z$ are the expected value and standard deviation of Z under the null hypothesis and the alternative, respectively.

The second termination procedure is used for the sequential tests presented in Chapters 7 and 8. Let the notation be the same as for the first termination procedure. Then, if the second termination procedure is used,

$$\alpha(m) \leqslant \alpha + A(\alpha, \beta)\Big\{\Phi\Big[(\sqrt{m}\sigma_0 Z)^{-1} \log_{10} [(1-\beta)/\alpha] - \sqrt{m}(E_0 Z)/\sigma_0 Z\Big] - \Phi\Big[(2\sqrt{m}\sigma_0 Z)^{-1} \log_{10} [\beta(1-\beta)/\alpha(1-\alpha)] - \sqrt{m}(E_0 Z)/\sigma_0 Z\Big]\Big\},$$

$$\beta(m) \leqslant \beta + B(\alpha, \beta)\Big\{\Phi\Big[(2\sqrt{m}\sigma_1 Z)^{-1} \log_{10} [\beta(1-\beta)/\alpha(1-\alpha)] - \sqrt{m}(E_1 Z)/\sigma_1 Z\Big] - \Phi\Big[(\sqrt{m}\sigma_1 Z)^{-1} \log_{10} [\beta/(1-\alpha)] - \sqrt{m}(E_1 Z)/\sigma_1 Z\Big]\Big\},$$

where $A(\alpha, \beta)$ is $1-\alpha$ if $\beta(1-\beta)/\alpha(1-\alpha) \geqslant 1$ and is unity otherwise; $B(\alpha, \beta)$ is $1-\beta$ if $\beta(1-\beta)/\alpha(1-\alpha) \leqslant 1$ and is unity otherwise.

For the third termination procedure, using the same notation,

$$\alpha(m) \leqslant \alpha + A(D)\Big\{\Phi\Big[(\sqrt{m}\sigma_0 Z)^{-1}\log_{10}[(1-\beta)/\alpha] - \sqrt{m}(E_0 Z)/\sigma_0 Z\Big] - \Phi\Big[(2\sqrt{m}\sigma_0 Z)^{-1}\log_{10} D - \sqrt{m}(E_0 Z)/\sigma_0 Z\Big]\Big\}$$
$$= \alpha + \alpha(m, D),$$
$$\beta(m) \leqslant \beta + B(D)\Big\{\Phi\Big[(2\sqrt{m}\sigma_1 Z)^{-1}\log_{10} D - \sqrt{m}(E_1 Z)/\sigma_1 Z\Big] - \Phi\Big[(\sqrt{m}\sigma_1 Z)^{-1}\log_{10}[\beta/(1-\alpha)] - \sqrt{m}(E_1 Z)/\sigma_1 Z\Big]\Big\}$$
$$= \beta + \beta(m, D),$$

where $A(D)$ is $1-\alpha$ if $D \geqslant 1$ and is unity otherwise; $B(D)$ is $1-\beta$ if $D \leqslant 1$ and unity otherwise. The value of D is determined from

$$\beta(m, D)\alpha = \alpha(m, D)\beta,$$

with $D = 1$ if this equation has no solution due to the discontinuity at $D = 1$.

In some respects, the third termination procedure seems to be most meaningful. However, a greater amount of computation is required for its use. Also, the termination procedures seem to be roughly equivalent, with respect to upper bounds for $\alpha(m)$ and $\beta(m)$, when the values of α and β do not differ very much.

As already mentioned, the sequential tests presented can be considered to be based on the ratio of two frequency functions and can be interpreted to have simple hypotheses. Thus, in principle, all three of these termination procedures can be applied and the stated upper bounds for $\alpha(m)$, $\beta(m)$ can be used. The material contained here is not repeated in the presentations; instead, reference to this material is made in the presentations.

Decision Theory Interpretations of Test—Remark

A probability-ratio sequential test can be interpreted as a statistical decision theory procedure for selecting one of two specified simple hypotheses. In fact, for a given *a priori* distribution for the hypotheses, a fixed cost per observation, and the appropriate loss function, a probability-ratio sequential test is optimal; that is, it is a Bayes nontruncated sequential procedure. This property of the probability-ratio sequential test is discussed in the next section (Statistical Decision Theory Procedures).

Outline of Presentations

A total of ten presentations are given for sequential results. The first of these is concerned with estimation of the value of a distribution function at a specified point. The second contains tests for a distribution function at a specified point. The third presents confidence regions for the value of a distribution function at a specified point.

The next three presentations contain tests of distribution functions for the continuous univariate case that are obtained by a transformation of variable. For the first of these, the transformation is to a generalization of the uniform (rectangular) distribution [0, 1]. The second contains a number of tests, including one with two separate alternatives (three hypotheses in all), for the case where the transformation is to normality. The transformation is to an exponential population for the third presentation of this type; these results are for use in life-testing situations.

The next presentation contains some general nature tests for arbitrary distribution functions. These tests are obtained by converting the sample data to a categorical form.

The final three presentations are concerned with tests for frequency functions. The first of these contains probability-ratio tests for simple hypotheses. The second contains tests for a moderately general class of composite hypotheses; here nuisance parameters are replaced by estimates that are based on supplementary information and on the sample values that have previously been obtained. The final presentation of this section contains tests where, on the basis of the simple hypotheses considered, the data are converted to a categorical form with three categories.

Fixed Material for Section

Assumptions 1 Random sample **Characteristics 3** Not used symmetrically.

Estimation of Distribution Function at Given Point

Data 1 Arbitrary, univariate or multivariate **2** None **3** $\{X(i)_j\}_m$ **4** $n_1 = \ldots = n_m = n \geqslant 1$; m not a fixed value **Description 1** Exact unbiased sequential point estimation **2** $F(x_1, \ldots, x_n)$ for a specified value $(x_1, \ldots, x_n)$, on basis of the m observations evaluated in performing a nontruncated test where observations obtained and used singly **Assumptions 2** None **3** None **Results 1** Let $y(t) = 1$ if $X(1)_t \leqslant x_1, \quad \ldots, X(n)_t \leqslant x_n$ and $=0$ otherwise. Test based on $\sum_{t=1}^{j} y(t)$ and terminated first time $\sum_{t=1}^{j} y(t)$ equals the value of a boundary pt. Test actually terminated when $j = m$ and with attainment of boundary pt. $(C_m, m - C_m)$, where first coordinate represents no. of the $y(t)$, $t \leqslant m$, that are 1's and second coordinate no. that are 0's. When jth sample value used, $1 \leqslant j \leqslant m$, the accessible boundary pts. (specified by the test procedure) are $(b_j, j - b_j)$ for $b_j \leqslant j$ and $(a_j, j - a_j)$ when $a_j \geqslant 0$; here $b_j \geqslant a_j$, $b_j \leqslant b_{j+1}$, $a_j \leqslant a_{j+1}$, and the a_j, b_j are integers. Let the set $(A_1, A'_1), \ldots, (A_R, A'_R)$, where $R \leqslant 2m - 1$ and the arrangement is such that $A_r + A_r' \leqslant A_{r+1} + A'_{r+1}$ with $A_r \leqslant A_{r+1}$, consist of

$(C_m, m-C_m)$ and the accessible boundary pts. for $j<m$; when the same pt. occurs more than once, it is included only once in this set. Let $N(A_1, A'_1)=1$. If $A_1=0$, express $\sum_{r=1}^{R} N(A_r, A'_r)p^{A_r}(1-p)^{A'_r}$ in terms of increasing powers of p and equate the coeff. of each positive power of p to zero. Starting with coeff. of p and proceeding according to increasing powers of p, determine $N(A_r, A'_r)$ for $r=2, \ldots, R$ in a stepwise fashion. If $A'_1=0$ (either $A_1=0$ or $A'_1=0$), express $\sum_{r=1}^{R} N(A_r, A'_r)q^{A'_r}(1-q)^{A_r}$ in terms of increasing powers of q and equate the coeff. of each positive power of q to zero. Starting with coeff. of q and proceeding according to increasing powers of q, determine $N(A_r, A'_r)$ for $r=2, \ldots, R$ in a stepwise fashion. By one of these methods, $N(A_R, A'_R)=N(C_m, m-C_m)$ is evaluated. Let the set $(B_1, B'_1), \ldots, (B_W, B'_W)$, where $W<R$ and the arrangement is such that $B_w+B'_w \leqslant B_{w+1}+B'_{w+1}$ with $B_w \leqslant B_{w+1}$, consist of $(C_m, m-C_m)$ and the accessible boundary pts. for $j<m$ where the first coordinate is nonzero. Let $N^*(B_1, B'_1)=1$. If $B_1=1$, express $\sum_{w=1}^{W} N^*(B_w, B'_w)p^{B_w-1}(1-p)^{B'_w}$ in terms of increasing powers of p and equate the coeff. of each positive power of p to zero. Starting with coeff. of p and proceeding according to increasing powers of p, determine $N^*(B_w, B'_w)$ for $w=2, \ldots, W$ in a stepwise fashion. If $B'_1=0$ (either $B_1=1$ or $B'_1=0$), express $\sum_{w=1}^{W} N^*(B_w, B'_w)q^{B'_w}(1-q)^{B_w-1}$ in terms of increasing powers of q and equate coeff. of each positive power of q to zero. Starting with coeff. of q and proceeding according to increasing powers of q, determine $N^*(B_w, B'_w)$ for $w=2, \ldots, W$ in a stepwise fashion. By one of these methods, $N^*(B_W, B'_W)=N^*(C_m, m-C_m)$ is evaluated **2** *Estimate*: $N^*(C_m, m-C_m)/N(C_m, m-C_m)$ is an unbiased estimate of $F(x_1, \ldots, x_n)$ **3** None **4** For given j, any pt. $(c, j-c)$ with c an integer and $0 \leqslant c \leqslant j$ is said to be accessible and of index j. The estimate presented is the unique unbiased estimate of $F(x_1, \ldots, x_n)$ obtainable on the basis of the $y(t)$ if every two accessible pts. of index j, $(j=1, \ldots, m)$, which are not boundary pts. cannot be separated on the line $c_1+c_2=j$, where c_1 is the first coordinate and c_2 the second coordinate for pts., by boundary pts. or pts. that are not accessible **Characteristics 1** Low to high, depending on m. Low only for very small m **2** Variance of estimate $\geqslant F(x_1, \ldots, x_n)[1-F(x_1, \ldots, x_n)]/E_F(m)$, where $E_F(m)$ is the average sample number, for the true value of $F(x_1, \ldots, x_n)$, for the sequential test yielding the data on which the estimate is based. Approx. upper bound for $E_F(m)$ furnished by next presentation **4** Sensitive to dependences involving more than a small percentage of observations. Moderately sensitive to variation among the values of the $P[y(t)=1]$ **5** Not difficult to decide on random sample condition **6** Only recommended for use as additional procedure for situations where a test is being conducted **Bibliography** Ref. 66, 204, 226, 264, 308, 417, 456, 598, 599.

Tests for Distribution Function at Given Point

Data 1 Arbitrary, univariate or multivariate **2** None **3** $\{X(i)_j\}_m$ **4** $n_1 = \ldots = n_m = n \geqslant 1$; m not a fixed value **Description 1** Approx. (nearly exact) one-sided and two-sided sequential signif. tests **2** $F(x_1, \ldots, x_n)$ for a specified value $(x_1, \ldots, x_n)$ **Assumptions 2** None **3** $0 < F(x_1, \ldots, x_n) < 1$ **Results 1** F_0, F_1, F_2 specified numbers between 0 and 1 such that $F_1 < F_0 < F_2$. Null hyp. H_0 is $F(x_1, \ldots, x_n) = F_0$. Altern. hyp. for one-sided tests are $F(x_1, \ldots, x_n) < F_0$ with emphasis on situations where $F(x_1, \ldots, x_n) \leqslant F_1$, and $F(x_1, \ldots, x_n) > F_0$ with emphasis on $F(x_1, \ldots, x_n) \geqslant F_2$. For the two types of two-sided tests, altern. hyp. is $F(x_1, \ldots, x_n) \neq F_0$ with emphasis on situations where $F(x_1, \ldots, x_n) \leqslant F_1$ or $F(x_1, \ldots, x_n) \geqslant F_2$. To a reasonable approx., all tests have signif. level α ($\alpha < \frac{1}{2}$). For one-sided tests, β is approximately max. prob. of type II error for situations emphasized. For one type of two-sided test, β = prob. of type II error when $F(x_1, \ldots, x_n) = w_1 F_1 + w_2 F_2$, where w_1 and w_2 non-negative, $w_1 + w_2 = 1$, and w_1 chosen so that larger of prob. of type II error at F_1 and F_2 minimized. For other type of two-sided test, β = prob. of type II error when $F(x_1, \ldots, x_n) = F_1^{w_1} F_2^{w_2}$, where w_1 and w_2 such that $0 < F_1^{w_1} F_2^{w_2} < 1$, $F_1^{w_1} F_2^{w_2} + (1 - F_1)^{w_1} (1 - F_2)^{w_2} = 1$, and w_1 chosen so that larger of prob. of type II error at F_1 and F_2 minimized. For both types of two-sided tests, method of evaluating w_1 stated in part 4 of Results. In all cases, $\alpha + \beta < 1$. Notation: $F = F(x_1, \ldots, x_n)$, $F^* = 1 - F$, $F_1^* = 1 - F_1$, $F_2^* = 1 - F_2$; F_3, F_4 = general symbols for numbers between 0 and 1, $F_3^* = 1 - F_3$, $F_4^* = 1 - F_4$. $a_J(F_3, F_4)$ is largest integer $\leqslant$ $\{\log_{10} [\beta/(1-\alpha)]\}/|\log_{10}(F_4 F_3^*/F_4^* F_3)| + J[\log_{10}(F_3^*/F_4^*)]/\log_{10}(F_4 F_3^*/F_3 F_4^*)$ and $b_J(F_3, F_4)$ is smallest integer $\geqslant$ $-\frac{1}{3} + \{\log_{10} [(1-\beta)/\alpha]\}/|\log_{10} (F_4 F_3^*/F_3 F_4^*)| + (J + \frac{2}{3})[\log_{10} (F_3^*/F_4^*)]/\log_{10} (F_4 F_3^*/F_3 F_4^*)$. Let $H'_1 = H'_1(F_4) = \{\log_{10} [F_4/F_0]\}/\log_{10} (F_0^*/F_4^*)$, $H'_2 = H'_2(F_4) = \{\log_{10} [(1-\alpha)/\beta]\}/\log_{10} (F_0^*/F_4^*)$, and $H'_3 = H'_3(F_4) = \{\log_{10} [(1-\beta)/\alpha]\}/\log_{10} (F_0^*/F_4^*) + \frac{2}{3} - (H'_1 + 1)/3$. When F_0, α, β, F_4 such that H'_1, H'_2, H'_3, and $(H'_2 + H'_3)/(H'_1 + 1)$ positive integers with $(H'_2 + H'_3)/(H'_1 + 1) \geqslant 2$, $V(F_4) = H'_1 + 1$ and $V_0(F_4) = H'_2 - (H'_1 + 1)$[largest integer in $H'_2/(H'_1 + 1)$]; otherwise $V(F_4) = V_0(F_4) = 1$. For J, V integers $\geqslant 1$, $N_J = \sum_{t=1}^{(J-1)V+V_0} y(t) = m F_m(x_1, \ldots, x_n)$ for $m = (J-1)V + V_0$, where $y(t) = 1$ if $X(1)_t \leqslant x_1, \ldots, X(n)_t \leqslant x_n$ and $= 0$ otherwise **2** *Tests*: Sequential sampling procedure starts with group of $m = V_0$ sample values and continues in groups of sample values with $m = V_0 + V, V_0 + 2V, \ldots$ until a decision is reached. Notation: $J(m) = 1 + (m - V_0)/V$. No prior conditions are imposed on tests when $J(m) = 1$. *One-sided test of* $F < F_0$: Here $(V, V_0) = (1, 1)$ or $\{V(F_1), V_0(F_1)\}$. Given that $a_J(F_0, F_1) < N_J < b_J(F_0, F_1)$ for $J \leqslant J(m) - 1$, accept H_0 if $N_{J(m)} \leqslant a_{J(m)}(F_0, F_1)$; accept $F < F_0$ with emphasis on $F \leqslant F_1$ if $N_{J(m)} \geqslant b_{J(m)}(F_0, F_1)$; otherwise take another V sample values and repeat procedure for increased sample size. *One-sided test of* $F > F_0$: Here $(V, V_0) = (1, 1)$ or $\{V(F_2), V_0(F_2)\}$. Given that $a_J(F_0, F_2) < N_J < b_J(F_0, F_2)$ for $J \leqslant J(m)-1$, accept H_0 if $N_{J(m)} \leqslant a_{J(m)}(F_0, F_2)$; accept $F > F_0$ with emphasis on $F \geqslant F_2$ if $N_{J(m)} \geqslant b_{J(m)}(F_0, F_2)$; otherwise take another V sample values and continue. *Two-sided test using* $w_1F_1 + w_2F_2$: Here $(V, V_0) = (1, 1)$ or $\{V(w_1F_1 + w_2F_2), V_0(w_1F_1 + w_2F_2)\}$. Given that $a_J(F_0, w_1F_1 + w_2F_2) < N_J < b_J(F_0, w_1F_1 + w_2F_2)$ for $J \leqslant J(m)-1$, accept H_0 if $N_{J(m)} \leqslant a_{J(m)}(F_0, w_1F_1 + w_2F_2)$; accept $F \neq F_0$ with emphasis on $F \leqslant F_1$ or $F \geqslant F_2$ if $N_{J(m)} \geqslant b_{J(m)}(F_0, w_1F_1 + w_2F_2)$; otherwise take another V sample values and continue. *Two-sided test using* $F_1{}^{w_1}F_2{}^{w_2}$: Here $(V, V_0) = (1, 1)$ or $\{V(F_1{}^{w_1}F_2{}^{w_2}), V_0(F_1{}^{w_1}F_2{}^{w_2})\}$. Given that $a_J(F_0, F_1{}^{w_1}F_2{}^{w_2}) < N_J < b_J(F_0, F_1{}^{w_1}F_2{}^{w_2})$ for $J \leqslant J(m)-1$, accept H_0 if $N_{J(m)} \leqslant a_{J(m)}(F_0, F_1{}^{w_1}F_2{}^{w_2})$; accept $F \neq F_0$ with emphasis on $F \leqslant F_1$ or $F \geqslant F_2$ if $N_{J(m)} \geqslant b_{J(m)}(F_0, F_1{}^{w_1}F_2{}^{w_2})$; otherwise take another V sample values and continue **3** None **4** The two-sided test using $w_1F_1 + w_2F_2$ is based on the conceptual random selection situation where, independently for each sample value, the altern. F_1 occurs with prob. w_1 and the altern. F_2 occurs with prob. w_2. For this test, subject to the restrictions stated in part 1 of Results, value for w_1 is that which minimizes max $[B_1(w_1, F_1), B_1(w_1, F_2)]$, where $B_1(w_1, F) = \{[(1-\beta)/\alpha]^{r_1(w_1, F)} - 1\}\{[(1-\beta)/\alpha]^{r_1(w_1, F)} - [\beta/(1-\alpha)]^{r_1(w_1, F)}\}$ and $r_1(w_1, F)$ is sol. for r of $[(w_1F_1 + w_2F_2)/F_0]^r F + [(1 - w_1F_1 - w_2F_2)/(1-F_0)]^r(1-F) = 1$. The two-sided test using $F_1{}^{w_1}F_2{}^{w_2}$ is based on a weighted geometric-mean type averaging of the dist. of $y(t)$ when $F = F_1$ and this dist. when $F = F_2$. For this test, subject to the restrictions stated in part 1 of Results, value for w_1 is that which minimizes max $[B_2(w_1, F_1), B_2(w_1, F_2)]$, where $B_2(w_1, F) = \{[(1-\beta)/\alpha]^{r_2(w_1, F)} - 1\}/\{[(1-\beta)/\alpha]^{r_2(w_1, F)} - [\beta/(1-\alpha)]^{r_2(w_1, F)}\}$ and $r_2(w_1, F)$ is sol. for r of $(F_1{}^{w_1}F_2{}^{w_2}/F_0)^r F + [(1 - F_1{}^{w_1}F_2{}^{w_2})/(1-F_0)]^r (1-F) = 1$. *Truncation*: See page 406. Whether truncated or not, one-sided test with altern. $F < F_0$ can also be considered as test of composite null hyp. $F \geqslant F_0$, and one-sided test of $F > F_0$ can also be considered as test of composite null hyp. $F \leqslant F_0$; both types of one-sided tests have a (generalized) signif. level of approx. α. These tests are special cases of probability-ratio test and can be interpreted as having simple hypotheses; decision theory implications of such tests considered in next sect. See page 396 for method of converting tests of simple hypotheses to tests of general modified composite hypotheses **Characteristics 1** Low to lower-medium for one-sided tests, depending on n and required sample size. Lower medium to medium for two-sided test using $w_1F_1 + w_2F_2$; medium to upper medium for two-sided test using $F_1{}^{w_1}F_2{}^{w_2}$ **2** For test of $F < F_0$, approx. operating characteristic (OC) fct. is $B_1(1, F)$; for test of $F > F_0$, OC fct. is $B_1(0, F)$; for test using $w_1F_1 + w_2F_2$, OC fct. is $B_1(w_1, F)$; for test using $F_1^{w_1}F_2^{w_2}$, OC fct. is $B_2(w_1, F)$. For the corresponding four tests, let $F_a =$ $F_1, F_2,$ $w_1F_1+w_2F_2,$ $F_1^{w_1}F_2^{w_2}$, respectively, and let $B(F)$ be the general notation for the OC fct. of a test; here the test considered is identified by the expression for F_a. Then $B(0)=1$, $B(1)=0$, $B(F_0)=1-\alpha$, $B(F_a)=\beta$, $B\{1/[H'_1(F_a)+1]\}=\{\log_{10}[(1-\beta)/\alpha]\}/\{\log_{10}[(1-\beta)/\alpha]+|\log_{10}[\beta/(1-\alpha)]|\}$ furnish five pts. for OC fct. of each test; interpolation furnishes other pts. To attain specified α and β, much smaller sample sizes needed, on the average, for sequential tests than for corresponding fixed sample size tests (see Chapter 10); often average sample no. less than $\frac{1}{2}$ of corresponding fixed sample size. For each test, to a reasonable approx., $E(m) \leqslant m'(F_a)$ for all F; here $m'(F_a)$ is the largest integer contained in $H'_2(F_a)H'_3(F_a)[1+H'_1(F_a)]^2/H'_1(F_a)+V/2$ that is of form V_0+(integral multiple of V) **4** Can be sensitive to dependences involving more than small percentage of observations. Moderately sensitive to variation among values of the $P[y(t)=1]$ **5** Not difficult to decide on random sample assumption **6** Results when sample values drawn in groups of other sizes obtainable from material in ref. 264 and 539 **Bibliography** Ref. 264, 539.

Confidence Regions for Distribution Function at Given Point

Data 1 Arbitrary, univariate or multivariate **2** None **3** $\{X(i)_j\}_m$ **4** $n_1 = \dots = n_m = n \geqslant 1$; m not a fixed value **Description 1** Theoretical-approx. two-sided confidence intervals **2** $F(x_1, \dots, x_n)$ for a specified value $(x_1, \dots, x_n)$ **Assumptions 2** None **3** $0 < F(x_1, \dots, x_n) < 1$ **Results 1** $y(0)=$ guess for value of $F=F(x_1, \dots, x_n)$ from supplementary information available at beginning of experiment; $y(0)=\frac{1}{2}$ if no supplementary information available. $y(j)=1$ if $X(1)_j \leqslant x_1, \dots, X(n)_j \leqslant x_n$ and $=0$ otherwise. F_{1j} and F_{2j} are the smaller and larger values of F, respectively, which satisfy $F^{y(1)+\dots+y(j)}(1-F)^{j-y(1)-\dots-y(j)} = (1-\epsilon)\{[y(0)+y(1)+\dots+y(j-1)]/j\}^{y(1)+\dots+y(j)}\{1-[y(0)+\dots+y(j-1)]/j\}^{j-y(1)-\dots-y(j)}$, where ϵ is lower limit for confidence coeff. of seq. confidence interval. $F_{Lm} = \max_{1 \leqslant j \leqslant m} F_{1j}$; $F_{Um} = \min_{1 \leqslant j \leqslant m} F_{2j}$. $r(F_{Lm}, F_{Um})$ is a specified relation that is satisfied for $F_{Um}-F_{Lm}$ sufficiently small. Example is $F_{Um}-F_{Lm} \leqslant D_1+D_2F_{Um}+D_3F_{Lm}$ with D_1, D_2, D_3 non-negative; $F_{Um}-F_{Lm} \leqslant D_1$ and $F_{Um}-F_{Lm} \leqslant D(F_{Um}+F_{Lm})$ are special cases **2** *Two-sided confidence interval*: Starting with $m=1$, continue taking single observations until $r(F_{Lm}, F_{Um})$ satisfied. For final m, $P(F_{Lm} \leqslant F \leqslant F_{Um}) \geqslant \epsilon$ **3** None **4** Based on binomial distribution part of Chapter 7. Advantage of these intervals is that endpoints satisfy specified relation, which can be selected with moderate generality. Expected sample size not determined, but it should not be excessively large unless $F(1-F)$ near zero and/or $r(F_{Lm}, F_{Um})$ not satisfied except when $F_{Um}-F_{Lm}$ very small. Since $y(1)+\dots+y(j)=$

$jF_j(x_1, \ldots, x_n)$, observational data occurs exclusively in terms of empirical dist. fct. for the sample values. **Characteristics 1** Lower medium to high, depending on n and final m, since F_{Lm} and F_{Um} evaluated for each new sample value. Computation reduced by only determining new values for F_{Lm} and F_{Um} every five observations, etc. **2** Unknown efficiency properties, but intuitive considerations indicate that efficiency at least moderately high; for many situations, this is the only available procedure **4** Can be sensitive to dependences involving more than a small percentage of the observations. Moderately sensitive to variation among values of the $P[y(j)=1]$ **5** Not difficult to decide on random sample condition **6** Useful when important that endpoints of confidence interval satisfy specified relation of $r(F_{Lm}, F_{Um})$ type **Bibliography** Ref. 539.

Tests by Transformation to Uniform Distribution—Univariate

Data 1 Continuous, univariate **2** None **3** $\{X(i)_j\}_m$ **4** $n_1 = \ldots = n_m = 1$; m not a fixed value **Description 1** Approx. (nearly exact) sequential signif. tests for simple null hyp. and for simple and modified composite altern. hyp. **2** $F(x)$ over all x, where $F(x)$ dist. fct. of $X(1)_j$. In general, simple hyp. considered assert that transformation $Y(j)=F_0[X(1)_j]$, where $F_0(x)$ completely specified continuous dist. fct., yields observation with freq. fct. of form $\exp[A(B, C)+By+Cy^2]$ for $0 \leqslant y \leqslant 1$ and equal to zero otherwise, where B and C any specified values. Null hyp. H_0 asserts that $B=C=0$. H_1 any simple altern. for which not both B and C zero. H_2 modified composite hyp. of form $B=w_1B_1+w_2B_2$, $C=w_1C_1+w_2C_2$ with weights w_1 and w_2 suitably chosen. General modified composite hyp. (null and altern.) obtainable by weighted geometric-mean type averaging of freq. fcts. corresponding to simple hyp. **Assumptions 2** Continuous population **3** None **Results 1** To a reasonable approx., all tests have signif. level α $(<\frac{1}{2})$ and prob. of type II error β $(<\frac{1}{2})$ at the altern. considered; in any case, signif. level $\leqslant \alpha$ and prob. of type II error at altern. $\leqslant \beta$. For altern. H_2, w_1 and w_2 such that freq. fct. is obtained and max. of prob. of type II error for simple hyp. $B=B_1$, $C=C_1$ and for simple hyp. $B=B_2$, $C=C_2$ is minimized; freq. fct. obtained when $w_1A(B_1, C_1)+w_2A(B_2, C_2)=A(w_1B_1+w_2B_2, w_1C_1+w_2C_2)$. Method of evaluating w_1 and w_2 given in part 4 of Results. $N_j(B, C)=jA(B, C)+B\sum_{t=1}^{j} Y(t)+C\sum_{t=1}^{j} Y(t)^2$ **2** *Tests*: Sequential sampling procedure such that one observation obtained and used at a time. No prior conditions imposed on tests when $m=1$. *Test of Altern.* H_1: Given that $\log_e[\beta/(1-\alpha)] < N_j(B, C) < \log_e[(1-\beta)/\alpha]$ for $j \leqslant m-1$, accept H_0 if $N_m(B, C) \leqslant \log_e[\beta/(1-\alpha)]$; accept H_1 if $N_m \geqslant \log_e[(1-\beta)/\alpha]$; otherwise take another sample value and repeat procedure for increased sample size. *Test of Altern.* H_2: Given that $\log_e[\beta/(1-\alpha)] < N_j(w_1B_1+w_2B_2, w_1C_1+$

$w_2C_2) < \log_e [(1-\beta)/\alpha]$ for $j \leqslant m-1$, accept H_0 if $N_m(w_1B_1+w_2B_2, w_1C_1+w_2C_2) \leqslant \log_e [\beta/(1-\alpha)]$; accept H_2 with emphasis on the simple hyp. $B=B_1, C=C_1$ and/or the simple hyp. $B=B_2, C=C_2$ if $N_m(w_1B_1+w_2B_2, w_1C_1+w_2C_2) \geqslant \log_e [(1-\beta)/\alpha]$; otherwise take another sample value and continue **3** In general, $A(B, C) = -\log_e \{\int_0^1 e^{By+Cy^2}dy\}$. When $C<0$, $A(B, C) = B^2/4C + \log_e(-C/\pi) - \log_e [\Phi(\sqrt{-2C} - B/\sqrt{-2C}) - \Phi(-B/\sqrt{-2C})]$. When $C>0$, $A(B, C) = B^2/4C + \log_e(2C) - \log_e [\text{sgn}(\sqrt{2C}+B/\sqrt{2C})\psi(|\sqrt{2C}+B/\sqrt{2C}|) - \text{sgn}(B)\psi(|B|/\sqrt{2C})]$, where $\psi(x) = \int_0^x e^{\frac{1}{2}z^2}dz$ with $x \geqslant 0$. When $C=0$ and $B \neq 0$, $A(B, C) = \log_e |B| - \log_e |e^B - 1|$. $A(0, 0)=0$ **4** $h = h(B', C'; B, C)$ is sol. for h of $hA(B, C) + A(B', C') = A(hB+B', hC+C')$. $L(B', C'; B, C) = \{[(1-\beta)/\alpha]^h - 1\}/\{[(1-\beta)/\alpha]^h - [\beta/(1-\alpha)]^h\}$. For H_2, relation for obtaining freq. fct. furnishes w_2 in terms of w_1, say $w_2 = w_2(w_1)$; value for w_1 is that which minimizes max of $L[B_1, C_1; w_1B_1+w_2(w_1)B_2, w_1C_1+w_2(w_1)C_2]$ and $L[B_2, C_2; w_1B_1+w_2(w_1)B_2, w_1C_1+w_2(w_1)C_2]$. Simple hypotheses occurring in these tests can be replaced by modified composite hyp. (see page 396). *Truncation*: See page 406 **Characteristics 1** Low to lower-medium for test of H_1, depending on final m and whether $F_0(x)$ already tabulated. Upper low to medium for test of H_2 **2** For test of H_1, approx. OC fct. is $L(B', C'; B, C)$ when altern. is B', C'; OC fct. is $L(B', C'; w_1B_1 + w_2B_2, w_1C_1+w_2C_2)$ for test of H_2. $E_1(B', C')$ denotes average sample no. for test of H_1 and true hyp. B', C'; $E_2(B', C')$ is average sample no. for test H_2. $E_1(B', C') \doteq \{L(B', C'; B, C) \log_e [(1-\beta)/\alpha] + [1 - L(B', C'; B, C)] \log_e[\beta/(1-\alpha)]\}/E[Y(1)|B', C']$; $E_2(B', C') \doteq \{L(B', C'; w_1B_1+w_2B_2, w_1C_1+w_2C_2) \log_e [(1-\beta)/\alpha] + [1 - L(B', C'; w_1B_1+w_2B_2, w_1C_1+w_2C_2)] \log_e [\beta/(1-\alpha)]\}/E[Y(1)|B', C']$ **4** Moderately sensitive to sample condition. Not sensitive to mild violations of continuity requirement **5** Not difficult to decide on sample and continuity assumptions **6** Useful when $F_0(x)$ representative of dists. of principal interest or best guess as to actual dist. **Bibliography** Ref. 539.

Tests by Transformation to Normal Distribution—Univariate (*Wald, etc.*)

Data 1 Continuous, univariate **2** None **3** $\{X(i)_j\}_m$ **4** $n_1 = \ldots = n_m = 1$; m not a fixed value **Description 1** Approx. (nearly exact) signif. tests for simple and composite hyp. **2** $F(x)$ over all x, where $F(x)$ dist. fct. of $X(1)_j$. In general, simple hyp. considered assert that transformation $Z(j) = -K_{p(j)}$, where $p(j) = F_0[X(1)_j]$ and $F_0(x)$ is completely specified continuous dist. fct., yields observation from normal dist. with mean μ and variance σ^2. Six different types of tests considered. Case (I): Simple hypotheses; yield one-sided test for μ when σ known and one-sided test for σ when μ known (see page 396). Case (II): Two-sided test of μ when σ known. Case (III): Two-sided test of μ when σ unknown. Case (IV): Test of μ with σ known that has two separate composite altern. hyp. and a composite null hyp. Case (V): One-sided test of σ when μ unknown. Case (VI): One-sided tests of $\mu+K_p\sigma$ when μ and σ unknown. For Case (I) modified composite hypotheses (see page 396) based on weighted geometric-mean type averaging of freq. fcts. for simple hyp. can be substituted for one or both simple hyp. Cases (I), (II), (IV) can be interpreted as tests of $\mu+K_p\sigma$. Ordinarily, $\mu=0$ when μ given and $\sigma=1$ when σ given; also, $\mu_0=0$ when $\mu=\mu_0$ tested and $\sigma_0=1$ when $\sigma=\sigma_0$ tested **Assumptions 2** Continuous population **3** None **Results 1** Freq. fct. for normal population with mean μ and variance σ^2 can be represented as $\exp[a(b, c)+bz-cz^2]$, with $b=\mu/\sigma$, $c=1/2\sigma^2$, $a(b, c)=-b^2/2+\log_e\sqrt{c/\pi}$; this form useful for tests with simple hyp., for developing modified composite hyp., and in determining OC fct. values. Except for Case (IV), to a reasonable approx., all tests have sig. level α ($<\frac{1}{2}$) and prob. of type II error β ($<\frac{1}{2}$). $N'_j(b_1, c_1; b_0, c_0)= j[a(b_1, c_1)-a(b_0, c_0)]+(b_1-b_0)\sum_{t=1}^{j} Z(t)-(c_1-c_0)\sum_{t=1}^{j} Z(t)^2$ **2** *Tests*: Sequential sampling procedure such that one observation obtained and used at a time. No prior conditions imposed on tests when $j=1$. *Case (I)*: Here null hyp. is b_0, c_0 and altern. is b_1, c_1. Given that $\log_e[\beta/(1-\alpha)]<N'_j(b_1, c_1; b_0, c_0)<\log_e[(1-\beta)/\alpha]$ for $j\leqslant m-1$, accept null hyp. if $N'_m(b_1, c_1; b_0, c_0)\leqslant\log_e[\beta/(1-\alpha)]$; accept altern. if $N'_m(b_1, c_1; b_0, c_0)\geqslant\log_e[(1-\beta)/\alpha]$; otherwise take another sample value and repeat procedure for increased sample size. *Case (II)*: Here null hyp. is $\mu=\mu_0$ and altern. is $\mu\neq\mu_0$ with emphasis on situations where $\mu\geqslant\mu_0+\delta\sigma$ or $\mu\leqslant\mu_0-\delta\sigma$, $(\delta>0)$. Given that $\log_e[\beta/(1-\alpha)]+j\delta^2/2<\log_e\cosh\{\delta\sum_{t=1}^{j}[Z(t)-\mu_0]/\sigma\}<\log_e[(1-\beta)/\alpha]+j\delta^2/2$ for $j\leqslant m-1$, accept null hyp. if $\log_e\cosh\{\delta\sum_{t=1}^{m}[Z(t)-\mu_0]/\sigma\}\leqslant\log_e[\beta/(1-\alpha)]+m\delta^2/2$; accept altern. if $\log_e\cosh\{\delta\sum_{t=1}^{m}[Z(t)-\mu_0]/\sigma\}\geqslant\log_e[\beta/(1-\alpha)]+m\delta^2/2$; otherwise take another sample value and continue. *Case (III)*: Here null and altern. hyp. same as for Case (II) but σ is unknown. Notation: $p_{1j}=\frac{1}{2}\int_0^\infty\sigma^{-j}\Big\{\exp[-\sum_{t=1}^{j}\{Z(t)-\mu_0-\delta\sigma\}^2/2\sigma^2]+\exp[-\sum_{t=1}^{j}\{Z(t)-\mu_0+\delta\sigma\}^2/2\sigma^2]\Big\}d\sigma$; $p_{0j}=\int_0^\infty\sigma^{-j}\exp\{-\sum_{t=1}^{j}[Z(t)-\mu_0]^2/2\sigma^2\}d\sigma$. Given that $\beta/(1-\alpha)<p_{1j}/p_{0j}<(1-\beta)/\alpha$ for $j\leqslant m-1$, accept null hyp. if $p_{1m}/p_{0m}\leqslant\beta/(1-\alpha)$; accept altern. if $p_{1m}/p_{0m}\geqslant(1-\beta)/\alpha$; otherwise take another sample value and continue. *Case (IV)*: Here three hyp. simultaneously tested, with the null hyp. being that where $\mu=0$ is one of its pts. H_1 is $\mu<\mu_1$; H_2 is $\mu_1\leqslant\mu\leqslant\mu_2$; H_3 is $\mu>\mu_2$. $\eta_1, \eta_2, \eta_3, \eta_4$ are specified numbers such that $\eta_1<\mu_1<\eta_2\leqslant\eta_3<\mu_2<\eta_4$, $\eta_1+\eta_2=2\mu_1$, $\eta_3+\eta_4=2\mu_2$, $\eta_2-\eta_1=\eta_4-\eta_3=\eta$. Test has properties: Prob. of wrong decision $\leqslant\gamma_1$ for $\mu\leqslant\eta_1$, $\leqslant\gamma_2$ for $\eta_1<\mu<\eta_4$, $\leqslant\gamma_3$ for $\mu\geqslant\eta_4$; here γ_1, γ_2, and γ_3

specified with values $<\frac{1}{2}$. Test consists of simultaneously conducting two tests, say T_1 and T_2, of type considered for Case (I). The "null" hyp. $\mu=\eta_1$ is tested against the "altern." $\mu=\eta_2$ for T_1, and the "null" hyp. η_3 is tested against the "altern." η_4 for T_2; $(\alpha, \beta)=(\gamma_1, \gamma_2)$ for T_1, and $(\alpha, \beta)=(\gamma_2, \gamma_3)$ for T_2. Separately but simultaneously, each of T_1 and T_2 is continued (using same observations) until it reaches a decision. Here, $[2(\mu_2-\mu_1)-\eta]/\eta \geqslant [\log_{10}(5/\gamma_2)]/\log_{10}\{[1-\max(\gamma_1, \gamma_3)]/\gamma_2\}$; see ref. 487 for approx. results when this relation not satisfied. If T_1 accepts η_1 and T_2 accepts η_3, then test accepts H_1. If T_1 accepts η_2 and T_2 accepts η_3, then H_2 accepted. If T_1 accepts η_2 and T_2 accepts η_4, then H_3 accepted (T_1 accepting η_1 and T_2 accepting η_4 not possible if $\gamma_2-\gamma_2{}^2+\gamma_1\gamma_3 \leqslant$ larger of γ_1 and γ_2, which is an additional condition). *Case* (*V*): Here null hyp. is $\sigma=\sigma_0$ and altern. $\sigma=\sigma_1$; one-sided test of $\sigma \leqslant \sigma_0$ against altern. $\sigma \geqslant \sigma_1$ obtained when $\sigma_0<\sigma_1$; one-sided test of $\sigma \geqslant \sigma_0$ against altern. $\sigma \leqslant \sigma_1$ obtained when $\sigma_0>\sigma_1$. Test starts when two sample values are available. Given that $2\log_e[\beta/(1-\alpha)]+2(j-1)\log_e(\sigma_1/\sigma_0) < (1/\sigma_0{}^2-1/\sigma_1{}^2)\sum_{t=1}^{j}[Z(t)-\sum_{v=1}^{j}Z(v)/j]^2 < 2\log_e[(1-\beta)/\alpha]+2(j-1)\log_e(\sigma_1/\sigma_0)$ for $j \leqslant m-1$, accept null hyp. if $(1/\sigma_0{}^2-1/\sigma_1{}^2)\sum_{t=1}^{j}[Z(t)-\sum_{v=1}^{j}Z(v)/j]^2 \leqslant 2\log_e[\beta/(1-\alpha)]+2(m-1)\log_e(\sigma_1/\sigma_0)$; accept altern. if $(1/\sigma_0{}^2-1/\sigma_1{}^2)\sum_{t=1}^{j}[Z(t)-\sum_{v=1}^{j}Z(v)/j]^2 \geqslant 2\log_e[(1-\beta)/\alpha]+2(m-1)\log_e(\sigma_1/\sigma_0)$; otherwise take another sample value and continue. Approx. to this test given in ref. 447. *Case* (*VI*): Here null hyp. is $(Z_0-\mu)/\sigma=K_{P(0)}$ and altern. is $(Z_0-\mu)/\sigma=K_{P(1)}$, where Z_0, $P(0)$, $P(1)$ specified. Notation: $N'_j=\frac{1}{2}(j-u_j{}^2)(K_{P(0)}^2-K_{P(1)}^2)+\log_e\{k_{j-1}[-u_jK_{P(1)}]k_{j-1}[-u_jK_{P(0)}]\}$, where $u_j=\{\sum_{t=1}^{j}[Z_0-Z(t)]\}/\{\sum_{t=1}^{j}[Z_0-Z(t)]^2\}^{1/2}$ and $k_j[x]=\int_0^\infty y^j(j!)^{-1}\exp[-\frac{1}{2}(y+x)^2]dy$. Test starts when two sample values are available. Given that $\log_e[\beta/(1-\alpha)]<N'_j<\log_e[(1-\beta)/\alpha]$ for $j \leqslant m-1$, accept null hyp. if $N'_m \leqslant \log_e[\beta/(1-\alpha)]$; accept altern. if $N'_j \geqslant \log_e[(1-\beta)/\alpha]$; otherwise take another sample value and continue **3** $k_j[x]$, with different notation, tabulated in ref. 4 **4** $h=h(b', c'; b_0, c_0, b_1, c_1)$ is sol. for h of $h[a(b_1, c_1)-a(b_0, c_0)]+a(b', c')= a[h(b_1-b_0)+b', h(c_1-c_0)+c']$ subj. to condition that $h(c_1-c_0)+c'>0$. Then, for Case (I) and simple hyp. b', c', OC fct. is $L(b', c'; b_0, c_0, b_1, c_1) \doteq \{[(1-\beta)/\alpha]^h-1\}/\{[(1-\beta)/\alpha]^h-[\beta/(1-\alpha)]^h\}$. For specified b' and c', average sample no. determined by method stated on page 405. Other OC fct., Em, and $P(m \leqslant m_0)$ results stated in part 2 of next heading **Characteristics 1** Case (I): Low to upper low, depending on final m. Case (II): Low to lower-medium. Case (III): Lower medium to lower high. Case (IV): Upper low to upper medium. Case (V): Low to lower-medium. Case (VI): Lower medium to high **2** No OC fct. or average sample no. results are given for Cases (II), (III), and (VI). However, at least for Case (II), a test can be expressed in a prob - ratio form where the methods stated in the introductory part of the sect.

are applicable; in particular, the lower bound for $P(m \leqslant m_0)$ can be used. For Case (IV), OC fct. stated for each of H_1, H_2, H_3: $L(\mu; H_1)$ = prob. of accepting H_1 when μ is true mean $\doteq \{[(1-\gamma_2)/\gamma_1]^{2(\mu_1-\mu)/\eta}-1\}/\{[(1-\gamma_2)/\gamma_1]^{2(\mu_1-\mu)/\eta}-[\gamma_2/(1-\gamma_1)]^{2(\mu_1-\mu)/\eta}\}$; $L(\mu; H_3) \doteq \{1-[\gamma_3/(1-\gamma_2)]^{2(\mu_2-\mu)/\eta}\}/\{[(1-\gamma_3)/\gamma_2]^{2(\mu_2-\mu)/\eta}-[\gamma_3/(1-\gamma_2)]^{2(\mu_2-\mu)/\eta}\}$; $L(\mu; H_2)=1-L(\mu; H_1)-L(\mu; H_3)$. Let $E_1(m|\mu)$ and $E_2(m|\mu)$ be the average sample no.'s for T_1 and T_2; then $E(m|\mu) \geqslant \max\,[E_1(m|\mu), E_2(m|\mu)]$. $E(m|\mu) \leqslant$ smaller of $\{\sigma^2 \log_e [\gamma_2/(1-\gamma_1)]\}/\eta(\mu-\mu_1)$ and $\{\sigma^2 \log_e [(1-\gamma_3)/\gamma_2]\}/\eta(\mu-\mu_2)$; this upper bound is close for $\mu \leqslant \eta_1$ and $\mu \geqslant \eta_4$ (to obtain closer bounds for $\eta_1 < \mu < \eta_4$, see ref. 487). For Case (V), the approx. OC fct. is $L(\sigma) = \{[(1-\beta)/\alpha]^{h(\sigma)}-1\}/\{[(1-\beta)/\alpha]^{h(\sigma)}-[\beta/(1-\alpha)]^{h(\sigma)}\}$, where $h(\sigma)$ is sol. for h of $(\sigma_1/\sigma_0)^h\sigma = (h/\sigma_1{}^2 - h/\sigma_0{}^2 + 1/\sigma)^{-1/2}\sqrt{2\pi}$. $E(m|\sigma) \doteq 1 + \{L(\sigma) \log_e [\alpha\beta/(1-\alpha)(1-\beta)] + \log_e [(1-\beta)/\alpha]\}/[\tfrac{1}{2}(1/\sigma_0{}^2 - 1/\sigma_1{}^2) + \log_e (\sigma_0/\sigma_1)]$ for denominator $\neq 0$; when denominator $=0$, $E(m|\sigma) \doteq 1 - \{\log_e [\beta/(1-\alpha)]\}\{\log_e [(1-\beta)/\alpha]\}/2[\log_e (\sigma_1/\sigma_0)]^2$ **4** Moderately sensitive to sample condition. Not overly sensitive to mild violations of continuity requirement **5** Not difficult to decide on sample and continuity assumptions **6** Useful when $F_0(x)$ representative of dists. of principal interest or best guess as to actual dist. **Bibliography** Ref. 4, 17, 21, 109, 140, 376, 447, 487, 539, 548.

Univariate Life-Testing—Transformation to Exponential (Epstein-Sobel)

Data 1 Continuous, univariate **2** Life test begins at same time for all items of initial group. For replacement case, another item immediately substituted for an item that fails **3** $X[1]_j$, where $X[1]_1 \leqslant \ldots \leqslant X[1]_m$, are order statistics of times to failure for initial group of items. $r(T)$ = total no. of failures, in initial group or among replacement items, at or before modified time T, which is a monotonically increasing fct. of the actual time τ **4** m = no. of items in initial group. $r(T) \leqslant m$ for no-replacement case (truncated test) and min value specified for m in part 2 of Results **Description 1** Approx. (nearly exact) signif. tests of simple hyp. (yield one-sided tests), also of a modified composite altern. hyp. **2** $F(x)$ over all x, where emphasis decreases as x increases; here $F(x)$ is dist. fct. of population sampled. In general, simple hyp. considered assert that transformation $y(j) = -\log_e \{1-F_0[X(1)_j]\}$, where $X(1)_j$ sample value from $F(x)$ and $F_0(x)$ completely specified continuous dist. fct., yields observation from population with freq. fct. = $\mu^{-1}e^{-y/\mu} = e^{-\log_e \mu - y/\mu}$ for $0 \leqslant y < \infty$ $(\mu > 0)$, and $=0$ otherwise; here μ is mean of transformed population. $y[j] = -\log_e \{1-F_0(X[1]_j)\}$, with $y[0]=0$. Modified time T determined from actual time τ by the relation $T = T(\tau) = -\log_e \{1-F_0(\tau)\}$. Tests of simple hyp. can be interpreted as one-sided tests (see page 396). Simple null hyp. H_0 asserts that $\mu = \mu_0$; ordinarily $\mu_0 = 1$. Simple altern. H_1

asserts that $\mu = \mu_1$. Modified composite altern. H_2 asserts that $\mu = (w_1/\mu_1 + w_2/\mu_2)^{-1}$ with weights w_1, w_2 suitably chosen. General modified composite hyp. (null and altern.) obtainable by weighted geometric-mean type averaging of freq. fcts. corresponding to simple hyp. Case (I) is that where no replacement occurs. Case (II) is that where a failed item is immediately replaced **Assumptions 1** The $X[1]_j$ are order statistics of sample of size m. The values for the replacement items are independent sample values from same population that yielded the $X[1]_j$ and are independent of the $X[1]_j$ **2** Continuous population **3** None **Results 1** To a reasonable approx., all tests have signif. level α ($<\frac{1}{2}$) and prob. of type II error β ($<\frac{1}{2}$). For altern. H_2, w_1 and w_2 such that freq. fct. obtained and such that max of prob. of type II error for simple hyp. $\mu = \mu_1$ and for simple hyp. $\mu = \mu_2$ is minimized. Freq. fct. obtained when $w_1 \log_e \mu_1 + w_2 \log_e \mu_2 = -\log_e (w_1/\mu_1 + w_2/\mu_2)$. Method of evaluating w_1 and w_2 given in part 4 of Results. $N_{\rm I}(\mu_0, \mu_1, T) = r(T) \log_e (\mu_0/\mu_1) + (1/\mu_0 - 1/\mu_1) \{\sum_{j=1}^{r(T)} y[j] + [m - r(T)](T - y[r(T)])\}$. $N_{\rm II}(\mu_0, \mu_1, T) = r(T) \log_e (\mu_0/\mu_1) + (1/\mu_0 - 1/\mu_1)mT$ **2** *Tests*: The sequential procedure starts at modified time $T = 0$, with $r(T) = 0$, and progresses time-wise until a decision is reached. *Case (I)*: Here the sequential procedure is necessarily truncated at sample size m; the value of m should be at least three times the larger of the average sample no. for the null hyp. and that for the altern. Either of the first two termination procedures outlined on page 406 can be used when no decision reached but all m items have failed. *Test of H_1 for Case (I)*: Continue test only as long as $\log_e [\beta/(1-\alpha)] < N_{\rm I}(\mu_0, \mu_1, T) < \log_e [(1-\beta)/\alpha]$ and $r(T) < m$. If test continued until $r(T) = m$ and no decision reached when this occurs, apply the termination procedure selected. If test discontinued because $N_{\rm I}(\mu_0, \mu_1, T) \leqslant \log_e [\beta/(1-\alpha)]$, accept H_0. If test discontinued because $N_{\rm I}(\mu_0, \mu_1, T) \geqslant \log_e [(1-\beta)/\alpha]$, accept H_1. *Test of H_2 for Case (I)*: Continue test only as long as $\log_e [\beta/(1-\alpha)] < N_{\rm I}[\mu_0, (w_1/\mu_1 + w_2/\mu_2)^{-1}, T] < \log_e [(1-\beta)/\alpha]$ and $r(T) < m$. If test continued until $r(T) = m$, but no decision reached, apply termination procedure selected. If test discontinued with $N_{\rm I}[\mu_0, (w_1/\mu_1 + w_2/\mu_2)^{-1}, T] \leqslant \log_e [\beta/(1-\alpha)]$, accept H_0. If test discontinued with $N_{\rm I}[\mu_0, (w_1/\mu_1 + w_2/\mu_2)^{-1}, T] \geqslant \log_e [(1-\beta)/\alpha]$ accept H_2. *Case (II)*: Here the sequential test is not necessarily truncated. *Test of H_1 for Case (II)*: Continue test only as long as $\log_e [\beta/(1-\alpha)] < N_{\rm II}(\mu_0, \mu_1, T) < \log_e [(1-\beta)/\alpha]$. If test discontinued because $N_{\rm II}(\mu_0, \mu_1, T) \leqslant \log_e [\beta/(1-\alpha)]$, accept H_0. If test discontinued because $N_{\rm II}(\mu_0, \mu_1, T) \geqslant \log_e [(1-\beta)/\alpha]$, accept H_1. *Test of H_2 for Case (II)*: Continue test only as long as $\log_e [\beta/(1-\alpha)] < N_{\rm II}[\mu_0, (w_1/\mu_1 + w_2/\mu_2)^{-1}, T] < \log_e [(1-\beta)/\alpha]$. If test discontinued because $N_{\rm II}[\mu_0, (w_1/\mu_1 + w_2/\mu_2)^{-1}, T] \leqslant \log_e [\beta/(1-\alpha)]$, accept H_0. If test discontinued because $N_{\rm II}[\mu_0, (w_1/\mu_1 + w_2/\mu_2)^{-1}, T] \geqslant \log_e [(1-\beta)/\alpha]$, accept

H_1 **3** None **4** $h = h[\mu; \mu_0, \mu_1]$ is sol. for h of $h \log_e(\mu_1/\mu_0) + \log_e \mu = -\log_e(h/\mu_1 - h/\mu_0 + 1/\mu)$. $L\{\mu; \mu_0, \mu_1\} = \{[(1-\beta)/\alpha]^h - 1\}/\{[(1-\beta)/\alpha]^h - [\beta/(1-\alpha)]^h\}$. Values of w_1 and w_2 for Case (I) same as those for Case (II). For H_2, relation for obtaining freq. fct. furnishes w_2 in terms of w_1, say $w_2 = w_2(w_1)$; value for w_1 is that which minimizes max of $L\{\mu_1; \mu_0, [w_1/\mu_1 + w_2(w_1)/\mu_2]^{-1}\}$ and $L\{\mu_2; \mu_0, [w_1/\mu_1 + w_2(w_1)/\mu_2]^{-1}\}$. Simple hypotheses can be replaced by modified composite hyp. (see page 396) **Characteristics 1** Low to upper medium for tests of H_1, depending on final $r(T)$, m, whether $F_0(x)$ already tabulated, and how frequently test statistic evaluated. Upper low to upper medium for tests of H_2 **2** The OC fcts. and average sample no.'s have approximately the same values for Cases (I) and (II). For tests with altern. H_1, OC fct. is approx. $L\{\mu; \mu_0, \mu_1\}$ for true value μ; OC fct. is approx. $L\{\mu; \mu_0, [w_1/\mu_1 + w_2/\mu_2]^{-1}\}$ for tests with altern. H_2. For tests of H_1, average sample no. $= E[r(T)|\mu] \doteq \big(L\{\mu; \mu_0, \mu_1\} \log_e[\beta/(1-\alpha)] + [1 - L\{\mu; \mu_0, \mu_1\}] \log_e[(1-\beta)/\alpha]\big)/[\log_e(\mu_0/\mu_1) - \mu(1/\mu_1 - 1/\mu_0)]$ if μ such that denominator $\neq 0$; if $\mu = [\log_e(\mu_0/\mu_1)]/(1/\mu_1 - 1/\mu_0)$, $E[r(T)|\mu] \doteq \log_e[(1-\alpha)/\beta] \log_e[(1-\beta)/\alpha]/[\log_e(\mu_0/\mu_1)]^2$; similarly for test of H_2, with μ_1 replaced by $(w_1/\mu_1 + w_2/\mu_2)^{-1}$. For Case (II), the expected modified time required to reach a decision for true value μ is $E[T(\tau)|\mu] = E[r(T)|\mu]\mu/m$; for Case (I), $E[T(\tau)|\mu] \doteq \mu \log_e \{m/(m - E[r(T)|\mu])\}$. By maximizing with respect to μ to determine an upper limit for $E[T(\tau)]$ and then evaluating the actual time τ corresponding to this estimate of T, a conservative value is obtained for the time required to reach a decision. For test of H_1, the values of the OC fct. at $\mu = 0, \mu_1, [\log_e(\mu_0/\mu_1)]/(1/\mu_1 - 1/\mu_0), \mu_0$, and ∞ are, respectively, $0, \beta, \{\log_e[(1-\beta)/\alpha]\}/\{\log_e[(1-\beta)/\alpha] - \log_e[\beta/(1-\alpha)]\}$, $1-\alpha$, and 1; likewise for test of H_2, with μ_1 replaced by $(w_1/\mu_1 + w_2/\mu_2)^{-1}$; these five pts., combined with interpolation, furnish approx. to OC fct. **4** Moderately sensitive to sample condition. Not overly sensitive to mild violations of continuity requirement **5** Not difficult to decide on sample and continuity assumptions **6** Useful when $F_0(x)$ representative of dists. of principal interest or best guess as to actual dist. Ref. 13 and 165 contain results for exponential populations when the situation is not of a life-testing nature **Bibliography** Ref. 6, 13, 165.

General Tests for Categorical Data

Data 1 Arbitrary, univariate or multivariate **2** None **3** $\{X(i)_j\}_m$ **4** $n_1 = \ldots = n_m = n \geqslant 1$; m not a fixed value **Description 1** Approx. (nearly exact) sequential signif. tests **2** $F(x_1, \ldots, x_n)$ over all $(x_1, \ldots, x_n)$, or over a specified set of pts. having nonzero prob., by conversion of data to categorical form (see page 440 for conversion advice) **Assumptions 2** Categories chosen in unbiased fashion **3** None **Results 1** Space of possible values for an observation divided into U mutually exclusive sets which are representative of situations of interest; each of these sets furnishes a category. Under null hyp. H_0, prob. of uth category is $p_u^{(0)} > 0$; prob. under altern. H_1 is $p_u^{(1)} > 0$; here $\sum_{u=1}^{U} p_u^{(0)} = \sum_{u=1}^{U} p_u^{(1)} = 1$. Only hyp. which are simple for multinomial dist. of the categorical data are considered; however, these simple hyp. can be replaced by modified composite hyp. (see page 396). To a reasonable approx., signif. level is α ($< \frac{1}{2}$) and prob. of type II error is β ($< \frac{1}{2}$) at the alternative considered; in any case, signif. level $\leqslant \alpha$ and prob. of type II error at altern. $\leqslant \beta$. $N_j^{(u)}$ = no. of times uth category has occurred for first j observations **2** *Test*: Sequential sampling procedure starts with single observation and continues with single observations until a decision is reached. No prior conditions imposed when $m = 1$. Given that $\log_{10} [\beta/(1-\alpha)] < \sum_{u=1}^{U} N_j^{(u)} \log_{10} (p_u^{(1)}/p_u^{(0)}) < \log_{10} [(1-\beta)/\alpha]$ for $j \leqslant m-1$, accept H_0 if $\sum_{u=1}^{U} N_m^{(u)} \log_{10} (p_u^{(1)}/p_u^{(0)}) \leqslant \log_{10} [\beta/(1-\alpha)]$; accept H_1 if $\sum_{u=1}^{U} N_m^{(u)} \log_{10} (p_u^{(1)}/p_u^{(0)}) \geqslant \log_{10} [(1-\beta)/\alpha]$; otherwise obtain another sample value and repeat this procedure **3** None **4** Truncation of tests of this nature is considered on page 406. Although hyp. simple for multinomial dist. of categorical data, they are composite for $F(x_1, \ldots, x_n)$ in sense that all dist. fcts. yielding same set of category probabilities are equivalent as far as test is concerned. By suitable choice of categories, tests for differences of dist. fct. values at specified pts. can often be obtained without great difficulty (see page 400). Results given are directly applicable to situation where sample values obtained in groups of equal size (see page 394) **Characteristics 1** Low to high, depending on final m, on U, on form of categories, on whether the $p_u^{(0)}$, $p_u^{(1)}$ merely stated values or are values computed from specified dist. fcts. $F_0(x_1, \ldots, x_n)$ and $F_1(x_1, \ldots, x_n)$, on whether these fcts. are already tabulated (if they are used), on whether modified composite hypotheses are used, etc. **2** $h = h(p_u^{(2)}; p_u^{(0)}, p_u^{(1)})$ is sol. for h of $\sum_{u=1}^{U} p_u^{(2)}[p_u^{(1)}/p_u^{(0)}]^h = 1$. For true probabilities $p_1^{(2)}, \ldots, p_U^{(2)}$, the OC fct. $B(p_u^{(2)}) \doteq \{[(1-\beta)/\alpha]^h - 1\}/\{[(1-\beta)/\alpha]^h - [\beta/(1-\alpha)]^h\}$. The average sample no. $E(m|p_u^{(2)}) \doteq \{B(p_u^{(2)}) \log_{10} [\beta/(1-\alpha)] + [1-B(p_u^{(2)})] \log_{10} [(1-\beta)/\alpha]\}/\{\sum_{u=1}^{U} p_u^{(2)} \log_{10} (p_u^{(1)}/p_u^{(0)})\}$ when denominator $\neq 0$; $E(m|p_u^{(0)}) \doteq \{\log_{10} [(1-\alpha)/\beta]\}\{\log_{10} [(1-\beta)/\alpha]\}/\{\sum_{u=1}^{U} p_u^{(2)}[\log_{10} (p_u^{(1)}/p_u^{(0)})]^2\}$ when $\sum_{u=1}^{U} p_u^{(2)} \log_{10} (p_u^{(1)}/p_u^{(0)}) = 0$. See page 406 for lower bounds for $P(m \leqslant m_0)$. Test consistent in sense of sampling from multinomial population but not consistent in general **4** Sample condition should be satisfied to reasonable approx. with respect to multinomial population **5** Not difficult to decide on sample condition **6** Tests presented have advantage that specified altern. hyp. is emphasized **Bibliography** Ref. 539.

Tests for Frequency Functions—Simple Hypotheses (*Wald*)

Data 1 Discrete or continuous, univariate or multivariate **2** None **3** $\{X(i)_j\}_m$ **4** $n_1 = \ldots = n_m = n \geqslant 1$; m not a fixed value **Description 1** Approx. (nearly exact) sequential signif. tests for simple hyp. **2** $f(x_1, \ldots, x_n)$, over all $(x_1, \ldots, x_n)$. Simple null hyp. H_0 asserts that $f(x_1, \ldots, x_n) = f_0(x_1, \ldots, x_n)$; simple altern. asserts that $f(x_1, \ldots, x_n) = f_1(x_1, \ldots, x_n)$. Modified composite hyp. can be used in place of simple hyp. **Assumptions 2** Population discrete or continuous and such that freq. fct. exists **3** None **Results 1** To a reasonable approx., all tests have signif. level $\alpha\ (<\frac{1}{2})$ and prob. of type II error $\beta\ (<\frac{1}{2})$ at the alternative considered; in any case, signif. level $\leqslant \alpha$ and prob. of type II error at altern. $\leqslant \beta$. $Z(j) = \sum_{t=1}^{j} \log_{10} \{f_1[X(1)_t, \ldots, X(n)_t]/f_0[X(1)_t, \ldots, X(n)_t]\}$ **2** *Test*: Sequential sampling procedure starts with a single observation and continues with single observations until a decision reached. No prior conditions imposed when $m = 1$. Given that $\log_{10}[\beta/(1-\alpha)] < Z(j) < \log_{10}[(1-\beta)/\alpha]$ for $j \leqslant m-1$, accept H_0 if $Z(m) \leqslant \log_{10}[\beta/(1-\alpha)]$; accept H_1 if $Z(m) \geqslant \log_{10}[(1-\beta)/\alpha]$; otherwise take another sample value and continue. If an observation occurs for which both $f_1[X(1)_j, \ldots, X(n)_j]$ and $f_0[X(1)_j, \ldots, X(n)_j]$ are zero, reject both H_1 and H_0 **3** None **4** Truncation of tests of this nature considered on page 406. Results given are directly applicable when sample values obtained in groups of equal size (see page 394) **Characteristics 1** Low to lower high, depending on final m, on whether $f_0(x_1, \ldots, x_n)$, $f_1(x_1, \ldots, x_n)$ already tabulated, and on whether modified composite hyp. are used **2** Methods for determining OC fct. values and average sample no.'s outlined in introductory part of sect. For given α and β, ordinarily much smaller no. of sample values required, on the average, than for corresponding fixed sample size tests of Chapter 10 **4** Sample condition should be satisfied to reasonable approx. Not very sensitive to requirement of discrete or continuous population for which freq. fct. exists **5** Not difficult to decide on assumptions **6** Nearly all sequential results are modifications of this sequential probability-ratio method. Information theory interpretation of this test given in ref. 313 **Bibliography** Ref. 313, 539.

Tests for Frequency Functions—Composite Hypotheses

Data 1 Discrete or continuous, univariate or multivariate **2** Guesses for values of unknown parameters, on basis of supplementary information, needed to start test procedure **3** $\{X(i)_j\}_m$ **4** $n_1 = \ldots = n_m = n \geqslant 1$; m not a fixed value **Description 1** Approx. sequential signif. tests for simple or composite null hyp. and altern. hyp. **2** $f(x_1, \ldots, x_n)$ over all $(x_1, \ldots, x_n)$, where $f(x_1, \ldots, x_n)$ considered to have the completely specified parametric form $f(x_1, \ldots, x_n; \xi_1, \ldots, \xi_r; \eta_1, \ldots, \eta_s)$; here $r \geqslant 1$, and $s = 0$ implies that

η's do not occur. Null hyp. H_0 asserts that $(\xi_1, \ldots, \xi_r) = (\xi_1^{(0)}, \ldots, \xi_r^{(0)})$. Altern. H_1 asserts $\xi_{r(1)} = \xi_{r(1)}^{(1)}, \ldots, \xi_{r(v)} = \xi_{r(v)}^{(1)}$, where $0 \leqslant v \leqslant r$ and $v = 0$ implies that none of the ξ's have specified values under H_1. $f(x_1, \ldots, x_n; \xi_1, \ldots, \xi_r; \eta_1, \ldots, \eta_s)$ such that when any zero or more of the ξ's have specified values, joint max likelihood estimates exist for the remaining ξ's and for the η's; also, these estimates have usual favorable asymptotic properties of max likelihood estimates **Assumptions 2** Population discrete or continuous and such that freq. fct. exists **3** Situation is such that procedure terminates with prob. 1 **Results 1** $W(j) = \sum_{t=0}^{j} \log_{10} \{f[X(1)_t, \ldots, X(n)_t; \hat{\xi}_1^{(t)}, \ldots, \hat{\xi}_r^{(t)}; \hat{\eta}_1^{(t)}, \ldots, \hat{\eta}_s^{(t)}]/f[X(1)_t, \ldots, X(n)_t; \xi_1^{(0)}, \ldots, \xi_r^{(0)}; \eta_1^{(t)}, \ldots, \eta_s^{(t)}]\}$, where $\hat{\eta}_u^{(t)} =$ [$(t-1)$(max likelihood estimate of η_u under H_1 on basis of first $t-1$ observations) + (supplementary information guess for η_u)]/t, $\eta_u^{(t)} =$ [$(t-1)$ (max likelihood estimate of η_u under H_0 on basis of first $t-1$ observations) + (supplementary information estimate of η_u)]/t, $\hat{\xi}_v^{(t)}$ = value specified for ξ_v by H_1 or, if no value specified, = [$(t-1)$(max likelihood estimate of ξ_v under H_1 on basis of first $t-1$ observations) + (supplementary information estimate of ξ_v)]/t. Max likelihood estimates computed as if available observations are unrestricted random sample from $f(x_1, \ldots, x_n; \xi_1, \ldots, \xi_r; \eta_1, \ldots, \eta_s)$. To reasonable approx., all tests have signif. level α ($< \frac{1}{2}$) and prob. of type II error β ($< \frac{1}{2}$) at altern.; in any case, signif. level $\leqslant \alpha$ and prob. of type II error at altern. $\leqslant \beta$ **2** *Tests*: Sequential sampling procedure starts with a single observation and continues with single observations until a decision reached. No prior conditions imposed when $m = 1$. Given that $\log_{10} [\beta/(1-\alpha)] < W(j) < \log_{10} [(1-\beta)/\alpha]$ for $j \leqslant m-1$, accept H_0 if $W(m) \leqslant \log_{10} [\beta/(1-\alpha)]$; accept H_1 if $W(m) \geqslant \log_{10} [(1-\beta)/\alpha]$; otherwise take another sample value and continue **3** None **4** Methods other than max likelihood may be more suitable for estimating the parameter values in some cases; i.e., have satisfactory properties and require less computation. A test which seems preferable but requires more computation is obtained by modifying $W(j)$ so that $\hat{\xi}_v^{(t)} = \hat{\xi}_v^{(j)}$, $\hat{\eta}_u^{(t)} = \hat{\eta}_u^{(j)}$, and $\eta_u^{(t)} = \eta_u^{(j)}$ for $t \leqslant j$ and all u, v. Results given are directly applicable when sample values obtained in groups of equal size (see page 394) **Characteristics 1** Upper low to high, depending final m, r, s, functional form of freq. fct., etc. Computational effort can be reduced by only determining new estimates of parameters every several observations (every five, ten, etc.) **2** Rough average sample no. values can be determined on basis of initial guesses for values of unspecified parameters. These rough approximations are improved as better estimates of the unspecified parameters are obtained on the basis of the sample values that have become available; estimates used as if they were true values in these determinations **4** Sample condition should be satisfied to reasonable approx. Also, to assure termination with prob. 1, population should have freq. fct. that is satisfactorily approximated by parametric form that is considered **5** Not difficult to determine a parametric freq. fct. form that is sufficiently general to approximate actual freq. fct. and to decide on other assumptions **6** Major disadvantage is that test properties not very well determined prior to sampling. Major advantage is general types of composite hyp. that can be handled **Bibliography** Ref. 539.

Trinomial Tests for Frequency Functions (*Tsao*)

Data 1 Continuous, univariate or multivariate **2** None **3** $\{X(i)_j\}_m$ **4** $n_1 = \ldots = n_m = n \geqslant 1$; m not a fixed value **Description 1** Exact sequential signif. tests for simple (or modified composite) hyp. **2** $f(x_1, \ldots, x_n)$ over all $(x_1, \ldots, x_n)$. Simple null hyp. H_0 is $f(x_1, \ldots, x_n) = f_0(x_1, \ldots, x_n)$ and simple altern. H_1 is $f(x_1, \ldots, x_n) = f_1(x_1, \ldots, x_n)$, where f_0 and f_1 continuous freq. fcts. such that $\{(x_1, \ldots, x_n) | f_1(x_1, \ldots, x_n)/f_0(x_1, \ldots, x_n) = V\}$ has zero prob. under H_0 and H_1 for all V. Modified composite hyp. can be used in place of simple hyp. **Assumptions 2** $f(x_1, \ldots, x_n)$ is continuous **3** None **Results 1** $\omega_0(t_0) = \{(x_1, \ldots, x_n) | f_1(x_1, \ldots, x_n) \leqslant t_0 f_0(x_1, \ldots, x_n)\}$; $\omega_1(t_1) = \{(x_1, \ldots, x_n) | f_1(x_1, \ldots, x_n) \geqslant t_1 f_0(x_1, \ldots, x_n)\}$; here $t_0 < t_1$. A and R are specified positive integers used in test. $A_k = \int_{\omega_0(t_0)} \cdots \int f_k(x_1, \ldots, x_n) dx_1 \ldots dx_n$, $R_k = \int_{\omega_1(t_1)} \cdots \int f_k(x_1, \ldots, x_n) dx_1 \ldots dx_n$, for $k = 0, 1, 2$; here $f_2(x_1, \ldots, x_k)$ denotes a general simple hyp. $\psi(k; A, R, t_0, t_1) = \psi(k; A, R, t_0, t_1; A_k, R_k) = \sum_{u=R}^{A+R-1} \binom{A+R-1}{u} (1 + A_k/R_k)^{-u} [A_k/R_k(1 + A_k/R_k)]^{A+R-1-u}$; t_0 and t_1 determined from $\psi(0; A, R, t_0, t_1) = \alpha$ and $\psi(1; A, R, t_0, t_1) = 1 - \beta$, where α is signif. level and β is prob. of type II error for H_1. $N_0(j)$ = no. of first j observations with values in $\omega_0(t_0)$; $N_1(j)$ = no. of first j observations with values in $\omega_1(t_1)$ **2** *Test*: Sequential sampling procedure starts with a single observation and continues with single observations until a decision is reached. No prior conditions imposed when $m = 1$. Given that $N_0(j) < A$ and $N_1(j) < R$ for $j \leqslant m - 1$, accept H_0 if $N_0(m) = A$; accept H_1 if $N_1(m) = R$; otherwise take another sample value and continue **3** $\psi(k; A, R, t_0, t_1)$ can be evaluated by use of a table of the binomial dist. with success prob. $= (1 + A_k/R_k)^{-1}$; likewise, table of incomplete beta fct. or approx. to binomial dist. (see Chapter 7) could be used **4** Truncation of tests of this nature is considered on page 406. $P(m \leqslant m_0 | f_k) = 2 - \psi(k; A, m_0 + 1, t_0, t_1; A_k, R_k) - \psi(k; R, m_0 + 1, t_0, t_1; R_k, A_k)$. Since A, R, α, β are all specified, the test can be optimized through the selection of A and R for given α and β. Although hyp. are simple for trinomial population, they are actually composite for $f(x_1, \ldots, x_n)$, since no distinction can be made between this dist. and any other yielding same prob. for the three categories. These results are directly applicable when sample values obtained in groups of equal size (see page 394) **Characteristics** **1** Low to lower medium, depending on final m, the difficulty in determining $\omega_0(t_0)$ and $\omega_1(t_1)$, the difficulty in determining t_0 and t_1, n, etc. **2** OC fct. for hyp. f_k is $1-\psi(k; A, R, t_0, t_1)$ and average sample no. is $(R/R_k)\{\psi(k; A, R, t_0, t_1) - \binom{A+R-1}{R}(1+A_k/R_k)^{-R}[A_R/R_k(1+A_R/R_k)]^A\} + (A/A_k)\{1-\psi(k; A, R, t_0, t_1) - \binom{A+R-1}{A}(1+A_k/R_k)^{-R}[A_k/R_k(1+A_k/R_k)]^A\}$. Test consistent in sense of sampling from a trinomial population but not consistent in general (see ref. 520 for def. of consistency). For sampling from normal population with known variance and $\alpha=\beta=.05$, efficiency (ratio of average sample no.'s) varies from about 35 per cent to about 90 per cent for $A=R=2$ and from about 10 per cent to about 85 per cent for $A=R=1$, depending on altern. considered; usually at least 60 per cent when H_0 and H_1 noticeably different **4** Sample condition should be satisfied to reasonable approx. for trinomial population. Continuity requirement for freq. fct. not very important except perhaps in efficiency sense test valid if the A_0, A_1 and R_0, R_1 values are accurate for null and altern. dists. **5** Not difficult to decide on random sample or continuity assumptions **6** Can be extended to case of more than three categories by using f_1/f_0 to determine categories and using general tests for categorical data **Bibliography** Ref. 520.

STATISTICAL DECISION THEORY PROCEDURES

Introduction

This section is mainly concerned with methods for incorporating supplementary information into procedures for estimating probability distributions and for selecting one of a finite number (two or more) hypotheses about a distribution. Only distribution functions at specified points are considered for the estimation procedures. The general material for selecting one of a finite number of hypotheses applies to frequency functions. However, by converting the data to a categorical form, these results can be used for distribution functions. Also, some procedures for selecting one of two or more hypotheses about distribution functions are presented for the continuous univariate case; these procedures are based on transformations of variable. Except for the continuous univariate cases, a distribution function can be from an arbitrary population and a frequency function can be from any discrete or absolutely continuous population; here a population can be univariate or multivariate. Besides the procedures that are given in the presentations, some descriptive material is given concerning statistical decision theory and the uses considered in this section, about types of procedures and hypotheses, about the use of transformations of variable, about truncated procedures, and about the decision theory properties of sequential tests. Also some methods of modifying the material presented are outlined.

Discussion of Statistical Decision Theory

As considered in this section, statistical decision theory is used for two kinds of problems. One of these problems is concerned with point estimation of a probability distribution on the basis of sample values and of any supplementary information (technical considerations, past experience, etc.) that may be available about this distribution. The other problem involves selecting one of a finite number of types of distributions as being the type of distribution yielding the sample values. For both problems, loss functions are given for quantitatively measuring the effects of erroneous decisions. The optimum decision, of the class being examined, is considered to be that for which the risk (expected value of the loss) is minimum. As throughout the handbook, a loss function depends on the hypothesis selected and the true hypothesis; the value of the loss is non-negative with zero loss occurring when the true hypothesis is selected.

The Bayes approach represents one method of incorporating supplementary information into decision making. Here, from the supplementary information, the relative *a priori* probabilities for the possible decisions (i.e., those considered) are specified. The risk is determined for each decision of the class considered on the basis of the loss function, the *a priori* distribution for the eligible decisions, and the sample values. The principal advantage of the Bayes approach is that it furnishes a direct method of incorporating supplementary information and that there are many situations where it can be applied without great difficulty. Its principal disadvantage is that an *a priori* distribution of this nature is a subjective concept so that the usual frequency interpretation for probability does not apply. That is, the expected value of the loss function is not an expected value in the sense of always being the average of what would result from an unlimited number of repetitions of this experimental situation.

The minimax principle is a special case of applying the Bayes approach. Here the *a priori* distribution is considered to be that which maximizes the minimum risk for the class of decisions being examined. Thus, strictly speaking, no supplementary information is incorporated into a minimax decision procedure. For this reason, minimax procedures for the investigation of distributions are not explicitly considered in this section, although they can be obtained as special cases of the Bayes procedures that are presented. Instead, they are presented in other sections and in Chapter 10. In fact, a decision procedure for a probability distribution is not considered in this section unless it specifically allows for the use of supplementary information in its application.

All but one of the presentations are based on the Bayes approach. This other presentation is of a sequential nature and is concerned with the selection of one out of several hypotheses that can be composite of a moderately general type. Supplementary information is introduced in the form of initial guesses for the values of parameters that are unspecified by the hypotheses. Probability has the usual interpretation for this kind of decision procedure.

Outline of Uses Considered

Bayes estimation of the value of an arbitrary distribution function at a specified point is considered for several types of loss functions. Bayes selection of an hypothesis about a distribution function over all points, on the basis of parametric procedures, is considered for the continuous univariate case; two methods, both based on a transformation of variable, are presented. In one case, the transformation is to a generalized uniform (rectangular) distribution; the transformation is to a normal distribution for the other case. The only sequential procedure for which a presentation is given involves the selection of a (possibly) composite hypothesis about a frequency function (over all points) and does not use the Bayes approach. Finally, the Bayes approach is used for selecting one of two or more specified simple hypotheses about a frequency function.

Some straightforward extensions can be made of the results that are given in the presentations. These include the replacement of simple hypotheses by modified composite hypotheses and the use of results for discrete frequency functions to investigate distribution functions, through conversion of the data to a categorical form. Also, the conversion of sequential tests to explicit statistical decision theory procedures is outlined. Truncated sequential decision procedures are discussed but no presentations are given.

As already mentioned, in this handbook statistical decision procedures are distinguished from significance tests by the fact that they make direct use of a specified loss function. Although this distinction is somewhat artificial, it is useful with respect to presentation of the material that is considered.

In some senses, much of the statistical decision theory material of this section can be considered to fall under the heading of discriminant analysis. That is, each hypothesis represents a possible classification and the classification with the smallest risk is preferable. However, the problem is somewhat different for discriminant analysis. Usually, the discriminant decision is made on the basis of a single observation, or individually for each of a group of observations. That is, each observation can be from a different population and the problem is to develop a satisfactory classification procedure for choosing one of a specified set of populations for a given observation. This differs from situations where all the observations are known to be from the same population and the classification problem is to suitably choose one of a specified set of populations.

Determination of Adequate Sample Sizes

As mentioned in Chapter 4, the value of the risk furnishes the basis for determining adequate sample sizes for nonsequential decision theory procedures. A maximum allowable value for the risk is specified and the smallest sample size for which the risk has at most this value is considered to be adequate. Risk function expressions are stated for all the nonsequential results that are presented in this section.

Types of Hypotheses Considered

For point estimation of a distribution function at a specified point, all values between zero and unity are considered to be possibilities. That is, the problem is to select one of a single-parameter nondenumerable family of hypotheses.

Various situations occur when the decision problem is not of a point estimation character. Here one of a finite number of hypotheses is to be selected and an hypothesis is either simple or composite. Several kinds of composite hypotheses are considered. A modified composite hypothesis consists of a weighted "average" of simple hypotheses and is itself of the same nature as a simple hypothesis. If the data are converted to a categorical form, all hypotheses are usually composite. That is, even though the hypotheses considered may be phrased as simple hypotheses, they are composite in the sense that no distinction can be made between the distribution specified by an hypothesis and any other distribution that yields the same probabilities for the categories. For the remaining type of composite hypotheses, a distribution is completely specified except for the values of some unknown parameters which, ordinarily, can have any values within specified limits.

The eligible hypotheses are of a specialized nature for continuous univariate situations where transformations to populations that are considered to be of a generalized uniform or of a normal form occur. That is, all hypotheses considered are special cases of a normal population when the transformation is to normality; also, all hypotheses are represented by uniform distributions or generalizations of uniform distributions when the transformation is to a generalization of uniform populations. Any hypothesis for a transformed distribution is a determinable hypothesis for the population actually sampled, since the transformation is completely specified. However, the amount of computation required to identify the composite hypothesis corresponding to a given composite hypothesis for the transformed distribution can be substantial.

Modified Composite Hypotheses

As mentioned in the preceding section (also see Chapter 10), modified composite hypotheses are weighted "averages" of specified simple hypotheses with the weights chosen so that simple hypotheses are obtained. That is, a modified composite hypothesis is a simple hypothesis which represents a composite hypothesis situation. Thus, composite hypotheses can be used for procedures that are developed to handle simple hypotheses. The three kinds of modified composite hypotheses described in the preceding section for tests can also be used in this section for decisions.

Estimation of Distribution Function

The Bayes estimates of the value of a distribution function at a specified point are obtained from the binomial distribution results of Chapter 7. Here the *a priori* distribution for the possible hypotheses (all values between zero and unity) can be any distribution which assigns zero probability to all values outside the interval (0, 1). Four different kinds of loss functions are considered. One is equal to a function of the true value times the square of the difference between the estimate and the true value. Another is equal to a function of the true value times the absolute value of the difference between the estimate and the true value. The third kind of loss function specifies zero loss if the difference between the estimate and the true value lies between two given numbers and specifies unit loss otherwise. The remaining kind of loss function specifies zero loss if the difference between the logarithm of the estimate and the logarithm of the true value lies between two given numbers and specifies unit loss otherwise. For the univariate case, these estimates are applicable when the values of some of the sample order statistics are not available, including situations where the sample is censored (e.g., life-testing situations). In all cases, the estimate is a function of the empirical distribution function for the sample values; moreover, the sample values occur only with respect to their use in the empirical distribution function.

General Results for Frequency Functions

Some rather general results are presented for the situation of frequency functions, simple hypotheses, and fixed sample sizes. Explicitly, any finite set of simple hypotheses, any loss function, and any *a priori* distribution for these hypotheses can be considered. By dividing the totality of simple hypotheses considered into subsets and picking an appropriate simple hypothesis to represent each subset, a reasonably thorough representation of the eligible hypotheses can sometimes be obtained without excessive effort being required for the application of the decision procedure. In particular, if the hypotheses considered are represented by a frequency function that depends on a single one-dimensional parameter, five or six simply hypotheses are often sufficient for representing the entire set of hypotheses; in some cases, two or three simple hypotheses may furnish a satisfactory representation.

Decisions Based on Categorical Data

The results for frequency functions, which are applicable for the discrete case, can be used to investigate arbitrary distribution functions over all points. This is accomplished by converting the data to a categorical form. Then the hypotheses about the distribution function become hypotheses about the frequency function of the resulting multinomial population, so that the problem is now concerned with the selection of an hypothesis about a frequency function.

Results for Univariate Case from Transformations

For the continuous univariate case, special transformations can be used to convert the data to samples that are considered to be from specified types of parametric populations. This conversion has the advantage that results which have been developed for these parametric populations can be used directly; also representation of all the hypotheses by a few simple hypotheses is not very difficult for the two types of parametric populations considered. The transformations used and the hypotheses considered for the transformed data are outlined here for the generalized uniform and the normality cases. Further remarks concerning the use of transformations in investigating distributions are given in the preceding section and in the introductory part of this chapter.

For both of the cases considered, the transformation depends on a completely specified continuous distribution function $F_0(x)$. For the generalized uniform distribution case, the transformation is $y = F_0(x)$ and the simple hypotheses considered for the transformed population assert that the frequency function of this population is of the form $\exp(A + By + Cy^2)$, where $0 \leqslant y \leqslant 1$. For the normality case, the transformation is

$z = -K_{F_0(x)}$ and the simple hypotheses considered for the transformed population assert that its frequency function is of the general normal form $(\sigma\sqrt{2\pi})^{-1} \exp[-\frac{1}{2}(z-\mu)^2/\sigma^2]$, where $-\infty < z < \infty$.

If the population sampled actually had the distribution function $F_0(x)$, the simple hypothesis $B = C = 0$ would occur for the generalized uniform distribution case and the simple hypothesis $\mu = 0$, $\sigma = 1$ would occur for the normal case. Thus, if $F_0(x)$ represents the experimenter's best guess concerning the actual distribution, or is representative of the distributions of principal interest, it would seem that $B = C = 0$ should be one of the simple hypotheses considered for the uniform distribution case and $\mu = 0$, $\sigma = 1$ should be considered for the normality case. For many situations, consideration of $(B, C) = (0, 0)$, $(0, |C'|)$, $(0, -|C''|)$, $(|B'|, 0)$, and $(-|B''|, 0)$, with C', C'', B', B'' suitably chosen, should be adequate for the generalized uniform distribution case. Also consideration of $(\mu, \sigma) = (0, 1)$, $(0, \sigma')$, $(0, \sigma'')$, $(|\mu'|, 1)$, and $(-|\mu''|, 1)$, with μ', μ'', $\sigma' > 1$, $\sigma'' < 1$ suitably chosen, should be adequate for many normality cases. Inclusion of four additional suitably chosen simple hypotheses of the forms $(|B_1|, |C_1|)$, $(-|B_2|, |C_2|)$, $(|B_3|, -|C_3|)$, and $(-|B_4|, -|C_4|)$, so that a total of nine simple hypotheses are considered, should satisfactorily handle nearly all situations for the generalized uniform distribution case. Likewise, inclusion of four additional suitably chosen simple hypotheses of the forms $(|\mu_1|, \sigma_1)$, $(-|\mu_2|, \sigma_2)$, $(|\mu_3|, \sigma_3)$, and $(-|\mu_4|, \sigma_4)$, with $\sigma_1 > 1$, $\sigma_2 > 1$, $\sigma_3 < 1$, $\sigma_4 < 1$, should be adequate for nearly all normality situations.

Sequential Decisions with Composite Hypotheses

Here frequency functions are investigated and the hypotheses considered are represented by a frequency function $f(x_1, \ldots, x_n; \eta_1, \ldots, \eta_s)$ which is completely specified except for the values of the one-dimensional parameters $\eta_1, \ldots, \eta_s$. The space of possible values for $\eta = (\eta_1, \ldots, \eta_s)$ is divided into R mutually exclusive sets and each of these sets represents an hypothesis (usually composite, but simple hypotheses are sometimes considered when η has a finite number of possible values). The loss is the same for all incorrect decisions and is standardized to have unit value. A sequential procedure is presented which has the property that the risk is at most equal to a specified value.

At the start of the sequential procedure, a guess based on the available supplementary information is used for the value of η. For later stages, the initial guess is combined with estimates based on the observation values that have already been obtained. These estimates are maximum likelihood estimates evaluated under the assumption that the available observations are a random sample, which is only approximately the case since some conditions must be satisfied in order for the sampling to continue; however, the resulting estimates should usually be satisfactory.

The principal advantage of this procedure lies in the generality of the situations that it is capable of handling. Its major disadvantages are that the loss function is of very restricted nature and that the expected sample size is not predetermined.

Truncated Sequential Decision Procedures

In principle, a rather general class of truncated sequential Bayes decision procedures can be obtained for frequency functions when only two simple hypotheses are considered. Here the maximum number of sample values, the loss function, and the *a priori* distribution can be chosen arbitrarily. Unfortunately, a substantial amount of computation is frequently required to apply one of these procedures. Consequently, this class of procedures, which is described on pages 263–65 of ref. 67, is not presented in the handbook.

Decision Theory Properties of Sequential Tests

As mentioned in the preceding section, the probability-ratio test for simple hypotheses concerning frequency functions is a Bayes nontruncated sequential procedure for a given *a priori* distribution for the two hypotheses, a fixed cost per observation, and the appropriate loss function. That is, this test furnishes an optimal decision procedure, in the Bayes sense, for selecting one of the two simple hypotheses considered when a suitable loss function is used. The purpose of the material given here is to outline an approximate method for determining this loss function.

The situation is standardized so that each observation used has unit cost. The simple hypotheses considered are H_0, for which the frequency function is $f_0(x_1, \ldots, x_n)$, and H_1, for which the frequency function is $f_1(x_1, \ldots, x_n)$. The probability of rejecting H_0 when true is α $(<\frac{1}{2})$ and the probability of rejecting H_1 when true is β $(<\frac{1}{2})$. The *a priori* probability of H_0 is p and $G_0(z)$, $G_1(z)$ are the distribution functions of

$$Z=\log_{10}\{f_1[X(1), \ldots, X(n)]/f_0[X(1), \ldots, X(n)]\}$$

under H_0 and H_1, respectively; E_0Z, $\sigma_0{}^2Z$ and E_1A, $\sigma_1{}^2Z$ are the expected value and variance of Z under H_0 and H_1, respectively. Let $L_0(1)$ be the desired value for the loss when H_0 is selected but H_1 is true while $L_1(0)$ is the loss value when H_1 is selected but H_0 is true; no loss occurs when the correct selection is made. When H_0 is true, the risk from the test is $E(m|H_0)+(1-\alpha)L_1(0)$ while the risk is $E(m|H_1)+(1-\beta)L_0(1)$ when H_1 is true.

Some additional notation is presented for use in the equations that determine $L_1(0)$ and $L_0(1)$:

$$b = \log_{10}[\beta/(1-\alpha)]$$

$$a_1 = [1+(1-p)(1-\beta)/\alpha p]^{-1}, \quad a_2 = [1+\beta(1-p)/(1-\alpha)p]^{-1}$$

$$A_u(z) = [1-10^{(1-2u)z}]/\{1-[\beta/(1-\alpha)]^{1-2u}\}, \qquad (u=0,\ 1)$$

$$B_u(z) = \{[(1-\alpha)/\beta]^{1-2u} - 10^{(1-2u)z}\}/\{[(1-\alpha)/\beta]^{1-2u} - 1\}, \quad (u=0,\ 1)$$

$$E[m;\, A_u(z)] = \{-z + A_u(z)\log_{10}[\beta/(1-\alpha)]\}/E_uZ, \qquad (\text{for } E_uZ \neq 0)$$

$$= -z\{z+\log_{10}[(1-\alpha)/\beta]\}/\sigma_u{}^2Z, \qquad (\text{for } E_uZ = 0)$$

$$E[m;\, B_u(z)] = \{-z+[1-B_u(z)]\log_{10}[(1-\alpha)/\beta]\}/E_uZ, \qquad (\text{for } E_uZ \neq 0)$$

$$= z\{-z+\log_{10}[(1-\alpha)/\beta]\}/\sigma_u{}^2Z. \qquad (\text{for } E_uZ = 0)$$

The values of $L_1(0)$ and $L_0(1)$ are obtained by simultaneously solving the two linear equations

$$a_1L_1(0) = 1 + a_1\Big\{L_1(0)[1-G_0(0-)] + \int_{b+}^{0-}\{E[m;\, A_0(z)] + L_1(0)[1-A_0(z)]\}dG_0(z)\Big\} + (1-a_1)\Big\{L_0(1)G_1(b) + \int_{b+}^{0-}\{E[m;\, A_1(z)] + L_0(1)A_1(z)\}dG_1(z)\Big\},$$

$$a_2L_0(1) = 1 + a_2\Big\{L_1(0)\{1-G_0[(-b)-]\} + \int_{0+}^{(-b)-}\{E[m;\, B_0(z)] + L_1(0)[1-B_0(z)]\}dG_0(z)\Big\} + (1-a_2)\Big\{L_0(1)G_1(0) + \int_{0+}^{(-b)-}\{E[m;\, B_1(z)] + L_0(1)B_1(z)\}dG_1(z)\Big\}.$$

The approximations used in obtaining the values for $L_1(0)$ and $L_0(1)$ are those given in ref. 539.

Generality of Results

The wide application range of the material of this section seems worthy of emphasis. For the Bayes type of procedures, the *a priori* distribution for the eligible hypotheses can be of almost any desired form. The hypotheses considered can be almost arbitrary. An arbitrary distribution function (univariate or multivariate) can be estimated at any given point. By conversion of the data to a categorical form, an arbitrary distribution function can be investigated over all points on the basis of the results for frequency functions. Continuous univariate distribution functions can be investigated over all points by special procedures. No point estimates are presented for frequency functions. For the discrete case, however, estimates of frequency functions can be obtained from estimates of distribution functions (see Chapter 10). Some rather general results are given for making decisions about frequency functions when the hypotheses are simple and the sample size is fixed. A reasonable representation of the entire class of eligible hypotheses can often be obtained by consideration of a moderate number of appropriately determined simple hypotheses. For the case of two simple hypotheses, some of the sequential results of the preceding section can be used. Results based on simple hypotheses can be generalized by replacing one or more of the simple hypotheses by suitable modified composite hypotheses. In addition to the Bayes methods, a sequential procedure is given which can handle moderately general composite hypotheses about frequency functions.

Outline of Presentations

There are a total of five presentations. The first three are concerned with distribution functions and the remaining two with frequency functions. The first presentation contains Bayes estimates for the value of an arbitrary distribution function at a specified point. The next two presentations contain Bayes decision procedures for continuous univariate distribution functions. In one case, the data are considered to be transformed into a sample from a generalized uniform distribution; in the other case, the transformation is to a normal distribution. The fourth presentation contains sequential decision procedures for a moderately general class of composite hypotheses concerning frequency functions; these procedures are not of the Bayes type. The final presentation is nonsequential and contains Bayes decision procedures for selecting one of a finite number of simple hypotheses concerning frequency functions.

Fixed Material for Section

Data 2 None **Assumptions 1** Random sample.

Bayes Estimation of Distribution Function at Given Point

Data 1 Arbitrary, univariate or multivariate **3** $\{X(i)_j\}_m$ **4** $n_1 = \ldots = n_m = n \geqslant 1$ **Description 1** Exact point estimation on basis of stat. decision theory **2** Bayes estimation of $F = F(x_1, \ldots, x_n)$ for specified $(x_1, \ldots, x_n)$, from sample values, stated *a priori* dist. of value for F (best guess from supplementary information) and specified loss fct. **Assumptions 2** None **3** None **Results 1** $\lambda(F) > 0$; $0 \leqslant h_m \leqslant 1$, where h_m an estimate of F. Loss fcts. considered are: $L_1(F, h_m) = \lambda(F)(F - h_m)^2$; $L_2(F, h_m) = \lambda(F)|F - h_m|$; $L_3(F, h_m) = 0$ if $-D_1 \leqslant F - h_m \leqslant D_2$, and is standardized to have the value 1 otherwise, where $D_1, D_2 \geqslant 0$; $L_4(F, h_m)=0$ if $-D_1 \leqslant \log_e F - \log_e h_m \leqslant D_2$ and is standardized to have the value 1 otherwise. $G(\xi)$ = specified *a priori* dist. fct. for unknown value of F $(0 \leqslant \xi \leqslant 1)$. $y(j)=1$ if $X(1)_j \leqslant x_1, \ldots, X(n)_j \leqslant x_n$ and $=0$ otherwise; $N' = \sum_{j=1}^{m} y(j) = mF_m(x_1, \ldots, x_n)$. $E[F^s\lambda(F)|N'] = [\int_0^1 \lambda(\xi)\xi^{N'+s}(1-\xi)^{m-N'}dG(\xi)]/[\int_0^1 \xi^{N'}(1-\xi)^{m-N'}dG(\xi)]$ for $s=0, 1, 2$. $\tau_1(h_m) = h_m{}^2 E[\lambda(F)|N'] - 2h_m E[F\lambda(F)|N'] + E[F^2\lambda(F)|N']$. $G_2(\xi'|N') = [\int_0^{\xi'} \lambda(\xi)\xi^{N'}(1-\xi)^{m-N'}dG(\xi)]/[\int_0^1 \lambda(\xi)\xi^{N'}(1-\xi)^{m-N'}dG(\xi)]$. $\tau_2(h_m) = \int_0^1 |\xi - h_m| dG_2(\xi|N')$. Fcts. occurring in def. of $\tau_1(h_m)$ and $\tau_2(h_m)$ such that these quantities finite for all h_m or, for given N', only finite for one value of h_m. $G_3[\xi'|r] = [\int_0^{\xi'} \xi^r(1-\xi)^{m-r}dG(\xi)]/[\int_0^1 \xi^r(1-\xi)^{m-r}dG(\xi)]$. $\tau_3(h_m|r) = G_3[\min(h_m+D_2, 1)|r] - G_3[\max(h_m - D_1, 0)|r]$. $\tau_4(h_m|r) = G_3\{\exp[\min(\log_e h_m + D_2, 1)]|r\} - G_3\{\exp[\max(\log_e h_m - D_1, 0)]|r\}$ **2** *General Bayes Estimates. Case of* L_1: Estimate is $t_1(N') = E[F\lambda(F)|N']/E[\lambda(F)|N']$ when $\tau_1(h_m) < \infty$ for all h_m, = value of h_m for which $\tau_1(h_m) < \infty$ otherwise. *Case of* L_2: Estimate $t_2(N')$ is median of $G_2(\xi|N')$ when $\tau_2(h_m) < \infty$ for all h_m, is value of h_m for which $\tau_2(h_m) < \infty$ otherwise. *Case of* L_3: Estimate $t_3(N')$ is value of h_m which maximizes $\tau_3(h_m|N')$. For given $G(\xi)$, $P[-D_1 \leqslant F - t_3(N') \leqslant D_2] = \sum_{r=0}^{m} \tau_3[t_3(r)|r]\binom{m}{r} \int_0^1 \xi^r(1-\xi)^{m-r}dG(\xi)$ = subjective prob. that measures extent to which estimate is so close to true value that no loss occurs. *Case of* L_4: Estimate $\log_e t_4(N')$ of $\log_e F$ is value of $\log_e h_m$ which maximizes $\tau_4(h_m|N')$. For given $G(\xi)$, $P[e^{-D_1} \leqslant F/t_4(h_m) \leqslant e^{D_2}] = \sum_{r=0}^{m} \tau_4[t_4(r)|r]\binom{m}{r} \int_0^1 \xi^r(1-\xi)^{m-r}dG(\xi)$ = subjective prob. that furnishes measure of extent to which estimate is so close to true value (in sense of ratio) that no loss occurs. *Examples of estimates for* L_1 *and* L_2: Here $G(\xi)$ continuous with freq. fct. $A(a, b)\xi^a(1-\xi)^b$, where $a, b > -1$; $\lambda(F) = F^c(1-F)^d$, where values of $-(a+c)$ and $-(b+d)$ not too large; a, b, c, d not necessarily integers. Many important combinations of $G(\xi)$ and $\lambda(F)$ can be approximated by allowable selections of values for a, b, c, d. *Case of* L_1: Here $-(a+c)$ and $-(b+d) < 3$. Then $t_1(N') = (N'+a+c+1)/(m+b+d+1)$ for $-(a+c+1) \leqslant N' \leqslant m+b+d+1$, $=0$ for $N' < -(a+c+1)$, $=1$ for $N' > m+b+d+1$. *Case of* L_2: Here $-(a+b)$ and $-(b+d) < 2$. Then $t_2(N')$ is median of beta dist. with freq. fct. $[\Gamma(m+b+d+1)\xi^{N'+a+c}(1-\xi)^{m+b+d-N'-a-c}]/\Gamma(N'+a+c+1)\Gamma(m+b+d-N'-a-c)$ for $-(a+c+1) \leqslant N' \leqslant m+b+d+1$, is 0 for $N' < -(a+c+1)$, is 1 for $N' > m+b+d+1$ **3** Median of beta dist. often obtainable from tables of incomplete beta dist. **4** If $D_1 = D_2 = 0$ and $G(\xi) = \xi$, $t_3(N')$ is max likelihood estimate of F and $\log_e t_4(N')$ is max likelihood estimate of $\log_e F$. Prob. relations stated for L_3 and L_4 do not represent probabilities in usual sense because they depend on *a priori* dist. of F. Except in special cases, expected value estimates not obtained. For the case of L_1, the risk equals $\sum_{r=0}^{m} \tau_1[t_1(r)]\binom{m}{r} \int_0^1 \xi^r(1-\xi)^{m-r}dG(\xi)$. The risk equals $\sum_{r=0}^{m}\tau_2[t_2(r)]\binom{m}{r} \int_0^1 \xi^r(1-\xi)^{m-r}\,dG(\xi)$ for the case of L_2. For L_3, the risk is $1-P[-D_1 \leqslant F-t_3(N') \leqslant D_2]$, and the risk is $1-P[e^{-D_1} \leqslant F-t_4(N') \leqslant e^{D_2}]$ for the case of L_4 **Characteristics 1** Low to upper low for examples for L_1, depending on n; low to lower medium for examples for L_2. Low to high for general situations **2** 100 per cent efficient for situations considered in sense of minimizing risk for given $G(\xi)$ and loss fct. **3** Used symmetrically **4** In general, properties of risk fct. can be very sensitive to dependences involving more than small percentage of observations. However, since N'/m is expected value estimate of F irrespective of dependence, F still estimated in at least rough sense for most cases when independence part of sample assumption violated. Let F_j be the value of the dist. fct. of $\{X(1)_j, \ldots, X(n)_j\}$ at $(x_1, \ldots, x_n)$. Estimates only mediumly sensitive to variation among values of the F_j if their arithmetic average considered to be estimated; here too dependences among observations can have large effect on risk fct. properties but $\sum_{j=1}^{m} F_j/m$ still estimated in at least rough sense for most situations, since N'/m is expected value estimate of $\sum_{j=1}^{m} F_j/m$ irrespective of dependence **5** Not so difficult to decide on independence but sometimes more difficult to verify that the F_j are equal **6** Useful when supplementary information available for selecting $G(\xi)$. Applicable to censored samples, including life-testing situations, for univariate case **Bibliography** Ref. 67.

Transformation to Uniform Distribution—Univariate Case

Data 1 Continuous, univariate **3** $\{X(i)_j\}_m$ **4** $n_1, = \ldots = n_m = 1$ **Description 1** Exact nonsequential Bayes procedures for selecting one of a finite no. of simple hyp. **2** $F(x)$ over all x, where $F(x)$ dist. fct. of $X(1)_j$. Simple hyp. considered assert that transformation $Y(j)=F_0[X(1)_j]$ where $F_0(x)$ completely specified continuous dist. fct., yields observation with freq. fct. of form $\exp[A(B, C)+By+Cy^2]$ for $0 \leqslant y \leqslant 1$ and equal to zero otherwise, where B and C any specified values. Hyp. considered are $(B, C)=(B_1, C_1), \ldots, (B_K, C_K)$; see page 431 for comments about selection of simple hyp. **Assumptions 2** Continuous population **3** None **Results 1** $L(k', k'')$=loss if the true hyp. is $(B_{k'}, C_{k'})$ and the hyp $(B_{k''}, C_{k''})$ is selected. $\xi(k)$=*a priori* prob. of (B_k, C_k), where $\sum_{k=1}^{K} \xi(k) = 1$. $p_k' = \exp[mA(B_k, C_k)+B_k \sum_{j=1}^{m} Y(j)+C_k \sum_{j=1}^{m} Y(j)^2]$. $R(k)=\sum_{k'=1}^{K} L(k', k)p'_k, \xi(k')$ **2** *Bayes decision procedure*: Hyp. (B_{k^*}, C_{k^*}) selected, where $k^*=k^*[Y(1), \ldots, Y(m)]$ determined by $R(k^*)=\min_{1 \leqslant k \leqslant K} R(k)$. If k^* not unique, any of the hyp. corresponding to the values for k^*

can be selected **3** When $C<0$, $A(B, C)= B^2/4C + \log_e(-C/\pi) - \log_e[\Phi(\sqrt{-2C}-B/\sqrt{-2C})-\Phi(-B/\sqrt{-2C})]$. When $C>0$, $A(B, C)= B^2/4C + \log_e(2C) - \log_e[\text{sgn}(\sqrt{2C}+B/\sqrt{2C})\psi(|\sqrt{2C}+B/\sqrt{2C}|) - \text{sgn}(B)\psi(|B|/\sqrt{2C})]$, where $\psi(x)=\int_0^x e^{\frac{1}{2}z^2}\,dz$ with $x \geqslant 0$. When $C=0$ and $B \neq 0$, $A(B, C)=\log_e|B| - \log_e|e^B-1|$. $A(0, 0)=0$ **4** The risk for the Bayes solution equals $\int_0^1 \ldots \int_0^1 R\{k^*(y_1, \ldots, y_m)\}dy_1 \ldots dy_m$ **Characteristics 1** Low to lower-medium, depending on m, K, and whether $F_0(x)$ already tabulated **2** 100 per cent efficient in sense that risk minimized for situation considered **3** Used symmetrically **4** Moderately sensitive to sample condition. Not very sensitive to moderate violations of continuity requirement **5** Not difficult to decide on sample and continuity assumptions **6** Useful when $F_0(x)$ representative of dists. of principal interest or best guess as to actual dist. **Bibliography** Ref. 67.

Transformation to Normal Distribution—Univariate Case

Data 1 Continuous, univariate **3** $\{X(i)_j\}_m$ **4** $n_1 = \ldots = n_m = 1$ **Description 1** Exact nonsequential Bayes procedures for selecting one of a finite no. of simple hyp.; also for selecting either a simple hyp. or a two-sided composite hyp. consisting of two simple hyp. **2** $F(x)$ over all x, where $F(x)$ dist. fct. of $X(1)_j$. Simple hyp. considered assert that transformation $Z(j) = -K_{p(j)}$, where $p(j)=F_0[X(1)_j]$ and $F_0(x)$ is completely specified continuous dist. fct., yields observation from normal dist. with mean μ and variance σ^2. This normal freq. fct. can be represented as $\exp(a'+b'z-c'z^2)$, with $a' = -\mu^2/2\sigma^2 - \log_e\sqrt{2\pi\sigma^2}$, $b' = \mu/\sigma$, $c'=1/2\sigma^2$; here $a'=a(b', c')$. Simple hyp. considered are $(b', c')=(b_1, c_1), \ldots, (b_T, c_T)$; see page 431 for advice about selection of simple hyp. For two-sided case, the simple hyp. H_1 is $(b', c')=(0, \frac{1}{2})$ and the composite hyp. H_2 is $(b', c')=(\mu, \frac{1}{2})$ or $(-\mu, \frac{1}{2})$, with $\mu>0$ and specified **Assumptions 2** Continuous population **3** None **Results 1** $L[t', t'']=$ loss if true hyp. is $(b_{t'}, c_{t'})$ and the hyp. $(b_{t''}, c_{t''})$ is selected, for case where only simple hyp. considered. For two-sided case, loss is standardized to have value unity if simple hyp. selected when composite hyp. true, and loss is w if composite hyp. selected when simple hyp. true. $\xi[t]=$ *a priori* prob. of (b_t, c_t), where $\sum_{t=1}^T \xi[t]=1$. For two-sided case, $\xi_1=$ *a priori* prob. of $(-\mu, \frac{1}{2})$, $\xi_2=$ *a priori* prob. of $(0, \frac{1}{2})$, and $\xi_3=$ *a priori* prob. of $(\mu, \frac{1}{2})$, where $\xi_1+\xi_2+\xi_3 =1$. $p'(t)=\exp[ma(b_t, c_t)+b_t\sum_{j=1}^m Z(j) - c_t\sum_{j=1}^m Z(j)^2]$. $R[t]=\sum_{t'=1}^T L[t', t]p'(t')\xi[t']$ **2** *Bayes decision procedures. Simple hyp. case*: Hyp. (b_{t^*}, c_{t^*}) selected, where $t^*=t^*[Z(1), \ldots, Z(m)]$ determined by $R[t^*]= \min_{1 \leqslant t \leqslant T} R[t]$. If t^* not unique, any hyp. corresponding to a value for t^* can be selected. *Two-sided case*: Select H_v, where $v=v[Z(1), \ldots, Z(m)]$ is 1 if $\xi_1\exp[-\mu\sum_{j=1}^m Z(j)]+\xi_3\exp[\mu\sum_{j=1}^m Z(j)] \leqslant \xi_2 w \exp(m\mu^2/2)$

and is 2 otherwise **3** None **4** For the simple hyp. case, risk is $\int_{-\infty}^{\infty} \cdots \int_{-\infty}^{\infty} R[t^*(z_1, \ldots, z_m)]\, dz_1 \ldots dz_m$. For the two-sided case, risk is $\int_{-\infty}^{\infty} \cdots \int_{-\infty}^{\infty} \Big\{ [2 - v(z_1, \ldots, z_m)] \Big[\xi_1 \exp\Big(ma(-\mu, \tfrac{1}{2}) - \mu \sum_{j=1}^{m} z_j - \tfrac{1}{2} \sum_{j=1}^{m} z_j^2 \Big) + \xi_3 \exp\Big(ma(\mu, \tfrac{1}{2}) + \mu \sum_{j=1}^{m} z_j - \tfrac{1}{2} \sum_{j=1}^{m} z_j^2 \Big) \Big] + [v(z_1, \ldots, z_m) - 1] w \xi_2 \exp\Big(ma(0, \tfrac{1}{2}) - \tfrac{1}{2} \sum_{j=1}^{m} z_j^2 \Big) \Big\} dz_1 \ldots dz_m$ **Characteristics 1** Low to lower-medium for simple hyp. case, depending on m, T, and whether $F_0(x)$ already tabulated. Low to upper-low for two-sided case **2** 100 per cent efficient in sense that risk minimized for situation considered **3** Used symmetrically **4** Moderately sensitive to sample condition. Not very sensitive to moderate violations of continuity requirement **5** Not difficult to decide on sample and continuity assumptions **6** Useful when $F_0(x)$ representative of dists. of principal interest or best guess as to actual dist. **Bibliography** Ref. 67.

Sequential Decisions—Composite Hypotheses (*Wald*)

Data 1 Discrete or continuous, univariate or multivariate **3** $\{X(i)_j\}_m$ **4** $n_1 = \ldots = n_m = n \geqslant 1$; m not a fixed value **Description 1** Approx. non-Bayes sequential decision procedures for selecting one of a finite no. of simple and/or composite hyp. **2** $f(x_1, \ldots, x_n)$ over all $(x_1, \ldots, x_n)$, where $f(x_1, \ldots, x_n)$ considered to have the completely specified parametric form $f(x_1, \ldots, x_n; \eta_1, \ldots, \eta_s)$. Space of possible values for $\eta = (\eta_1, \ldots, \eta_s)$ divided into R mutually exclusive sets $\omega_1, \ldots, \omega_R$. Hyp. H_r asserts that $\eta \epsilon \omega_r$, $(r = 1, \ldots, R)$; usually hyp. are composite but are sometimes simple when no. of possible values for η is finite. $f(x_1, \ldots, x_n; \eta)$ such that max likelihood estimate exists for η and has usual favorable asymptotic properties of max likelihood estimates. Value of η to start sequential procedure obtained as best guess on basis of available supplementary information **Assumptions 2** Population continuous or discrete and such that freq. fct. exists **3** Situation such that decision reached with prob. 1 **Results 1** Loss same for all incorrect decisions and standardized to have value 1. Upper bound for value of risk is r_0. $\hat{\eta}_{j'} = [(j'-1)(\text{max likelihood estimate of } \eta \text{ from first } j'-1 \text{ observations}) + (\text{supplementary information guess for } \eta)]/j'$. Max likelihood estimates computed as if available observations are unrestricted random sample from $f(x_1, \ldots, x_n; \eta)$. $W_j(\eta) = \sum_{j'=0}^{j} \log_{10} \{ f[X(1)_{j'}, \ldots, X(n)_{j'}; \hat{\eta}_{j'}] / f[X(1)_{j'}, \ldots, X(n)_{j'}; \eta] \}$. $\eta'(j) =$ set of eligible values for η such that $W_j(\eta) < -\log_{10} r_0$ **2** *Decision procedure*: Sequential sampling procedure starts with a single observation and continues with single observations until a decision reached. No prior conditions imposed when $m = 1$. Given that $\eta'(j)$ is not completely contained in any one of $\omega_1, \ldots, \omega_R$ for $j \leqslant m-1$, accept H_r if $\eta'(m)$ is completely contained in ω_r $(r = 1, \ldots, R)$; otherwise take another sample value and repeat procedure for increased sample size **3** None **4** Methods other than max likelihood may be more suitable for estimating η in some cases; i.e., have satisfactory properties and require less computation. A modification of the decision procedure which seems preferable but requires more computation is obtained by modifying $W_j(\eta)$ so that $\hat{\eta}_{j'}=\hat{\eta}_j$ for $j'\leqslant j$ **Characteristics 1** Upper low to high, depending on m, s, R, the ω_r, functional form of freq. fct., etc. Computation can be reduced by only determining new estimate of η every several observations (every five, ten, etc.) **2** Risk $\leqslant r_0$. However, r_0 may be substantially larger than true risk in some cases **3** Not used symmetrically **4** Sample condition should be satisfied to reasonable approx. To assure termination of procedure with prob. 1, population freq. fct. should be satisfactorily approximated by parametric form considered **5** Not difficult to determine a parametric freq. fct. form general enough to approximate actual freq. fct. and to decide on other assumptions **6** Major disadvantages are restricted form of risk fct. and lack of information about average sample no. and efficiency. Major advantage is general types of hyp. that can be handled **Bibliography** Ref. 539.

Bayes Decisions for Fixed Sample Sizes—Simple Hypotheses

Data 1 Discrete or continuous, univariate or multivariate **2** None **3** $\{X(i)_j\}_m$ **4** $n_1=\ldots=n_m=n\geqslant 1$; m fixed **Description 1** Exact Bayes decision procedures for selecting one of a finite no. of simple hyp. **2** $f(x_1,\ldots,x_n)$ over all $(x_1,\ldots,x_n)$. Hyp. considered are $H_1,\ldots,H_U$, where H_u asserts that $f(x_1,\ldots,x_n)=f_u(x_1,\ldots,x_n)$; see page 430 for comments about selection of the hyp. **Assumptions 1** Random sample **2** Population discrete or continuous and such that freq. fct. exists **3** None **Results 1** $L(u',u'')=$ loss if true hyp. is $H_{u'}$ and the hyp. $H_{u''}$ is selected. $\xi\{u\}=$ *a priori* prob. of H_u, where $\sum_{u=1}^{U}\xi\{u\}=1$. $p'[u]=\prod_{j=1}^{m}f_u[X(1)_j,\ldots,X(n)_j]$. $r(u)=\sum_{u'=1}^{U}L(u',u)p'[u']\xi\{u'\}$ **2** *Bayes decision procedure*: Hyp. H_{u*} selected, where $u^*=\ u^*[\{X(1)_1,\ldots,X(n)_1\},\ldots,\{X(1)_m,\ldots,X(n)_m\}]$ determined by $r(u^*)=\min_{1\leqslant u\leqslant U}r(u)$. If u^* not unique, any hyp. corresponding to a value for u^* can be selected **3** None **4** Risk equals $\int_{-\infty}^{\infty}\cdots\int_{-\infty}^{\infty}r(u^*[\{x_1^{(1)},\ldots,x_n^{(1)}\},\ldots,\{x_1^{(m)},\ldots,x_n^{(m)}\}])\,dx_1^{(1)}\ldots dx_n^{(m)}$ for the Bayes solution **Characteristics 1** Low to medium, depending on m, n, U, and the $f_u(x_1,\ldots,x_n)$ **2** 100 per cent efficient in sense that risk minimized for situation considered **3** Used symmetrically **4** Sample condition should be satisfied to reasonable approx. **5** Not difficult to decide on assumptions **6** By using enough suitably selected simple hyp., many situations of importance can be reasonably approximated **Bibliography** Ref. 67.

NONSEQUENTIAL CATEGORICAL DATA RESULTS—INTRODUCTION

Discussion

The remainder of this chapter contains tests, and a decision procedure, for investigating probability distributions on the basis of categorical type data. These results are based on a sample from the population whose distribution is being investigated. The categorical data are obtained by grouping these sample values in some suitable fashion. The tests presented have advantages and disadvantages with respect to the tests that can be obtained on the basis of the material of Chapter 10. Some of the advantages are that categorical data tests have general applicability, that some of these tests can be used for composite null hypotheses of a rather general nature, and that, for many of the tests, the distribution can be tested over any specified region that has nonzero probability under the null hypothesis.

Conversion of Data to Categorical Form

The tests presented are used to investigate whether the probability distribution of the population sampled is of the type specified by the null hypothesis. The available data are a sample of size m from this population, which can be multivariate, univariate, continuous, arbitrary, etc. To use the results given in the remaining parts of this chapter, these data are converted to a categorical form. This conversion is accomplished by dividing the space of possible values for the random variable into a specified finite number of disjoint sets. Each of these sets represents a category and the only information used about a sample value is the identification of the category in which its value falls.

The disjoint sets used to determine categories should be chosen so as to yield nonzero null expectations for all the categories. Ideally, their choice should not depend on the values of the sample. Otherwise the amount of bias introduced by the use of this unwarranted additional information may be enough to destroy even the approximate validity of tests based on the resulting categories. For tests with simple null hypotheses, the methods suggested for selecting categories allow this ideal situation to be attained. For tests with composite null hypotheses, some knowledge about the sample values is used in the selection of the categories. However, in this case, the sample information used should not introduce very much bias into tests based on the resulting categories.

When a probability distribution is to be investigated over a specified set of points (with nonzero probability under the null hypothesis), one category is determined by all points that do not belong to this specified set. That is, all categories but one are based exclusively on the points of the specified set that is being considered. Within this specified set, the disjoint sets used to determine categories should be chosen according to the principles already outlined (nonzero null expectations, etc.).

In some situations, especially for the univariate case, the interest may be in testing the distribution function value at several specified points. If the dimensionality of the random variable is small, this can usually be accomplished without much difficulty by a suitable choice of the categories. Ordinarily, the resulting categorical data test has a simple null hypothesis. However, in some cases where the distribution function is investigated over a subregion of the points where it is defined, the null hypothesis can be composite in the sense that only differences of the distribution function values at the specified points have given values. For example, this can be the situation for the univariate case where the subregion over which the distribution function is considered consists of the interval from the smallest of the specified points to the largest of the specified points. That is, the given probability values are those for the consecutive differences of the distribution function values at the specified points; however, the distribution function values at these points are not given.

One situation where the use of categorical type data can be almost equivalent to the use of actual data is that where the population is discrete with not too large a number of possible values (which are known). Here each possible population value is considered to represent a separate category.

Since data from any type of population can be converted to a categorical form, results based on categorical data have an extremely broad area of application. For many situations where the population sampled is not continuous and univariate, the only available procedures for investigating a probability distribution are those based on categorical data. Even for the continuous univariate case, categorical data tests are the only nonsequential procedures that are available for testing a distribution over an arbitrary region and/or for testing nearly all types of composite null hypotheses.

Advice on Selection of Categories

Although categories can be determined in an unlimited number of ways, some selection methods are more desirable than others for given situations. In general, the null expectation for any given category can either be evaluated or estimated; it can be exactly determined for the case of a simple null hypothesis and can be estimated for the case of a composite null hypothesis (estimation of null expectations is discussed on page 455).

General guides for selecting categories can be stated in terms of their null expectations.

When the probability distribution is to be investigated over all points, selection of the disjoint sets so that they have nearly the same null expectations seems to be desirable. If the probability distribution is to be investigated over a specified restricted set of points, the categories are chosen so that all points not in the specified set represent a single category. Then selection of the other categories so that they have about the same null expectations seems desirable. Ref. 441 outlines a method for determining categories with equal null expectations in the continuous multivariate case.

For some of the procedures, an additional problem is that of deciding on the number of categories to be used. Ideally, this selection should be made independently of the values of the sample, so that biases are avoided. The available rules for handling this problem were developed for the special situation of a large sample, a chi-square goodness of fit test with a simple null hypothesis, and a continuous population that is considered over all points (see ref. 330 and 592). These rules apply to the case of equal null expectations for all categories and indicate that, for significance level α ($\alpha < \frac{1}{2}$) and $m \geqslant 200$, the number of categories should lie between

$$2[2(m-1)^2/K_\alpha{}^2]^{1/5} \quad \text{and} \quad 1+4[2(m-1)^2/K_\alpha{}^2]^{1/5}.$$

These limits can also be used for smaller values of m but with less theoretical basis. The number of categories determined by the lower limit should be reasonably satisfactory for m and α combinations such that $m \geqslant 20$ and also m divided by this number of categories is at least 5.

For lack of anything better, this set of rules is also suggested for the other situations considered where a probability distribution is investigated over all points and the number of categories is a choice of the experimenter. However, for the composite null hypothesis situations, the m and α combinations for which the number of categories furnished by the lower limit seem to be satisfactory are modified. Let $m-1-K$ be the number of degrees of freedom for the asymptotic null distribution of the chi-square statistic for the composite null hypothesis considered. Then the number of categories determined by the lower limit would seem to be reasonably satisfactory for m, α combinations such that $m/\sqrt{K+1} \geqslant 20$ and also $m/\sqrt{K+1}$ divided by this number of categories is at least 5. These modified conditions represent a practical compromise. That is, the numbers of categories allowed by the rules should be satisfactory for nearly all practical type situations where these conditions hold but less conservative conditions on m and α might be applicable in many cases.

Next consider selecting the number of categories to be used for cases where the probability distribution is investigated over a specified restricted set of points. This selection can be made on the basis of the number U of categories that would be chosen, according to the rules stated above, under the assumption that the probability distribution is investigated over all points. Let N be the expected number of sample values that will fall in the specified restricted set when the null hypothesis is satisfied. Then the use of a total number of categories equal to the greater of two and the largest integer contained in

$$1 + NU/m$$

seems to be at least moderately satisfactory for many situations. Here one category is represented by the set consisting of all points not in the specified set and all the other categories have the same (or nearly the same) expectations under the null hypothesis.

Subject to the above considerations, the disjoint sets used to determine categories should be chosen so as to emphasize the regions of the probability distribution which are of principal interest to the investigator. Also the amount of effort required to determine or estimate the null expectations and to determine which set contains a given observed value can be important in selecting the disjoint sets on which the categories are based.

Remark on Pooling of Categories

In some cases, the desired set of categories is determined from technical and/or computational considerations. For even these situations, however, the null expectations for the categories can not ordinarily be ignored. Namely, many of the tests presented in this chapter are based on approximations to the null distribution of the test statistic. Usually, these approximations are not applicable when the null expectations (exact or estimated) are too small for some of the categories. This difficulty is frequently handled by combining adjacent categories until the resulting set of categories has satisfactory null expectations.

This pooling of categories can introduce substantial probability bias if it is not done in a suitable manner. If the null expectations are exactly known (i.e., not estimated), the procedure used to combine categories should be specified without any knowledge about the sample values. If the null expectations are estimated, the values of these estimates should be the only knowledge about the sample values that is used in the procedure adopted for pooling categories.

Another consideration is that the pooling of categories tends to reduce the power of a test, especially when categories pertaining to the distribution tails are pooled. The distribution tails are often the places where the difference between the null hypothesis and an alternative of major interest stands out most clearly. Thus, only the minimum pooling required for obtaining an acceptable approximation to the null distribution of the test statistic should ordinarily be used.

Multinomial Form of Testing Problem

After the observations are converted to a categorical form, the problem is that of testing the distribution of a multinomial population on the basis of a sample from that population. Here the probabilities for the categories of the multinomial population are completely determined for the case of a simple null hypothesis and are determined except for the values of some unknown constants for the case of a composite null hypothesis. Specifically, let the population sampled be n-variate ($n \geqslant 1$) and let the null hypothesis be expressed in the form

$$F(x_1, \ldots, x_n) = F_0(x_1, \ldots, x_n),$$

where $F_0(x_1, \ldots, x_n)$ is either completely specified or is specified except for the values of some unknown constants $c_1, \ldots, c_K$. Suppose that there are U categories and let s_u be the set of points that determines the uth category ($u = 1, \ldots, U$). Then

$$p_u^{(0)} = \int_{s_u} \cdots \int dF_0(x_1, \ldots, x_n)$$

is the probability of the uth category under the null hypothesis (depends on the c's for the composite case), where $p_1^{(0)} + \ldots + p_U^{(0)} = 1$.

For given $x_1, \ldots, x_U$, different $F_0(x_1, \ldots, x_n)$ can yield the same values for $p_1^{(0)}, \ldots, p_U^{(0)}$. Thus tests obtained by grouping data into categories are not consistent against general alternatives.

In this chapter, the observed number of sample values belonging to the uth category is denoted by m_u, where $m_1 + \ldots + m_U = m$. The expectation for the uth category is $mp_u^{(0)}$ when the null hypothesis is satisfied.

Methods for Obtaining Exact Tests of Simple Null Hypotheses

In principle, exact tests for simple null hypotheses can always be developed on the basis of test statistics that are expressed in terms of the m_u and the $p_u^{(0)}$. However, unless m is very small, the amount of effort required to develop a test can be huge. To illustrate the method, let us consider a procedure for obtaining an exact one-sided test with significance level approximately equal to α; here the null hypothesis is rejected if the value of the test statistic is too large.

First determine the largest possible value for the test statistic. Let this value be denoted by X_R and consider all possible combinations of values for the m_u such that the statistic has this value. Then $P_0(X_R)$ denotes the sum of the null probabilities for these combinations. If the value of $P_0(X_R)$ is sufficiently near α, the test consists in rejecting the null hypothesis when the value of the test statistic equals X_R; this test has significance level $P_0(X_R)$. When $P_0(X_R)$ is much smaller than α, the next to largest value of the test statistic, denoted by X_{R-1}, is determined and its null probability evaluated. If $P_0(X_R)+P_0(X_{R-1})$, is sufficiently near α, the test used rejects the null hypothesis when the test statistic value is at least equal to X_{R-1}; this test has significance level $P_0(X_R)+P_0(X_{R-1})$. Continuing in this manner, if $P_0(X_R)+\ldots+P_0(X_{R-t})$ is sufficiently near α, the test used rejects the null hypothesis when the test statistic value is at least equal to X_{R-t} and has significance level $P_0(X_R)+\ldots+P_0(X_{R-t})$.

If the categories are chosen in the suggested manner, with equal null expectations for all categories, or for all but one category, the amount of computation required to determine the $P_0(X_R), \ldots, P_0(X_{R-t})$ may be substantially reduced. This is an additional motivation for following the stated advice concerning the selection of categories.

Another method for obtaining exact tests with significance levels approximately equal to α consists in direct selection of critical regions in the space of the possible values for the m_u. Here the recommended procedure for building up the critical region consists in first selecting a combination of values for the m_u that has minimum probability under the null hypothesis. The next combination chosen has the next to smallest null probability (could be equal to the minimum probability). This procedure is continued until the sum of the null probabilities for the points chosen is sufficiently near α. Here, too, selection of the categories in the manner suggested on page 441 has computational advantages.

Considerations in Testing Material Deviations from Null Hypothesis

Ordinarily, a significance test investigates whether the null hypothesis differs too much from the true situation in a probability sense. In many cases, however, the principal interest lies in whether the "deviation" of the null hypothesis from the true situation is too great in a material sense. To define what is meant by a material sense some "distance" function must be developed to measure the deviation between the null hypothesis and the true situation. For the multinomial population considered when the data are categorical, the hypotheses are identified by the values of the probabilities for the categories. Thus, if $p=(p_1, \ldots, p_U)$ and $p^{(0)}=(p_1^{(0)}, \ldots, p_U^{(0)})$, the "distance" between the points p and $p^{(0)}$ measures the deviation between the null hypothesis and the actual situation in a material sense. Here the distance function, denoted by $\Delta(p, p^{(0)})$, is chosen so that the alternatives of greatest interest are emphasized; in some cases, $\Delta(p, p^{(0)})$ may be chosen as ordinary Euclidean distance between the points p and $p^{(0)}$. Matusita's distance definition (see page 471) has favorable properties and should be useful for many situations.

The "deviation" of a simple null hypothesis from the actual situation is said to be too great in a material sense if $\Delta(p, p^{(0)})$ exceeds a specified critical value. When the null hypothesis is composite, the requirement imposed is that $\Delta(p, p^{(0)})$ exceeds a specified critical value for all allowable values of $p^{(0)}$.

Confidence Regions for Categorical Data Distributions

The tests with simple null hypothesis can be used to obtain confidence regions for the multinomial population from which the categorical data are a sample. The method used to determine these confidence regions is as follows: Suppose that there are U possible categories and let the probabilities of these categories be denoted by $p_1, \ldots, p_U$, where the sum of these probabilities is unity. Then the multinomial probability distribution for the categorical data is completely identified by the value of the $(U-1)$-dimensional point $(p_1, \ldots, p_{U-1})$, and a confidence region for the distribution is obtained by determining a confidence region for this point.

The tests with simple null hypotheses presented for categorical type data are based on relations involving statistics which depend on the observed numbers of values in the categories and on the hypothetically true value of $(p_1, \ldots, p_{U-1})$. The complements of the regions (in the space of possible values for $p_1, \ldots, p_{U-1}$) determined by the relations that the statistics satisfy for the tests determine confidence regions for $(p_1, \ldots, p_{U-1})$. These regions have confidence coefficients whose values equal unity minus the values of the significance levels for the tests.

Remark on Simple Null Hypotheses

Although many of the categorical data tests presented are said to have simple null hypotheses, in actuality these null hypotheses are simple only from the viewpoint of sampling from a multinomial population. This is the reason that the tests are only consistent from the viewpoint of sampling from a multinomial population. The null distribution $F_0(x_1, \ldots, x_n)$ which yields the null multinomial distribution is not unique. An unlimited number of other distributions can also yield this multinomial distribution.

Situations Considered

The following two sections are devoted to presentations. The first of these sections is concerned with the chi-square test for goodness of fit and some related tests. The other section contains some additional tests, and a decision procedure, that are based on categorical data. Included are grouped data versions of the Neyman smooth test and of Smirnov's version of the Cramér-von Mises type tests.

CHI-SQUARE GOODNESS OF FIT AND RELATED TESTS

Introduction

This section is concerned with Karl Pearson's well-known chi-square test for goodness of fit and with some modifications and some closely related substitutes for this test. The advantages and disadvantages of the standard chi-square test are discussed and motivations are presented for using the substitutes and modifications that are considered. The problems of testing composite null hypotheses and of determining power function values and adequate sample sizes are examined. Also some methods are stated for approximating the null hypothesis distribution of the chi-square goodness of fit statistic.

Discussion of Chi-Square Test of Fit

When the null hypothesis is simple, the chi-square goodness of fit test is based on the statistic

$$\sum_{u=1}^{U} (m_u - mp_u^{(0)})^2/mp_u^{(0)} = -m + \sum_{u=1}^{U} m_u^2/mp_u^{(0)}$$

and, ordinarily, is a one-sided test where the null hypothesis is rejected when this statistic is too large. Since the $p_u^{(0)}$ are known values, the distribution of this statistic under the null hypothesis can be exactly determined. However, to avoid computational difficulties, approximations to this distribution are nearly always used.

When the null hypothesis is composite, involving K unknown one-dimensional constants $c_1, \ldots, c_K$ with $K < U$, the null probabilities for the categories are of the forms

$$p_u^{(0)} = p_u^{(0)}(c_1, \ldots, c_K) = \int_{S_u}\!\!\cdots\!\int dF_0(x_1, \ldots, x_n; c_1, \ldots, c_K).$$

Then, on the basis of the categorical data, the values of $c_1, \ldots, c_K$ are jointly estimated in a suitable manner (e.g., by maximum likelihood). Let the estimate be $\hat{c}_1, \ldots, \hat{c}_K$ and let the resulting estimates of the $p_u^{(0)}$ be

$$\hat{p}_u^{(0)} = p_u^{(0)}(\hat{c}_1, \ldots, \hat{c}_K), \qquad (\hat{p}_1^{(0)} + \ldots + \hat{p}_U^{(0)} = 1).$$

For this composite null hypothesis case, the chi-square goodness of fit test is based on the statistic

$$\sum_{u=1}^{U} (m_u - m\hat{p}_u^{(0)})^2/m\hat{p}_u^{(0)} = -m + \sum_{u=1}^{U} m_u^2/m\hat{p}_u^{(0)}$$

and, ordinarily, is one-sided with the null hypothesis rejected when this statistic is too large. Since, in general, the $p_u^{(0)}$ depend on $c_1, \ldots, c_K$, the distribution of this statistic depends on the values of these constants. However, under the null hypothesis, the asymptotic distribution of this statistic is, for nearly all situations of interest, independent of $c_1, \ldots, c_K$ and of the functional forms for the $p_u^{(0)}(c_1, \ldots, c_K)$; explicitly, this distribution is χ^2 with $U-1-K$ degrees of freedom. Thus, this version of chi-square goodness of fit test can be applied when the sample size is not too small.

Let us outline some of the advantages and disadvantages of the chi-square test for goodness of fit. First, this test has the general advantages and disadvantages of tests based on categorical type data. Namely, it has the advantages of being relatively easy to apply and of being applicable to investigating probability distributions over specified restricted sets of points. On the other hand, it has the problem of selecting categories in a suitable and unbiased fashion. Also this test is not consistent against general alternatives and seems to be somewhat insensitive unless the sample size is large.

The chi-square test of fit has the additional advantages of being able to handle composite null hypotheses and of being asymptotically equivalent to the corresponding maximum likelihood ratio test for a multinomial population. Moreover the chi-square statistic can be expressed as a sum of asymptotically independent components which emphasize specified properties of interest and, asymptotically, this statistic represents an intuitively meaningful measure of the deviation of the categorical data from the multinomial population (see ref. 51). As an example of subdivision into components, the results for single categories can be compared with those for groupings of categories by the subdivision stated in ref. 258. As another example, the first few sample moments can be compared with the corresponding hypothetical population moments by the method outlined in ref. 303. In general, linear functions of the m_u can be compared with their null expectations by use of the method given in ref. 105.

The chi-square test of fit also has some additional disadvantages. First, the signs of the deviations of the m_u from the $mp_u^{(0)}$, or the $m\hat{p}_u^{(0)}$, and the order in which these signs occur, are not taken into consideration. Second, the relative locations of the disjoint sets from which the categories are determined are not considered. Third, there are some difficulties of a computational nature. For the composite null hypothesis case, determination of the estimates $\hat{c}_1, \ldots, \hat{c}_K$ can require a large amount of computational effort, especially if $K \geqslant 2$. Also difficulties occur in determining the null distribution, even to a reasonable approximation, when m is only moderately large; these difficulties can be substantial for cases involving composite null hypotheses. Fourth, as for many significance tests, the chi-square test only investigates whether the deviation of the null hypothesis situation from the actual situation is too great in a probability sense; often the proximity of these two situations in a material sense is of at least as much interest. Finally, the chi-square test is of a general nature with respect to the alternatives emphasized; i.e., no special alternative hypothesis is emphasized.

Modifications and Substitutes for Chi-Square Test

The other tests considered in this section are either direct modifications for the chi-square test of fit or are closely related substitutes for this test. In all cases, these other tests are designed to offset some of the difficulties that occur for the standard chi-square test.

Methods for obtaining exact tests on the basis of categorical data are discussed on page 444. These methods, which can be used to yield an exact version of the chi-square test, can be applied to situations involving small sample sizes and simple null hypotheses. Ref. 209 contains a method for computing exact probabilities for the special case where all the categories have the same probability.

An asymptotically equivalent substitute for the chi-square test is presented which can also handle both simple and composite null hypotheses. This substitute consists of the corresponding likelihood ratio test, for a multinomial population, and has the advantage of not requiring much in the way of continuity corrections when the sample size and the number of categories are small. In addition, the use of a likelihood ratio statistic has an intuitive appeal even when the sample size is not large. Some other asymptotically equivalent substitutes considered in the statistical literature are obtained by using $m_u + 2$ (or m_u) in place of $mp_u^{(0)}$, or $m\hat{p}_u^{(0)}$, in the denominator of the standard chi-square statistic (see ref. 137, 227 and 381).

Two modifications of the standard chi-square test are presented. For one case, involving a simple null hypothesis, the test used consists of a combination of a test based on runs in the signs of the differences $m_u - mp_u^{(0)}$ and the chi-square test of fit; this is referred to as the chi-square "smooth" test. Here the order in which the categories occur is taken into consideration. The other modification is concerned with testing whether the deviation of the actual multinomial situation from the null hypothesis situation is too great in a material sense. Here a distance function is introduced and the maximum allowable "distance" between the null hypothesis situation and the actual situation is specified. This second modification can be used for both simple and composite null hypotheses.

A third type of modification (no presentation given) which emphasizes a specified alternative can be obtained along the lines of the results outlined on page 338. The Neyman-Pearson lemma furnishes the motivation for this modification, which tests a specified simple (or modified composite) null hypothesis for the categorical data distribution against a simple (or modified composite) alternative hypothesis for this multinomial distribution. By analogy with the corresponding continuous case, the efficiency of these results, compared to any competitive results based on categorical data, should be quite high.

According to the simple null hypothesis, the (nonzero) probabilities for the categories are $p_1^{(0)}, \ldots, p_U^{(0)}$ while they are $p_1^{(1)}, \ldots, p_U^{(1)}$ for the simple alternative. The test statistic is

$$\sum_{u=1}^{U} m_u \log_{10} [p_u^{(1)}/p_u^{(0)}]$$

and the null hypothesis is rejected if the value of this statistic is too large.

Although the multinomial distribution is discrete, the distribution of the test statistic is approximately continuous except for small m. The null distribution of this statistic can be approximated by computing its first few moments under the assumption that the null hypothesis holds and using the first few terms of the Edgeworth series based on these moments; the first four moments should be satisfactory for most situations. A similar procedure can be used to approximate the power of the test for a specified alternative set of allowable values for $p_1, \ldots, p_U$.

Remarks About Chi-Square "Smooth" Test

As already mentioned, this test is for simple null hypotheses and consists of a combination of a chi-square test of fit and a run test based on the signs of the $m_u - mp_u^{(0)}$; here only the nonzero differences $m_u - mp_u^{(0)}$ are considered in a run test and the sequence of signs begins with that for $u = 1$ and ends with that for $u = U$. The run test used rejects the null hypothesis when the total number of runs (of both signs) is too small. Thus the method used to determine which is the uth category is important in determining the alternative hypotheses that are emphasized. That is, for the alternative to be protected against, the numbering of the categories should be such that the number of runs tends to be small when this alternative holds. Of course, such a selection is only possible for restricted types of alternatives. As an illustration of selecting the categories so as to emphasize a specified type of alternative, consider the univariate case and slippage alternatives of the form $F(x)=F_0(x+a)$, where $F(x)=F_0(x)$ is the null hypothesis. Then choice of the s_u as consecutive intervals along the x axis tends to yield small numbers of runs in the signs of the $m_u-mp_u^{(0)}$ when a is large in magnitude.

If none of the $mp_u^{(0)}$ is integral, runs of U signs are considered. When some of the $mp_u^{(0)}$ are integral, however, less than U nonzero differences can occur, and the resulting run test is of a conditional nature. In some cases, such as when $p_u^{(0)}=1/m$, it is possible for no signs to be available. Except for this case, the number of runs is at least two, since the sum of the differences $m_u-mp_u^{(0)}$ is necessarily zero.

Discussion of Test for Material Deviations

The test presented consists in first selecting a distance function $\Delta(f', p^{(0)})$ to measure material deviations between the sample and the null hypothesis. Then this function is examined for all possible values of $p^{(0)}$; here $f'=(m_1/m, \ldots, m_U/m)$. The result is adjudged to not be significant in a material sense when $\Delta(f', p^{(0)})$ is less than or equal to a specified critical value for at least one allowable value of $p^{(0)}$. That is, the deviation from the null hypothesis is considered to be unimportant in a material sense when this situation occurs. When this situation does not occur, the determination of whether the result is significant or not in a material sense is made by the use of a significance test of a chi-square type. Although this test can have a composite null hypothesis, the $\hat{p}_u^{(0)}$ are not used in its application and therefore do not have to be evaluated.

Power Function—Adequate Sample Sizes

For the chi-square test of fit, and asymptotically equivalent substitutes, large sample values of the power can be determined for alternatives that are expressed in terms of the quantity

$$C_m=m\sum_{u=1}^{U}(p_u-p_u^{(0)})^2/p_u^{(0)}.$$

Here

$$p_u=\int_{s_u}\cdots\int dF(x_1, \ldots, x_n)$$

is the actual probability for the uth category. If the p_u are fixed and $p_u\neq p_u^{(0)}$ for at least one value of u, the asymptotic power of a test is unity (then $C_m\rightarrow\infty$).

A more interesting situation is that where the p_u are not fixed with respect to m. Let

$$p_u = p_u^{(0)} + a_u/\sqrt{m}, \qquad (u=1, \ldots, U)$$

where the a_u are specified constants (independent of m). Then,

$$C_m = \sum_{u=1}^{U} a_u^2/p_u^{(0)}$$

has a fixed value and the asymptotic distribution of the test statistic is noncentral χ^2 with parameter C_m. For a simple null hypothesis, this noncentral χ^2 distribution has $U-1$ degrees of freedom. If the null hypothesis is composite and nontrivially involves unknown constants $c_1, \ldots, c_K$, i.e., $p_u^{(0)}$ is of the form $p_u^{(0)}(c_1, \ldots, c_K)$, the noncentral χ^2 distribution has $U-1-K$ degrees of freedom. Power function values can be determined, for specified C_m, by use of tables and approximations for the noncentral χ^2 distribution (given in ref. 179 and 402). Consideration of the power function for this situation (i.e., with the p_u expressed in this form) seems to have many worthwhile uses.

One important application of the asymptotic power function is to approximately determine adequate sample sizes. This can be accomplished by specifying the values of the p_u (fixed) and the corresponding value for the power function. Then, the minimum value of m for which this power is attained by the asymptotic power function is determined. This determination is accomplished by considering the asymptotic power function to be noncentral χ^2 with parameter C_m (see the preceding paragraph for the determination of the degrees of freedom). Often, the resulting value of m is sufficiently large for approximate accuracy of the asymptotic power function and, consequently, is satisfactory for use as the minimum adequate sample size.

Methods for Determining the $\hat{p}_u^{(0)}$

In general, a composite null hypothesis can be expressed in the form

$$F(x_1, \ldots, x_n) = F_0(x_1, \ldots, x_n; c_1, \ldots, c_K),$$

where F_0 is completely specified (as a function of $x_1, \ldots, x_n$) except for the values of the real constants $c_1, \ldots, c_K$. That is, there exists a set of values for $c_1, \ldots, c_K$ such that this equality is satisfied. Then, as already mentioned,

$$p_u^{(0)} = p_u^{(0)}(c_1, \ldots, c_K) = \int_{s_u} \cdots \int dF_0(x_1, \ldots, x_n; c_1, \ldots, c_K).$$

The problem is to determine suitable estimates for $c_1, \ldots, c_K$ on the basis of the observed values $m_1, \ldots, m_U$ $(K < U)$ and subject to some regularity conditions on the $p_u^{(0)}$ as functions of the c's. Alternately, the problem is to directly estimate the values of the $p_u^{(0)}$ For each estimation method outlined, the resulting set of estimates is suitable for use in the statistics for the chi-square test of fit and the likelihood ratio test. That is, for sufficiently large sample sizes, sets of estimates obtained by the various methods given here have approximately equivalent properties and can be used in the statistics of tests for composite null hypotheses. These estimates of the $p_u^{(0)}$ are the $\hat{p}_u^{(0)}$ that are mentioned in the discussion of the chi-square test of fit.

Several regularity conditions are imposed on the $p_u^{(0)}$ for situations involving composite null hypotheses. These require that, for all $c_1, \ldots, c_K$ in the nondegenerate K-dimensional region considered,

(1) The values of the $p_u^{(0)}$ are bounded away from zero
(2) $p_1^{(0)} + \ldots + p_U^{(0)} = 1$
(3) The $\partial p_u^{(0)}/\partial c_{k'}$ and the $\partial^2 p_u^{(0)}/\partial c_{k'}\partial c_{k''}$ exist and are continuous $(u = 1, \ldots, U;\ k', k'' = 1, \ldots, K)$
(4) The matrix $\|\partial p_u^{(0)}/\partial c_k\|$, where $u = 1, \ldots, U$ and $k = 1, \ldots, K$, is of rank K.

All estimation methods considered are for situations where the $p_u^{(0)}$ satisfy these conditions.

Three different types of approaches are outlined for handling the estimation problem. For the first two approaches, the estimates are the values for $c_1, \ldots, c_K$ which maximize or minimize specified functions of the c's and the categorical data. In one case, the estimates are determined directly, through the use of numerical techniques. In the other case, the estimates are determined by partial differentiation. The same functions of the c's and the categorical data are considered for these two types of approaches. The third type of approach consists in direct estimation of the $p_u^{(0)}$ rather than estimation of the c's. Only one estimation method is outlined for this third approach. Computational convenience should probably be the principal criterion in choosing among the various estimation methods that are considered.

Three estimation methods are outlined for the first type of approach. In one case the estimates are the values of $c_1, \ldots, c_K$ which minimize

$$\sum_{u=1}^{U} (m_u - mp_u^{(0)})^2/mp_u^{(0)}, \quad \text{or equivalently,} \quad \sum_{u=1}^{U} m_u^2/p_u^{(0)},$$

since the condition that

$$p_1^{(0)} + \ldots + p_U^{(0)} = 1$$

is always imposed on the $p_u^{(0)}$. In the second case, the estimates are the values of the c's which maximize the likelihood function; i.e., which maximize

$$[p_1^{(0)}]^{m_1} \dots [p_U^{(0)}]^{m_U}.$$

For the third case, the estimates are the values of the c's which minimize

$$\sum_{u=1}^{U} (m_u - mp_u^{(0)})^2/(m_u+2), \quad \text{or} \quad \text{equivalently}, \quad \sum_{u=1}^{U} (mp_u^{(0)}+2)^2/(m_u+2).$$

Various numerical techniques, some of which use high-speed computers, have been developed for determining the maximum or the minimum of a function of a number of variables subject to stated conditions. For many situations, use of one of these estimation methods, combined with a suitable numerical technique, may be most desirable from a computational viewpoint.

Three estimation methods are also outlined for the second type of approach. Here the estimates yielded by the first method for this second approach are the same as those yielded by the first method for the type of approach just considered, although they are determined by partial differentiation. Likewise, the estimates yielded by the second methods, and those yielded by the third methods, are the same for the two types of approaches. For the first method of the second type of approach, the estimates are the values for the c's that satisfy the simultaneous equations

$$\sum_{u=1}^{U} \{(m_u - mp_u^{(0)})/p_u^{(0)} + [(m_u - mp_u^{(0)})/p_u^{(0)}]^2/2m\} \partial p_u^{(0)}/\partial c_k = 0. \qquad (k=1, \dots, K)$$

For the second method, the estimates are the values for $c_1, \dots, c_K$ that satisfy the simultaneous equations

$$\sum_{u=1}^{U} (m_u/p_u^{(0)}) \partial p_u^{(0)}/\partial c_k = 0. \qquad (k=1, \dots, K)$$

For the third method, the estimates are the values for the c's that satisfy the simultaneous equations

$$\sum_{u=1}^{U} [(mp_u^{(0)}+2)/(m_u+2)] \partial p_u^{(0)}/\partial c_k = 0. \qquad (k=1, \dots, K)$$

The second method will usually require less computational effort than the first method.

The third approach is concerned with direct estimation of the $p_u^{(0)}$. In addition to the condition

$$h_0(p_1^{(0)}, \dots, p_U^{(0)}) = \sum_{u=1}^{U} p_u^{(0)} - 1 = 0,$$

K other conditions of the form

$$h_k(p_1^{(0)}, \ldots, p_U^{(0)}) = 0, \qquad (k = 1, \ldots, K)$$

are obtained by eliminating the constants $c_1, \ldots, c_K$ from the equations

$$p_u^{(0)}(c_1, \ldots, c_K) = p_u^{(0)}.$$

Thus the problem is to estimate the $p_u^{(0)}$ subject to these $K+1$ conditions.

On the basis of the method given in ref. 381, which uses Lagrange multipliers, the values of the $p_u^{(0)}$ which minimize

$$\sum_{u=1}^{U} (m_u - mp_u^{(0)})^2/m(m_u+2)$$
$$+ \sum_{k=0}^{K} \lambda_k[h_k(m_1/m, \ldots, m_U/m) + \sum_{u=0}^{U} h_k^{(u)}(m_1/m, \ldots, m_U/m)(p_u^{(0)} - m_u/m)]$$

furnish suitable estimates. Here $\lambda_0, \ldots, \lambda_K$ are Lagrange multipliers and

$$h_k^{(u)}(p_1^{(0)}, \ldots, p_U^{(0)}) = \partial h_k(p_1^{(0)}, \ldots, p_U^{(0)})/\partial p_u^{(0)}.$$

The values of the estimates for the $p_u^{(0)}$ are found by simultaneous solution of the $U+K+1$ linear equations in $U+K+1$ unknowns

$$2 \sum_{u=1}^{U} (mp_u^{(0)} - m_u)/(m_u+2) + \sum_{k=0}^{K} \lambda_k h_k^{(u)}(m_1/m, \ldots, m_U/m) = 0$$

$$h_k(m_1/m, \ldots, m_U/m) + \sum_{u=1}^{U} h_k^{(u)}(m_1/m, \ldots, m_U/m)(p_u^{(0)} - m_u/m) = 0,$$

where $u = 1, \ldots, U$ and $k = 0, 1, \ldots, K$.

Although the third approach may seem to require the least computational effort, since the estimates can be determined by the simultaneous solution of linear equations, this is not necessarily the case. The reason is that much effort may be required to determine the $h_k(m_1/m, \ldots, m_U/m)$ and the $h_k^{(u)}(m_1/m, \ldots, m_U/m)$ for $k = 1, \ldots, K$.

For all three estimation approaches, the data used are the m_u. That is, the $p_u^{(0)}$ are not estimated by direct use of the sample values from the distribution being tested. As shown in ref. 93, estimation of these constants directly from the sample values can introduce large biases when the estimates are used in the test statistics.

Estimation of Null Expectations

Although direct estimation of $c_1, \ldots, c_K$ from the sample values is not desirable for use in the test statistic, this estimation can be helpful in determining suitable categories. The methods outlined for determining the $\hat{p}_u^{(0)}$ can not be used for this purpose because they require that the categories already be determined.

Let $c'_1, \ldots, c'_K$ be estimates of the c's determined from the sample values. Then, the estimated null expectation for a category based on a specified set s_u is

$$m \int_{s_u} \cdots \int dF_0(x_1, \ldots, x_n; c'_1, \ldots, c'_K).$$

Thus, in determining suitable categories, the null hypothesis distribution function is considered to be $F_0(x_1, \ldots, x_n; c'_1, \ldots, c'_K)$, which is completely specified.

Various methods could be used in estimating the c's directly from the sample values. Maximum likelihood estimation is one possibility. The method of moments (i.e., equating population moments to the corresponding sample moments) is another estimation possibility.

This estimation of the c's has another important use besides that of determining suitable categories. Namely, this set of estimates should be somewhere near in value to the sets of estimates that can be used to determine the $\hat{p}_u^{(0)}$. Thus, starting with this initial set of values and a given estimation method, a few iterations should yield the values of the estimates for determining the $\hat{p}_u^{(0)}$ which are used in the test statistic.

Use of $c'_1, \ldots, c'_K$ for determining categories places some conditional effects on the data. However, for cases where tests of composite null hypotheses are obtainable, these conditional effects are believed to be relatively unimportant.

An alternative method consists in arbitrarily choosing a set of categories, independently of the sample values, and determining estimates of $c_1, \ldots, c_K$ on the basis of this set of categories. In many cases, however, this method is much more difficult to apply than direct estimation from the sample values. Also, unless the set of categories used for this purpose differs very little from that ultimately selected for use, the estimates of $c_1, \ldots, c_K$ should be recomputed for the categories actually used for a test. An exception to this occurs when the only change in categories consists in pooling adjacent categories that have small estimated expectations (see, e.g., ref. 385). If pooling is used, the decision as to how pooling will take place should be made independently of the sample values except with respect to the estimates of the expectations.

Approximations to Null Distributions

The first part of the material given here is concerned with statement of a few rough rules for deciding when the continuous χ^2 distribution is acceptable for approximating some specified null distributions (a suitable continuity correction may also be needed in some cases). The null distributions considered are that for the chi-square statistic for fit and that of the statistic that equals $-2 \log_e$ (likelihood ratio statistic). These rules are stated in terms of the null expectations, or their estimates (composite null hypothesis case), for the categories that occur. The second part contains some continuous approximations which can be used for the null distribution of the chi-square statistic for goodness of fit when some or all of the null expectations are small; suitable corrections for continuity may also be needed for some uses of these approximations. Finally, the question of when continuity corrections are needed is considered and methods for introducing these corrections are outlined.

First let us consider the extent of the null expectation situations which might be encountered when deciding on the acceptability of the continuous χ^2 approximation to the null distribution. In converting the data to a categorical form, the recommended procedure is to have approximately equal null expectations for the categories that correspond to the specified set of points over which the probability distribution is being investigated. That is, under the null hypothesis, either all the expectations for the categories are nearly equal or all but one of the expectations are nearly equal. However, for various reasons, the categories may have almost any values for their null expectations. As an example, technical considerations may have a strong influence on the grouping used for the sample values, and yield categories whose null expectations differ appreciably. As another example, for composite null hypotheses, estimates of the null expectations may not be available until after a definite grouping is selected, so that not much control can be exercised over these expectations. Also computational convenience can have a strong influence on the groupings used to obtain the categories.

For the case of a simple null hypothesis, the continuous χ^2 approximation is considered to be satisfactory for obtaining a test with significance level α when

(a) $U-1=1,\quad \alpha(1-\alpha)\geqslant 5/4[m \max_u p_u^{(0)}][m\sum_{u=1}^{U} p_u^{(0)}/U],$
$m \min_u p_u^{(0)}\geqslant 5$

(b) $2\leqslant U-1\leqslant 60,\quad \alpha(1-\alpha)\geqslant (U+\tfrac{1}{2})^2/9(U-\tfrac{3}{2})^{11/5}\,[m \max_u p_u^{(0)}][m\sum_{u=1}^{U} p_u^{(0)}/U],\quad m\min_u p_u^{(0)}\geqslant 3(U+\tfrac{1}{2})/2(U-\tfrac{3}{2}),\quad m\max_u p_u^{(0)}\geqslant[3U+7(U-3)^{4/3}/4+\tfrac{3}{2}]/2(U-\tfrac{3}{2})$

(c) $U-1>60,\quad \alpha(1-\alpha)\geqslant 1/9U^{1/5}[m\max_u p_u^{(0)}][m\sum_{u=1}^{U} p_u^{(0)}/U],$
$m\min_u p_u^{(0)}\geqslant \tfrac{3}{2},\quad m\max_u p_u^{(0)}\geqslant 5.$

Corrections for continuity may be needed for (a); also for (b) when m and U are small.

When the null hypothesis is composite, it seems impossible to specify sample sizes that are satisfactory for all cases. Thus a practical compromise is adopted. Namely, rules are adopted which should furnish sample sizes that are definitely larger than those which would ordinarily be required for most of the practical applications that have occurred for the chi-square statistic. On the other hand, situations exist where these sample sizes are too small for reasonably accurate use of the continuous χ^2 approximation. For the case of a composite null hypothesis with K unknown real constants, the continuous χ^2 approximation is considered to be satisfactory when

(a′) $U-1=1$, $\alpha(1-\alpha)\geqslant 5(K+1)/4[m \max_u \hat{p}_u^{(0)}][m \sum_{u=1}^{U} \hat{p}_u^{(0)}/U]$, $m \min_u \hat{p}_u^{(0)} \geqslant 5\sqrt{K+1}$

(b′) $2\leqslant U-1\leqslant 60$, $\alpha(1-\alpha)\geqslant (U+\frac{1}{2})^2(K+1)/9(U-\frac{3}{2})^{11/5}[m \max_u \hat{p}_u^{(0)}][m \sum_{u=1}^{U} \hat{p}_u^{(0)}/U]$, $m \min_u \hat{p}_u^{(0)} \geqslant 3(U+\frac{1}{2})\sqrt{K\quad 1}/2(U-\frac{3}{2})$, $m \max_u \hat{p}_u^{(0)} \geqslant [3U+7(U-3)^{4/3}/4+\frac{3}{2}]\sqrt{K+1}/2(U-\frac{3}{2})$

(c′) $U+1>60$, $\alpha(1-\alpha)\geqslant (K+1)/9U^{1/5}[m \max_u \hat{p}_u^{(0)}][m \sum_{u=1}^{U} \hat{p}_u^{(0)}/U]$, $m \min_u \hat{p}_u^{(0)} \geqslant 3\sqrt{K+1}/2$, $m \max_u \hat{p}_u^{(0)} \geqslant 5\sqrt{K+1}$.

Next let us consider obtaining approximations to the chi-square test of fit which are applicable to the case of a simple null hypothesis when none of the rules (a)–(c) is satisfied. Two different methods are outlined for obtaining continuous approximations to the null distribution of the chi-square statistic. In one case, the continuous χ^2 distribution is used, but with the degrees of freedom modified; then the approximation has the same mean, variance, and nonzero range as the actual null distribution. For the other case, the continuous approximation is expanded so that the terms neglected are of order $1/m^2$. In both cases, rough rules are given for deciding when these approximations are applicable. Continuity corrections may be needed for some situations.

The approximation using a modification of the degrees of freedom is based on ref. 409. Here the continuous χ^2 distribution is considered for nonintegral degrees of freedom, with probabilities determined by interpolation, by use of the incomplete gamma distribution, etc. Explicitly, the continuous χ^2 distribution with

$$(U-1)/[1-1/m-U^2/2(U-1)m+\sum_{u=1}^{U} 1/2(U-1)p_u^{(0)}]$$

degrees of freedom is considered to be satisfactory for obtaining a test with significance level α when

$$m \geqslant 10,\ \alpha(1-\alpha) \geqslant 1/9[m \max_u p_u^{(0)}][m \sum_{u=1}^{U} p_u^{(0)}/U],\ mp_u^{(0)} \geqslant (U+1)/2(U-1).$$

A continuity correction may be needed when m and U are small.

The other approximation is based on ref. 252 and consists of a sum of continuous χ^2 distributions with various integral degrees of freedom. Let $G_v(x)$ denote the distribution function for χ^2 with v degrees of freedom. Then the approximation to the null distribution function of the chi-square statistic for arbitrary but specified x is

$$G_{U-1}(x)+\frac{1}{8m}\left[\sum_{u=1}^{U} 1/p_u^{(0)}-(U^2+2U-2)\right]\left[G_{U+3}(x)-2G_{U+1}(x)+G_{U-1}(x)\right]$$
$$+\frac{1}{24m}\left[5\sum_{u=1}^{U} 1/p_u^{(0)}-(3U^2+6U-4)\right]$$
$$\left[G_{U+5}(x)-3G_{U+3}(x)+3G_{U+1}(x)-G_{U-1}(x)\right].$$

Let ϵ denote the value of this approximation to the distribution function, where $\epsilon=\epsilon_1+\epsilon_2$ and $\epsilon_1=G_{U-1}(x)$. Then, for $\epsilon_1 \leqslant \frac{1}{2}$, this approximation is considered to be applicable when $\epsilon_1 \geqslant 10\epsilon_2$; for $\epsilon_1 > \frac{1}{2}$, this approximation is considered to be applicable when $1-\epsilon_1 \geqslant 10\epsilon_2$.

Continuity corrections are seldom needed in applying the stated continuous approximations to the null distributions for the likelihood ratio test, the chi-square test with a composite null hypothesis, and the chi-square test with a simple null hypothesis and $U-1>2$. If $U-1=1$, the use of a continuity correction should always be considered for a chi-square test with a simple null hypothesis; if $U-1=2$, a continuity correction may be needed when m is small and/or the null expectations are small for all categories.

A correction for continuity can be introduced by modifying the value of the chi-square test statistic on the basis of the set of values that it can attain (see ref. 105). Let $X_1^2 < \ldots < X_R^2$ be the possible values of this statistic for given values of m and the $p_u^{(0)}$; also let its observed value be X_r^2. Then, if $H(x)$ is a suitable continuous approximation to the null distribution function of the chi-square statistic for the situation where a continuity correction is used ($x \geqslant 0$),

$$P[\tfrac{1}{2}(X_r^2 + X_{r+1}^2) \geqslant x] \doteq 1 - H(x), \quad P[\tfrac{1}{2}(X_{r-1}^2 + X_r^2) \leqslant x] \doteq H(x)$$

when the null hypothesis holds. Here, by definition,

$$X_0^2 = 0 \quad \text{and} \quad X_{R+1}^2 = 2X_R^2 - X_{R-1}^2.$$

That is, X_r^2 is replaced by $\frac{1}{2}(X_r^2 + X_{r+1}^2)$ if values at least equal to a specified value are of interest and by $\frac{1}{2}(X_{r-1}^2 + X_r^2)$ if values at most equal to a specified value are of interest. These continuity corrections tend to furnish the greatest accuracy with respect to the use of a continuous approximation $H(x)$ when x is one of the possible values for the chi-square statistic.

Another type of continuity correction, in which the value of the chi-square statistic is not modified, can also be determined on the basis of its possible values (see ref. 105 and 600). Let $X_{s(x)}^2$ be the largest among $X_0^2, X_1^2, \ldots, X_R^2$ that is less than x, while $X_{t(x)}^2$ equals $X_{s(x)+1}^2$ if x is not one of $X_1^2, \ldots, X_R^2$ and equals $X_{s(x)+2}^2$ otherwise. Then, under the null hypothesis,

$$P[X_r^2 \geqslant \tfrac{1}{2}(x + X_{s(x)}^2)] \doteq 1 - H(x)$$

$$P[X_r^2 \leqslant \tfrac{1}{2}(x + X_{t(x)}^2)] \doteq H(x).$$

As for the other type, these continuity corrections tend to furnish the greatest accuracy with respect to the use of $H(x)$ when x is one of the values $X_1^2, \ldots, X_R^2$.

In general, the values of X_{r-1}^2, X_{r+1}^2, $X_{s(x)}^2$, $X_{t(x)}^2$ are determined by trial-and-error methods. In some cases, a moderately large amount of effort can be required to determine one of these values.

Appropriateness of Two-Sided Tests

As already mentioned, the chi-square test of fit is ordinarily a one-sided test where the null hypothesis is rejected when the test statistic is too large. Two-sided versions of this test have also been proposed; i.e., the null hypothesis is also rejected if it agrees too closely with the observational data. The motivation for rejection when the agreement is very close stems from the possibility that not all of the assumptions underlying the test are satisfied to a reasonable approximation. Since violations of assumptions are not considered to represent legitimate alternative hypotheses, the viewpoint adopted is that only the standard one-sided version of the chi-square test should be used (also see ref. 500). However, if the agreement between the null hypothesis and the observational data is very close, the reasons for accepting the assumptions on which the test is based (including that of unbiased selection of categories) should be carefully examined. For similar reasons, this viewpoint is also adopted for the other tests presented in this section, i.e., only the appropriate one-sided versions are considered.

Fixed Material for Section

Data 1 Arbitrary; univariate or multivariate **3** $\{X(i)_j\}_m$ **4** $n_1 = \ldots = n_m = n \geqslant 1$ **Description 2** $F(x_1, \ldots, x_n)$ over all $(x_1, \ldots, x_n)$ or over a specified set of pts. having nonzero prob. under null hyp. (see page 440) **Assumptions 1** Random sample **2** Categories chosen in unbiased fashion **3** None **Characteristics 3** Used symmetrically **4** Sample condition should be satisfied to reasonable approx. Moderately sensitive to biases in selection of categories **5** Not difficult to decide on sample assumption and to select categories in unbiased fashion.

K. Pearson's Chi-Square Test for Goodness of Fit

Data 2 None **4** Rules for deciding when approximations applicable given on page 456 **Description 1** Theoretical-approx. one-sided tests **2** Simple and composite null hyp. considered. Simple null hyp. asserts that $F(x_1, \ldots, x_n) = F_0(x_1, \ldots, x_n)$ while composite null hyp. asserts that $F(x_1, \ldots, x_n)$ is of the form $F_0(x_1, \ldots, x_n; c_1, \ldots, c_K)$. Tests obtained by converting data to categorical form, as described on page 440. Then simple null hyp. expressed as $p_u = p_u^{(0)}$ for all u, and composite null hyp. expressed as $p_u = p_u^{(0)}(c_1, \ldots, c_K)$ for all u and some set of values for the c's, where, as already mentioned, $p_u = \int_{s_u} \cdots \int dF(x_1, \ldots, x_n)$. Here the $p_u^{(0)}(c_1, \ldots, c_K)$ satisfy the regularity conditions stated on page 453 **Results 1** The $\hat{p}_u^{(0)}$ are determined by one of methods outlined on page 452. $Y = -m + \sum_{u=1}^{U} m_u^2/mp_u^{(0)}$; $\hat{Y} = -m + \sum_{u=1}^{U} m_u^2/m\hat{p}_u^{(0)}$; m_u defined on page 444 **2** *Test of simple null hyp.*: Reject null hyp. if $Y \geqslant Y_\alpha$. *Test of composite null hyp.*: Reject null hyp. if $\hat{Y} \geqslant \hat{Y}_\alpha$ **3** Only approx. values are considered for Y_α and $\hat{Y}_\alpha$. The available values, and situations where they are applicable, furnished by approx. to null dist. that are stated on page 456; for one type of continuity correction, statistic Y is slightly modified. Exact version of test for simple null hyp. obtainable by method discussed on page 444 **4** Method for suitable selection of categories outlined on page 441. Procedure for determining adequate sample sizes mentioned on page 451. Stratified sample form of chi-square test of fit considered in ref. 14 **Characteristics 1** Low to medium for simple null hyp., depending on m, U, the s_u, and $F_0(x_1, \ldots, x_n)$. Upper low to high for composite null hyp., depending on m, U, K, the s_u, and $F_0(x_1, \ldots, x_n; c_1, \ldots, c_K)$ **2** Method for determining asymptotic power fct. outlined on page 451. Test where all categories have same null expectation is unbiased for case of simple null hyp. Test consistent against multinomial population altern. which differ from multinomial pop. null hyp. but not consistent against general altern. for population sampled. Test is asymptotically optimum (for multinomial population) in an information theory sense **6** Useful when altern. of interest only described in rather vague and general terms. Other tests of sect. are modifications or substitutes for this test **Bibliography** Ref. 14, 46, 51, 53, 85, 93, 105, 118 (p. 424), 162, 172, 174, 175, 209, 215, 225, 252, 258, 301, 303, 312, 323, 330, 381, 384, 385, 394, 406, 409, 500, 528, 592, 600.

Likelihood Ratio Test (Neyman, E. S. Pearson, Wilks)

Data 2 None **4** Rules for deciding when approximations applicable given on page 456 **Description 1** Theoretical-approx. one-sided tests **2** Simple and composite null hyp. considered. Simple null hyp. asserts that $F(x_1, \ldots, x_n) = F_0(x_1, \ldots, x_n)$ while composite null hyp. asserts that $F(x_1, \ldots, x_n)$ is of the form $F_0(x_1, \ldots, x_n; c_1, \ldots, c_K)$, where $c_1, \ldots, c_K$ are unknown real constants. Tests obtained by converting data to categorical form, as described on page 440. Then simple null hyp. expressed as $p_u = p_u^{(0)}$ for all u, and composite null hyp. expressed as $p_u = p_u^{(0)}(c_1, \ldots, c_K)$ for all u and some set of values for the c's, where, as already mentioned, $p_u = \int_{s_u} \cdots \int dF(x_1, \ldots, x_n)$. Here the $p_u^{(0)}(c_1, \ldots, c_K)$ satisfy the regularity conditions stated on page 453 **Results 1** The $\hat{p}_u^{(0)}$ are determined by one of methods outlined on page 452. $Z = -2\sum_{u=1}^{U} m_u \log_e(m_u/mp_u^{(0)})$; $\hat{Z} = -2\sum_{u=1}^{U} m_u \log_e (m_u/m\hat{p}_u^{(0)})$, m_u defined on page 444 **2** *Test of simple null hyp.*: Reject null hyp. if $Z \geqslant Z_\alpha$. *Test of composite null hyp.*: Reject null hyp. if $\hat{Z} \geqslant \hat{Z}_\alpha$ **3** Only approx. values are considered for Z_α and $\hat{Z}_\alpha$. The available values, and outline of situations where they are applicable, furnished by approx. to null dist. that are stated on page 456. Exact version for test of simple null hyp. obtainable by method discussed on page 444 **4** Method for suitable selection of categories outlined on page 441. Procedure for determining adequate sample sizes discussed on page 451. This test asymptotically equivalent to chi-square test of fit **Characteristics 1** Low to medium for simple null hyp., depending on m, U, and s_u, and $F_0(x_1, \ldots, x_n)$. Upper low to high for composite null hyp., depending on m, U, K, the s_u, and $F_0(x_1, \ldots, x_n; c_1, \ldots, c_K)$ **2** Has intuitively desirable property of being likelihood ratio test for multinomial population considered and all sample sizes. May be more powerful than chi-square test of fit for the smaller sample sizes but this is not firmly established. Method for determining asymptotic power fct. outlined on page 451. Consistent against multinomial population altern. which differ from multinomial pop. null hyp. but not consistent against general altern.

for population sampled. Has optimum properties (for multinomial population) from information theory viewpoint **6** Substitute for chi-square test of fit (see discussion in first part of sect.) **Bibliography** Ref. 93, 105, 301, 381, 384, 385, 587.

Chi-Square "Smooth" Test (F. N. David)

Data 2 Numbering of categories used in grouping data (the s_u) should be such that altern. hyp. of interest emphasized by run part of test **4** Rules for deciding when tests applicable given in part 4 of Results **Description 1** Combination of exact run test and theoretical-approx. one-sided chi-square test of fit **2** Simple null hyp., asserts that $F(x_1, \ldots, x_n) = F_0(x_1, \ldots, x_n)$. Tests obtained by converting data to categorical form, as described on page 440. Then null hyp. expressed as $p_u = p_u^{(0)}$ for all u, where, as already mentioned, $p_u = \int_{s_u} \cdots \int dF(x_1, \ldots, x_n)$ and $p_u^{(0)} = \int_{s_u} \cdots \int dF_0(x_1, \ldots, x_n)$ **Results 1** m_u is no. of sample values falling in uth category (i.e., with values in s_u). r_1 = no. of + signs and r_2 = no. of − signs among the $m_u - mp_u^{(0)}$. T = observed total no. of runs of +'s and −'s in the sequence $\operatorname{sgn}(m_1 - mp_1^{(0)}), \ldots, \operatorname{sgn}(m_U - mp_U^{(0)})$, where $\operatorname{sgn}(m_u - mp_u^{(0)})$ excluded from consideration when $m_u - mp_u^{(0)} = 0$. $p_r(t)$ = prob., under null hyp., that t or fewer runs occur, given r_1 and r_2. $Y = -m + \sum_{u=1}^{U} m_u^2/mp_u^{(0)}$. $p_c(y) = \int_y^\infty g(\chi^2)d\chi^2$, where $g(\chi^2)$ freq. fct. of continuous χ^2 dist. with $U-1$ d.f. **2** *Test*: Reject null hyp. if $p_r(T)p_c(Y) < A_\alpha$ **3** When $r_1 = r_2 = 0$, $p_r(T) = 1$ and chi-square signif. pts. used. $p_c(y)$ evaluated by use of Table 2 at end of book. Table 11.1 contains values of $p_r(t) = p_r(t; r_1, r_2)$ for $5 \leqslant r_1 + r_2 \leqslant 14$ and $r_1 \geqslant r_2$; values for $r_2 \geqslant r_1$ obtainable from $p_r(t; r_1, r_2) = p_r(t; r_2, r_1)$. Table 11.2 contains values of $A_\alpha = A_\alpha(r_1, r_2)$ for $5 \leqslant r_1 + r_2 \leqslant 14$, $r_1 \geqslant r_2$, and $\alpha = .01, .05$; values for $r_2 \geqslant r_1$ obtainable from $A_\alpha(r_1, r_2) = A_\alpha(r_2, r_1)$. Method given in ref. 133 can be used to determine $p_r(t)$ and A_α for other values of $r_1 + r_2$ and α **4** Tests applicable when $U > 3$, $A_\alpha(1 - A_\alpha) \geqslant (U + \frac{1}{2})^2/9(U - \frac{3}{2})^{11/5}$ $[m \max_u p_u^{(0)}][m \sum_{u=1}^{U} p_u^{(0)}/U]$, $m \min_u p_u^{(0)} \geqslant 3(U + \frac{1}{2})/2(U - \frac{3}{2})$, and $m \max_u p_u^{(0)} \geqslant [3U + 7(U-3)^{4/3}/4 + \frac{3}{2}]/2(U - \frac{3}{2})$. Method for suitable selection of categories discussed on page 441 **Characteristics 1** Low to high, depending on m, U, the s_u, $F_0(x_1, \ldots, x_n)$ and whether $p_r(T)$ and A_α tabulated **2** The run test is not very powerful by itself, unless $r_1 + r_2$ is quite large. However, the combination of this test and the chi-square test should be more powerful against altern. where the no. of runs tends to be small (smooth altern.) than either test by itself **6** Only test considered in this sect. which allows for the ordering of the categories and the signs of the $m_u - mp_u^{(0)}$ **Bibliography** Ref. 105, 133, 135.

TABLE 11.1. VALUES OF $p_r(t)=p_r(t; r_1, r_2)$ FOR $5 \leqslant r_1+r_2 \leqslant 14$ AND $r_1 \geqslant r_2$ (TO THREE SIGNIFICANT FIG. ACCURACY)*

r_1	r_2 \ t	2	3	4	5	6	7	8	9	10	11	12	13	14
4	1	.400	1.000											
3	2	.200	.500	.900	1.000									
5	1	.333	1.000											
4	2	.133	.400	.800	1.000									
3	3	.100	.300	.700	.900	1.000								
6	1	.286	1.000											
5	2	.0953	.333	.714	1.000									
4	3	.0572	.200	.543	.800	.971	1.000							
7	1	.250	1.000											
6	2	.0714	.285	.643	1.000									
5	3	.0357	.143	.429	.714	.929	1.000							
4	4	.0286	.114	.371	.629	.885	.971	1.000						
8	1	.222	1.000											
7	2	.0556	.250	.583	1.000									
6	3	.0238	.107	.345	.642	.881	1.000							
5	4	.0159	.0714	.262	.500	.786	.928	.992	1.000					
9	1	.200	1.000											
8	2	.0444	.222	.533	1.000									
7	3	.0167	.0833	.283	.583	.833	1.000							
6	4	.00952	.0476	.190	.405	.691	.882	.976	1.000					
5	5	.00794	.0397	.167	.357	.643	.833	.960	.992	1.000				
10	1	.182	1.000											
9	2	.0364	.200	.491	1.000									
8	3	.0121	.0667	.236	.533	.788	1.000							
7	4	.00606	.0333	.143	.333	.606	.833	.955	1.000					
6	5	.00433	.0238	.110	.260	.521	.738	.912	.976	.998	1.000			
11	1	.167	1.000											
10	2	.0303	.182	.454	1.000									
9	3	.00910	.0546	.200	.491	.745	1.000							
8	4	.00404	.0241	.109	.279	.533	.788	.929	1.000					
7	5	.00253	.0152	.0758	.197	.424	.651	.853	.954	.992	1.000			
6	6	.00217	.0130	.0671	.176	.392	.608	.826	.934	.988	.998	1.000		
12	1	.154	1.000											
11	2	.0256	.167	.423	1.000									
10	3	.00699	.0454	.171	.454	.706	1.000							
9	4	.00280	.0182	.0853	.236	.471	.746	.902	1.000					
8	5	.00156	.0101	.0536	.144	.347	.577	.795	.930	.984	1.000			
7	6	.00117	.00758	.0426	.121	.296	.500	.733	.878	.966	.992	.999	1.000	
13	1	.143	1.000											
12	2	.0220	.154	.395	1.000									
11	3	.00550	.0385	.148	.423	.671	1.000							
10	4	.00200	.0140	.0680	.203	.419	.707	.875	1.000					
9	5	.00100	.00700	.0390	.119	.287	.511	.735	.903	.973	1.000			
8	6	.000667	.00467	.0280	.0864	.227	.413	.646	.822	.937	.985	.998	1.000	
7	7	.000583	.00408	.0251	.0775	.209	.384	.617	.792	.924	.976	.996	.999	1.000

* Taken from ref. 133: A χ^2-"smooth" test of fit, F. N. David, *Biometrika*, Vol. 34, 1947, pages 299–310. Used with the kind permission of the author, F. N. David, and of the Editor of *Biometrika*.

TABLE 11.2. VALUES OF $A_\alpha = A_\alpha(r_1, r_2)$ FOR $5 \leqslant r_1 + r_2 \leqslant 14$, $r_1 \geqslant r_2$, AND $\alpha = .01, .05$*

r_1	r_2	$A_{.05}$	$A_{.01}$	r_1	r_2	$A_{.05}$	$A_{.01}$
4	1	.03125	.00625	10	1	.02755	.0055
3	2	.0213	.0043	9	2	.0171	.0034
				8	3	.0144	.0028
5	1	.0300	.0060	7	4	.0144	.0025
4	2	.0211	.0042	6	5	.0140	.0024
3	3	.0195	.0039				
				11	1	.0273	.0055
6	1	.0292	.0058	10	2	.0174	.0035
5	2	.0197	.00395	9	3	.0149	.0027
4	3	.0174	.0035	8	4	.0142	.0024
				7	5	.0135	.0022
7	1	.0286	.0057	6	6	.0131	.0021
6	2	.0188	.0038				
5	3	.0160	.0032	12	1	.0271	.0054
4	4	.0153	.0031	11	2	.0165	.0033
				10	3	.0151	.0026
8	1	.0281	.0056	9	4	.0138	.0023
7	2	.0180	.0036	8	5	.0137	.0022
6	3	.0153	.0031	7	6	.0138	.00225
5	4	.0140	.0028				
				13	1	.0269	.0054
9	1	.0278	.0056	12	2	.0163	.0033
8	2	.0175	.0035	11	3	.0151	.0025
7	3	.0143	.0029	10	4	.0135	.00225
6	4	.0143	.0026	9	5	.0138	.0023
5	5	.0143	.0025	8	6	.0136	.0022
				7	7	.0134	.0022

* Taken from ref. 133: A χ^2-"smooth" test of fit, F. N. David, *Biometrika*, Vol. 34, 1947, pages 299–310. Used with the kind permission of the author, F. N. David, and of the Editor of *Biometrika*.

Test for Specified Material Deviations from Null Hypothesis (*Hodges-Lehmann*)

Data 2 None **4** Rules for deciding when approx. applicable given in part 4 of Results **Description 1** Theoretical-approx. one-sided tests **2** Simple & composite null hyp. considered. Simple null hyp. asserts that $F(x_1, \ldots, x_n) = F_0(x_1, \ldots, x_n)$ while composite null hyp. asserts that $F(x_1, \ldots, x_n)$ is of the form $F_0(x_1, \ldots, x_n; c_1, \ldots, c_K)$. Tests obtained by converting data to categorical form, as described on page 440. Then simple null hyp. expressed as $p_u = p_u^{(0)}$ for all u, and composite null hyp. expressed as $p_u = p_u^{(0)}(c_1, \ldots, c_K)$ for all u and some set of values for the c's, where, as already mentioned, $p_u = \int_{s_u} \ldots \int dF(x_1, \ldots, x_n)$ **Results 1** $\Delta(p, p^{(0)}) =$

appropriately chosen fct. for measuring distance between $p=(p_1, \ldots, p_U)$ and $p^{(0)}=(p_1^{(0)}, \ldots, p_U^{(0)})$. $d(p)=\Delta(p, p^{(0)})$ for case of simple null hyp. and $= \inf_{c_1, \ldots, c_K} \Delta[p, p^{(0)}(c_1, \ldots, c_K)]$ for case of composite null hyp., where $p^{(0)}(c_1, \ldots, c_K)=\{p_1^{(0)}(c_1, \ldots, c_K), \ldots, p_U^{(0)}(c_1, \ldots, c_K)\}$. Fct. $d(p)$ required to possess continuous first and second partial derivatives with respect to the p_u. $b_u=\partial d(p)/\partial p_u$ evaluated at $p=f'$, where $f'=(m_1/m, \ldots, m_U/m)$ and m_u is no. of sample values falling in uth category (s_u). Deviation between null hyp. and altern. hyp. p considered unimportant in a material sense if and only if $d(p) \leqslant D$; being unimportant in a material sense represents a weakened type of null hyp. $W=m\{\sum_{u=1}^{U}[d(f')-D]^2\}/\{\sum_{u=1}^{U} m_u(b_u-\bar{b})^2/m\}$, where $\bar{b}=\sum_{u=1}^{U} b_u m_u/m$ **2** *Test*: Accept that the deviation of the null hyp. from the true situation is unimportant in a material sense if $d(f') \leqslant D$ or if $d(f')>D$ and $W \leqslant \chi_{2\alpha}^2(1)$; otherwise accept that this deviation is important in a material sense. Here α is sig. level $(\alpha<\frac{1}{2})$ **3** Value of $\chi_{2\alpha}^2(1)$ obtainable from Table 2 at end of book **4** Test considered applicable if $\min_u m_u \geqslant 6\sqrt{K+1}$ and $\alpha \geqslant 6(K+1)/4(\max_u m_u)(\sum_{u=1}^{U} m_u/U)$. Method for suitable selection of categories outlined on page 441. Considerations involved in use of this test discussed on page 451 **Characteristics 1** Low to upper medium, depending on m, U, the s_u, the null hyp., and the distance fct. **2** Power fct. $\beta_m(p)$ for altern. hyp. p has properties: $\lim_{m\to\infty}\beta_m(p)=0$ when $d(p)<D$; $\lim_{m\to\infty}\beta_m(p)=\alpha$ when $d(p)=D$; $\lim_{m\to\infty}\beta_m(p)=1$ when $d(p)>D$ **6** Only procedure in sect. which explicitly tests for material deviations from null hyp. **Bibliography** Ref. 240.

SOME TESTS AND DECISION PROCEDURES FOR GROUPED DATA

Introduction

The preceding section contains some procedures for testing probability distributions on the basis of grouped data. Some additional procedures of this nature are given in this section. One of these is a grouped data version of the Neyman smooth test while another is a grouped data form of a Cramér-von Mises type test that was presented for the continuous univariate case. All but three of the tests are concerned with situations where the groups have the same null expectations. One presentation contains both tests and decision procedures; these results are based on a specified type of distance function for measuring the deviation of the sample from the null distribution and the deviation of the null distribution from the actual distribution. All of the procedures are based on categorical type data and can be used to investigate a probability distribution over all points; only a few of the results can also be used to investigate distributions over specified sets of points. Only simple null hypotheses are considered and, as applied, nearly all of the procedures are of a theoretical-approximate nature. The population sampled can be arbitrary and univariate or multivariate; however, one of the types of tests is principally useful for univariate situations.

Categorical Nature of Data Groupings Considered

As already mentioned, two of the tests represent grouped data versions of tests for the continuous univariate case. However, these and all the other procedures presented in this section are based on categorical type data. That is, the data used are the numbers of sample values falling in specified categories, and the probability distribution investigated is represented by the probabilities for these categories. Thus, all of the procedures are applicable to both univariate and multivariate situations, also for arbitrary kinds of populations (continuous, discrete, etc.). However, the grouped data version of the Neyman smooth test is oriented toward the univariate case, since the alternatives emphasized are based on the univariate situation.

Outline of Procedures Presented

The first test presented represents a grouped data version of the Neyman smooth test. The second presentation contains a grouped data version of the Smirnov form of the Cramér-von Mises type tests; here the categories are required to have the same null expectations. The statistic for the two types of tests of the third presentation, which are of an exact nature, is the number of the categories of a specified set that contain no observed values. For one type of test, the statistic is based on all the categories and each category has a null expectation of unity. For the other type, the statistic is based on all but one of the categories and each of these $U-1$ categories has a null expectation of $\frac{1}{2}$; this test represents a situation where the probability distribution is investigated over a specified set of points.

The fourth and fifth presentations require categories with equal null expectations. The tests for the fourth presentation are based on specified combinatorial functions of the numbers of values falling in the categories. The fifth test is based on the maximum of the numbers of values for the categories; i.e., the statistic used is $\max_u m_u$, where m_u is the observed number of values falling in the uth category ($u=1, \ldots, U; m_1+\ldots+m_U=m$). The sixth and final presentation contains some tests and decision procedures that are based on a definition of the distance between a sample and a population, also between two populations, that has been developed by K. Matusita. These results can be used to investigate whether the hypothetical population differs from the actual population in a material sense.

Relation of Tests Presented to Chi-Square Test of Fit

The tests given in this section are not considered to be direct modifications or direct substitutes for the chi-square test of fit. However, some of these results protect against a general class of alternatives and are applicable for small sample sizes. Consequently, they can be used in place of the chi-square test of fit for small sample sizes. Moreover, an extreme form of the Neyman smooth test for grouped data is equivalent to the corresponding chi-square test of fit; also one of the combinatorial test statistics is a linear function of the corresponding chi-square statistic. In many cases, however, these results emphasize situations that are different from those emphasized by the chi-square test of fit.

Alternatives Emphasized by Tests

The Neyman smooth test for grouped data is designed to handle univariate situations. When the distribution is considered over all points, the alternatives emphasized by this test are essentially the same as those emphasized by the Neyman smooth test for continuous distribution functions that is based on ungrouped data (see page 360). The alternatives considered are identified in the presentation of the Neyman smooth test for grouped data. This test can also be used to test a distribution over a specified set of points; then the alternatives emphasized also depend on the specified set of points that is considered.

The grouped data version of a Cramér-von Mises type test which is considered should be at least roughly sensitive to alternative hypotheses that are expressed in terms of the metric

$$m\int_{-\infty}^{\infty}\cdots\int_{-\infty}^{\infty}[F_0(x_1,\ldots,x_n)-F(x_1,\ldots,x_n)]^2dF_0(x_1,\ldots,x_n),$$

where the null hypothesis asserts that $F(x_1,\ldots,x_n)=F_0(x_1,\ldots,x_n)$ for all $(x_1,\ldots,x_n)$. This metric should be especially suitable for this purpose when $n=1$.

The test based on the number of empty categories, with all categories considered, is of a general purpose type. That is, this test protects against any violation of the null distribution for the categorical data. The corresponding test where all but one of the categories are considered, and the number of these that are empty is the test statistic, is sensitive to special classes of alternatives. That is, the selection of the categories establishes the alternatives that are emphasized.

The remaining tests protect against alternatives of a general type. In addition to this general protection, the test based on the maximum of the observed numbers for equiprobable categories emphasizes situations where the actual probabilities are much larger than their hypothetical values for a few categories. For the test based on Matusita's distance definition, the alternatives are stated in terms of the distance between the null distribution and the actual distribution. For the other tests, the alternatives are stated directly in terms of the actual distribution; that is, simple alternatives are considered.

Power Function Discussion

In the case of the Neyman smooth test for grouped data, the class of alternatives for which power function values are considered is similar to the class $H_s^{(2)}$ that was considered for the ungrouped version of this test (see page 360). In fact, the power functions for the grouped and ungrouped situations are nearly the same when the sample size is not too small, the categories have roughly the same null expectations, and the number of categories is not too small. For a specified alternative, the asymptotic distribution of the test statistic is that of a noncentral χ^2 variable with a determined parameter value and number of degrees of freedom.

No direct power expressions or values are given for the grouped data version of a Cramér-von Mises type test. However, if the number of categories is not too small, the results for the ungrouped version of this test should furnish an indication of how its power compares with that of the corresponding chi-square test for large sample sizes.

If the sample size is not too small and the alternatives do not differ too much from the null hypothesis, approximate power function values can be obtained for both types of tests that are based on the number of empty equiprobable categories. For a given alternative, the test statistic is nearly normally distributed when the sample size is sufficiently large. Likewise, for a given alternative, the statistic for the test based on combinatorial functions of data for equiprobable categories has a distribution that is asymptotically normal.

Upper and lower bounds are determined for the power function of the test based on the maximum of the numbers of values for the categories. These bounds may be rather far apart for some situations where the power is at least moderately large. An exact method can be used for cases where the bounds are too far apart; however, use of the exact method can require a large amount of effort.

The power function values obtained for the test based on Matusita's distance definition are expressed in terms of the distance between the actual and the hypothetical distributions. The values furnished are lower bounds for the actual power and are not applicable unless the sample size exceeds a specified value.

Determination of Adequate Sample Sizes

Adequate sample sizes for the grouped data version of the Neyman smooth test can be obtained on the basis of the asymptotic power function. Here the degrees of freedom for the variable with a noncentral χ^2 distribution are fixed and the minimum sample size such that the power has at least a specified value is determined on the basis of the parameter for this distribution. Usually, the resulting sample size is sufficiently large for the actual power function to be approximated by the asymptotic power function.

No method is given for determining adequate sample sizes for the grouped data form of a Cramér-von Mises type test. However, for this test, the minimum allowable sample size is reasonably large and should also be an adequate sample size for many situations of interest.

For both types of tests that are based on the number of empty equiprobable categories, adequate sample sizes can be determined by use of the asymptotic power functions. Specifically, a representative alternative hypothesis is chosen and the minimum adequate sample size is determined by the requirement that power have at least a specified value when this alternative holds. Ordinarily, the asymptotic power function furnishes a sufficiently accurate approximation to the true power function for the resulting sample sizes. This procedure can also be used for the test based on combinatorial functions of data for categories that are equiprobable under the null hypothesis.

Next let us consider the determination of adequate sample sizes for the test based on the maximum of the numbers of observations in the categories. If the representative alternative is such that the lower power bound for this alternative tends to unity as the sample size increases, a conservative (perhaps highly conservative) adequate sample size can be determined by use of this bound. Thus the alternative investigated should be chosen, if such a choice is reasonable, so that the lower bound for the power function increases monotonically to unity as the sample size becomes infinite.

Determination of adequate sample sizes is relatively easy for the test based on Matusita's distance definition. To obtain a specified lower bound for the power function value, the sample size is required to equal or exceed a specified number. For a suitably chosen alternative (expressed in terms of Matusita's distance between the actual and hypothetical distributions) and a sufficiently large value for the power lower bound, the required sample size is also an adequate sample size. Upper bounds for the risk can be used to determine adequate sample sizes for Matusita's decision procedure.

Discussion of Matusita's Distance Definition

This definition of the distance between two probability distributions, or of the distance between the observed empirical distribution and a probability distribution, is applicable only for multinomial populations with the same set of categories. Let the category probabilities for one multinomial population be denoted by $p_1^{(1)}, \ldots, p_U^{(1)}$ while those for a second population having the same categories are denoted by $p_1^{(2)}, \ldots, p_U^{(2)}$. Then, the square of the Matusita distance between these two multinomial populations is given by

$$\sum_{u=1}^{U}\left[\sqrt{p_u^{(1)}}-\sqrt{p_u^{(2)}}\right]^2=2\left[1-\sum_{u=1}^{U}\sqrt{p_u^{(1)}p_u^{(2)}}\right].$$

Let m_u be the number of observations with values in the uth category ($u=1, \ldots, U; m_1+\ldots+m_U=m$). Then the square of the Matusita distance between the empirical distribution determined by the m_u and the multinomial population with probabilities $p_1, \ldots, p_U$ is given by

$$\sum_{u=1}^{U}\left[\sqrt{p_u}-\sqrt{m_u/m}\right]^2=2\left[1-\sum_{u=1}^{U}\sqrt{p_u m_u/m}\right].$$

This distance definition has desirable properties and furnishes a basis for some tests and decision procedures.

In the tests presented, the null hypothesis asserts that the Matusita distance between the true and the hypothetical multinomial population is zero while the alternative hypothesis asserts that this distance is at least a specified amount. The alternative is accepted if the distance between the observed empirical distribution and the hypothetical multinomial distribution is too large; otherwise the null hypothesis is accepted.

For the decision procedures, there are two possible decisions. One decision asserts that the actual multinomial distribution belongs to a specified class of multinomial distributions. The other decision asserts that the minimum distance between the actual multinomial distribution and any distribution of the specified class is at least a stated amount. The decision rule results in accepting that the actual distribution belongs to the specified class if the minimum distance from the observed empirical distribution is at most a stated amount for the distributions of this class. Otherwise the other possible decision is accepted.

The Matusita definition of distance has the favorable property that categories with small probabilities are not emphasized. The metric associated with the chi-square test of fit tends to emphasize categories with small probabilities.

Remark

For the case of the Neyman smooth test for grouped data and a univariate population, the sets s_u used to determine the categories are most meaningfully defined as consecutive intervals of points, with s_1 being unbounded from below and s_U unbounded from above. Then the test emphasizes a specified class of alternative hypotheses.

Fixed Material for Section

Data 1 Arbitrary, univariate or multivariate **2** None **3** $\{X(i)_j\}_m$ **4** $n_1 = \ldots = n_m = n \geqslant 1$ **Assumptions 1** Random sample **2** Categories chosen in unbiased fashion **3** None **Characteristics 3** Used symmetrically **4** Sample condition should be satisfied to reasonable approx. Moderately sensitive to biases in selection of categories **5** Not difficult to decide on sample assumption and to select categories in unbiased fashion.

Neyman Smooth Test for Grouped Data (Barton, Scott)

Data 4 Min allowable m stated in Results **Description 1** Theoretical-approx. one-sided sig. tests **2** Simple null hyp. H_0, which asserts that $F(x_1, \ldots, x_n) = F_0(x_1, \ldots, x_n)$. Tests based on categorical data. Method of converting data to categorical form outlined on page 440. Then simple null hyp. expressed as $p_u = p_u^{(0)}$, $(u = 1, \ldots, U)$. Univariate case of principal interest when prob. dist. investigated over all pts.; then s_u should be consecutive intervals, with s_1 unbounded from below and s_U unbounded from above **Results 1** $w_u = \frac{1}{2}p_u^{(0)} - \frac{1}{2} + \sum_{w=1}^{u-1} p_w^{(0)}$. $\pi_1(y) = 2\sqrt{3}y$; $\pi_2(y) = \sqrt{5}(6y^2 - \frac{1}{2})$; $\pi_3(y) = \sqrt{7}(20y^3 - 3y)$; $\pi_4(y) = 210y^4 - 45y^2 + \frac{9}{8}$; $\pi_{t+1}(y) = 2y[(2t+3)(2t+1)]^{1/2}\pi_t(y)/(t+1) - t[(2t+3)/(2t-1)]^{1/2}\pi_{t-1}(y)/(t+1)$. $P'_{tu} = (1/p_u^{(0)}) \int_{w_u - 1/2p_u^{(0)}}^{w_u + 1/2p_u^{(0)}} \pi_t(y)dy$. $I_{tr} = I_{rt} = \sum_{u=1}^{U} P'_{tu}P'_{ru}p_u^{(0)}$. $\Delta_t = \|I_{rs}\|$, $r = 1, \ldots, t$ and $s = 1, \ldots, t$. $i_{rs} =$ cofactor of I_{rs} in Δ_t. $P_{0u} = 1$; $P_{tu} = |\Delta_{t-1}\Delta_t|^{-1/2} \sum_{r=1}^{t} P'_{ru}i_{tr}$ for $t \geqslant 1$. $\gamma_{uj} = 1$ if $\{X(1)_j, \ldots, X(n)_j\} \epsilon s_u$ and is zero otherwise. $Q_{tj} = \sum_{u=1}^{U} P_{tu}\gamma_{uj}$. $\Psi_k^2 = \sum_{t=1}^{k} [\sum_{j=1}^{m} Q_{tj}/\sqrt{m}]^2$ **2** *Test*: Reject H_0 if $\Psi_k^2 \geqslant \chi_\alpha^2(k)$ **3** Table 2 at end of book contains values of $\chi_\alpha^2(k)$ **4** Min allowable $m \geqslant [.2/\min(.01, \alpha) + 3k/2]/U \min_u p_u^{(0)}$. Value of k chosen on basis of altern. emphasized (see part 2 of Characteristics); use of $k \leqslant 4$ seems suitable for most applications. Adequate m can be determined on basis of asymptotic power fct. Method for suitable selection of categories discussed on page 441. The P_{tu}, which are polynomials in the w_t, are standardized Chebychev polynomials when the categories have equal null expectations. Ψ_{U-1}^2 equals statistic for chi-square test of fit applied to same categories and data. In the limit, as

$\max_u p_u \to 0$, Ψ_k^2 has same prob. properties as test statistic for ungrouped continuous univariate data **Characteristics 1** Low to medium, depending on m, n, k, U, the s_u, and $F_0(x_1, \ldots, x_n)$ **2** Altern. hyp. of class considered assert that $p_u = \{1 + \sum_{t=1}^{T} \xi_t P'_{tu}\} p_u^{(0)}$. Asymptotic dist. of Ψ_k^2 is that of a noncentral χ^2 variable with parameter $m \sum_{t=1}^{\min(k,T)} \xi_t^2$ and k degrees of freedom (see ref. 179 and 402 for prob. values of noncentral χ^2). Thus if altern. (unknown) that actually occurs requires $T > k$, the values of $\xi_1, \ldots, \xi_k$ for this altern. will be tested for large m even though $\xi_{k+1}, \ldots, \xi_T$ are not tested. Preferably k should equal value of T corresponding to class of altern. of principal interest. Actual power fct. at least roughly same as asymptotic power fct. if $m \geqslant$ min allowable value **6** Case of composite null hyp. considered in ref. 31; then test no longer nonparametric since even asymptotic dist. depends on form of dist. fct. specified by null hyp. **Bibliography** Ref. 30, 31, 465.

Cramér-von Mises Type Test for Grouped Data (Watanabe, Kondo)

Data 4 Min allowable m stated in Results **Description 1** Theoretical-approx. one-sided sig. tests **2** Simple null hyp. H_0, which asserts that $F(x_1, \ldots, x_n) = F_0(x_1, \ldots, x_n)$. Tests based on categorical data, where categories selected so as to have equal null expectations. Method of converting data to categorical form outlined on page 440. Then simple null hyp. expressed as $p_u = p_u^{(0)}$, $(u = 1, \ldots, U)$ **Results 1** $\omega_{mU}^2 = (1/mU) \sum_{v=1}^{U-1} \sum_{u=1}^{v} (m_u - m/U)^2$, where m_u = no. of observations in uth category **2** *Test*: Reject H_0 if $\omega_{mU}^2 > W_\alpha(U)$; usable when m is sufficiently large **3** Let $\alpha_U(W)$ be the value of α obtained for given values of U and $W = W_\alpha(U)$. Table 11.3 contains values of $\alpha_\infty(W)$ for $W = .2(.01)1.0(.1)$

TABLE 11.3. VALUES OF $\alpha_\infty(W)$ FOR $W = .2(.01)1.0(.1)1.3$*

W	.00	.01	.02	.03	.04	.05	.06	.07	.08	.09
.2	.267	.249	.232	.216	.202	.188	.176	.165	.154	.144
.3	.135	.127	.119	.112	.105	.0983	.0924	.0868	.0816	.0768
.4	.0722	.0680	.0641	.0600	.0568	.0535	.0504	.0475	.0448	.0422
.5	.0398	.0376	.0355	.0335	.0316	.0298	.0281	.0266	.0251	.0237
.6	.0224	.0211	.0200	.0189	.0178	.0169	.0159	.0151	.0142	.0135
.7	.0127	.0120	.0114	.0108	.0102	.00964	.00912	.00863	.00817	.00773
.8	.00732	.00692	.00655	.00620	.00587	.00556	.00526	.00498	.00472	.00447
.9	.00423	.00401	.00380	.00359	.00340	.00322	.00305	.00289	.00274	.00260

W	1.0	1.1	1.2	1.3
$\alpha_\infty(W)$	.00246	.00144	.00084	.0005

* Based on ref. 281: K-sample analogues of the Kolmogorov-Smirnov and Cramér-v. Mises tests, J. Kiefer, *Annals of Mathematical Statistics*, Vol. 30, 1959, pages 420–47 and on ref. 574: On the ω^2 distribution, Y. Watanabe, *Journal of the Gakugei College, Tokushima University*, Vol. 2, 1952, pages 21–30. Used with the kind permission of the authors, J. Kiefer and Y. Watanabe.

1.3; also see Table 10.4 on page 362. Approx values of $\alpha_U(W)$ can be obtained from $\alpha_U(W) \doteq \alpha_\infty(W)+4U^{-7/3}\alpha_\infty(W)^{.84}(W-2.764/U+3.82/U^2)$ for $.2 \leqslant W \leqslant 1.3$ and $U \geqslant 2$ **4** Min allowable $m \geqslant 3/\alpha+2U$ for $\alpha \leqslant \frac{1}{4}$. Smirnov's modification of the Cramér-von Mises type test statistics for continuous univariate populations, denoted by $W_n^{(1)}$ in Chapter 10 (page 361), asymptotically has same null dist. as that of $\omega_{mU}{}^2$ when $U \to \infty$ and $m \to \infty$. For univariate case, the s_u used to determine categories should be consecutive intervals, with s_1 unbounded from below and s_U unbounded from above. Min allowable m should also be adequate m for many situations; however, depending somewhat on the s_u, min m may be much smaller than adequate m for some situations **Characteristics 1** Low to medium, depending on m, n, U, the s_u, and $F_0(x_1, \ldots, x_n)$ **2** Should be at least roughly sensitive to altern. hyp. that are expressed in terms of the metric $m\int_{-\infty}^{\infty} \cdots \int_{-\infty}^{\infty} [F_0(x_1, \ldots, x_n)-F(x_1, \ldots, x_n)]^2 dF_0(x_1, \ldots, x_n)$; this metric should be especially suitable for univariate cases. Results for continuous univariate case indicate that this test more powerful than corresponding chi-square test of fit for altern. expressed in terms of this metric when m is large and U not too small (say, $U > 8$) **6** Mainly useful as grouped data version of $W_n^{(1)}$ test for continuous univariate case **Bibliography** Ref. 289, 574.

Two Types of Tests Based on Number of Empty Categories (F. N. David, Stevens)

Description 1 Two types of exact sig. tests, denoted by Case (I) and Case (II). Only one-sided tests considered for Case (I); one-sided and two-sided tests considered for Case (II) **2** Simple null hyp. H_0, which asserts that $F(x_1, \ldots, x_n)=F_0(x_1, \ldots, x_n)$. Tests based on categorical data (method of converting data to categorical form, outlined on page 440). Then simple null hyp. expressed as $p_u=p_u^{(0)}$, $(u=1, \ldots, U)$. For Case (I), $U=m$ and all categories have null expectations equal to 1. For Case (II), $U=m+1$, one category has a null expectation of $m/2$, and the other categories have null expectations of $\frac{1}{2}$ **Results 1** Z_1=no. of empty categories for Case (I). For Case (II), Z_2=no. of empty categories among those that have null expectations of $\frac{1}{2}$. $E(Z_1|H_0)=m(1-1/m)^m$; $\sigma^2(Z_1|H_0)= m[(m-1)(1-2/m)^m+(1-1/m)^m-m(1-1/m)^{2m}]$. $E(Z_2|H_0) =m(1-1/2m)^m$; $\sigma^2(Z_2|H_0)= m^2[(1-1/m)^m-(1-1/2m)^{2m}]-m[(1-1/m)^m -(1-1/2m)^m]$ **2** *Case (I)*: Accept that $EZ_1 > E(Z_1|H_0)$ if $Z_1 > Z_1(\alpha)$. *Case (II)*: Accept that $EZ_2 > E(Z_2|H_0)$ if $Z_2 > Z_2(\alpha)$. Accept that $EZ_2 < E(Z_2|H_0)$ if $Z_2 < Z'_2(\alpha)$. Accept that $EZ_2 \neq E(Z_2|H_0)$ if $Z_2 > Z_2(\alpha_1)$ or $Z_2 < Z'_2(\alpha_2)$, where $\alpha_1+\alpha_2 < 1$; sig. level is $\alpha_1+\alpha_2$ **3** Table 11.4 contains values of $Z_1(\alpha)$ for $m=5(1)20$; a single value of α is considered for each value of m. Table 11.5 contains values of $Z_2(\alpha_1)$ and $Z'_2(\alpha_2)$ for

TABLE 11.4. VALUES OF $Z_1(\alpha)$ FOR $m=5(1)20$*

m	α	$Z_1(\alpha)$	m	α	$Z_1(\alpha)$
5	.002	3	13	.042	6
6	.020	3	14	.013	7
7	.003	4	15	.034	7
8	.020	4	16	.011	8
9	.064	4	17	.027	8
10	.018	5	18	.057	8
11	.052	5	19	.022	9
12	.015	6	20	.045	9

* Taken from ref. 136: Two combinatorial tests of whether a sample has come from a given population, F. N. David, *Biometrika*, Vol. 37, 1950, pages 97–110. Used with the kind permission of the author, F. N. David, and of the Editor of *Biometrika*.

$m=3(1)10$; a single value of α_1 and of α_2 is considered for each value of m. For $m \geqslant 20$ and $1/2m \leqslant \alpha \leqslant 1-1/2m$, $Z_1(\alpha) \doteq -\frac{1}{2}+E(Z_1|H_0)+K_\alpha\sigma(Z_1|H_0)$ for α such that this quantity is integral. For $m>10$ and

TABLE 11.5. VALUES OF $Z_2(\alpha_1)$ AND $Z'_2(\alpha_2)$ FOR $m=3(1)10$*

m	α_1	$Z_2(\alpha_1)$	α_2	$Z'_2(\alpha_2)$	m	α_1	$Z_2(\alpha_1)$	α_2	$Z'_2(\alpha_2)$
3			.0278	1	7	.0078	6	.0489	3
4	.0625	3	.0059	1	8	.0528	6	.0168	3
5	.0312	4	.0432	2	9	.0298	7	.0501	4
6	.0156	5	.0125	2	10	.0165	8	.0193	4

* Taken from ref. 136: Two combinatorial tests of whether a sample has come from a given population, F. N. David, *Biometrika*, Vol. 37, 1950, pages 97–110. Used with the kind permission of the author, F. N. David, and of the Editor of *Biometrika*.

$1/2m \leqslant \alpha_1, \alpha_2 \leqslant 1-1/2m$, $Z_2(\alpha_1) \doteq -\frac{1}{2}+E(Z_2|H_0)+K(\alpha_1)\sigma(Z_2|H_0)$ for α_1 such that this quantity integral; $Z'_2(\alpha_2) \doteq \frac{1}{2}+E(Z_2|H_0)-K(\alpha_2)\sigma(Z_2|H_0)$ for α_2 such that this quantity integral 4 In general, $EZ_1=\sum_{u=1}^{U}(1-p_u)^m$ and $\sigma^2Z_1=2\sum_{u>v=1}^{U}(1-p_u-p_v)^m+EZ_1-(EZ_1)^2$. EZ_1 is min when $p_u=1/m$ for all u. $\sigma^2Z_1 \doteq U[(U-1)(1-2/U)^m+(1-1/U)^m-U(1-1/U)^{2m}]+[EZ_1-U(1-1/U)^m][1+2(U-2)(1-2/U)^{m-2}(1-1/U)^{-m+2}-2U(1-1/U)^m]$, with the approx. improving as the variation among the p_u decreases. If Z_2 based on categories $1,\ldots,U-1$, in general, $EZ_2=\sum_{u=1}^{U-1}(1-p_u)^m$ and $\sigma^2Z_2=2\sum_{u>v=1}^{U-1}(1-p_u-p_v)^m+EZ_2-(EZ_2)^2$. When $U=m$, $m^{-4/3} \leqslant p_u \leqslant m^{-2/3}$, $m^{5/6} \geqslant 25$, $1/m \leqslant \xi \leqslant 1-1/m$, and ξ such that $-\frac{1}{2}+EZ_1+K_\xi\sigma Z_1$ integral, $P[Z_1>-\frac{1}{2}+EZ_1+K_\xi\sigma Z_1] \doteq \xi$; if ξ such that $\frac{1}{2}+EZ_1-K_\xi\sigma Z_1$ integral, $P[Z_1<\frac{1}{2}+EZ_1-K_\xi\sigma Z_1] \doteq \xi$. When $U=m+1$, $\frac{1}{2}m^{-4/3} \leqslant p_u \leqslant \frac{1}{2}m^{-2/3}$ for $u \leqslant U-1$,

$m^{-1/3} \leqslant p_U \leqslant 1 - m^{-1/3}$, $m^{5/6} \geqslant 20$, $1/m \leqslant \xi \leqslant 1-1/m$, and ξ such that $-\frac{1}{2}+EZ_2+K_\xi \sigma Z_2$ integral, $P[Z_2 > -\frac{1}{2}+EZ_2+K_\xi\sigma Z_2] \doteq \xi$; if ξ such that $\frac{1}{2}+EZ_2-K_\xi\sigma Z_2$ integral, $P[Z_2 < \frac{1}{2}+EZ_2-K_\xi\sigma Z_2] \doteq \xi$. These approx. prob. results form basis for one-sided and two-sided tests where none of categories necessarily have same null expectations; also furnish approx. power fct. values for altern. not differing greatly from null hyp. Adequate m can usually be determined on basis of these large sample power fct. results. Combined with approx. relation expressing $\sigma^2 Z_1$ in terms of EZ_1, the approx. prob. results for Z_1 yield one-sided and two-sided confidence intervals for EZ_1 when variation among the p_u known to not be too great. Exact prob. for Case (I) can be computed on basis of material of ref. 136 **Characteristics 1** Low to medium, depending on m, n, the s_u, and $F_0(x_1, \ldots, x_n)$ **2** For Case (I), no particular class of altern. hyp. emphasized. For Class (II), specified set of pts., with total null expectation of $m/2$, is emphasized; i.e., tests for Case (II) sensitive to given specialized classes of altern. The tests for Case (I) are unbiased for all altern. and consistent with respect to a very general class of altern. For the situation $n=2$, a rectangular type grid, and the altern. such that items tend to cluster, Case (I) test not very powerful for $m \leqslant 25$ but reasonably powerful if $m \geqslant 100$. When $m=30$, Class (I) test seems to have roughly same power as chi-square test of fit. For Case (II) and one-sided test for mean of normal population with known variance, power of Z_2 test approx. .65 for altern. such that power of t-test is .9 **6** None **Bibliography** Ref. 136, 393, 394, 494, 514.

Tests Based on Combinatorial Functions of Categorical Data (Okamoto)

Data 4 Min allowable m stated in Results **Description 1** Theoretical-approx. one-sided sig. tests **2** Simple null hyp. H_0, which asserts that $F(x_1, \ldots, x_n) = F_0(x_1, \ldots, x_n)$. Tests based on categorical data, where categories selected so as to have equal null expectations. Method of converting data to categorical form outlined on page 440. Then simple null hyp. expressed as $p_u = p_u^{(0)}$, $(u=1, \ldots, U)$ **Results 1** C_d = no. among the $\binom{m}{d}$ sets of d pts. $\{X(1)_{j(1)}, \ldots, X(n)_{j(1)}\}, \ldots, \{X(1)_{j(d)}, \ldots, X(n)_{j(d)}\}$, $1 \leqslant j(1) < \ldots < j(d) \leqslant m$, that fall in the same category (i.e., in same set s_u), where $d \geqslant 2$. $E_0 = U(m/U)^d/d!$; $\sigma_0{}^2 = U(m/U)^{2d} \sum_{b=2}^{d} (m/U)^{-b}\binom{d}{b}/d!$ **2** *Test*: Reject H_0 if $C_d > C_d(\alpha)$ **3** For $m \geqslant 50d^{1/3}$, $1/m \leqslant \alpha \leqslant 1-1/m$, and $.1 \leqslant U/m \leqslant 5$, $C_d(\alpha) \doteq -\frac{1}{2}+E_0+K_\alpha\sigma_0$ for α such that this quantity integral **4** Let $E_a = m^d \sum_{u=1}^{U} p_u{}^d/d!$ and $\sigma_a{}^2 = m^{2d-1}\{-(\sum_{u=1}^{U} p_u{}^d)^2/[(d-1)!]^2 + \sum_{b=1}^{d} \sum_{u=1}^{U} p_u{}^{2d-b}/m^{b-1}b![(d-b)!]^2\}$. For any given constant A such that $A \geqslant 1$, $1/mA \leqslant p_u \leqslant A/m$, $m \geqslant 50A^{1/2}d^{1/3}$, $1/m \leqslant \xi \leqslant 1-1/m$,

$.1 \leqslant U/m \leqslant 5$, and for ξ such that $-\frac{1}{2}+E_a+K_\xi\sigma_a$ integral, $P[C_d > -\frac{1}{2}+E_a+K_\xi\sigma_a] \doteq \xi$; if ξ such that $\frac{1}{2}+E_a-K_\xi\sigma_a$ integral, $P[C_d<\frac{1}{2}+E_a-K_\xi\sigma_a] \doteq \xi$. These approx. prob. results form basis for one-sided and two-sided tests where none of categories necessarily have same null expectations; also furnish approx. power fct. values for altern. not differing greatly from null hyp. Adequate m can usually be determined on basis of these large sample power fct. results. C_2 is linear fct. of corresponding statistic for chi-square test of fit. When $m/U \leqslant \frac{1}{2}$, test based on C_2 approx. equiv. to test based on no. of empty equiprobable categories (see preceding presentation) **Characteristics 1** Low to upper medium depending on m, n, d, U, the s_u, and $F_0(x_1, \ldots, x_n)$ **2** No particular class of altern. hyp. emphasized. Test unbiased against all altern. and consistent against altern. for which $\sum_{u=1}^{U} p_u{}^d$ is $O(m^{-d+1})$ **6** None **Bibliography** Ref. 395.

Test Based on Maximum of Numbers of Values in Equiprobable Categories (Kozelka)

Description 1 Theoretical-approx. one-sided sig. tests (exact results attainable but usually require large effort) **2** Simple null hyp. H_0, which asserts that $F(x_1, \ldots, x_n)=F_0(x_1, \ldots, x_n)$. Tests based on categorical data, where categories selected so as to have equal null expectations. Method of converting data to categorical form outlined on page 440. Then simple null hyp. expressed as $p_u=p_u{}^{(0)}$, $(u=1, \ldots, U)$ **Results 1** m_u = no. observations in uth category $(u=1, \ldots, U)$ and $Y=\max_u m_u$. Y_α = sol. for y of $\sum_{j=y}^{m} \binom{m}{j}(1/U)^j(1-1/U)^{m-j}=\alpha/U$, where α such that Y_α integral **2** *Test*: Reject H_0 if $Y \geqslant Y_\alpha$; sig. level bounded by $\alpha-(1-1/U)\alpha^2$ and α **3** Y_α can be determined by use of tables for incomplete beta fct., tables for binomial dist., approx. to binomial dist. (see Chapter 7), and, in some cases, tables for Poisson dist. When normal approx. to binomial dist. applicable, values of Y_α given in ref. 294 for $\alpha=.01, .05$ and $U=2, \ldots, 25$ **4** Let $b_u(y)=\sum_{j=1}^{m}\binom{m}{j}p_u{}^j(1-p_u)^{m-j}$. In general, $\sum_{u=1}^{U} b_u(y) - 2\sum_{u>v=1}^{U} b_u(y)b_v(y) \leqslant P(Y\geqslant y) \leqslant \sum_{u=1}^{U} b_u(y)$. This result furnishes basis for tests where none of categories necessarily have same null expectations; also furnishes approx. power fct. values for altern. where bounds reasonably close together. Adequate m can often be obtained on basis of these prob. bounds. Some moments for Y when $U=2$ and 3 given in ref. 212. Exact value of $P(Y\geqslant y)$ is unity minus $m!$ times coeff. of x^m in $\prod_{u=1}^{U} [1+p_u x+p_u{}^2x^2/2!+\ldots+p^{y-1}_u x^{y-1}/(y-1)!]$ **Characteristics 1** Low to lower medium, depending on m, n, U, the s_u, $F_0(x_1, \ldots, x_n)$, and the method used to determine Y_α **2** Protects against any altern. where not all the p_u equal $1/U$. Emphasizes situations where one or more p_u are much larger than $1/U$. For given $p_1, \ldots, p_U$, value of power fct. is $1 - P(Y \geqslant Y_\alpha)$ **6** None **Bibliography** Ref. 209, 212, 294.

Tests and Decision Procedures Based on Matusita's Distance Definition

Description 1 Theoretical-approx. one-sided sig. tests and decision procedures **2** Tests investigate simple null hyp. H_0, which asserts that $F(x_1, \ldots, x_n) = F_0(x_1, \ldots, x_n)$. Altern. hyp. asserts that Matusita distance between hypothetical and actual distributions is at least a specified amount. Decision procedures investigate whether $F(x_1, \ldots, x_n)$ belongs to a specified class of dist. fcts. Two decisions are possible: Either $F(x_1, \ldots, x_n)$ belongs to the specified class or the min. Matusita distance of $F(x_1, \ldots, x_n)$ from this class is at least a stated amount. Results for both tests and decision procedures based on categorical data. Method of converting data to categorical form outlined on page 440. Then simple null hyp. expressed as $p_u = p_u^{(0)}$, $(u = 1, \ldots, U)$, while specified class of dist. fcts. is represented by a set of possible values for $p = (p_1, \ldots, p_U)$ **Results 1** m_u = no. of observations in uth category. $p' = (p'_1, \ldots, p'_U)$, $f' = (m_1/m, \ldots, m_U/m)$, $p^{(0)} = (p_1^{(0)}, \ldots, p_U^{(0)})$, and $\{p_0\}$ is the specified set of possible values for p that is being investigated. $D^2(p, f')$ = square of Matusita distance between empirical dist. and actual dist. $= \sum_{u=1}^{U} (\sqrt{p_u} - \sqrt{f'})^2 = 2(1 - \sum_{u=1}^{U} \sqrt{p_u m_u/m})$; $D(p, p^{(0)})$ = Matusita distance between hypothetical dist. and actual dist. $D_0^2(f') = \inf_{p' \in \{p_0\}} D^2(p', f')$. $\alpha = \alpha(B, m, U, p^{(0)}) = \{U^2 - 1 + [2 - U - U^2 + \sum_{u=1}^{U} 1/p_u^{(0)}]m^{-1}\}/(U-1)^2 B^2$, where $B > 0$ **2** *General Test*: Reject H_0 if $D^2(p^{(0)}, f') \geqslant (U-1)B/m$; sig. level $\leqslant \min(\alpha, 1/B)$. *Test for Specified Material Deviation*: For $m \geqslant 4(U-1)B/\delta^2$, accept H_0 if $D^2(p^{(0)}, f') < (U-1)B/m$; otherwise accept $D(p^{(0)}, p) \geqslant \delta$; sig. level $\leqslant \min(\alpha, 1/B)$. *Decision Rule*: When $D_0(f') \leqslant \eta$, decide that $p \epsilon \{p_0\}$; otherwise decide that $D_0(p) \geqslant \gamma$; here γ and η are specified with $\gamma > \eta$. Risk implications of decision rule stated in part 2 of Characteristics **3** None **4** When $m \min_u p_u \geqslant 3U/(U-1)$ and $\xi(1-\xi) \geqslant (U+\frac{1}{2})^2/5(U-\frac{3}{2})^{11/5}(m \max_u p_u)(m \sum_{u=1}^{U} p_u/U)$, $P[D^2(p, f') \geqslant \chi_\xi^2(U-1)/4m] \doteq \xi$; furnishes basis for large sample form of test. Also, if these relations satisfied for both the p_u and the $p_u^{(0)}$, $P\{D^2(p^{(0)}, f') \geqslant [\delta - \chi_\xi(U-1)/2\sqrt{m}]^2\} \dot{\geqslant} \xi$ when $D(p^{(0)}, p) \geqslant \delta > \chi_\xi(U-1)/2\sqrt{m}$; useful for determining lower bound power function values for large sample form of test In general, $P[D_0(f') \leqslant \eta] \geqslant 1 - (U-1)/m\eta^2$ when $p \epsilon \{p_0\}$, and $P[D_0(f') > \eta] \geqslant 1 - (U-1)/m(\gamma - \eta)^2$ when $D_0(p) \geqslant \gamma > \eta$. Also, in general, $P[D_0(f') \leqslant \eta] \geqslant 1 - 2U \exp(-m\eta^4/2U^2)$ when $p \epsilon \{p_0\}$, and $P[D_0(f') > \eta] \geqslant 1 - 2U \exp[-m(\gamma - \eta)^4/2U^2]$ when $D_0(p) \geqslant \gamma > \eta$. If the relations which furnish a basis for the large sample form of the test are satisfied, $P[D_0(f') \leqslant \eta] \geqslant 1 - \xi(1)$ when $p \epsilon \{p_0\}$, where $\xi(1)$ determined by

$\chi_{\xi(1)}{}^2(U-1)=4m\eta^2$; also $P[D_0(f')>\eta]\geqslant 1-\xi(2)$ when $D_0(p)\geqslant\gamma>\eta$, where $\xi(2)$ determined by $\chi_{\xi(2)}{}^2(U-1)=4m(\gamma-\eta)^2$. In all cases, m, η, and γ should be selected so that the set of p' such that $D_0(p')\geqslant\gamma>\eta$ is not vacuous; for given $\eta<\gamma<2$, this set can be made nonempty by using a large enough value for m. Method for suitable selection of categories discussed on page 441 **Characteristics 1** Low to lower medium for tests, depending on m, n, U, the s_u, and $F_0(x_1,\ldots,x_n)$. Low to upper medium for decision procedures, depending on m, n, U, $\{p_0\}$, η, γ, the s_u, and $F_0(x_1,\ldots,x_n)$ **2** If $m\geqslant 4(U-1)B/\delta^2$, power of test $\geqslant$ $1-1/B$ for $D(p^{(0)},p)\geqslant\delta$. If relations for large sample form of test stated in part 4 of Results satisfied, power of test $\geqslant$ $1-\xi'$ (approx.) when $D(p^{(0)},p)\geqslant\delta$, where ξ' determined from $\chi_{\xi'}{}^2(U-1)=4m[\delta-\sqrt{(U-1)B/m}]^2$ and is such that $\delta^2>\chi_{\xi'}{}^2(U-1)/4m$. If loss is 0 for correct decision and 1 for incorrect decision, risk from using decision rule $\leqslant$ $\min\{\max[(U-1)/m\eta^2,\ (U-1)/m(\gamma-\eta)^2],\ \max[2U\exp(-m\eta^4/2U^2),\ 2U\exp(-m\{\gamma-\eta\}^4/2U^2)]\}$; when m sufficiently large and all coordinates positive for all $p'\epsilon\{p_0\}$, risk $\leqslant$ $\max[\xi(1),\xi(2)]$ **6** These are only procedures in this sect. that specifically consider material deviations between actual and hypothetical populations **Bibliography** Ref. 339, 340, 341.

Tables

TABLE 1*. VALUES OF α AND $\varphi(K_\alpha)$ FOR $K_\alpha = K(\alpha) = .00(.01)3.99$

K_α	α	$\varphi(K_\alpha)$	K_α	α	$\varphi(K_\alpha)$	K_α	α	$\varphi(K_\alpha)$
.00	.50000	.39894	.35	.36317	.37524	.70	.24196	.31225
.01	.49601	.39892	.36	.35942	.37391	.71	.23885	.31006
.02	.49202	.39886	.37	.35569	.37255	.72	.23576	.30785
.03	.48803	.39876	.38	.35197	.37115	.73	.23270	.30563
.04	.48405	.39862	.39	.34827	.36973	.74	.22965	.30339
.05	.48006	.39844	.40	.34458	.36827	.75	.22663	.30114
.06	.47608	.39822	.41	.34090	.36678	.76	.22363	.29887
.07	.47210	.39797	.42	.33724	.36526	.77	.22065	.29659
.08	.46812	.39767	.43	.33360	.36371	.78	.21770	.29431
.09	.46414	.39733	.44	.32997	.36213	.79	.21476	.29200
.10	.46017	.39695	.45	.32636	.36053	.80	.21186	.28969
.11	.45620	.39654	.46	.32276	.35889	.81	.20897	.28737
.12	.45224	.39608	.47	.31918	.35723	.82	.20611	.28504
.13	.44828	.39559	.48	.31561	.35553	.83	.20327	.28269
.14	.44433	.39505	.49	.31207	.35381	.84	.20045	.28034
.15	.44038	.39448	.50	.30854	.35207	.85	.19766	.27798
.16	.43644	.39387	.51	.30503	.35029	.86	.19489	.27562
.17	.43251	.39322	.52	.30153	.34849	.87	.19215	.27324
.18	.42858	.39253	.53	.29806	.34667	.88	.18943	.27086
.19	.42465	.39181	.54	.29460	.34482	.89	.18673	.26848
.20	.42074	.39104	.55	.29116	.34294	.90	.18406	.26609
.21	.41683	.39024	.56	.28774	.34105	.91	.18141	.26369
.22	.41294	.38940	.57	.28434	.33912	.92	.17879	.26129
.23	.40905	.38853	.58	.28096	.33718	.93	.17619	.25888
.24	.40517	.38762	.59	.27760	.33521	.94	.17361	.25647
.25	.40129	.38667	.60	.27425	.33322	.95	.17106	.25406
.26	.39743	.38568	.61	.27093	.33121	.96	.16853	.25164
.27	.39358	.38466	.62	.26763	.32918	.97	.16602	.24923
.28	.38974	.38361	.63	.26435	.32713	.98	.16354	.24681
.29	.38591	.38251	.64	.26109	.32506	.99	.16109	.24439
.30	.38209	.38139	.65	.25785	.32297	1.00	.15866	.24197
.31	.37828	.38023	.66	.25463	.32086	1.01	.15625	.23955
.32	.37448	.37903	.67	.25143	.31874	1.02	.15386	.23713
.33	.37070	.37780	.68	.24825	.31659	1.03	.15150	.23471
.34	.36693	.37654	.69	.24510	.31443	1.04	.14917	.23230

* $\varphi(-K_\alpha) = \varphi(K_\alpha)$. The relation $K_\alpha = t_\alpha(\infty)$ and the use of Table 3 furnishes values of K_α for $\alpha = .0005, .005, .01, .025, .05, .10, .15, .20, .25, .30, .35, .40, .45$.

K_α	α	$\varphi(K_\alpha)$	K_α	α	$\varphi(K_\alpha)$	K_α	α	$\varphi(K_\alpha)$
1.05	.14686	.22988	1.55	.06057	.12001	2.05	.02018	.04879
1.06	.14457	.22747	1.56	.05938	.11816	2.06	.01970	.04780
1.07	.14231	.22506	1.57	.05821	.11632	2.07	.01923	.04682
1.08	.14007	.22265	1.58	.05705	.11450	2.08	.01876	.04586
1.09	.13786	.22025	1.59	.05512	.11270	2.09	.01831	.04491
1.10	.13567	.21785	1.60	.05480	.11092	2.10	.01786	.04398
1.11	.13350	.21546	1.61	.05370	.10915	2.11	.01743	.04307
1.12	.13136	.21307	1.62	.05262	.10741	2.12	.01700	.04217
1.13	.12924	.21069	1.63	.05155	.10567	2.13	.01659	.04128
1.14	.12714	.20831	1.64	.05050	.10396	2.14	.01618	.04041
1.15	.12507	.20594	1.65	.04947	.10226	2.15	.01578	.03955
1.16	.12302	.20357	1.66	.04846	.10059	2.16	.01539	.03871
1.17	.12100	.20121	1.67	.04746	.09893	2.17	.01500	.03788
1.18	.11900	.19886	1.68	.04648	.09728	2.18	.01463	.03706
1.19	.11702	.19652	1.69	.04551	.09566	2.19	.01426	.03626
1.20	.11507	.19419	1.70	.04457	.09405	2.20	.01390	.03547
1.21	.11314	.19186	1.71	.04363	.09246	2.21	.01355	.03470
1.22	.11123	.18954	1.72	.04272	.09089	2.22	.01321	.03394
1.23	.10935	.18724	1.73	.04182	.08933	2.23	.01287	.03319
1.24	.10749	.18494	1.74	.04093	.08780	2.24	.01255	.03246
1.25	.10505	.18265	1.75	.04006	.08628	2.25	.01222	.03174
1.26	.10383	.18037	1.76	.03920	.08478	2.26	.01191	.03103
1.27	.10204	.17810	1.77	.03836	.08329	2.27	.01160	.03034
1.28	.10027	.17585	1.78	.03754	.08183	2.28	.01130	.02965
1.29	.09853	.17360	1.79	.03673	.08038	2.29	.01101	.02898
1.30	.09680	.17137	1.80	.03593	.07895	2.30	.01072	.02833
1.31	.09510	.16915	1.81	.03515	.07754	2.31	.01044	.02768
1.32	.09342	.16694	1.82	.03438	.07614	2.32	.01017	.02705
1.33	.09176	.16474	1.83	.03362	.07477	2.33	.00990	.02643
1.34	.09012	.16256	1.84	.03288	.07341	2.34	.00964	.02582
1.35	.08851	.16038	1.85	.03216	.07206	2.35	.00939	.02522
1.36	.08691	.15822	1.86	.03144	.07074	2.36	.00914	.02463
1.37	.08534	.15608	1.87	.03074	.06943	2.37	.00889	.02406
1.38	.08379	.15395	1.88	.03005	.06814	2.38	.00866	.02349
1.39	.08226	.15183	1.89	.02938	.06687	2.39	.00842	.02294
1.40	.08076	.14973	1.90	.02872	.06562	2.40	.00820	.02239
1.41	.07927	.14764	1.91	.02807	.06439	2.41	.00798	.02186
1.42	.07780	.14556	1.92	.02743	.06316	2.42	.00776	.02134
1.43	.07636	.14350	1.93	.02680	.06195	2.43	.00755	.02083
1.44	.07493	.14146	1.94	.02619	.06077	2.44	.00734	.02033
1.45	.07353	.13943	1.95	.02559	.05959	2.45	.00714	.01984
1.46	.07214	.13742	1.96	.02500	.05844	2.46	.00695	.01936
1.47	.07078	.13542	1.97	.02442	.05730	2.47	.00676	.01889
1.48	.06944	.13344	1.98	.02385	.05618	2.48	.00657	.01842
1.49	.06811	.13147	1.99	.02330	.05508	2.49	.00639	.01797
1.50	.06681	.12952	2.00	.02275	.05399	2.50	.00621	.01753
1.51	.06552	.12758	2.01	.02222	.05292	2.51	.00604	.01709
1.52	.06426	.12566	2.02	.02169	.05186	2.52	.00587	.01667
1.53	.06301	.12376	2.03	.02118	.05082	2.53	.00570	.01625
1.54	.06178	.12188	2.04	.02068	.04980	2.54	.00554	.01585

K_α	α	$\varphi(K_\alpha)$	K_α	α	$\varphi(K_\alpha)$	K_α	α	$\varphi(K_\alpha)$
2.55	.00539	.01545	3.05	.00114	.00381	3.55	.00019	.00073
2.56	.00523	.01506	3.06	.00111	.00370	3.56	.00019	.00071
2.57	.00508	.01468	3.07	.00107	.00358	3.57	.00018	.00068
2.58	.00494	.01431	3.08	.00103	.00348	3.58	.00017	.00066
2.59	.00480	.01394	3.09	.00100	.00337	3.59	.00017	.00063
2.60	.00466	.01358	3.10	.00097	.00327	3.60	.00016	.00061
2.61	.00453	.01323	3.11	.00094	.00317	3.61	.00015	.00059
2.62	.00440	.01289	3.12	.00090	.00307	3.62	.00015	.00057
2.63	.00427	.01256	3.13	.00087	.00298	3.63	.00014	.00055
2.64	.00415	.01223	3.14	.00084	.00288	3.64	.00014	.00053
2.65	.00402	.01191	3.15	.00082	.00279	3.65	.00013	.00051
2.66	.00391	.01160	3.16	.00079	.00271	3.66	.00013	.00049
2.67	.00379	.01130	3.17	.00076	.00262	3.67	.00012	.00047
2.68	.00368	.01100	3.18	.00074	.00254	3.68	.00012	.00046
2.69	.00357	.01071	3.19	.00071	.00246	3.69	.00011	.00044
2.70	.00347	.01042	3.20	.00069	.00238	3.70	.00011	.00042
2.71	.00336	.01014	3.21	.00066	.00231	3.71	.00010	.00041
2.72	.00326	.00987	3.22	.00064	.00224	3.72	.00010	.00039
2.73	.00317	.00961	3.23	.00062	.00216	3.73	.00010	.00038
2.74	.00307	.00935	3.24	.00060	.00210	3.74	.00009	.00037
2.75	.00298	.00909	3.25	.00058	.00203	3.75	.00009	.00035
2.76	.00289	.00885	3.26	.00056	.00196	3.76	.00008	.00034
2.77	.00280	.00861	3.27	.00054	.00190	3.77	.00008	.00033
2.78	.00272	.00837	3.28	.00052	.00184	3.78	.00008	.00031
2.79	.00264	.00814	3.29	.00050	.00178	3.79	.00008	.00030
2.80	.00256	.00792	3.30	.00048	.00172	3.80	.00007	.00029
2.81	.00248	.00770	3.31	.00047	.00167	3.81	.00007	.00028
2.82	.00240	.00748	3.32	.00045	.00161	3.82	.00007	.00027
2.83	.00233	.00727	3.33	.00043	.00156	3.83	.00006	.00026
2.84	.00226	.00707	3.34	.00042	.00151	3.84	.00006	.00025
2.85	.00219	.00687	3.35	.00040	.00146	3.85	.00006	.00024
2.86	.00212	.00668	3.36	.00039	.00141	3.86	.00006	.00023
2.87	.00205	.00649	3.37	.00038	.00136	3.87	.00005	.00022
2.88	.00199	.00631	3.38	.00036	.00132	3.88	.00005	.00021
2.89	.00193	.00613	3.39	.00035	.00127	3.89	.00005	.00021
2.90	.00187	.00595	3.40	.00034	.00123	3.90	.00005	.00020
2.91	.00181	.00578	3.41	.00032	.00119	3.91	.00005	.00019
2.92	.00175	.00562	3.42	.00031	.00115	3.92	.00004	.00018
2.93	.00169	.00545	3.43	.00030	.00111	3.93	.00004	.00018
2.94	.00164	.00530	3.44	.00029	.00107	3.94	.00004	.00017
2.95	.00159	.00514	3.45	.00028	.00104	3.95	.00004	.00016
2.96	.00154	.00499	3.46	.00027	.00100	3.96	.00004	.00016
2.97	.00149	.00485	3.47	.00026	.00097	3.97	.00004	.00015
2.98	.00144	.00471	3.48	.00025	.00094	3.98	.00003	.00014
2.99	.00139	.00457	3.49	.00024	.00090	3.99	.00003	.00014
3.00	.00135	.00433	3.50	.00023	.00087			
3.01	.00131	.00430	3.51	.00022	.00084			
3.02	.00126	.00417	3.52	.00022	.00081			
3.03	.00122	.00405	3.53	.00021	.00079			
3.04	.00118	.00393	3.54	.00020	.00076			

TABLE 2.* VALUES OF $\chi^2_\alpha(k)$ FOR $.005 \leq \alpha \leq .995$ AND $k = 1(1)30$. WHEN $k > 30$ AND $2/7k \leq \alpha \leq 1 - 1/2k$, $\chi^2_\alpha(k) = k(1 - 2/9k + K_\alpha \sqrt{2/9k}$

k \ α	.995	.990	.980	.975	.950	.900	.800	.750	.700	.500
1	393×10^{-7}	157×10^{-6}	628×10^{-6}	982×10^{-6}	393×10^{-5}	.0158	.0642	.1015	.148	.4549
2	.0100	.0201	.0404	.0506	.1026	.2107	.446	.5754	.713	1.386
3	.0717	.1148	.185	.2158	.3518	.5844	1.005	1.213	1.424	2.366
4	.2070	.2971	.429	.4844	.7107	1.064	1.649	1.923	2.195	3.357
5	.4117	.5543	.752	.8312	1.145	1.610	2.343	2.675	3.000	4.351
6	.6757	.8721	1.134	1.237	1.635	2.204	3.070	3.455	3.828	5.348
7	.9893	1.269	1.564	1.690	2.167	2.833	3.822	4.255	4.671	6.346
8	1.344	1.646	2.032	2.180	2.733	3.490	4.594	5.071	5.527	7.344
9	1.735	2.088	2.532	2.700	3.325	4.168	5.380	5.899	6.393	8.343
10	2.156	2.558	3.059	3.247	3.940	4.865	6.179	6.737	7.267	9.342
11	2.603	3.053	3.609	3.816	4.575	5.578	6.989	7.584	8.148	10.34
12	3.074	3.571	4.178	4.404	5.226	6.304	7.807	8.438	9.034	11.34
13	3.565	4.107	4.765	5.009	5.892	7.042	8.634	9.299	9.926	12.34
14	4.075	4.660	5.368	5.629	6.571	7.790	9.467	10.17	10.82	13.34
15	4.601	5.229	5.985	6.262	7.261	8.547	10.31	11.04	11.72	14.34
16	5.142	5.812	6.614	6.908	7.962	9.312	11.15	11.91	12.62	15.34
17	5.697	6.408	7.255	7.564	8.672	10.09	12.00	12.79	13.53	16.34
18	6.265	7.015	7.906	8.231	9.390	10.86	12.86	13.68	14.44	17.34
19	6.844	7.633	8.567	8.907	10.12	11.65	13.72	14.56	15.35	18.34
20	7.434	8.260	9.237	9.591	10.85	12.44	14.58	15.45	16.27	19.34
21	8.034	8.897	9.915	10.28	11.59	13.24	15.45	16.34	17.18	20.34
22	8.643	9.542	10.60	10.98	12.34	14.04	16.31	17.24	18.10	21.34
23	9.260	10.20	11.29	11.69	13.09	14.85	17.19	18.15	19.02	22.34
24	9.886	10.86	11.99	12.40	13.85	15.66	18.06	19.04	19.94	23.34
25	10.52	11.52	12.70	13.12	14.61	16.47	18.94	19.94	20.87	24.34
26	11.16	12.20	13.41	13.84	15.38	17.29	19.82	20.84	21.79	25.34
27	11.81	12.88	14.13	14.57	16.15	18.11	20.70	21.75	22.72	26.34
28	12.46	13.56	14.85	15.31	16.93	18.94	21.59	22.66	23.65	27.34
29	13.12	14.26	15.57	16.05	17.71	19.77	22.48	23.57	24.58	28.34
30	13.79	14.95	16.31	16.79	18.49	20.60	23.36	24.48	25.51	29.34

* Based on table in *Statistical methods for research workers* (12th ed.), R. A. Fisher, Oliver and Boyd, Ltd., and on the table of the paper: Tables of percentage points of the incomplete beta function and of the chi-square distribution, C. M. Thompson, *Biometrika*, Vol. 32, 1941, pp. 188–89. Used with the kind permission of the authors, R. A. Fisher and C. M. Thompson, and of the publishers.

k \ α	.300	.250	.200	.100	.050	.025	.020	.010	.005
1	1.074	1.323	1.642	2.706	3.841	5.024	5.412	6.635	7.879
2	2.408	2.773	3.219	4.605	5.991	7.378	7.824	9.210	10.60
3	3.665	4.108	4.642	6.251	7.815	9.348	9.837	11.34	12.84
4	4.878	5.385	5.989	7.779	9.488	11.14	11.67	13.28	14.86
5	6.064	6.626	7.289	9.236	11.07	12.83	13.39	15.09	16.75
6	7.231	7.841	8.558	10.64	12.59	14.45	15.03	16.81	18.55
7	8.383	9.037	9.803	12.02	14.07	16.01	16.62	18.48	20.28
8	9.524	10.22	11.03	13.36	15.51	17.53	18.17	20.09	21.96
9	10.66	11.39	12.24	14.68	16.92	19.02	19.68	21.67	23.59
10	11.78	12.55	13.44	15.99	18.31	20.48	21.16	23.21	25.19
11	12.90	13.70	14.63	17.28	19.68	21.92	22.62	24.72	26.76
12	14.01	14.85	15.81	18.55	21.03	23.34	24.05	26.22	28.30
13	15.12	15.98	16.99	19.81	22.36	24.74	25.47	27.69	29.82
14	16.22	17.12	18.15	21.06	23.68	26.12	26.87	29.14	31.32
15	17.32	18.25	19.31	22.31	25.00	27.49	28.26	30.58	32.80
16	18.42	19.37	20.47	23.54	26.30	28.85	29.63	32.00	34.27
17	19.51	20.48	21.62	24.77	27.59	30.19	31.00	33.41	35.72
18	20.60	21.60	22.76	25.99	28.87	31.53	32.35	34.81	37.16
19	21.69	22.72	23.90	27.20	30.14	32.85	33.69	36.19	38.58
20	22.78	23.83	25.04	28.41	31.41	34.17	35.02	37.57	40.00
21	23.86	24.93	26.17	29.62	32.67	35.48	36.34	38.93	41.40
22	24.94	26.04	27.30	30.81	33.92	36.78	37.66	40.29	42.80
23	26.02	27.14	28.43	32.01	35.17	38.08	38.97	41.64	44.18
24	27.10	28.24	29.55	33.20	36.42	39.36	40.27	42.98	45.56
25	28.17	29.34	30.68	34.38	37.65	40.65	41.57	44.31	46.93
26	29.25	30.43	31.80	35.56	38.89	41.92	42.86	45.64	48.29
27	30.32	31.53	32.91	36.74	40.11	43.19	44.14	46.96	49.64
28	31.39	32.62	34.03	37.92	41.34	44.46	45.42	48.28	50.99
29	32.46	33.71	35.14	39.09	42.56	45.72	46.69	49.59	52.34
30	33.53	34.80	36.25	40.26	43.77	46.98	47.96	50.89	53.67

* Based on table in *Statistical methods for research workers* (12th ed.), R. A. Fisher, Oliver and Boyd, Ltd., and on the table of the paper: Tables of percentage points of the incomplete beta function and of the chi-square distribution, C. M. Thompson, *Biometrika*, Vol. 32, 1941, pp. 188–89. Used with the kind permission of the authors, R. A. Fisher and C. M. Thompson, and of the publishers.

k \ α	.45	.40	.35	.30	.25	.20	.15	.10	.05	.025	.01	.005	.0005
1	.158	.325	.510	.727	1.000	1.376	1.963	3.078	6.314	12.706	31.821	63.657	636.619
2	.142	.289	.445	.617	.816	1.061	1.386	1.886	2.920	4.303	6.965	9.925	31.598
3	.137	.277	.424	.584	.765	.978	1.250	1.638	2.353	3.182	4.541	5.841	12.924
4	.134	.271	.414	.569	.741	.941	1.190	1.533	2.132	2.776	3.747	4.604	8.610
5	.132	.267	.408	.559	.727	.920	1.156	1.476	2.015	2.571	3.365	4.032	6.869
6	.131	.265	.404	.553	.718	.906	1.134	1.440	1.943	2.447	3.143	3.707	5.959
7	.130	.263	.402	.549	.711	.896	1.119	1.415	1.895	2.365	2.998	3.499	5.408
8	.130	.262	.399	.546	.706	.889	1.108	1.397	1.860	2.306	2.896	3.355	5.041
9	.129	.261	.398	.543	.703	.883	1.100	1.383	1.833	2.262	2.821	3.250	4.781
10	.129	.260	.397	.542	.700	.879	1.093	1.372	1.812	2.228	2.764	3.169	4.587
11	.129	.260	.396	.540	.697	.876	1.088	1.363	1.796	2.201	2.718	3.106	4.437
12	.128	.259	.395	.539	.695	.873	1.083	1.356	1.782	2.179	2.681	3.055	4.318
13	.128	.259	.394	.538	.694	.870	1.079	1.350	1.771	2.160	2.650	3.012	4.221
14	.128	.258	.393	.537	.692	.868	1.076	1.345	1.761	2.145	2.624	2.977	4.140
15	.128	.258	.393	.536	.691	.866	1.074	1.341	1.753	2.131	2.602	2.947	4.073
16	.128	.258	.392	.535	.690	.865	1.071	1.337	1.746	2.120	2.583	2.921	4.015
17	.128	.257	.392	.534	.689	.863	1.069	1.333	1.740	2.110	2.567	2.898	3.965
18	.127	.257	.392	.534	.688	.862	1.067	1.330	1.734	2.101	2.552	2.878	3.922
19	.127	.257	.391	.533	.688	.861	1.066	1.328	1.729	2.093	2.539	2.861	3.883
20	.127	.257	.391	.533	.687	.860	1.064	1.325	1.725	2.086	2.528	2.845	3.850
21	.127	.257	.391	.532	.686	.859	1.063	1.323	1.721	2.080	2.518	2.831	3.819
22	.127	.256	.390	.532	.686	.858	1.061	1.321	1.717	2.074	2.508	2.819	3.792
23	.127	.256	.390	.532	.685	.858	1.060	1.319	1.714	2.069	2.500	2.807	3.767
24	.127	.256	.390	.531	.685	.857	1.059	1.318	1.711	2.064	2.492	2.797	3.745
25	.127	.256	.390	.531	.684	.856	1.058	1.316	1.708	2.060	2.485	2.787	3.725
26	.127	.256	.390	.531	.684	.856	1.058	1.315	1.706	2.056	2.479	2.779	3.707
27	.127	.256	.389	.531	.684	.855	1.057	1.314	1.703	2.052	2.473	2.771	3.690
28	.127	.256	.389	.530	.683	.855	1.056	1.313	1.701	2.048	2.467	2.763	3.674
29	.127	.256	.389	.530	.683	.854	1.055	1.311	1.699	2.045	2.462	2.756	3.659
30	.127	.256	.389	.530	.683	.854	1.055	1.310	1.697	2.042	2.457	2.750	3.646
40	.127	.255	.388	.529	.681	.851	1.050	1.303	1.684	2.021	2.423	2.704	3.551
60	.127	.254	.387	.527	.679	.848	1.046	1.296	1.671	2.000	2.390	2.660	3.460
120	.126	.254	.386	.526	.677	.845	1.041	1.289	1.658	1.980	2.358	2.617	3.373
∞	.126	.253	.385	.524	.674	.842	1.036	1.282	1.645	1.960	2.326	2.576	3.291

* Based on table in *Statistical methods for research workers* (12th ed.), R. A. Fisher, Oliver and Boyd, Ltd., and on the table in *Statistical tables for biological, agricultural, and medical research* (5th rev. ed.), R. A. Fisher and F. Yates, Oliver and Boyd, Ltd. Used with the kind permission of the authors, R. A. Fisher and F. Yates, and of the publisher, Oliver and Boyd, Ltd. The value of $t_{.50}(k)$ is zero for all k; for $k > 30$ and $k_1 \leq k < k_2 \leq \infty$,

$$t_\alpha(k) \doteq t_\alpha(k_2) + \{[(1/k) - (1/k_2)]/[(1/k_1) - (1/k_2)]\}[t_\alpha(k_1) - t_\alpha(k_2)].$$

TABLE 4*. VALUES OF $F_\alpha(k_1, k_2)$ FOR $\alpha = .005, .01, .025, .05, .10$ AND $1 \le k_1, k_2 \le 30, 40, 60, 120, \infty$

$\alpha = .10$

k_2 \ k_1	1	2	3	4	5	6	7	8	9	10	12	15	20	24	30	40	60	120	∞
1	39.86	49.50	53.59	55.83	57.24	58.20	58.91	59.44	59.86	60.20	60.70	61.22	61.74	62.00	62.26	62.53	62.79	63.06	63.33
2	8.53	9.00	9.16	9.24	9.29	9.33	9.35	9.37	9.38	9.39	9.41	9.42	9.44	9.45	9.46	9.47	9.47	9.48	9.49
3	5.54	5.46	5.39	5.34	5.31	5.28	5.27	5.25	5.24	5.23	5.22	5.20	5.18	5.18	5.17	5.16	5.15	5.14	5.13
4	4.54	4.32	4.19	4.11	4.05	4.01	3.98	3.95	3.94	3.92	3.90	3.87	3.84	3.83	3.82	3.80	3.79	3.78	3.76
5	4.06	3.78	3.62	3.52	3.45	3.40	3.37	3.34	3.32	3.30	3.27	3.24	3.21	3.19	3.17	3.16	3.14	3.12	3.10
6	3.78	3.46	3.29	3.18	3.11	3.05	3.01	2.98	2.96	2.94	2.90	2.87	2.84	2.82	2.80	2.78	2.76	2.74	2.72
7	3.59	3.26	3.07	2.96	2.88	2.83	2.78	2.75	2.72	2.70	2.67	2.63	2.59	2.58	2.56	2.54	2.51	2.49	2.47
8	3.46	3.11	2.92	2.81	2.73	2.67	2.62	2.59	2.56	2.54	2.50	2.46	2.42	2.40	2.38	2.36	2.34	2.32	2.29
9	3.36	3.01	2.81	2.69	2.61	2.55	2.51	2.47	2.44	2.42	2.38	2.34	2.30	2.28	2.25	2.23	2.21	2.18	2.16
10	3.28	2.92	2.73	2.61	2.52	2.46	2.41	2.38	2.35	2.32	2.28	2.24	2.20	2.18	2.16	2.13	2.11	2.08	2.06
11	3.23	2.86	2.66	2.54	2.45	2.39	2.34	2.30	2.27	2.25	2.21	2.17	2.12	2.10	2.08	2.05	2.03	2.00	1.97
12	3.18	2.81	2.61	2.48	2.39	2.33	2.28	2.24	2.21	2.19	2.15	2.10	2.06	2.04	2.01	1.99	1.96	1.93	1.90
13	3.14	2.76	2.56	2.43	2.35	2.28	2.23	2.20	2.16	2.14	2.10	2.05	2.01	1.98	1.96	1.93	1.90	1.88	1.85
14	3.10	2.73	2.52	2.39	2.31	2.24	2.19	2.15	2.12	2.10	2.05	2.01	1.96	1.94	1.91	1.89	1.86	1.83	1.80
15	3.07	2.70	2.49	2.36	2.27	2.21	2.16	2.12	2.09	2.06	2.02	1.97	1.92	1.90	1.87	1.85	1.82	1.79	1.76
16	3.05	2.67	2.46	2.33	2.24	2.18	2.13	2.09	2.06	2.03	1.99	1.94	1.89	1.87	1.84	1.81	1.78	1.75	1.72
17	3.03	2.64	2.44	2.31	2.22	2.15	2.10	2.06	2.03	2.00	1.96	1.91	1.86	1.84	1.81	1.78	1.75	1.72	1.69
18	3.01	2.62	2.42	2.29	2.20	2.13	2.08	2.04	2.00	1.98	1.93	1.89	1.84	1.81	1.78	1.75	1.72	1.69	1.66
19	2.99	2.61	2.40	2.27	2.18	2.11	2.06	2.02	1.98	1.96	1.91	1.86	1.81	1.79	1.76	1.73	1.70	1.67	1.63
20	2.97	2.59	2.38	2.25	2.16	2.09	2.04	2.00	1.96	1.94	1.89	1.84	1.79	1.77	1.74	1.71	1.68	1.64	1.61

TABLE 4*—(continued)

$\alpha = .10$

k_2 \ k_1	1	2	3	4	5	6	7	8	9	10	12	15	20	24	30	40	60	120	∞
21	2.96	2.57	2.36	2.23	2.14	2.08	2.02	1.98	1.95	1.92	1.88	1.83	1.78	1.75	1.72	1.69	1.66	1.62	1.59
22	2.95	2.56	2.35	2.22	2.13	2.06	2.01	1.97	1.93	1.90	1.86	1.81	1.76	1.73	1.70	1.67	1.64	1.60	1.57
23	2.94	2.55	2.34	2.21	2.11	2.05	1.99	1.95	1.92	1.89	1.84	1.80	1.74	1.72	1.69	1.66	1.62	1.59	1.55
24	2.93	2.54	2.33	2.19	2.10	2.04	1.98	1.94	1.91	1.88	1.83	1.78	1.73	1.70	1.67	1.64	1.61	1.57	1.53
25	2.92	2.53	2.32	2.18	2.09	2.02	1.97	1.93	1.89	1.87	1.82	1.77	1.72	1.69	1.66	1.63	1.59	1.56	1.52
26	2.91	2.52	2.31	2.17	2.08	2.01	1.96	1.92	1.88	1.86	1.81	1.76	1.71	1.68	1.65	1.61	1.58	1.54	1.50
27	2.90	2.51	2.30	2.17	2.07	2.00	1.95	1.91	1.87	1.85	1.80	1.75	1.70	1.67	1.64	1.60	1.57	1.53	1.49
28	2.89	2.50	2.29	2.16	2.06	2.00	1.94	1.90	1.87	1.84	1.79	1.74	1.69	1.66	1.63	1.59	1.56	1.52	1.48
29	2.89	2.50	2.28	2.15	2.06	1.99	1.93	1.89	1.86	1.83	1.78	1.73	1.68	1.65	1.62	1.58	1.55	1.51	1.47
30	2.88	2.49	2.28	2.14	2.05	1.98	1.93	1.88	1.85	1.82	1.77	1.72	1.67	1.64	1.61	1.57	1.54	1.50	1.46
40	2.84	2.44	2.23	2.09	2.00	1.93	1.87	1.83	1.79	1.76	1.71	1.66	1.61	1.57	1.54	1.51	1.47	1.42	1.38
60	2.79	2.39	2.18	2.04	1.95	1.87	1.82	1.77	1.74	1.71	1.66	1.60	1.54	1.51	1.48	1.44	1.40	1.35	1.29
120	2.75	2.35	2.13	1.99	1.90	1.82	1.77	1.72	1.68	1.65	1.60	1.54	1.48	1.45	1.41	1.37	1.32	1.26	1.19
∞	2.71	2.30	2.08	1.94	1.85	1.77	1.72	1.67	1.63	1.60	1.55	1.49	1.42	1.38	1.34	1.30	1.24	1.17	1.00

* Based on tables in paper: Tables of percentage points of the inverted beta (F) distribution, M. Merrington and C. M. Thompson, *Biometrika*, Vol. 33, 1943–46, pp. 73–88. Used with the kind permission of the authors, M. Merrington and C. M. Thompson, and of the Editor of *Biometrika*. For at least one of $k_1, k_2 > 30$ and $k'_1 \le k_1 < k''_2 \le \infty$, $k'_2 \le k_2 < k''_2 \le \infty$,

$$F_\alpha(k_1, k_2) \doteq F_\alpha(k_1, k'_2) + \{[(1/k_2)-(1/k''_2)]/[(1/k'_2)-(1/k''_2)]\}[F_\alpha(k_1, k'_2)-F_\alpha(k_1, k''_2)],$$

where

$$F_\alpha(k_1, k'_2) = F_\alpha(k'_1, k'_2) + \{[(1/k_1)-(1/k''_1)]/[(1/k'_1)-(1/k''_1)]\}[F_\alpha(k'_1, k'_2)-F_\alpha(k''_1, k'_2)],$$
$$F_\alpha(k_1, k''_2) = F_\alpha(k'_1, k''_2) + \{[(1/k_1)-(1/k''_1)]/[(1/k'_1)-(1/k''_1)]\}[F_\alpha(k'_1, k''_2)-F_\alpha(k''_1, k''_2)].$$

TABLE 4*—(continued)

$\alpha = .05$

k_2 \ k_1	1	2	3	4	5	6	7	8	9	10	12	15	20	24	30	40	60	120	∞
1	161.45	199.50	215.71	224.58	230.16	233.99	236.77	238.88	240.54	241.88	243.91	245.95	248.01	249.05	250.09	251.14	252.20	253.25	254.32
2	18.51	19.00	19.16	19.25	19.30	19.33	19.35	19.37	19.38	19.40	19.41	19.43	19.45	19.45	19.46	19.47	19.48	19.49	19.50
3	10.13	9.55	9.28	9.12	9.01	8.94	8.89	8.85	8.81	8.79	8.74	8.70	8.66	8.64	8.62	8.59	8.57	8.55	8.53
4	7.71	6.94	6.59	6.39	6.26	6.16	6.09	6.04	6.00	5.96	5.91	5.86	5.80	5.77	5.75	5.72	5.69	5.66	5.63
5	6.61	5.79	5.41	5.19	5.05	4.95	4.88	4.82	4.77	4.74	4.68	4.62	4.56	4.53	4.50	4.46	4.43	4.40	4.36
6	5.99	5.14	4.76	4.53	4.39	4.28	4.21	4.15	4.10	4.06	4.00	3.94	3.87	3.84	3.81	3.77	3.74	3.70	3.67
7	5.59	4.74	4.35	4.12	3.97	3.87	3.79	3.73	3.68	3.64	3.57	3.51	3.44	3.41	3.38	3.34	3.30	3.27	3.23
8	5.32	4.46	4.07	3.84	3.69	3.58	3.50	3.44	3.39	3.35	3.28	3.22	3.15	3.12	3.08	3.04	3.01	2.97	2.93
9	5.12	4.26	3.86	3.63	3.48	3.37	3.29	3.23	3.18	3.14	3.07	3.01	2.94	2.90	2.86	2.83	2.79	2.75	2.71
10	4.96	4.10	3.71	3.48	3.33	3.22	3.14	3.07	3.02	2.98	2.91	2.84	2.77	2.74	2.70	2.66	2.62	2.58	2.54
11	4.84	3.98	3.59	3.36	3.20	3.09	3.01	2.95	2.90	2.85	2.79	2.72	2.65	2.61	2.57	2.53	2.49	2.45	2.40
12	4.75	3.89	3.49	3.26	3.11	3.00	2.91	2.85	2.80	2.75	2.69	2.62	2.54	2.51	2.47	2.43	2.38	2.34	2.30
13	4.67	3.81	3.41	3.18	3.03	2.92	2.83	2.77	2.71	2.67	2.60	2.53	2.46	2.42	2.38	2.34	2.30	2.25	2.21
14	4.60	3.74	3.34	3.11	2.96	2.85	2.76	2.70	2.65	2.60	2.53	2.46	2.39	2.35	2.31	2.27	2.22	2.18	2.13
15	4.54	3.68	3.29	3.06	2.90	2.79	2.71	2.64	2.59	2.54	2.48	2.40	2.33	2.29	2.25	2.20	2.16	2.11	2.07
16	4.49	3.63	3.24	3.01	2.85	2.74	2.66	2.59	2.54	2.49	2.42	2.35	2.28	2.24	2.19	2.15	2.11	2.06	2.01
17	4.45	3.59	3.20	2.96	2.81	2.70	2.61	2.55	2.49	2.45	2.38	2.31	2.23	2.19	2.15	2.10	2.06	2.01	1.96
18	4.41	3.55	3.16	2.93	2.77	2.66	2.58	2.51	2.46	2.41	2.34	2.27	2.19	2.15	2.11	2.06	2.02	1.97	1.92
19	4.38	3.52	3.13	2.90	2.74	2.63	2.54	2.48	2.42	2.38	2.31	2.23	2.16	2.11	2.07	2.03	1.98	1.93	1.88
20	4.35	3.49	3.10	2.87	2.71	2.60	2.51	2.45	2.39	2.35	2.28	2.20	2.12	2.08	2.04	1.99	1.95	1.90	1.84

TABLE 4*—(continued)

$\alpha = .05$

k_2 \ k_1	1	2	3	4	5	6	7	8	9	10	12	15	20	24	30	40	60	120	∞
21	4.32	3.47	3.07	2.84	2.68	2.57	2.49	2.42	2.37	2.32	2.25	2.18	2.10	2.05	2.01	1.96	1.92	1.87	1.81
22	4.30	3.44	3.05	2.82	2.66	2.55	2.46	2.40	2.34	2.30	2.23	2.15	2.07	2.03	1.98	1.94	1.89	1.84	1.78
23	4.28	3.42	3.03	2.80	2.64	2.53	2.44	2.37	2.32	2.27	2.20	2.13	2.05	2.00	1.96	1.91	1.86	1.81	1.76
24	4.26	3.40	3.01	2.78	2.62	2.51	2.42	2.36	2.30	2.25	2.18	2.11	2.03	1.98	1.94	1.89	1.84	1.79	1.73
25	4.24	3.39	2.99	2.76	2.60	2.49	2.40	2.34	2.28	2.24	2.16	2.09	2.01	1.96	1.92	1.87	1.82	1.77	1.71
26	4.23	3.37	2.98	2.74	2.59	2.47	2.39	2.32	2.27	2.22	2.15	2.07	1.99	1.95	1.90	1.85	1.80	1.75	1.69
27	4.21	3.35	2.96	2.73	2.57	2.46	2.37	2.31	2.25	2.20	2.13	2.06	1.97	1.93	1.88	1.84	1.79	1.73	1.67
28	4.20	3.34	2.95	2.71	2.56	2.45	2.36	2.29	2.24	2.19	2.12	2.04	1.96	1.91	1.87	1.82	1.77	1.71	1.65
29	4.18	3.33	2.93	2.70	2.55	2.43	2.35	2.28	2.22	2.18	2.10	2.03	1.94	1.90	1.85	1.81	1.75	1.70	1.64
30	4.17	3.32	2.92	2.69	2.53	2.42	2.33	2.27	2.21	2.16	2.09	2.01	1.93	1.89	1.84	1.79	1.74	1.68	1.62
40	4.08	3.23	2.84	2.61	2.45	2.34	2.25	2.18	2.12	2.08	2.00	1.92	1.84	1.79	1.74	1.69	1.64	1.58	1.51
60	4.00	3.15	2.76	2.53	2.37	2.25	2.17	2.10	2.04	1.99	1.92	1.84	1.75	1.70	1.65	1.59	1.53	1.47	1.39
120	3.92	3.07	2.68	2.45	2.29	2.18	2.09	2.02	1.96	1.91	1.83	1.75	1.66	1.61	1.55	1.50	1.43	1.35	1.25
∞	3.84	3.00	2.60	2.37	2.21	2.10	2.01	1.94	1.88	1.83	1.75	1.67	1.57	1.52	1.46	1.39	1.32	1.22	1.00

* Based on tables in paper: Tables of percentage points of the inverted beta (F) distribution, M. Merrington and C. M. Thompson, *Biometrika*, Vol. 33, 1943–46, pp. 73–88. Used with the kind permission of the authors, M. Merrington and C. M. Thompson, and of the Editor of *Biometrika*. For at least one of $k_1, k_2 > 30$ and $k'_1 \le k_1 < k''_2 \le \infty$, $k'_2 \le k_2 < k''_2 \le \infty$,

$$F_\alpha(k_1, k_2) \doteq F_\alpha(k_1, k'_2) + \{[(1/k_2) - (1/k''_2)]/[(1/k'_2) - (1/k''_2)]\}[F_\alpha(k_1, k'_2) - F_\alpha(k_1, k''_2)],$$

where

$$F_\alpha(k_1, k'_2) = F_\alpha(k'_1, k'_2) + \{[(1/k_1) - (1/k''_1)]/[(1/k'_1) - (1/k''_1)]\}[F_\alpha(k'_1, k'_2) - F_\alpha(k''_1, k'_2)],$$
$$F_\alpha(k_1, k''_2) = F_\alpha(k'_1, k''_2) + \{[(1/k_1) - (1/k''_1)]/[(1/k'_1) - (1/k''_1)]\}[F_\alpha(k'_1, k''_2) - F_\alpha(k''_1, k''_2)].$$

$\alpha = .025$

k_2 \ k_1	1	2	3	4	5	6	7	8	9	10	12	15	20	24	30	40	60	120	∞
1	647.79	799.50	864.16	899.58	921.85	937.11	948.22	956.66	963.28	968.63	976.71	984.87	993.10	997.25	1001.4	1005.6	1009.8	1014.0	1018.3
2	38.51	39.00	39.16	39.25	39.30	39.33	39.36	39.37	39.39	39.40	39.42	39.43	39.45	39.46	39.46	39.47	39.48	39.49	39.50
3	17.44	16.04	15.44	15.10	14.88	14.74	14.62	14.54	14.47	14.42	14.34	14.25	14.17	14.12	14.08	14.04	13.99	13.95	13.90
4	12.22	10.65	9.98	9.60	9.36	9.20	9.07	8.98	8.90	8.84	8.75	8.66	8.56	8.51	8.46	8.41	8.36	8.31	8.26
5	10.01	8.43	7.76	7.39	7.15	6.98	6.85	6.76	6.68	6.62	6.52	6.43	6.33	6.28	6.23	6.18	6.12	6.07	6.02
6	8.81	7.26	6.60	6.23	5.99	5.82	5.70	5.60	5.52	5.46	5.37	5.27	5.17	5.12	5.07	5.01	4.96	4.90	4.85
7	8.07	6.54	5.89	5.52	5.29	5.12	4.99	4.90	4.82	4.76	4.67	4.57	4.47	4.42	4.36	4.31	4.25	4.20	4.14
8	7.57	6.06	5.42	5.05	4.82	4.65	4.53	4.43	4.36	4.30	4.20	4.10	4.00	3.95	3.89	3.84	3.78	3.73	3.67
9	7.21	5.71	5.08	4.72	4.48	4.32	4.20	4.10	4.03	3.96	3.87	3.77	3.67	3.61	3.56	3.51	3.45	3.39	3.33
10	6.94	5.46	4.83	4.47	4.24	4.07	3.95	3.85	3.78	3.72	3.62	3.52	3.42	3.37	3.31	3.26	3.20	3.14	3.08
11	6.72	5.26	4.63	4.28	4.04	3.88	3.76	3.66	3.59	3.53	3.43	3.33	3.23	3.17	3.12	3.06	3.00	2.94	2.88
12	6.55	5.10	4.47	4.12	3.89	3.73	3.61	3.51	3.44	3.37	3.28	3.18	3.07	3.02	2.96	2.91	2.85	2.79	2.72
13	6.41	4.97	4.35	4.00	3.77	3.60	3.48	3.39	3.31	3.25	3.15	3.05	2.95	2.89	2.84	2.78	2.72	2.66	2.60
14	6.30	4.86	4.24	3.89	3.66	3.50	3.38	3.29	3.21	3.15	3.05	2.95	2.84	2.79	2.73	2.67	2.61	2.55	2.49
15	6.20	4.76	4.15	3.80	3.58	3.41	3.29	3.20	3.12	3.06	2.96	2.86	2.76	2.70	2.64	2.58	2.52	2.46	2.40
16	6.12	4.69	4.08	3.73	3.50	3.34	3.22	3.12	3.05	2.99	2.89	2.79	2.68	2.63	2.57	2.51	2.45	2.38	2.32
17	6.04	4.62	4.01	3.66	3.44	3.28	3.16	3.06	2.98	2.92	2.82	2.72	2.62	2.56	2.50	2.44	2.38	2.32	2.25
18	5.98	4.56	3.95	3.61	3.38	3.22	3.10	3.01	2.93	2.87	2.77	2.67	2.56	2.50	2.44	2.38	2.32	2.26	2.19
19	5.92	4.51	3.90	3.56	3.33	3.17	3.05	2.96	2.88	2.82	2.72	2.62	2.51	2.45	2.39	2.33	2.27	2.20	2.13
20	5.87	4.46	3.86	3.51	3.29	3.13	3.01	2.91	2.84	2.77	2.68	2.57	2.46	2.41	2.35	2.29	2.22	2.16	2.09

TABLE 4*—(continued)

$\alpha = .025$

k_2 \ k_1	1	2	3	4	5	6	7	8	9	10	12	15	20	24	30	40	60	120	∞
21	5.83	4.42	3.82	3.48	3.25	3.09	2.97	2.87	2.80	2.73	2.64	2.53	2.42	2.37	2.31	2.25	2.18	2.11	2.04
22	5.79	4.38	3.78	3.44	3.22	3.05	2.93	2.84	2.76	2.70	2.60	2.50	2.39	2.33	2.27	2.21	2.14	2.08	2.00
23	5.75	4.35	3.75	3.41	3.18	3.02	2.90	2.81	2.73	2.67	2.57	2.47	2.36	2.30	2.24	2.18	2.11	2.04	1.97
24	5.72	4.32	3.72	3.38	3.15	2.99	2.87	2.78	2.70	2.64	2.54	2.44	2.33	2.27	2.21	2.15	2.08	2.01	1.94
25	5.69	4.29	3.69	3.35	3.13	2.97	2.85	2.75	2.68	2.61	2.51	2.41	2.30	2.24	2.18	2.12	2.05	1.98	1.91
26	5.66	4.27	3.67	3.33	3.10	2.94	2.82	2.73	2.65	2.59	2.49	2.39	2.28	2.22	2.16	2.09	2.03	1.95	1.88
27	5.63	4.24	3.65	3.31	3.08	2.92	2.80	2.71	2.63	2.57	2.47	2.36	2.25	2.19	2.13	2.07	2.00	1.93	1.85
28	5.61	4.22	3.63	3.29	3.06	2.90	2.78	2.69	2.61	2.55	2.45	2.34	2.23	2.17	2.11	2.05	1.98	1.91	1.83
29	5.59	4.20	3.61	3.27	3.04	2.88	2.76	2.67	2.59	2.53	2.43	2.32	2.21	2.15	2.09	2.03	1.96	1.89	1.81
30	5.57	4.18	3.59	3.25	3.03	2.87	2.75	2.65	2.57	2.51	2.41	2.31	2.20	2.14	2.07	2.01	1.94	1.87	1.79
40	5.42	4.05	3.46	3.13	2.90	2.74	2.62	2.53	2.45	2.39	2.29	2.18	2.07	2.01	1.94	1.88	1.80	1.72	1.64
60	5.29	3.93	3.34	3.01	2.79	2.63	2.51	2.41	2.33	2.27	2.17	2.06	1.94	1.88	1.82	1.74	1.67	1.58	1.48
120	5.15	3.80	3.23	2.89	2.67	2.52	2.39	2.30	2.22	2.16	2.05	1.94	1.82	1.76	1.69	1.61	1.53	1.43	1.31
∞	5.02	3.69	3.12	2.79	2.57	2.41	2.29	2.19	2.11	2.05	1.94	1.83	1.71	1.64	1.57	1.48	1.39	1.27	1.00

* Based on tables in paper: Tables of percentage points of the inverted beta (F) distribution, M. Merrington and C. M. Thompson, *Biometrika*, Vol. 33, 1943–46, pp. 73–88. Used with the kind permission of the authors, M. Merrington and C. M. Thompson, and of the Editor of *Biometrika*. For at least one of k_1, $k_2 > 30$ and $k'_1 \leq k_1 < k''_2 \leq \infty$, $k'_2 \leq k_2 < k''_2 \leq \infty$,

$$F_\alpha(k_1, k_2) \doteq F_\alpha(k_1, k'_2) + \{[(1/k_2) - (1/k''_2)]/[(1/k'_2) - (1/k''_2)]\}[F_\alpha(k_1, k'_2) - F_\alpha(k_1, k''_2)],$$

where

$$F_\alpha(k_1, k'_2) = F_\alpha(k'_1, k'_2) + \{[(1/k_1) - (1/k''_1)]/[(1/k'_1) - (1/k''_1)]\}[F_\alpha(k'_1, k'_2) - F_\alpha(k''_1, k'_2)],$$
$$F_\alpha(k_1, k''_2) = F_\alpha(k'_1, k''_2) + \{[(1/k_1) - (1/k''_1)]/[(1/k'_1) - (1/k''_1)]\}[F_\alpha(k'_1, k''_2) - F_\alpha(k''_1, k''_2)].$$

TABLE 4*—(continued)

$\alpha = .01$

k_2 \ k_1	1	2	3	4	5	6	7	8	9	10	12	15	20	24	30	40	60	120	∞
1	4052.2	4999.5	5403.3	5624.6	5763.7	5859.0	5928.3	5981.6	6022.5	6055.8	6106.3	6157.3	6208.7	6234.6	6260.7	6286.8	6313.0	6339.4	6366.0
2	98.50	99.00	99.17	99.25	99.30	99.33	99.36	99.37	99.39	99.40	99.42	99.43	99.45	99.46	99.47	99.47	99.48	99.49	99.50
3	34.12	30.82	29.46	28.71	28.24	27.91	27.67	27.49	27.34	27.23	27.05	26.87	26.69	26.60	26.50	26.41	26.32	26.22	26.12
4	21.20	18.00	16.69	15.98	15.52	15.21	14.98	14.80	14.66	14.55	14.37	14.20	14.02	13.93	13.84	13.74	13.65	13.56	13.46
5	16.26	13.27	12.06	11.39	10.97	10.67	10.46	10.29	10.16	10.05	9.89	9.72	9.55	9.47	9.38	9.29	9.20	9.11	9.02
6	13.74	10.92	9.78	9.15	8.75	8.47	8.26	8.10	7.98	7.87	7.72	7.56	7.40	7.31	7.23	7.14	7.06	6.97	6.88
7	12.25	9.55	8.45	7.85	7.46	7.19	6.99	6.84	6.72	6.62	6.47	6.31	6.16	6.07	5.99	5.91	5.82	5.74	5.65
8	11.26	8.65	7.59	7.01	6.63	6.37	6.18	6.03	5.91	5.81	5.67	5.52	5.36	5.28	5.20	5.12	5.03	4.95	4.86
9	10.56	8.02	6.99	6.42	6.06	5.80	5.61	5.47	5.35	5.26	5.11	4.96	4.81	4.73	4.65	4.57	4.48	4.40	4.31
10	10.04	7.56	6.55	5.99	5.64	5.39	5.20	5.06	4.94	4.85	4.71	4.56	4.41	4.33	4.25	4.17	4.08	4.00	3.91
11	9.65	7.21	6.22	5.67	5.32	5.07	4.89	4.74	4.63	4.54	4.40	4.25	4.10	4.02	3.94	3.86	3.78	3.69	3.60
12	9.33	6.93	5.95	5.41	5.06	4.82	4.64	4.50	4.39	4.30	4.16	4.01	3.86	3.78	3.70	3.62	3.54	3.45	3.36
13	9.07	6.70	5.74	5.21	4.86	4.62	4.44	4.30	4.19	4.10	3.96	3.82	3.66	3.59	3.51	3.43	3.34	3.25	3.17
14	8.86	6.51	5.56	5.04	4.70	4.46	4.28	4.14	4.03	3.94	3.80	3.66	3.51	3.43	3.35	3.27	3.18	3.09	3.00
15	8.68	6.36	5.42	4.89	4.56	4.32	4.14	4.00	3.89	3.80	3.67	3.52	3.37	3.29	3.21	3.13	3.05	2.96	2.87
16	8.53	6.23	5.29	4.77	4.44	4.20	4.03	3.89	3.78	3.69	3.55	3.41	3.26	3.18	3.10	3.02	2.93	2.84	2.75
17	8.40	6.11	5.18	4.67	4.34	4.10	3.93	3.79	3.68	3.59	3.46	3.31	3.16	3.08	3.00	2.92	2.83	2.75	2.65
18	8.29	6.01	5.09	4.58	4.25	4.01	3.84	3.71	3.60	3.51	3.37	3.23	3.08	3.00	2.92	2.84	2.75	2.66	2.57
19	8.18	5.93	5.01	4.50	4.17	3.94	3.77	3.63	3.52	3.43	3.30	3.15	3.00	2.92	2.84	2.76	2.67	2.58	2.49
20	8.10	5.85	4.94	4.43	4.10	3.87	3.70	3.56	3.46	3.37	3.23	3.09	2.94	2.86	2.78	2.69	2.61	2.52	2.42

TABLE 4*—(continued)

$\alpha = .01$

k_2 \ k_1	1	2	3	4	5	6	7	8	9	10	12	15	20	24	30	40	60	120	∞
21	8.02	5.78	4.87	4.37	4.04	3.81	3.64	3.51	3.40	3.31	3.17	3.03	2.88	2.80	2.72	2.64	2.55	2.46	2.36
22	7.95	5.72	4.82	4.31	3.99	3.76	3.59	3.45	3.35	3.26	3.12	2.98	2.83	2.75	2.67	2.58	2.50	2.40	2.31
23	7.88	5.66	4.76	4.26	3.94	3.71	3.54	3.41	3.30	3.21	3.07	2.93	2.78	2.70	2.62	2.54	2.45	2.35	2.26
24	7.82	5.61	4.72	4.22	3.90	3.67	3.50	3.36	3.26	3.17	3.03	2.89	2.74	2.66	2.58	2.49	2.40	2.31	2.21
25	7.77	5.57	4.68	4.18	3.86	3.63	3.46	3.32	3.22	3.13	2.99	2.85	2.70	2.62	2.54	2.45	2.36	2.27	2.17
26	7.72	5.53	4.64	4.14	3.82	3.59	3.42	3.29	3.18	3.09	2.96	2.82	2.66	2.58	2.50	2.42	2.33	2.23	2.13
27	7.68	5.49	4.60	4.11	3.78	3.56	3.39	3.26	3.15	3.06	2.93	2.78	2.63	2.55	2.47	2.38	2.29	2.20	2.10
28	7.64	5.45	4.57	4.07	3.75	3.53	3.36	3.23	3.12	3.03	2.90	2.75	2.60	2.52	2.44	2.35	2.26	2.17	2.06
29	7.60	5.42	4.54	4.04	3.73	3.50	3.33	3.20	3.09	3.00	2.87	2.73	2.57	2.49	2.41	2.33	2.23	2.14	2.03
30	7.56	5.39	4.51	4.02	3.70	3.47	3.30	3.17	3.07	2.98	2.84	2.70	2.55	2.47	2.39	2.30	2.21	2.11	2.01
40	7.31	5.18	4.31	3.83	3.51	3.29	3.12	2.99	2.89	2.80	2.66	2.52	2.37	2.29	2.20	2.11	2.02	1.92	1.80
60	7.08	4.98	4.13	3.65	3.34	3.12	2.95	2.82	2.72	2.63	2.50	2.35	2.20	2.12	2.03	1.94	1.84	1.73	1.60
120	6.85	4.79	3.95	3.48	3.17	2.96	2.79	2.66	2.56	2.47	2.34	2.19	2.03	1.95	1.86	1.76	1.66	1.53	1.38
∞	6.63	4.61	3.78	3.32	3.02	2.80	2.64	2.51	2.41	2.32	2.18	2.04	1.88	1.79	1.70	1.59	1.47	1.32	1.00

* Based on tables in paper: Tables of percentage points of the inverted beta (F) distribution, M. Merrington and C. M. Thompson, *Biometrika*, Vol. 33, 1943–46, pp. 73–88. Used with the kind permission of the authors, M. Merrington and C. M. Thompson, and of the Editor of *Biometrika*. For at least one of $k_1, k_2 > 30$ and $k'_1 \leq k_1 < k''_2 \leq \infty$, $k'_2 \leq k_2 < k''_2 \leq \infty$,

$$F_\alpha(k_1, k_2) \doteq F_\alpha(k_1, k'_2) + \{[(1/k_2) - (1/k''_2)]/[(1/k'_2 - (1/k''_2)]\}[F_\alpha(k_1, k'_2) - F_\alpha(k_1, k''_2)],$$

where

$$F_\alpha(k_1, k'_2) = F_\alpha(k'_1, k'_2) + \{[(1/k_1) - (1/k''_1)]/[(1/k'_1) - (1/k''_1)]\}[F_\alpha(k'_1, k'_2) - F_\alpha(k''_1, k'_2)],$$
$$F_\alpha(k_1, k''_2) = F_\alpha(k'_1, k''_2) + \{[(1/k_1) - (1/k''_1)]/[(1/k'_1) - (1/k''_1)]\}[F_\alpha(k'_1, k''_2) - F_\alpha(k''_1, k''_2)].$$

TABLE 4*—(continued)

$\alpha = .005$

k_2 \ k_1	1	2	3	4	5	6	7	8	9	10	12	15	20	24	30	40	60	120	∞
1	16211	20000	21615	22500	23056	23437	23715	23925	24091	24224	24426	24630	24836	24940	25044	25148	25253	25359	25465
2	198.50	199.00	199.17	199.25	199.30	199.33	199.36	199.37	199.39	199.40	199.42	199.43	199.45	199.46	199.47	199.47	199.48	199.49	199.51
3	55.55	49.80	47.47	46.20	45.39	44.84	44.43	44.13	43.88	43.69	43.39	43.08	42.78	42.62	42.47	42.31	42.15	41.99	41.83
4	31.33	26.28	24.26	23.16	22.46	21.98	21.62	21.35	21.14	20.97	20.70	20.44	20.17	20.03	19.89	19.75	19.61	19.47	19.32
5	22.78	18.31	16.53	15.56	14.94	14.51	14.20	13.96	13.77	13.62	13.38	13.15	12.90	12.78	12.66	12.53	12.40	12.27	12.14
6	18.64	14.54	12.92	12.03	11.46	11.07	10.79	10.57	10.39	10.25	10.03	9.81	9.59	9.47	9.36	9.24	9.12	9.00	8.88
7	16.24	12.40	10.88	10.05	9.52	9.16	8.89	8.68	8.51	8.38	8.18	7.97	7.75	7.64	7.53	7.42	7.31	7.19	7.08
8	14.69	11.04	9.60	8.81	8.30	7.95	7.69	7.50	7.34	7.21	7.01	6.81	6.61	6.50	6.40	6.29	6.18	6.06	5.95
9	13.61	10.11	8.72	7.96	7.47	7.13	6.88	6.69	6.54	6.42	6.23	6.03	5.83	5.73	5.62	5.52	5.41	5.30	5.19
10	12.83	9.43	8.08	7.34	6.87	6.54	6.30	6.12	5.97	5.85	5.66	5.47	5.27	5.17	5.07	4.97	4.86	4.75	4.64
11	12.23	8.91	7.60	6.88	6.42	6.10	5.86	5.68	5.54	5.42	5.24	5.05	4.86	4.76	4.65	4.55	4.44	4.34	4.23
12	11.75	8.51	7.23	6.52	6.07	5.76	5.52	5.35	5.20	5.09	4.91	4.72	4.53	4.43	4.33	4.23	4.12	4.01	3.90
13	11.37	8.19	6.93	6.23	5.79	5.48	5.25	5.08	4.94	4.82	4.64	4.46	4.27	4.17	4.07	3.97	3.87	3.76	3.65
14	11.06	7.92	6.68	6.00	5.56	5.26	5.03	4.86	4.72	4.60	4.43	4.25	4.06	3.96	3.86	3.76	3.66	3.55	3.44
15	10.80	7.70	6.48	5.80	5.37	5.07	4.85	4.67	4.54	4.42	4.25	4.07	3.88	3.79	3.69	3.58	3.48	3.37	3.26
16	10.58	7.51	6.30	5.64	5.21	4.91	4.69	4.52	4.38	4.27	4.10	3.92	3.73	3.64	3.54	3.44	3.33	3.22	3.11
17	10.38	7.35	6.16	5.50	5.07	4.78	4.56	4.39	4.25	4.14	3.97	3.79	3.61	3.51	3.41	3.31	3.21	3.10	2.98
18	10.22	7.21	6.03	5.37	4.96	4.66	4.44	4.28	4.14	4.03	3.86	3.68	3.50	3.40	3.30	3.20	3.10	2.99	2.87
19	10.07	7.09	5.92	5.27	4.85	4.56	4.34	4.18	4.04	3.93	3.76	3.59	3.40	3.31	3.21	3.11	3.00	2.89	2.78
20	9.94	6.99	5.82	5.17	4.76	4.47	4.26	4.09	3.96	3.85	3.68	3.50	3.32	3.22	3.12	3.02	2.92	2.81	2.69

TABLE 4*—(continued)

$\alpha = .005$

k_2 \ k_1	1	2	3	4	5	6	7	8	9	10	12	15	20	24	30	40	60	120	∞
21	9.83	6.89	5.73	5.09	4.68	4.39	4.18	4.01	3.88	3.77	3.60	3.43	3.24	3.15	3.05	2.95	2.84	2.73	2.61
22	9.73	6.81	5.65	5.02	4.61	4.32	4.11	3.94	3.81	3.70	3.54	3.36	3.18	3.08	2.98	2.88	2.77	2.66	2.55
23	9.63	6.73	5.58	4.95	4.54	4.26	4.05	3.88	3.75	3.64	3.47	3.30	3.12	3.02	2.92	2.82	2.71	2.60	2.48
24	9.55	6.66	5.52	4.89	4.49	4.20	3.99	3.83	3.69	3.59	3.42	3.25	3.06	2.97	2.87	2.77	2.66	2.55	2.43
25	9.48	6.60	5.46	4.84	4.43	4.15	3.94	3.78	3.64	3.54	3.37	3.20	3.01	2.92	2.82	2.72	2.61	2.50	2.38
26	9.41	6.54	5.41	4.79	4.38	4.10	3.89	3.73	3.60	3.49	3.33	3.15	2.97	2.87	2.77	2.67	2.56	2.45	2.33
27	9.34	6.49	5.36	4.74	4.34	4.06	3.85	3.69	3.56	3.45	3.28	3.11	2.93	2.83	2.73	2.63	2.52	2.41	2.29
28	9.28	6.44	5.32	4.70	4.30	4.02	3.81	3.65	3.52	3.41	3.25	3.07	2.89	2.79	2.69	2.59	2.48	2.37	2.25
29	9.23	6.40	5.28	4.66	4.26	3.98	3.77	3.61	3.48	3.38	3.21	3.04	2.86	2.76	2.66	2.56	2.45	2.33	2.21
30	9.18	6.35	5.24	4.62	4.23	3.95	3.74	3.58	3.45	3.34	3.18	3.01	2.82	2.73	2.63	2.52	2.42	2.30	2.18
40	8.83	6.07	4.98	4.37	3.99	3.71	3.51	3.35	3.22	3.12	2.95	2.78	2.60	2.50	2.40	2.30	2.18	2.06	1.93
60	8.49	5.80	4.73	4.14	3.76	3.49	3.29	3.13	3.01	2.90	2.74	2.57	2.39	2.29	2.19	2.08	1.96	1.83	1.69
120	8.18	5.54	4.50	3.92	3.55	3.28	3.09	2.93	2.81	2.71	2.54	2.37	2.19	2.09	1.98	1.87	1.75	1.61	1.43
∞	7.88	5.30	4.28	3.72	3.35	3.09	2.90	2.74	2.62	2.52	2.36	2.19	2.00	1.90	1.79	1.67	1.53	1.36	1.00

* Based on tables in paper: Tables of percentage points of the inverted beta (F) distribution, M. Merrington and C. M. Thompson, *Biometrika*, Vol. 33, 1943–46, pp. 73–88. Used with the kind permission of the authors, M. Merrington and C. M. Thompson, and of the Editor of *Biometrika*. For at least one of $k_1, k_2 > 30$ and $k'_1 \le k_1 < k''_2 \le \infty$, $k'_2 \le k_2 < k''_2 \le \infty$,

$$F_\alpha(k_1, k_2) \doteq F_\alpha(k_1, k'_2) + \{[(1/k_2) - (1/k''_2)]/[(1/k'_2) - (1/k''_2)]\}[F_\alpha(k_1, k'_2) - F_\alpha(k_1, k''_2)],$$

where

$$F_\alpha(k_1, k'_2) = F_\alpha(k'_1, k'_2) + \{[(1/k_1) - (1/k''_1)]/[(1/k'_1) - (1/k''_1)]\}[F_\alpha(k'_1, k'_2) - F_\alpha(k''_1, k'_2)],$$
$$F_\alpha(k_1, k''_2) = F_\alpha(k'_1, k''_2) + \{[(1/k_1) - (1/k''_1)]/[(1/k'_1) - (1/k''_1)]\}[F_\alpha(k'_1, k''_2) - F_\alpha(k''_1, k''_2)].$$

ABBREVIATIONS FOR PLACE OF PUBLICATION

AE	Annals of Eugenics
AISM	Annals of the Institute of Statistical Mathematics (Tokyo)
AMS	Annals of Mathematical Statistics
BA	Biometrika
BAMS	Bulletin of the American Mathematical Society
BS	Biometrics
CRAS	C.R. (Doklady) Akademii Sci. URSS (N.S.)
DAN	Dokladŷ Akademii Nauk SSSR (N.S.)
E	Econometrica
JASA	Journal of the American Statistical Association
JISAS	Journal of the Indian Society of Agricultural Statistics
JRSS	Journal of the Royal Statistical Society
JRSSB	Journal of the Royal Statistical Society, Series B (Through 1947, called Journal of the Royal Statistical Society, Supplement)
JWS	John Wiley and Sons
MH	McGraw-Hill Book Company
PAMS	Proceedings of the American Mathematical Society
PBS	Proceedings of the Berkeley Symposium on Mathematical Statistics and Probability, University of California Press
PCPS	Proceedings of the Cambridge Philosophical Society
PKNAW	Proceedings Koninklijke Nederlandse Akademie van Wetenschappen
PKNAWA	Proceedings Koninklijke Nederlandse Akademie van Wetenschappen, Series A
PNAS	Proceedings of the National Academy of Science, U.S.A.
PSBS	Proceedings of the Second Berkeley Symposium on Probability and Statistics, University of California Press
PTBS	Proceedings of the Third Berkeley Symposium on Mathematical Statistics and Probability, University of California Press
S	Sankhyā
SA	Skandinavisk Aktuarietidskrift
TAMS	Transactions of the American Mathematical Society
TE	Trabajos Estadística

BIBLIOGRAPHY—AUTHOR INDEX FOR REFERENCES

The format used for stating references is described on pages 23–24. Not all of the material listed is explicitly referred to in the body of the handbook. When explicit referral does occur on one or more pages in other sections of the handbook (nearly all cases), these pages are listed in square brackets at the end of the statement of the reference. The bibliography is:

1 Aggarwal, O. P., Some minimax invariant procedures for estimating a cumulative distribution function, *AMS* 26, '55, 450–63, [301, 304]

2 Agnew, R. P., Global versions of the central limit theorem, *PNAS* 40, '54, 800–04, [192]

3 Agnew, R. P., Estimates for global central limit theorems, *AMS* 28, '57, 26–42, [94, 105, 106]

4 Airey, J. R., *Tables of Hh function*, British Assoc. Math. Tables 1, '31, [417, 418]

5 Akaike, H., An approximation to the density function, *AISM* 6, '54, 127–32, [293]

6 Albert, G. E., Accurate sequential tests on the mean of an exponential distribution, *AMS* 27, '56, 460–70, [420]

7 Amato, V., Sui limiti di applicabilita della formula di Poisson, *Statistica Milano* 10, '50, 149–52, [184]

8 Andersen, E. S., On the number of positive sums of random variables, *SA* 32, '49, 27–36, [192]

9 Anderson, T. W., and Darling, D. A., Asymptotic theory of certain "goodness of fit" criteria based on stochastic processes, *AMS* 23, '52, 193–212, [318, 329, 362]

10 Anderson, T. W., and Darling, D. A., A test of goodness of fit, *JASA* 49, '54, 765–69, [362]

11 Anscombe, F. J., Linear sequential rectifying inspection for controlling fraction defective, *JRSSB* 8, '46, 216–22, [189]

12 Anscombe, F. J., The transformation of Poisson, binomial, and negative binomial data, *Supplement to the Journal of the Royal Statistical Society* 35, '48, 246–54, [192]

13 Anscombe, F. J., and Pages, E. S., Sequential tests for binomial and exponential populations, *BA* 41, '54, 252–53, [189, 420]

14 Aoyama, H., On the chi-square test for weighted samples, *AISM* 5, '53, 25–28, [461, 462]

15 Aoyama, H., A study of the stratified random sampling, *AISM* 6, '54, 1–36, [87]

16 Aoyama, H., On the evaluation of the sampling error of a certain determinant, *AISM* 8, '56, 27–33, [115]

17 Armitage, P., Some sequential tests of Student's hypothesis, *JRSSB* 9, '47, 250–63, [418]

18 Austin, T., Fagan, R., Lehrer, T., and Penney, W., The distribution of the number of locally maximal elements in a random sample, *AMS* 28, '57, 786–90, [67]

19 Bahadur, R. R., and Savage, L. J., The nonexistence of certain statistical procedures in nonparametric problems, *AMS* 27, '56, 1115–22, [120, 318]

20 Barankin, E. W., Conditional expectation and convex functions, *PSBS*, '51, 167–69, [184]

21 Barnard, G. A., The frequency justification of certain sequential tests, *BA* 39, '52, 144–50; also *Addendum* in *BA* 40, '53, 468–69, [418]

22 Barnard, G. A., Sequential tests in industrial statistics, *JRSSB* 8, '46, 1–21, [189]

23 Bartholomew, D. J., Note on the use of Sherman's statistics as a test for randomness, *BA* 41, '54, 556–58, [364]

24 Bartholomew, D. J., Tests for randomness in a series of events where the alternative is a trend, *JRSSB* 18, '56, 234–39, [324, 329, 370]

25 Bartky, W., Multiple sampling with constant probability, *AMS* 14, '43, 363–77, [189]

26 Bartlett, M. S., The effect of non-normality on the t-distribution, *PCPS* 31, '35, 223–31, [152, 165, 192]

27 Bartlett, M. S., The use of transformations, *BS* 3, '47, 39–51, [192]

28 Barton, D. E., On Neyman's smooth test of goodness of fit and its power with respect to a particular system of alternatives, *SA* 36, '53, 24–63, [360, 361]

29 Barton, D. E., The probability distribution function of a sum of squares, *TE* 4, '53, 199–207, [360, 361]

30 Barton, D. E., A form of Neyman's $\psi_K{}^2$ test of goodness of fit applicable to grouped and discrete data, *SA* 38, '55, 1–21, [361, 473]

31 Barton, D. E., Neyman's $\psi_K{}^2$ test of goodness of fit when the null hypothesis is composite, *SA* 39, '56, 216–45, [361, 473]

32 Barton, D. E., A comparison of two sorts of tests for a change of location applicable to truncated data, *JRSSB* 19, '57, 119–24, [226]

33 Barton, D. E., and David, F. N., Sums of ordered intervals and distances, *Mathematika* 2, '55, 150–59, [368, 370]

34 Barton, D. E., and David, F. N., Tests for randomness of points on a line, *BA* 43, '56, 104–12, [369]

35 Barton, D. E., and David, F. N., "Spearman's rho" and the matching problem, *British Journal of Statistical Psychology* 9, '56, 69–73, [71, 72]

36 Barton, D. E., and David, F. N., Some notes on ordered random intervals, *JRSSB* 18, '56, 79–94, [367, 368]

37 Barton, D. E., and David, F. N., Multiple runs, *BA* 44, '57, 168–78, [64, 65]
38 Barton, D. E., and Dennis, K. E., The conditions under which the Gram-Charlier and Edgeworth curves are positive definite and unimodal, *BA* 39, '52, 425–27, [46, 47, 48]
39 Bateman, G., On the power function of the longest run as a test for randomness in a sequence of alternatives, *BA* 35, '48, 97–112, [64, 65]
40 Béjar, J., Maxima and minima of the coefficients of asymmetry and kurtosis in finite populations, *TE* 3, '52, 3–11, [115]
41 Bennett, B. M., On a rank-order test for the equality of probability of an event, *SA* 39, '56, 11–18, [192]
42 Bennett, C. A., Application of tests for randomness, *Industrial and Engineering Chemistry* 43, '51, 2063–67, [64, 71]
43 Benson, F., A note on the estimation of mean and standard deviation from quantiles, *JRSSB* 11, '49, 91–100, [128, 134]
44 Berge, P. O., A note on a form of Tchebycheff's theorem for two variables, *BA* 29, '37, 405–06, [108, 110]
45 Bergström, H., On the central limit theorem in the case of not equally distributed random variables, *SA* 32, '49, 37–62, [107]
46 Berkson, J., Some difficulties of interpretation encountered in the application of the chi-square test, *JASA* 33, '38, 526–36, [462]
47 Bernstein, S., Sur une modification de l'inégalité de Tchebichef, *Ann. Sc. Instit. Sav. Ukraine, Sect. Math. I*, '24 (Russian; French summary), [100]
48 Bernstein, S., Sur quelques modifications de l'inégalité de Tchebycheff, *CRAS* 17, '37, 279–82, [100]
49 Berry, A. C., The accuracy of the Gaussian approximation to the sum of independent variables, *TAMS* 49, '41, 122–36, [106, 192]
50 Bhate, D. H., A note on the estimates of centre of location of symmetrical populations, *Bulletin of the Calcutta Stat. Assoc.* 4, '51, 33–35, [128]
51 Bhattacharyya, A., On the measure of divergence of two multinomial populations, *S* 7, '46, 401–06, [448, 462]
52 Bienaymé, J., Considérations à l'appuie de la découverte de Laplace sur la loi des probabilitiés dans la méthode des moindres carrés, *Compte Rendus* (Paris) 37, 1853, 309–26, [87]
53 Billingsley, P., Asymptotic distributions of two goodness of fit criteria, *AMS* 27, '56, 1123–29, [462]
54 Birnbaum, Z. W., On random variables with comparable peakedness, *AMS* 19, '48, 76–81, [102]
55 Birnbaum, Z. W., Numerical tabulation of the distribution of Kolmogorov's statistic for finite sample size, *JASA* 47, '52, 425–41, [325–29]
56 Birnbaum, Z. W., Distribution-free tests of fit for continuous distribution functions, *AMS* 24, '53, 1–8, [317, 324, 329, 352, 362]
57 Birnbaum, Z. W., On the power of a one-sided test of fit for continuous probability functions, *AMS* 24, '53, 484–89, [324]
58 Birnbaum, Z. W., Raymond, J., and Zuckerman, H. S., A generalization of Tshebyshev's inequality to two dimensions, *AMS* 18, '47, 70–79, [101, 109]

59 Birnbaum, Z. W., and Rubin, H., On distribution-free statistics, *AMS* 25, '54, 593–98, [317, 352]

60 Birnbaum, Z. W., and Tingey, F. H., One-sided confidence contours for probability distribution functions, *AMS* 22, '51, 592–96, [324]

61 Birnbaum, Z. W., and Zuckerman, H. S., An inequality due to H. Hornich, *AMS* 15, '44, 328–29, [115]

62 Birnbaum, Z. W., and Zuckerman, H. S., A graphical determination of sample size for Wilks' tolerance limits, *AMS* 20, '49, 313–16, [250]

63 Blackman, J., On the approximation of a distribution function by an empiric distribution, *AMS* 26, '55, 256–67, [363]

64 Blackman, J., An extension of the Kolmogorov distribution, *AMS* 27, '56, 513–20, [329]

65 Blackman, J., Correction to "An extension of the Kolmogorov distribution", *AMS* 29, '58, 318–22, [329]

66 Blackwell, D., Conditional expectation and unbiased sequential estimation, *AMS* 18, '47, 105–10, [182, 410]

67 Blackwell, D., and Girshick, M. A., *Theory of games and statistical decisions*, *JWS*, '54, [29, 178, 184, 188, 189, 287, 348, 432, 436–39]

68 Blank, A. A., Existence and uniqueness of a uniformly most powerful randomized unbiased test for the binomial, *BA* 43, '56, 465–66, [186]

69 Block, H. D., Estimates of error for two modifications of the Robbins-Monro stochastic approximation process, *AMS* 28, '57, 1003–10, [203, 208, 209]

70 Blom, G., Transformations of the binomial, negative binomial, Poisson and χ^2 distributions, *BA* 41, '54, 302–16, [192]

71 Blum, J. R., and Fattu, N. A., Tests of goodness of fit, *Review of Educational Research* 24, '54, 467–87, [324, 329]

72 Boas, R. P., Jr., Representation of probability distributions by Charlier series, *AMS* 20, '49, 376–92, [48]

73 Bose, R. C., The patch number problem, *Science and Culture* 12, '46, 199–200, [77]

74 Bose, R. C., On a problem of two dimensional probability, *S* 10, '50, 13–28, [77]

75 Box, G. E. P., and Andersen, S. L., Permutation theory in the derivation of robust criteria and the study of departures from assumptions, *JRSSB* 17, '55, 1–34, [165]

76 Bradley, R. A., *The statistical sign test*, Rutgers Univ. (Notes), '55, [148, 201, 206]

77 Bradt, R. N., and Karlin, S., On the design and comparison of certain dichotomous experiments, *AMS* 27, '56, 390–409, [192]

78 Brown, G. W., and Mood, A. M., On median tests for linear hypotheses, *PSBS*, '51, 159–66, [74]

79 Buehler, R. J., Confidence intervals for the product of two binomial parameters, *JASA* 52, '57, 482–93

80 Burkholder, D. L., *On a certain class of stochastic approximation processes* (Thesis), University of North Carolina, '55, [393]

81 Burkholder, D. L., On a class of stochastic approximation processes, *AMS* 27, '56, 1044–59, [197, 203, 209, 393]

82 Burman, J. P., Sequential sampling formulas for a binomial population, *JRSSB* 8, '46, 98–103, [189]

83 Burr, I. W., Cumulative frequency functions, *AMS* 13, '42, 215–32, [48]

84 Camp, B. H., A new generalization of Tchebycheff's statistical inequality, *BAMS* 28, '22, 427–32, [95]

85 Camp, B. H., Further interpretations of the chi-square test, *JASA* 33, '38, 537–42, [462]

86 Camp, B. H., Generalization to N dimensions of inequalities of the Tchebycheff type, *AMS* 19, '48, 568–74, [110]

87 Camp, B. H., Approximation to the point binomial, *AMS* 22, '51, 130–31, [184]

88 Cantelli, F. P., Intorno ad un teorema fundementale della teoria del rischio, *Bolletino dell'Associazione degli Attuari Italiani, Milan*, '10, 1–23, [87]

89 Cantelli, F. P., Sui confini della probabilitá, *Atti del Congresso Internazional del Matematici, Bologna* 6, '28, 47–59, [88, 90]

90 Chang, L.-C., On the ratio of an empirical distribution function to the theoretical distribution function, *Acta Math. Sinica* 5, '55, 347–68, (Chinese; English summary), [336]

91 Chang, T.-T., On asymptotic expansions connected with sums of independent random variables, *Acta Math. Sinica* 5, '55, 91–108 (Chinese; English summary), [192]

92 Chapelon, J. M., Sur l'inégalité fondamentale du cacul des probabilités, *Bulletin de la Société Mathematique de France* 65, '37, 100–08, [109]

93 Chernoff, H., and Lehmann, E. L., The use of maximum likelihood estimates in χ^2 tests for goodness of fit, *AMS* 25, '54, 579–86, [455, 462, 463]

94 Chu, J. T., On the distribution of the sample median, *AMS* 26, '55, 112–16, [201, 206]

95 Chu, J. T., The "inefficiency" of the sample median for many familiar symmetric distributions, *BA* 42, '55, 520–21, [127, 128]

96 Chu, J. T., Some uses of quasi-ranges, *AMS* 28, '57, 173–80, [224]

97 Chung, K. L., The approximate distribution of Student's statistic, *AMS* 17, '46, 447–65, [164, 165]

98 Chung, K. L., Asymptotic distribution of the maximum cumulative sum of independent random variables, *BAMS* 54, '48, 1162–70, [192]

99 Chung, K. L., On the maximum partial sums of sequences of independent random variables, *TAMS* 64, '48, 205–33, [192]

100 Chung, K. L., An estimate concerning the Kolmogoroff limit distribution, *TAMS* 67, '49, 36–50, [329]

101 Chung, K. L., On a stochastic approximation method, *AMS* 25, '54, 463–83, [203, 209]

102 Churchill, E., Information given by odd moments, *AMS* 17, '46, 244–46, [85]

103 Clopper, C. J., and Pearson, E. S., The use of confidence or fiducial limits illustrated in the case of the binomial, *BA* 26, '34, 404–13, [186]
104 Cochran, W. G., The statistical analysis of field counts of diseased plants, *JRSSB* 3, '36, 49–67, [77]
105 Cochran, W. G., The χ^2 test of goodness of fit, *AMS* 23, '52, 315–45, [448, 459, 460, 462, 463]
106 Cole, R. H., Relations between moments of order statistics, *AMS* 22, '51, 308–10, [131]
107 Combes, B., Le probléme de la généralisation de l'inégalité de Bienaymé, *Bulletin Trimestriel de l'Institut des Actuaires Français* 52, '53, 61–69, [115]
108 Cornish, E. A., and Fisher, R. A., Moments and cumulants in the specification of distributions, *Revue de l'Instit. International Stat.* 5, '37, 307, [48]
109 Cox, D. R., Sequential tests for composite hypotheses, *PCPS* 48, '52, 290–99, [418]
110 Cox, D. R., The mean and coefficient of variation of range in small samples from non-normal populations, *BA* 41, '54, 469–81, [134, 167]
111 Cox, D. R., Some statistical methods connected with series of events, *JRSSB* 17, '55, 129–51, [373]
112 Cox, D. R., and Stuart, A., Some quick sign tests for trend in location and dispersion, *BA* 42, '55, 80–95, [72–74, 79]
113 Craig, C. C., On the Tchebycheff inequality of Bernstein, *AMS* 4, '33, 94–102, [100]
114 Craig, C. C., A new exposition and chart for the Pearson system of frequency curves, *AMS* 7, '36, 16–28, [48]
115 Cramer, G. F., An approximation to the binomial summation, *AMS* 19, '48, 592–94, [184]
116 Cramér, H., On the composition of elementary errors, *SA* 11, '28, 13–74 and 141–80, [362]
117 Cramér, H., Sus un nouveau théoréme-limite de la théorie des probabilitas, *Actualités, scientifiques et industrielles* (Paris), No. 736, '38, [48]
118 Cramér, H., *Mathematical methods of statistics*, Princeton Univ. Press, '46, [46, 115, 137, 175, 191, 200, 201, 206, 207, 214, 219, 224, 462]
119 Crow, E. L., Confidence intervals for a proportion, *BA* 43, '56, 423–35, [185, 186]
120 Dandekar, V. M., Certain modified forms of binomial and Poisson distributions, *S* 15, '55, 237–50, [192]
121 Daniels, H. E., Rank correlation and population models, *JRSSB* 12, '50, 171–81, [71, 72]
122 Daniels, H. E., Note on Durbin and Stuart's formula for $E(r_s)$, *JRSSB* 13, '51, 310, [71, 72]
123 Daniels, H. E., Saddlepoint approximations in statistics, *AMS* 25, '54, 631–50, [48]
124 van Dantzig, D., Une nouvelle généralisation de l'inégalité de Bienaymé, *Annals of the Institute of H. Poincaré* 12, '51, 31–43, [94, 95]

125 van Dantzig, D., and Hemelrijk, J., Statistical methods based on few assumptions, *Bulletin of the International Statistical Institute* 34 (2nd part), '54, 3–31, [71]

126 Darling, D. A., On a test for homogeneity and extreme values, *AMS* 23, '52, 450–56, [372]

127 Darling, D. A., On a class of problems related to the random division of an interval, *AMS* 24, '53, 239–53, [364, 365]

128 Darling, D. A., The Cramér-Smirnov test in the parametric case, *AMS* 26, '55, 1–20, [349]

129 Darling, D. A., The Kolmogorov-Smirnov, Cramér-von Mises tests, *AMS* 28, '57, 823–38, [301, 324, 329, 362, 372, 381]

130 Darling, D. A., and Erdös, P., A limit theorem for the maximum of normalized sums of independent random variables, *Duke Mathematical Journal* 23, '56, 143–55, [192]

131 David, F. N., On the P_{λ_n} test for randomness: Remarks, further illustration, and table for P_{λ_n} for given values of $-\log_{10}\lambda_n$, *BA* 26, '34, 1–11, [360]

132 David, F. N., On Neyman's "smooth" test for goodness of fit. I. Distribution of the criterion ψ^2 when the hypothesis tested is true, *BA* 31, '39, 191–99, [361]

133 David, F. N., A χ^2-"Smooth" test of fit, *BA* 34, '47, 299–310, [463–65]

134 David, F. N., A power function for tests of randomness in a sequence of alternatives, *BA* 34, '47, 335–39, [64]

135 David, F. N., Correlations between χ^2 cells, *BA* 35, '48, 418–22, [463]

136 David, F. N., Two combinatorial tests of whether a sample has come from a given population, *BA* 37, '50, 97–110, [475, 476]

137 David, F. N., An alternative form of χ^2, *BA* 37, '50, 448–51, [449]

138 David, F. N., and Johnson, N. L., Statistical treatment of censored data. Part I Fundamental formulae, *BA* 41, '54, 228–40, [136–38, 199, 200, 201, 370]

139 David, H. A., The distribution of range in certain non-normal populations, *BA* 41, '54, 463–68, [134]

140 David, H. T., and Kruskal, W. H., The WAGR *t*-test reaches a decision with probability one, *AMS* 27, '56, 797–805, [418]

141 David, S. T., Kendall, M. G., and Stuart, A., Some questions of distribution in the theory of rank correlation, *BA* 38, '51, 131–40, [71, 72]

142 deBoer, J., Sequential test with three possible decisions for testing an unknown probability, *Applied Scientific Research, Sect. B* 3, '53, 249–59, [189]

143 deMunter, P., Fonction de puissance de certains tests du caractére aléatoire d'un échantillon, *Acad. Roy. Belg. Bull. Cl. Sci.* (5) 42, '56, 291–312, [71, 72, 74]

144 de Oliveira, J. Tiago, Distribution-free tests of goodness of fitting for distribution functions, *Univ. de Lisboa. Revista da Faculdade de Ciencias. Serié A. Ciencias Matemáticas* 5, '55–'56, 113–18, [362]

145 Derman, C., Stochastic approximation, *AMS* 27, '56, 879–86, [203, 209, 393]

146 Derman, C., Non-parametric up-and-down experimentation, *AMS* 28, '57, 795–98, [203]

147 Dananda, P. H., The central limit theorem for m-dependent variables asymptotically stationary to second order, *PCPS* 50, '54, 287–92, [192]

148 Diananda, P. H., The central limit theorem for m-dependent variables, *PCPS* 51, '55, 92–95, [192]

149 Dixon, W. J., Power functions of the sign test and power efficiency for normal alternatives, *AMS* 24, '54, 467–73, [148]

150 Dixon, W. J., and Mood, A. M., The statistical sign test, *JASA* 41, '46, 557–66, [148]

151 Dodd, E. L., The problem of assigning a length to the cycle to be found in a simple moving average and a double moving average of chance data, *E* 9, '41, 25–37, [64, 65]

152 Donsker, M. D., Justification and extension of Doob's heuristic approach to the Kolmogorov-Smirnov theorems, *AMS* 23, '52, 277–81, [324, 329, 362]

153 Doob, J. L., Heuristic approach to Kolmogorov-Smirnov theorems, *AMS* 20, '49, 393–403, [324, 329, 362]

154 Downton, F., Least squares estimates using order observations, *AMS* 25, '54, 303–16, [128]

155 Durbin, J., and Stuart, A., Inversions and rank correlation coefficients, *JRSSB* 13, '51, 303–09, [71, 72]

156 Dvoretzky, A., On stochastic approximation, *PTBS* 1, '56, 39–55, [203, 208, 209]

157 Dvoretzky, A., Kiefer, J., and Wolfowitz, J., Asymptotic minimax character of the sample distribution function and of the classical multinomial estimator, *AMS* 27, '56, 642–69, [301]

158 van Eeden, C., and Benard, A., *General theorems on Wilcoxon's test for symmetry*, Mathematische Centrum. Amsterdam, Rept. S 209, '56, [148, 150, 152, 155, 156]

159 van Eeden, C., and Benard, A., A general class of distribution free tests for symmetry containing the tests of Wilcoxon and Fisher I, II, III, *PKNAWA* 60, '57, 382–408, [148, 150–53, 155, 156]

160 Elderton, W. P., *Frequency curves and correlation* (4th Ed.), Harren Press, '53, [48]

161 Elfving, G., and Whitlock, J. H., A simple trend test with application to Erythrocyte size data, *BS* 6, '50, 282–88, [71]

162 El Shanawany, M. R., An illustration of the accuracy of the χ^2 approximation, *BA* 26, '36, 179–87, [462]

163 Epstein, B., Tables for the distribution of the number of exceedances, *AMS* 25, '54, 762–68, [273–75]

164 Epstein, B., and Sobel, M., Life testing, *JASA* 48, '53, 486–502, [220, 290, 356]

165 Epstein, B., and Sobel, M., Sequential life tests in the exponential case, *AMS* 26, '55, 82–93, [420]

166 Esseen, C. G., Fourier analysis of distribution functions, *Acta Math.* 77, '44, 1–125, [48]

167 Feller, W., Generalization of a probability limit theorem of Cramér, *TAMS* 54, '43, 361–72, [48]
168 Feller, W., On the normal approximation to the binomial distribution, *AMS* 16, '45, 319–29, [184, 186]
169 Feller, W., The fundamental limit theorems in probability, *BAMS* 51, '45, 800–32, [192]
170 Feller, W., On the Kolmogorov-Smirnov limit theorems for empirical distributions, *AMS* 19, '48, 177–89, [324, 329]
171 Feller, W., The asymptotic distribution of the range of sums of independent random variables, *AMS* 22, '51, 427–32, [192]
172 Feuell, A. J., and Rybicka, S. M., Quality-control chart based on goodness-of-fit test, *Nature* 167, '51, 194–95, [462]
173 Finney, D. J., The significance of associations in a square point lattice, *JRSSB* 9, '47, 99–103, [77]
174 Fisher, R. A., On the interpretation of chi-square from contingency tables, and the calculation of *P*, *JRSS* 85, '22, 87–94, [462]
175 Fisher, R. A., The conditions under which χ^2 measures the discrepancy between observation and hypothesis, *JRSS* 87, '24, 442–50, [462]
176 Fisher, R. A., *The design of experiments*, Hafner Publishing Co. (5th Ed.), '49, [152]
177 Fisher, R. A., *Statistical methods for research workers* (12th Ed.), Oliver and Boyd, '54, [Table 2, Table 3]
178 Fisher, R. A., and Yates, F., *Statistical tables for biological, agricultural and medical research* (5th Ed.), Oliver and Boyd, '57, [76, 133, Table 3]
179 Fix, E., *Tables of the noncentral* χ^2, Univ. of Calif. Pub. in Stat. 1, '49, 15–19, [361, 452, 473]
180 Foster, F. G., and Stuart, A., Distribution-free tests in time series based on the breaking of records, *JRSSB* 16, '54, 1–22, [67, 71, 72, 74, 79]
181 Foster, F. G., and Teichroew, D., A sampling experiment on the powers of the records test for trend in a time series, *JRSSB* 17, '55, 115–21, [74]
182 Fraser, D. A. S., Sequentially determined statistically equivalent blocks, *AMS* 22, '51, 372–81, [235, 260–62, 269]
183 Fraser, D. A. S., Nonparametric tolerance regions, *AMS* 24, '53, 44–55, [235, 240, 261, 262, 269]
184 Fraser, D. A. S., Non-parametric theory: Scale and location parameters, *Canadian Journal of Mathematics* 6, '54, 46–68, [206, 207, 214, 240, 242, 254]
185 Fraser, D. A. S., Most powerful rank type tests, *AMS* 28, '57, 1040–43, [151]
186 Fraser, D. A. S., *Nonparametric methods in statistics*, *JWS*, '57, [30, 32, 49, 67, 71, 72, 76, 79, 126, 127, 148, 150, 152, 161, 192, 242, 243, 254, 261, 262, 269]
187 Fraser, D. A. S., and Guttman, I., Tolerance regions, *AMS* 27, '56, 162–79, [242, 243]
188 Fraser, D. A. S., and Wormleighton, R., Nonparametric estimation IV, *AMS* 22, '51, 294–98, [235, 261, 262, 269]
189 Frechét, M., Sur une limitation très générale de la dispersion de la médiane, *Journal de la Société Statistique de Paris* 81, '40, 67–76, [127, 128]

190 Frechét, M., A general relation between the mean and mode for a discontinuous variate, *AMS* 18, '47, 290–93, [115]

191 Freeman, M. F., and Tukey, J. W., Transformations related to the angular and the square root, *AMS* 21, '50, 607–11, [184]

192 Gayen, A. K., The distribution of "Student's" *t* in random samples of any size drawn from non-normal universes, *BA* 36, '49, 353–69, [164, 165]

193 Gayen, A. K., Significance of difference between the means of two non-normal samples, *BA* 37, '50, 399–408, [169]

194 Gayen, A. K., The inverse hyperbolic sine transformation on Student's *t* for non-normal samples, *S* 12, '52, 105–08, [165]

195 Geary, R. C., The distribution of "Student's" ratio for non-normal samples, *JRSSB* 3, '36, 178–84, [165]

196 Geffroy, J., Sur une propriété de l'ecart maximum entre les fonctions de répartition theorique et empirique d'un échantillon de *n* points à deux dimensions, *CR* 242, '56, 2283–85, [374]

197 Gheorghiu, S., Quelques problémes concernant la division d'un segment par des points pris au hasard, *Acad. R.P. Romîne Stud. Cerc. Mat.* 6, '55, 243–72 (Romanian; French and Russian Summaries), [368, 369]

198 Ghosh, B., Topographic variation in statistical fields, *Bull. of the Calcutta Stat. Assoc.* 2, '49, 11–28, [77]

199 Ghosh, M. N., A test for field uniformity based on the space correlation method, *S* 9, '48, 39–46, [77]

200 Ghosh, M. N., Asymptotic distribution of serial statistics and applications to problems of nonparametric tests of hypotheses, *AMS* 25, '54, 218–51, [67–69, 71]

201 Ghurye, S. G., On the use of Student's *t*-test in an asymmetrical population, *BA* 36, '49, 426–30, [165]

202 Ghurye, S. G., and Robbins, H., Two-stage procedures for estimating the difference between means, *BA* 41, '54, 146–52, [130]

203 Girshick, M. A., Karlin, S., and Royden, H. L., Multistage statistical decision procedures, *AMS* 28, '57, 111–25, [184]

204 Girshick, M. A., Mosteller, F., and Savage, L. J., Unbiased estimates for certain binomial sampling problems with applications, *AMS* 17, '46, 13–23, [182, 410]

205 Girshick, M. A., and Savage, L. J., Bayes and minimax estimates for quadratic loss functions, *PSBS*, '51, [184]

206 Gnedenko, B. V., and Kolmogorov, A. N., *Limit distributions for sums of independent random variables*, Addison-Wesley, '54, [175, 192]

207 Gnedenko, B. V., and Mihalevič, V. S., On the distribution of the number of places in which one empirical distribution function exceeds another, *DAN* 82, '52, 841–43 (Russian), [372]

208 Godwin, H. J., On generalizations of Tchebychef's inequality, *JASA* 50, '55, 923–45, [87–92, 94–98, 100, 102, 103, 105–11]

209 Good, I. J., Saddle point methods for the multinomial distribution, *AMS* 28, '57, 861–81, [449, 462, 478]

210 Goodman, L. A., Kolmogorov-Smirnov tests for psychological research, *Psychological Bulletin* 51, '54, 160–68, [324, 329]
211 Grant, A. M., Some properties of runs in smoothed random series, *BA* 39, '52, 198–204, [64, 65]
212 Greenwood, R. E., and Glascow, M. O., Distribution of maximum and minimum frequencies in a sample drawn from a multinomial distribution, *AMS* 21, '50, 416–24, [477, 478]
213 Gronow, D. G. C., Non-normality in two-sample t-tests, *BA* 40, '53, 223–25, [169]
214 Gumbel, E. J., Simple tests for given hypotheses, *BA* 32, '42, 317–33, [362]
215 Gumbel, E. J., On the reliability of the classical χ^2 test, *AMS* 14, '43, 253–63, [462]
216 Gumbel, E. J., The maxima of the mean largest value and of the range, *AMS* 25, '54, 76–84, [113, 114]
217 Gumbel, E. J., and Carlson, P. G., On the asymptotic covariance of the sample mean and standard deviation, *Metron* 18, '56, 113–19, [137]
218 Gumbel, E. J., and Schelling, H. von, The distribution of the number of exceedances, *AMS* 21, '50, 247–62, [275]
219 Gurland, J., A moment inequality with application to the central limit theorem, *SA* 39, '56, 160–70, [107]
220 Guttman, L., An inequality for kurtosis, *AMS* 19, '48, 277–78, [88]
221 Guttman, L., A distribution-free confidence interval for the mean, *AMS* 19, '48, 410–13, [100]
222 Hájek, J., The asymptotic efficiency of a certain sequence of tests, *Čehoslovackiĭ Matematičeskiĭ Žurnal* 6 (81), '56, 26–30, [148, 150]
223 Hájek, J., and Rényi, A., Generalization of an inequality of Kolmogorov, *Hungarica Acta Mathematica* 6, '55, 281–83, [103]
224 Hald, A., *Statistical theory with engineering applications*, *JWS*, '52, [64, 65, 67, 68, 71, 184, 186]
225 Haldane, J. B. S., The exact value of the moments of the distribution of χ^2, used as a test of goodness of fit, when expectations are small, *BA* 29, '37, 133–43, [462]
226 Haldane, J. B. S., On a method of estimating frequencies, *BA* 33, '45, 222–25, [182, 410]
227 Haldane, J. B. S., Substitutes for χ^2, *BA* 42, '55, 265–66, [449]
228 Haldane, J. B. S., and Smith, C. A. B., A simple exact test for the birth-order effect, *AE* 14, '47–'49, 117–24, [71]
229 Halmos, P. R., The theory of unbiased estimation, *AMS* 17, '46, 34–44, [49, 126, 181]
230 Hamaker, H. C., "Average Confidence" limits for binomial probabilities, *Revue de l'Institut International de Statistique* 21, '53, 17–27, [185, 186]
231 Harris, L. B., On a limiting case for the distribution of exceedances with an application to life testing, *AMS* 23, '52, 295–98, [275]
232 Hartley, H. O., and David, H. A., Universal bounds for mean range and extreme observation, *AMS* 25, '54, 85–99, [113, 114]

233 Hatke, M. A., A certain cumulative probability function, *AMS* 20, '49, 461–63, [48]

234 Hawkins, D. T., A new method of approximating the binomial and hypergeometric probabilities, *Journal of the Royal Statistical Society of New South Wales* 81, '47, 38–47, [184]

235 Hemelrijk, J., *Tests for symmetry and other applications of the theory of Neyman and Pearson*, Univ. of Amsterdam (Ph.D. thesis), '50, [155]

236 Hemelrijk, J., *A symmetry test*, Mathematische Centrum, Amsterdam, rept. ZW-1950-015, '50 (Dutch), [155]

237 Hemelrijk, J., A family of parameter-free tests for symmetry with respect to a given point, I, II, *PKNAW* 53, '50, 945–55 and 1186–98, [141, 155]

238 Hemelrijk, J., A theorem on the sign test when ties are present, *PKNAWA* 55, '52, 322–26, [148, 215]

239 Hodges, J. L., Jr., and Lehmann, E. L., Some problems in minimax point estimation, *AMS* 21, '50, 182–97, [129, 181, 192]

240 Hodges, J. L., Jr., and Lehmann, E. L., Testing the approximate validity of statistical hypotheses, *JRSSB* 16, '54, 216–68, [466]

241 Hodges, J. L., Jr., and Lehmann, E. L., The efficiency of some nonparametric competitors of the *t*-test, *AMS* 27, '56, 324–35, [148, 150]

242 Hodges, J. L., Jr., and Lehmann, E. L., Two approximations to the Robbins-Monro process, *PTBS* 1, '56, 95–104, [203, 209]

243 Hoeffding, W., A class of statistics with asymptotically normal distribution, *AMS* 19, '48, 293–325, [49, 71, 72, 126, 127]

244 Hoeffding, W., The large sample power of tests based on permutations of observations, *AMS* 23, '52, 169–93, [40, 76, 152]

245 Hoeffding, W., On the distribution of the expected values of order statistics, *AMS* 24, '53, 93–100, [301]

246 Hoeffding, W., The extreme of the expected value of a function of independent random variables, *AMS* 26, '55, 268–75, [85]

247 Hoeffding, W., On the distribution of the number of successes in independent trials, *AMS* 27, '56, 713–21, [190]

248 Hoeffding, W., The role of assumptions in statistical decisions, *PTBS* 1, '56, 105–14, [165]

249 Hoeffding, W., and Robbins, H., The central limit theorem for dependent random variables, *Duke Mathematical Journal* 15, '48, 773–80, [192]

250 Hoeffding, W., and Rosenblatt, J. R., The efficiency of tests, *AMS* 26, '55, 52–63, [148, 324]

251 Hoeffding, W., and Shrikhande, S. S., Bounds for the distribution function of a sum of independent identically distributed random variables, *AMS* 26, '55, 439–49, [102]

252 Hoel, P. G., On the chi-square distribution for small samples, *AMS* 9, '38, 158–65, [459, 462]

253 Hoel, P. G., *Introduction to mathematical statistics* (2nd Ed.), *JWS*, '54, [348]

254 Homma, T., On the limit distributions of some ranges, *Reports of Stat. Application Res., Union of Japanese Scientists and Engineers* 1, '52, 15–26, [192]

255 Hotelling, H., and Pabst, M. R., Rank correlation and tests of significance involving no assumption of normality, *AMS* 7, '36, 29–43, [72]

256 Hsu, P. L., The approximate distributions of the mean and variance of a sample of independent variables, *AMS* 16, '45, 1–29, [192]

257 Hsu, P. L., On the approximate distribution of ratios, *AMS* 16, '45, 204–10, [192]

258 Irwin, J. O., A note on the subdivision of χ^2 into components, *BA* 36, '49, 130–34, [448, 462]

259 Ivanoic, B., Précision de la déviation standards pour une répartition quelconque, *Srpska Akademija Nauka, Zbornik Radova* 18, '52, 173–80 (Serbo-Croatian, French), [87]

260 Jacobson, P. H., The relative power of three statistics, *JASA* 42, '47, 575–84, [220]

261 Jiřina, M., Sequential estimation of distribution-free tolerance limits, *Čehoslovackiĭ Matematičeskiĭ Žurnal* 2 (77), '52, 221–32 (Russian; English summary); also *Correction* 3 (78): '53, 283, [242]

262 Johns, M. V., Jr., Nonparametric empirical Bayes procedures, *AMS* 28, '57, 649–69, [179, 184]

263 Johnson, N. L., and Rogers, C. A., The moment problem for unimodal distributions, *AMS* 22, '51, 433–39, [115]

264 Jones, H. L., Formulas for the group sequential sampling of attributes, *AMS* 23, '52, 72–87 [182, 189, 410, 413]

265 Jung, J., On linear estimates defined by continuous weight function, *Arkiv för Matematik* 15, '55, 199–209, [128]

266 Kac, M., On deviations between theoretical and empirical distributions, *PNAS* 35, '49, 252–57, [329, 362, 372]

267 Kac, M., Kiefer, J., and Wolfowitz, J., On tests of normality and other tests of goodness of fit based on distance methods, *AMS* 26, '55, 189–211, [329, 362]

268 Kallianpur, G., On a limit theorem for dependent random variables, *DAN* 101, '55, 13–16 (Russian), [192]

269 Kaplansky, I., The asymptotic distribution of runs of consecutive elements, *AMS* 16, '45, 200–03, [75]

270 Kaplansky, I., and Riordan, J., The problem of the rooks and its applications, *Duke Mathematical Journal* 13, '46, 259–68

271 Keeping, E. S., The problem of birth ranks, *BS* 8, '52, 112–19, [71]

272 Kemperman, J. H. B., Generalized tolerance limits, *AMS* 27, '56, 180–86, [235, 261, 262, 269]

273 Kendall, M. G., A new measure of rank correlation, *BA* 30, '38, 81–93, [71]

274 Kendall, M. G., Note on the distribution of quantiles for large samples, *JRSSB* 7, '40–'41, 83–85, [138]

275 Kendall, M. G., *The advanced theory of statistics, Vol. I*, Charles Griffin and Company, '47, [48]

276 Kendall, M. G., *Rank Correlation methods* (2nd Ed.), Hafner Publishing Company, '55, [71, 72]

277 Kendall, M. G., Kendall, S. F. H., and Smith, B. B., The distribution of Spearman's coefficient of rank correlation in a universe in which all rankings occur an equal number of times, *BA* 30, '38, 251–73, [71, 72]
278 Kerawala, S. M., On bounds of skewness and kurtosis, *Bull. of the Calcutta Math. Soc.* 40, '48, 41–44, [115]
279 Kermack, W. O., and McKendrick, A. G., Some distributions associated with a randomly arranged set of numbers, *Proc. of the Royal Soc. of Edinburgh* 57, '36–'37, 332–76, [65, 68]
280 Khamis, S. H., On the reduced moment problem, *AMS* 25, '54, 113–22, [105]
281 Kiefer, J., *K*-sample analogues of the Kolmogorov-Smirnov and Cramér-v. Mises tests, *AMS* 30, '59, 420–47, [362, 473]
282 Kimball, B. F., Some basic theorems for developing tests of fit for the case of the non-parametric probability distribution function, I, *AMS* 18, '47, 540–48, [365]
283 Kimball, B. F., On the asymptotic distribution of the sum of powers of unit frequency differences, *AMS* 21, '50, 263–71, [365]
284 Kivéliovitch, M., and Vialar, J., Quelques nouveaux tests pour l'étude des séries chronologiques II, *Journal Sci. Météoral.* 6, '54, 151–66, [66]
285 Kolmogoroff, A. N., Über die Summen durch den Zufall bestimmter unabhängiger Grössen, *Mathematische Annalen* 99, '28, 309–19, [103]
286 Kolmogoroff, A. N., Bemerkungen zu meiner Arbeit "Über die Summen Zufalligen Grössen", *Mathematische Annalen* 102, '29, 484–88, [103]
287 Kolmogoroff, A. N., Confidence limits for an unknown distribution, *AMS* 12, '41, 461–63, [308, 324, 328, 329]
288 Kolmogorov, A. N., Sulla determinazione empirica di une legge di distribuzione, *Giornale dell'Institute Italiano degli Attuari* 4, '33, 83–91, [328, 329]
289 Kondo, T., Evaluation of some $\omega_n{}^2$ distribution, *Jour. of the Gakugei College, Tokushima Univ.* 4, '54, 45–47, [474]
290 Konijn, H. S., Some nonparametric tests for treatment effect in paired replications, *JISAS* 9, '57, 145–67, [147, 148, 150, 152, 156]
291 Koopman, B. O., Necessary and sufficient conditions for Poisson's distribution, *PAMS* 1, '50, 813–23, [191]
292 Korolyuk, V. S., Asymptotic expansions for A. N. Kolmogorov's and N. V. Smirnov's criteria of fit, *DAN* 55, '54, 443–46 (Russian), [324, 329]
293 Korolyuk, V. S., On the discrepancy of empiric distributions for the case of two independent samples, *Investiya Akademii Nauk SSSR Seriya Matemat.* 19, '55, 81–86 (Russian), [329]
294 Kozelka, R. M., Approximate upper percentage points for extreme values in multinomial sampling, *AMS* 27, '56, 507–12, [477, 478]
295 Krishna Iyer, P. V., The theory of probability distributions of points on a line, *JISAS* 1, '48, 173–95, [64, 65]
296 Krishna Iyer, P. V., The first and second moments of some probability distributions arising from points on a lattice and their application, *BA* 36, '49, 135–41, [77]
297 Krishna Iyer, P. V., The theory of probability distributions of points on a lattice, *AMS* 21, '50, 198–217, [77]

298 Krishna Iyer, P. V., Further contributions to the theory of probability distributions of points on a line—II, *JISAS* 3, '51, 80–93, [64, 65]

299 Krishna Iyer, P. V., Further contributions to the theory of probability distributions of points on a line—III, *JISAS* 4, '52, 50–71, [67]

300 Krishna Iyer, P. V., Factorial moments and cumulants of distributions arising in Markoff chains, *JISAS* 4, '52, 113–23, [77]

301 Kullback, S., and Leibler, R. A., On information and sufficiency, *AMS* 22, '51, 79–86, [186, 462, 463]

302 Lal, D. N., A note on a form of Tchebycheff's inequality for two or more variables, *S* 15, '55, 317–20, [108, 110]

303 Lancaster, H. O., A reconciliation of χ^2, considered from metrical and enumerative aspects, *S* 13, '53, 1–10, [448, 462]

304 Lawley, D. N., A general method for approximating to the distribution of the likelihood ratio criteria, *BA* 43, '56, 295–303, [343]

305 Lehmann, E. L., A general concept of unbiasedness, *AMS* 22, '51, 587–92, [296, 350, 373]

306 Lehmann, E. L., A theory of some multiple decision problems, I, *AMS* 28, '57, 1–25, [302, 303, 329, 373]

307 Lehmann, E. L., and Stein, C., On the theory of some non-parametric hypotheses, *AMS* 20, '49, 28–45, [33, 56, 71, 76, 152, 161, 192]

308 Lehmann, E. L., and Stein, C., Completeness in the sequential case, *AMS* 21, '50, 376–85, [182, 410]

309 Leser, C. E. V., Inequalities for multivariate frequency distributions, *BA* 32, '42, 284–93, [110]

310 Levene, H., On the power function of tests of randomness based on runs up and down, *AMS* 23, '52, 34–56, [67–69]

311 Levene, H., and Wolfowitz, J., The covariance matrix of runs up and down, *AMS* 15, '44, 58–69, [67–69]

312 Lewis, D., and Burke, C. J., The use and misuse of the chi-square test, *Psychological Bulletin* 46, '49, 433–89, [462]

313 Lindley, D. V., On the measure of the information provided by an experiment, *AMS* 27, '56, 986–1005, [422]

314 Lindley, D. V., Binomial sampling schemes and the concept of information, *BA* 44, '57, 179–86, [186]

315 Lloyd, E. H., Least squares estimation of location and scale parameters using order statistics, *BA* 39, '52, 88–95, [128]

316 Ludwig, O., Über die stochastiche Theorie der Merkmalsiterationen, *Mitteilungsblatt für Mathematische Statistik* 8, '56, 49–82, [64, 65]

317 Lurquin, C., Sur un théorème de limite pour la probabilité au sens de Bienaymé, *Bulletin Acad. Bruxelles* (5) 14, '28, 641–58, [92]

318 Lurquin, C., Sur une inégalité fondamentale de probabilité, *Comptes Rendus* (Paris) 187, '28, 868–70, [87]

319 McNemar, Q., *Psychological statistics*, *JWS*, '55, [72]

320 Mack, C., An exact formula for $Q_k(n)$, the probable number of k-aggregates in a random distribution of n points, *Philosophical Magazine* (7) 39, '48, 778–90, [373]

321 MacStewart, W., A note on the power of the sign test, *AMS* 12, '41, 468–70, [147, 148]

322 Madow, W. G., On the limiting distributions of estimates based on samples from finite universes, *AMS* 19, '48, 535–45, [192]

323 Mainland, D., Statistical methods in medical research, *Canadian Jour. of Res., Sect. E* 26, '48, 1–166, [462]

324 Mallows, C. L., Generalizations of Tchebycheff's inequalities, *JRSSB* 18, '56, 139–76, [91, 95]

325 Malmquist, S., On a property of order statistics from a rectangular distribution, *SA* 33, '50, 214–22, [360, 373]

326 Malmquist, S., On certain contours for distribution functions, *AMS* 25, '54, 523–33, [309, 330, 331, 333]

327 Maniya, G. M., Generalization of the criterion of A. N. Kolmogorov for an estimate for the law of distribution for empirical data, *DAN* 69, '49, 495–97 (Russian), [333]

328 Mann, H. B., On a test for randomness based on signs of differences, *AMS* 16, '45, 193–99, [67]

329 Mann, H. B., Non-parametric tests against trend, *E* 13, '45, 245–59, [71, 72]

330 Mann, H. B., and Wald, A., On the choice of the number of intervals in the application of the chi-square test, *AMS* 13, '42, 306–17, [442, 462]

331 Mann, H. B., and Wald, A., On stochastic limit and order relationships, *AMS* 14, '43, 217–26, [44]

332 Markoff, A., Démonstration de certaines inégalités de M. Tchébychef, *Mathematische Annalen* 24, '84, 172–80, [87]

333 Marsaglia, G., Iterated limits and the central limit theorem for dependent variables, *PAMS* 5, '54, 987–91, [192]

334 Marshall, A. W., and Walsh, J. E., Some tests for comparing percentage points of two arbitrary continuous populations, *Proc. Internat. Congress of Mathematicians* 1, '50 (published '52), 582–83, [227]

335 Maruyama, G., Fourier analytic treatment of some problems on the sums of random variables, *Nat. Sci. Rep. Ochanomizu Univ.* 6, '55, 7–24, [192]

336 Massey, F. J., Jr., A note on the estimation of a distribution function by confidence limits, *AMS* 21, '50, 116–19, [329]

337 Massey, F. J., Jr., A note on the power of a non-parametric test, *AMS* 21, '50, 440–43, [329]

338 Massey, F. J., Jr., The Kolmogorov-Smirnov test for goodness of fit, *JASA* 46, '51, 68–78, [328, 329]

339 Matusita, K., On estimation by the minimum distance method, *AISM* 5, '54, 59–65, [479]

340 Matusita, K., Decision rules, based on the distance, for problems of fit, two samples, and estimation, *AMS* 26, '55, 631–40, [479]

341 Matusita, K., and Akaike, H., Decision rules, based on distance for the problems of independence, invariance, and two samples, *AISM* 7, '56, 67–80, [479]

342 Mauldon, J. G., Random division of an interval, *PCPS* 47, '51, 331–36, [368]

343 Meidell, B., Sur un probleme du calcul des probabilités et les statistiques mathématiques, *Comptes Rendus* (Paris) 175, '22, 806–08, [95]
344 Merrington, M., and Thompson, C. M., Tables of percentage points of the inverted beta (F) distribution, *BA* 33, '43–'46, 73–88, [Table 4]
345 Midzuno, H., On certain groups of inequalities (confidence intervals for the mean), *AISM* 2, '50, 21–33, [101]
346 Miller, L. H., Table of percentage points of Kolmogorov statistics, *JASA* 51, '56, 11–21, [321–24, 329]
347 von Mises, R., *Warscheinlichkeitsrechnung*, Leipzig-Wien, '31, [362]
348 von Mises, R., Sur une inégalité pour les moments d'une distribution quasi-convexe, *Bulletin des Sciences Mathématiques* (2) 62, '38, 68–71, [94]
349 von Mises, R., The limits of a distribution function if two expected values are given, *AMS* 10, '39, 99–104, [88]
350 von Mises, R., On the asymptotic distribution of differentiable statistical functions, *AMS* 18, '47, 309–48, [362]
351 Mood, A. M., The distribution theory of runs, *AMS* 11, '40, 367–92, [64, 65]
352 Mood, A. M., *Introduction to the theory of statistics*, *MH*, '50, 394–98, [225, 226]
353 Moore, G. H., and Wallis, W. A., Times series significance tests based on signs of differences, *JASA* 38, '43, 153–64, [67, 68]
354 Moore, P. G., A test for randomness in a sequence of two alternatives involving a 2×2 table, *BA* 35, '49, 305–16, [64]
355 Moore, P. G., A sequential test for randomness, *BA* 40, '53, 111–15, [77]
356 Moran, P. A. P., The random division of an interval, *JRSSB* 9, '47, 92–98, [365]
357 Moran, P. A. P., Random associations on a lattice, *PCPS* 43, '47, 321–28, [77]
358 Moran, P. A. P., Rank correlation and permutation distributions, *PCPS* 44, '48, 142–44, [71]
359 Moran, P. A. P., The interpretation of statistical maps, *JRSSB* 10, '48, 243–51, [77]
360 Moran, P. A. P., A curvilinear ranking test, *JRSSB* 12, '50, 292–95, [74]
361 Moriguti, S., Extremal properties of extreme value distributions, *AMS* 22, '51, 523–36, [114]
362 Moriguti, S., A lower bound for a probability moment of any absolutely continuous distribution with finite variance, *AMS* 23, '52, 286–89, [115]
363 Moriguti, S., Bounds for second moments of the sample range, *Reports of Stat. Application Res. Union of Japanese Scientists and Engineers* 3, '54, 57–64, [114]
364 Moses, L. E., Non-parametric statistics for psychological research, *Psychological Bulletin* 49, '52, 122–43, [152]
365 Mosteller, F., Note on an application or runs to quality control charts, *AMS* 12, '41, 228–32, [65, 66]
366 Mosteller, F., On some useful "inefficient" statistics, *AMS* 17, '46, 377–408, [128]

367 Mosteller, F., and Bush, R. R., Selected quantitative techniques, *Handbook of social psychology*, Addison-Wesley, '54, 289–334, [192]
368 Mosteller, F., and Tukey, J. W., The uses and usefulness of binomial probability paper, *JASA* 44, '49, 174–212, [184, 186, 192]
369 Mulholland, H. P., On distributions for which the Hartley-Khamis solution of the moment problem is exact, *BA* 38, '51, 74–89, [48]
370 Murphy, R. B., Non-parametric tolerance limits, *AMS* 19, '48, 581–89, [247–49]
371 Murty, V. N., The distribution of the quotient of maximum values in sampling from a rectangular population, *JASA* 50, '55, 1136–41, [373]
372 Nagler, H., On the best unbiased quadratic estimate of the variance, *BA* 37, '50, 444–45, [126]
373 Nair, A. N. K., Distribution of Students' "t" and the correlation coefficient in samples from non-normal populations, *S* 5, '41, 383–400, [163]
374 Nair, K. R., A note on the exact distribution of λ_n, *S* 3, '37, 171–74, [360]
375 Nair, K. R., The median in tests by randomization, *S* 4, '40, 543–50, [153]
376 Nandi, H. K., Use of well-known statistics in sequential analysis, *S* 8, '48, 339–44, [418]
377 Narumi, S., On further inequalities with possible application to problems in the theory of probability, *BA* 15, '23, 245–53, [96]
378 National Bureau of Standards, Applied Math. Series 6, *Tables of the binomial probability distribution*, '50, [147, 186, 190]
379 Navarro, S., On a generalization of Pearson curves, *Las Ciencas*, 17, '52, 435–41, [48]
380 Neyman, J., "Smooth test" for goodness of fit, *SA* 20, '37, 149–99, [361]
381 Neyman, J., Contribution to the theory of the χ^2 test, *PBS*, '49, 239–73, [449, 455, 462, 463]
382 Neyman, J., Sur une famille de tests asymptotiques des hypotheses statistiques composees, *TE* 5, '54, 161–68, [342]
383 Neyman, J., and Pearson, E. S., On the use and interpretation of certain test criteria for purposes of statistical inference, Part I, *BA* 20A, '28, 175–240, [348, 386]
384 Neyman, J., and Pearson, E. S., On the use and interpretation of certain test criteria for purposes of statistical inference, Part II, *BA* 20A, '28, 263–94, [348, 386, 462, 463]
385 Neyman, J., and Pearson, E. S., Further notes on the χ^2 distribution, *BA* 22, '31, 298–305, [456, 462, 463]
386 Noether, G. E., On confidence limits for quantiles, *AMS* 19, '48, 416–19, [206]
387 Noether, G. E., Confidence limits in the non-parametric case, *JASA* 44, '49, 89–100, [186, 301–03, 320, 382, 383]
388 Noether, G. E., Asymptotic properties of the Wald-Wolfowitz test of randomness, *AMS* 21, '50, 231–46, [71]
389 Noether, G. E., On a connection between confidence and tolerance intervals, *AMS* 22, '51, 603–04, [261]

390 Noether, G. E., Two sequential tests against trend, *JASA* 51, '56, 440–50, [77]
391 Noether, G. E., *The efficiency of nonparametric methods*, Boston Univ. Math. Dept., 1 Dec. '57, [31]
392 Offord, A. C., An inequality for sums of independent random variables, *Proc. of the London Math. Soc.* (2) 48, '45, 467–77, [100]
393 Okamoto, M., On a non-parametric test, *Osaka Mathematics Jour.* 4, '52, 77–85, [476]
394 Okamoto, M., Unbiasedness in the test of goodness of fit, *Osaka Mathematics Jour.* 4, '52, 211–14, [462, 476]
395 Okamoto, M., Some combinatorial tests of goodness of fit, *Osaka Mathematics Jour.* 4, '53, 215–28, [477]
396 Olds, E. G., Distributions of sums of squares of rank differences for small numbers of individuals, *AMS* 9, '38, 133–48, [71, 72]
397 Olds, E. G., The 5% significance levels for sums of squares of rank differences and a correction, *AMS* 20, '49, 117–18, [72]
398 Olekiewicz, M., Tables of expected values and variances of numbers of runs in random sequences with probabilities of exceeding expected values, *Annales Univ. Mariae-Curie-Sklodowska, Ser. A* 5, '51, 147–59 (Polish; Russian summary), [64]
399 Olmstead, P. S., Note on theoretical and observed distribution of repetitive occurrences, *AMS* 11, '40, 363–66, [192]
400 Olmstead, P. S., Distribution of sample arrangements for runs up and down, *AMS* 17, '46, 24–33, [68]
401 Owen, D. B., Tables for computing bivariate normal probabilities, *AMS* 27, '56, 1075–90, [332, 333]
402 Patnaik, P. B., The noncentral χ^2- and F-distributions and their applications, *BA* 36, '49, 202–32, [361, 452, 473]
403 Pearson, E. S., The probability integral transformation for testing goodness of fit and combining independent tests of significance, *BA* 30, '38, 134–48, [360, 361]
404 Pearson, E. S., and Adyanthāya, N. K., The distribution of frequency constants in small samples from symmetrical populations, *BA* 20A, '28, 356–60, [128, 134, 167]
405 Pearson, E. S. (assisted by N. K. Adyanthāya and others), The distribution of frequency constants in small samples from non-normal symmetrical and skew populations, 2nd paper: The distribution of "Student's" *z*, *BA* 21, '29, 259–86, [163]
406 Pearson, K., On the criterion that a given system of deviations from the probable in the case of a correlated system of variables is such that it can reasonably supposed to have arisen from random sampling, *Philosophical Magazine 5 Series* 50, '00, 157–72, [462]
407 Pearson, K., On generalized Tchebycheff theorems in the mathematical theory of statistics, *BA* 12, '19, 284–96, [87, 108]
408 Pearson, K., *Tables of the incomplete beta function*, Cambridge Univ. Press, '48, [184, 186, 190]

409 Pearson, K., Experimental discussion of the (χ^2, P) test for goodness of fit, *BA* 24, '32, 351–81, [458, 462]

410 Pearson, K., On a method of determining whether a sample of size n supposed to have been drawn from a parent population having a known probability integral has probably been drawn at random, *BA* 25, '33, 379–410, [360]

411 Pearson, K., On a new method of determining "goodness of fit", *BA* 26, '34, 425–42, [360]

412 Peterson, R. P., Uniformly best constant risk and minimax point estimates, *Journal of Research, National Bureau of Standards* 48, '52, 49–53, [184]

413 Petrov, V. V., Extension of Cramér's limit theorem to non-identically distributed independent quantities, *Vestnik Leningrad. Univ.* 8, '53, 13–25 (Russian), [192]

414 Petrov, V. V., On precise estimates in limit theorems, *Vestnik Leningrad. Univ.* 10, '55, 57–58 (Russian), [192]

415 Picard, H. C., A note on the maximum value of kurtosis, *AMS* 22, '51, 480–82, [115]

416 Plackett, R. L., Limits of the ratio of mean range to standard deviation, *BA* 34, '47, 120–22, [113]

417 Plackett, R. L., Boundaries on minimum size in binomial sampling, *AMS* 19, '48, 575–80, [182, 189, 410]

418 Putter, J., The treatment of ties in some nonparametric tests, *AMS* 26, '55, 368–86, [148, 215]

419 Quenouille, M. H., The joint distribution of serial correlation coefficients, *AMS* 20, '49, 561–71, [71]

420 Quensel, C.-E., The distribution of second order moments in random samples from non-normal multivariate universes, *Lunds Univ. Arsskrift, Ny Foljt, Andra Avdelningen, Nova Series* 48, '52, 11, [165]

421 Raff, M. S., On approximating the point binomial, *JASA* 51, '56, 293–303, [184]

422 Raj, D., Relative efficiency of gauging and exact measurement in estimating the proportion of a population between given limits, *S* 15, '55, 191–96, [192]

423 Rényi, A., Some remarks on independent random variables, *Hungarica Acta Mathematica* 1, '49, 17–20, [104]

424 Rényi, A., On a new generalization of the central limit theorem of probability theory, *A Magyar Tudományos Akadémia Matematikai és Termeszettudományi Osztályának Kozleményei* 1, '51, 351–55 (Hungarian), [192]

425 Rényi, A., On the theory of order statistics, *Acta Mathematica Academiae Scientiarum Hungaricae* 4, '53, 191–232, [333–36]

426 Richter, H., Parameterfree Abschätzung und Realisierung von Erwartungswerten, *Blätter Deutscher Gesellschaft Versicherungs-Mathemat.* 3, '57, 147–62, [87, 88, 90, 91, 115]

427 Rider, P. R., On the distribution of the ratio of mean to standard deviation in small samples from non-normal universes, *BA* 21, '29, 124–43, [163]

428 Rider, P. R., The distribution of the product of ranges in samples from a rectangular population, *JASA* 48, '53, 546–49, [373]
429 Rider, P. R., The distribution of the product of maximum values in samples from a rectangular population, *JASA* 50, '55, 1142–43, [373]
430 Rider, P. R., The midrange of a sample as an estimator of the population midrange, *JASA* 52, '57, 537–43, [128]
431 Rietz, H. L., On the distribution of the "Student" ratio for small samples from certain non-normal populations, *AMS* 10, '39, 265–74, [163]
432 Robbins, H., On distribution-free tolerance limits in random samples, *AMS* 15, '44, 214–16, [242]
433 Robbins, H., Some remarks on the inequality of Tchebychef, *Courant Anniversary Vol.*, Interscience Publishers, '48, 345–50, [101]
434 Robbins, H., An empirical Bayes approach to statistics, *PTBS* 1, '56, 157–63, [192]
435 Robbins, H., and Monro, S., A stochastic approximation method, *AMS* 22, '51, 400–07, [197, 203]
436 Romaní, J., Nonparametric tests in sequential form, *TE* 7, '56, 43–96, (Spanish; English summary), [77, 218]
437 Romanovskiĭ, V. I., On inductive conclusions in statistics, *CRAS* 27, '40, 419–21 (Russian), [111]
438 Romanovskii, V. I., Quantile criteria for testing the hypothesis that a sample comes from a specified population, *Akad. Nauk Uzbek. SSR. Trudy Inst. Mat. Meh.* 11, '53, 12–15 (Russian), [371]
439 Rosander, A. C., The use of inversions as a test of random order, *JASA* 37, '42, 352–58, [71]
440 Rosenbaum, S., Tables for a nonparametric test of dispersion, *AMS* 24, '53, 663–68, [275]
441 Rosenblatt, M., Remarks on a multi-variate transformation, *AMS* 23, '52, 470–72, [376, 442]
442 Rosenblatt, M., Limit theorems associated with variants of the von Mises statistic, *AMS* 23, '52, 617–23, [376]
443 Rosenblatt, M., Remarks on some nonparametric estimates of a density function, *AMS* 27, '56, 832–37, [305]
444 Roy, J., On some quick decision methods in multivariate and univariate analysis, *S* 17, '56, 77–88, [346, 384]
445 Royden, H. L., Bounds on a distribution function when its first n moments are given, *AMS* 24, '53, 361–76, [90, 91, 96]
446 Ruist, E., Comparison of tests for non-parametric hypotheses, *Arkiv för Matematik* 3, '54, 133–63, [148, 150, 152, 155, 156, 160]
447 Rushton, S., On a sequential t-test, *BA* 37, '50, 326–33, [417, 418]
448 Rustagi, J. S., On minimizing and maximizing a certain integral with statistical applications, *AMS* 28, '57, 309–28, [115]
449 Sarhan, A. E., Estimation of the mean and standard deviation by order statistics, *AMS* 25, '54, 317–28, [128]
450 Sarhan, A. E., Estimation of the mean and standard deviation by order statistics. Part II, *AMS* 26, '55, 505–11, [128]

451 Sarhan, A. E., Estimation of the mean and standard deviation by order statistics. Part III, *AMS* 26, '55, 576–92, [128]

452 Sarhan, A. E., and Greenberg, B. G., Estimation of location and scale parameters by order statistics from singly and doubly censored samples, Part I. The normal distribution up to samples of size 10, *AMS* 27, '56, 427–51, [128]

453 Savage, I. R., Contributions to the theory of rank order statistics—the "trend" case *AMS* 28, '57, 968–77, [71, 73–75, 79]

454 Savage, I. R., On the independence of tests of randomness and other hypotheses, *JASA* 52, '57, 53–57, [56]

455 Savage, I. R., Nonparametric statistics, *JASA* 52, '57, 331–44, [71]

456 Savage, L. J., A uniqueness theorem for unbiased sequential binomial estimation, *AMS* 18, '47, 295–97, [182, 410]

457 Savage, L. J., *The foundations of statistics*, *JWS*, '54, [184]

458 Scheffé, H., On solutions of the Behrens-Fisher problem based on the t-distribution, *AMS* 14, '43, 35–44, [226]

459 Scheffé, H., Note on the use of tables of percentage points of the incomplete beta function to calculate small sample confidence intervals for binomial p, *BA* 33, '43–'46, 181, [186]

460 Scheffé, H., and Tukey, J. W., A formula for sample sizes for population tolerance limits, *AMS* 15, '44, 217, [246]

461 Scheffé, H., and Tukey, J. W., Nonparametric estimation, I. Validation of order statistics, *AMS* 16, '45, 187–92, [261, 262]

462 Schmid, P., Sur les théorèmes asymptotiques de Kolmogoroff et Smirnov pour des functions de distribution discontinues, *Comptes Rendus* (Paris) 243, '56, 349–51, [324, 329, 357]

463 Schützenberger, M. P., An *ABAC* for the sample range, *Psychometrika* 13, '48, 95–97, [246]

464 Schützenberger, M. P., Valeurs caractéristiques du coefficient de corrélation par rang de Kendall dans le cas general, *Comptes Rendus* (Paris) 226, '48, 2122–23, [71]

465 Scott, E. L., Distribution of the longitude of periastron of spectroscopic binaries, *Astrophysical Jour.* 109, '49, 194–207, [473]

466 Selberg, H. L., Über eine Ungleichung de Mathematischen Statistik, *SA* 23, '40, 114–20, [95]

467 Selberg, H. L., Zwei Ungleichnungen zur Ergängzung des Tchebycheffschen Lemmas, *SA* 23, '40, 121–25, [87]

468 Shenton, L. R., Efficiency of the method of moments and the Gram-Charlier type *A* distribution, *BA* 38, '51, 58–73, [48]

469 Sherman, B., A random variable related to the spacing of sample values, *AMS* 21, '50, 339–61, [364]

470 Sherman, B., Percentiles of the ω_n statistic, *AMS* 28, '57, 259–61, [364]

471 Shohat, J. A., Inequalities for moments of frequency functions and for various statistical constants, *BA* 21, '29, 361–70, [97]

472 Shohat, J. A., and Tamarkin, J. D., *The problems of moments*, Amer. Math. Soc. Publication, '43, 77–80, [91, 93, 94, 115]

473 Shone, K. J., Relations between the standard deviation and the distribution of range in non-normal populations, *JRSSB* 11, '49, 85–88, [134]

474 Siegel, S., *Nonparametric statistics: for the behavioral sciences, MH*, '56

475 Sillitto, G. P., Interrelations between certain linear systematic statistics of samples from any continuous population, *BA* 38, '51, 377–82, [130, 131]

476 Silverstone, H., A note on the cumulants of Kendall's *S*-distribution, *BA* 37, '50, 231–35, [71]

477 Simpson, P. B., Note on the estimation of a bivariate distribution function, *AMS* 22, '51, 476–78, [374, 384]

478 Smirnov, N. V., Sur la distribution de ω^2 criterium de M. R. v. Mises, *Comptes Rendus* (Paris) 202, '36, 449–52, [362]

479 Smirnov, N. V., On the distribution of the $\omega_n{}^2$ criterion of von Mises, *Rec. Math.* (*NS*) 2, '37, 963–93 (Russian), [362]

480 Smirnov, N. V., Sur les ecarts de la courbe de distribution empirique, *Rec. Math.* (*NS*) 6, '39, 3–26 (Russian; French summary), [324, 373]

481 Smirnov, N. V., Sur une critere de symétrie de la loi de distribution d'une variable aleatoire, *CRAS* 56, '47, 11–14, [155]

482 Smirnov, N. V., On the construction of confidence regions for the density distribution of random variables, *DAN* 74, '50, 189–91 (Russian), [345]

483 Smith, C. D., On generalized Tchebycheff inequalities in mathematical statistics, *Amer. Jour. of Math.* 52, '30, 109–26, [97]

484 Smith, C. D., On Tchebycheff approximation for decreasing functions, *AMS* 10, '39, 190–92, [97]

485 Smith, C. D., Tchebycheff inequalities as a basis for statistical tests, *Mathematics Magazine* 28, '55, 185–95, [97, 108, 111]

486 Smith, K., Distribution-free statistical methods and the concept of power efficiency, *Research methods in the behavioral sciences*, Dryden Press, '53, Chapter 12, [64, 71, 72]

487 Sobel, M., and Wald, A., A sequential test for choosing one of three hypotheses concerning the unknown mean of a normal distribution, *AMS* 20, '49, 502–22, [417, 418]

488 Sophister, Discussion of small samples drawn from an infinite skew population, *BA* 20A, '28, 389–423, [163, 167, 175]

489 Spearman, C., The proof and measurement of association between two things, *Amer. Jour. of Psychology* 15, '04, 72–101, [72]

490 Statistical Research Group, Columbia University, *Sequential analysis of statistical data: Applications*, Columbia Univ. Press, '45, [189]

491 Stein, C., Efficient nonparametric testing and estimation, *PTBS* 1, '56, 187–95, [154]

492 Steinhaus, H., The problem of estimation, *AMS* 28, '57, 633–48, [181, 184, 301, 381]

493 Stephan, F. F., The expected value and variance of the reciprocal and other negative powers of a positive Bernoullian variate, *AMS* 16, '45, 50–61, [192]

494 Stevens, W. L., Significance of grouping, *AE* 8, '37, 57–69, [77, 476]

495 Stevens, W. L., Distributions of groups in a sequence of alternatives, *AE* 9, '39, 10–17, [64]

496 Stevens, W. L., Shorter intervals for the parameter of the binomial and Poisson distributions, *BA* 44, '57, 436–40, [185, 186]

497 Stoker, D. J., *Oor 'n Klas van toetsingsgroothede vir die probleem van twee steekproeve*, Univ. of Amsterdam (Ph.D. Thesis), '55, [106]

498 Stuart, A., The correlation between variate-values and ranks in samples from a continuous distribution, *Brit. Jour. of Stat. Psychology* 7, '51, 37–44, [71, 72, 98]

499 Stuart, A., The power of two difference-sign tests, *JASA* 47, '52, 416–24, [67]

500 Stuart, A., Too good to be true?, *Applied Statistics* 3, '54, 29–32, [460, 462]

501 Stuart, A., Asymptotic relative efficiencies of distribution-free tests of randomness against normal alternatives, *JASA* 49, '54, 147–57, [64, 67, 71, 72, 79]

502 Stuart, A., The efficiencies of tests of randomness against normal regression, *JASA* 51, '56, 285–87, [67, 71–74, 79]

503 Stuart, A., The efficiency of the records test for trend in normal regression, *JRSSB* 19, '57, 149–53, [74]

504 Sukhatme, B. V., Random association of points on a lattice, *JISAS* 2, '49, 60-85, [77]

505 Sukhatme, B. V., On certain probability distributions arising from points on a line, *JRSSB* 13, '51, 219–32, [64]

506 Sukhatme, B. V., Joint asymptotic distribution of the median and a *U*-statistic, *JRSSB* 19, '57, 144–48, [192]

507 Swed, F., and Eisenhart, C., Tables for testing randomness of grouping in a sequence of alternatives, *AMS* 14, '43, 66–87, [64, 65]

508 Takashima, M., Tables for testing randomness by means of lengths of runs, *Bulletin of Math. Stat.* 6, '55, 17–23, [65]

509 Tate, M. W., and Clelland, R. C., *Nonparametric and shortcut statistics: in the social, biological, and medical sciences*, Interstate Printers and Publishers, Inc., '56, [192]

510 Tchebycheff, P. L., Des valeurs moyennes, *Jour. de Mathematiques (Liouville, 2nd Series)* 12, 1867, 177–84, [87]

511 Teichroew, D., Tables of expected values of order statistics and products of order statistics for samples of size twenty and less from the normal distribution, *AMS* 27, '56, 410–26, [76, 151]

512 Terpstra, T. J., A generalization of Kendall's rank correlation statistic I, *PKNAWA* 58, '55, 690–96, [71]

513 Terry, M. E., Some rank order tests which are most powerful against specific parametric alternatives, *AMS* 23, '52, 346–66, [76]

514 Thomas, M., Some tests for randomness in plant population, *BA* 38, '51, 102–11, [77, 476]

515 Thompson, C. M., Tables of percentage points of the incomplete beta function and of the chi-square distribution, *BA* 32, '41, 188–89, [Table 2]

516 Thompson, G. W., Bounds for the ratio of range to standard deviation, *BA* 42, '55, 268–69, [114]
517 Tocher, K. D., Extension of the Neyman-Pearson theory of tests to discontinuous variates, *BA* 37, '50, 130–44, [185, 186]
518 Todd, H., Note on random associations in a square point lattice, *JRSSB* 7, '40–'41, 78–82, [77]
519 Toranzos, F. I., An asymmetric bell-shaped frequency curve, *AMS* 23, '52, 467–69, [48]
520 Tsao, C. K., A simple procedure for testing statistical hypotheses, *AMS* 25, '54, 687–702, [425]
521 Tsao, C. K., Rank sum tests of fit, *AMS* 26, '55, 94–104, [347, 385]
522 Tsao, C. K., Distribution of the sum in random samples from a discrete population, *AMS* 27, '56, 703–12, [192]
523 Tukey, J. W., An inequality for deviations from medians, *AMS* 17, '46. 75–78, [115]
524 Tukey, J. W., Nonparametric estimation, II. Statistically equivalent blocks and tolerance regions—the continuous case, *AMS* 18, '47, 529–39, [235, 261, 262, 269]
525 Tukey, J. W., Nonparametric estimation, III. Statistically equivalent blocks and multivariate tolerance regions—the discontinuous case, *AMS* 19, '48, 30–39, [235, 261, 262, 269]
526 Tukey, J. W., *The simplest signed-rank tests*, Princeton Univ. Stat. Res. Group, Memo Rept. No. 17, July '49, [149, 150, 160, 173, 174]
527 Tukey, J.W., Sums of random partitions of ranks, *AMS* 28,'57, 987-92, [150]
528 Tumanyan, S. H., On the asymptotic distribution of the χ^2 criterion, *DAN* 94, '54, 1011–12 (Russian), [462]
529 Ulin, B., An extremal problem in mathematical statistics, *SA* 36, '53, 158–67, [95]
530 Uranisi, H., The distribution of statistics drawn from the Gram-Charlier Type A population, *Bulletin of Math. Stat.* 4, '50, 1–14, [165]
531 Vora, S. A., Bounds on the distribution of Chi-square, *S* 11, '51, 365–78, [112]
532 Votaw, D. F., Jr., The probability distribution of the measure of a random linear set, *AMS* 17, '46, 240–44, [373]
533 Waerden, B. L. van der, Testing a distribution function, *PKNAWA* 56, '53, 201–07, [324]
534 Wald, A., A generalization of the inequality of Markoff, *AMS* 9, '38, 244–55, [88]
535 Wald, A., Limits of a distribution function determined by absolute moments and inequalities satisfied by absolute moments, *TAMS* 46, '39, 280–306, [90]
536 Wald, A., An extension of Wilks' method for setting tolerance limits, *AMS* 14, '43, 45–55, [269]
537 Wald, A., Sequential tests of statistical hypotheses, *AMS* 16, '45, 117–86, [189]
538 Wald, A., Limit distribution of the maximum and minimum of successive cumulative sums of random variables, *BAMS* 53, '47, 142–53, [192]

539 Wald, A., *Sequential analysis*, *JWS*, '47, [186, 189, 394, 397, 404, 407, 413–15, 418, 421, 422, 424, 433, 439]
540 Wald, A., On the distribution of the maximum of successive cumulative sums of independently but not identically distributed chance variables, *BAMS* 54, '48, 422–30, [192]
541 Wald, A., *Statistical decision functions*, *JWS*, '50, [178, 184, 188, 189]
542 Wald, A., Asymptotic minimax solutions of sequential point estimation problems, *PSBS*, '51, 1–11, [184]
543 Wald, A., and Wolfowitz, J., Confidence limits for continuous distribution functions, *AMS* 10, '39, 105–18, [318, 324, 329]
544 Wald, A., and Wolfowitz, J., On a test of whether two samples are from the same population, *AMS* 11, '40, 147–62, [30, 64]
545 Wald, A., and Wolfowitz, J., Note on confidence limits for continuous distribution functions, *AMS* 12, '41, 118–19, [324, 329]
546 Wald, A., and Wolfowitz, J., An exact test for randomness in the nonparametric case based on serial correlation, *AMS* 14, '43, 378–88, [71]
547 Wald, A., and Wolfowitz, J., Optimum character of the sequential probability ratio test, *AMS* 19, '48, 326–39, [189]
548 Wallis, W. A., *Selected techniques of statistical analysis*, *MH*, '47, Chapter 1, [418]
549 Wallis, W. A., and Moore, G. H., A significance test for time series analysis, *JASA* 36, '41, 401–09, [68]
550 Wallis, W. A., and Moore, G. H., *A significance test for time series and other ordered observations*, Tech. Paper No. 1, Nat'l Bur. Econ. Res., N.Y., '41, [68]
551 Wallis, W. A., and Roberts, H. V., *Statistics, a new approach*, Free Press, '56, [64, 67, 71, 72]
552 Walsh, J. E., On the power function of the sign test for slippage of means, *AMS* 17, '46, 358–62, [148]
553 Walsh, J. E., *On the power function of a sign test formed by using subsamples*, Douglas Aircraft Co. (Project RAND), '48
554 Walsh, J. E., Some significance tests for the median which are valid under very general conditions, *AMS* 20, '49, 64–81, [159, 160]
555 Walsh, J. E., On the range-midrange test and some tests with bounded significance levels, *AMS* 20, '49, 257–67, [168, 173]
556 Walsh, J. E., Applications of some significance tests for the median which are valid under very general conditions, *JASA* 44, '49, 342–55, [160]
557 Walsh, J. E., Some estimates and tests based on the r smallest values in a sample, *AMS* 21, '50, 386–97, [220]
558 Walsh, J. E., On a generalization of the Behrens-Fisher problem, *Human Biology* 22, '50, 125–35, [226]
559 Walsh, J. E., Some bounded significance level properties of the equal-tail sign test, *AMS* 22, '51, 408–17, [170, 172]
560 Walsh, J. E., A large sample t-statistic which is insensitive to nonrandomness, *JASA* 46, '51, 79–88, [166]
561 Walsh, J. E., Large sample validity of the binomial distribution for lives with unequal mortality rates, *SA* 35, '52, 11–15, [191]

562 Walsh, J. E., Large sample confidence intervals for density function values at percentage points, *S* 12, '53, 265–76, [200, 201, 307, 344]
563 Walsh, J. E., Analytic tests and confidence intervals for the mean value, probabilities, and percentage points of a Poisson distribution, *S* 14, '54, 25–38, [191]
564 Walsh, J. E., Bounded significance level tests for comparing quantiles of two possibly different continuous populations, *AISM* 6, '55, 213–22, [227]
565 Walsh, J. E., The Poisson distribution as a limit for dependent binomial events with unequal probabilities, *Jour. of the Operations Res. Soc. of Amer.* 3, '55, 198–209, [191]
566 Walsh, J. E., Approximate probability values for observed number of "successes" from statistically independent binomial events with unequal probabilities, *S* 15, '55, 281–90, [190]
567 Walsh, J. E., Validity of approximate normality values for $\mu \pm k\sigma$ areas of practical type continuous populations, *AISM* 8, '56, 79–86, [175]
568 Walsh, J. E., Asymptotic efficiencies of a nonparametric life test for smaller percentiles of a gamma distribution, *JASA* 51, '56, 467–80, [220]
569 Walsh, J. E., Actuarial validity of the binomial distribution for large numbers of lives with small mortality probabilities, *SA* 39, '56, 39–46, [190, 191]
570 Walsh, J. E., Estimating population mean, variance, and percentage points from truncated data, *SA* 39, '56, 47–58, [135, 202]
571 Walsh, J. E., Nonparametric mean estimation of percentage points and density function values, *AISM* 8, '57, 167–80, [136, 199, 200, 201, 305, 306]
572 Walsh, J. E., Estimating future from past in life testing, *AMS* 28, '57, 432–41, [136, 201]
573 Walter, E., Über die Ausnützung der Irrtumswahrscheinlichkeit, *Mitteilungsblatt für Mathematische Statistik* 6, '54, 170–79, [148, 155, 215]
574 Watanabe, Y., On the ω^2 distribution, *Jour. of the Gakugei College, Tokushima Univ.* 2, '52, 21–30, [473, 474]
575 Watson, G. S., Sufficient statistics, similar regions and distribution-free tests, *JRSSB* 19, '57, 262–67, [76]
576 Weingarten, H., On the probability of large deviations for sums of bounded chance variables, *AMS* 27, '56, 1170–74, [103]
577 Weiss, L., A certain class of tests of fit, *AMS* 27, '56, 1165–70, [365]
578 Weiss, L., The convergence of certain functions of sample spacings, *AMS* 28, '57, 778–82, [373]
579 Weiss, L., The asymptotic power of certain tests of fit based on sample spacings, *AMS* 28, '57, 783–86, [365]
580 Weiss, L., Tests of fit in the presence of nuisance location and scale parameters, *AMS* 28, '57, 1016–20, [373]
581 Welker, E. L., The distribution of the mean, *AMS* 18, '47, 111–17, [175]
582 Whitfield, J. W., Intra-class rank correlation, *BA* 36, '49, 463–67, [71]
583 Wilcoxon, F., Individual comparisons by ranking methods, *Biometrics Bulletin* 1, '45, 80–83, [150]

584 Wilcoxon, F., Individual comparisons of grouped data by ranking methods, *Jour. of Economic Entomology* 39, '46, 269–70, [150]
585 Wilcoxon, F., Probability tables for individual comparisons by ranking methods, *BS* 3, '47, 119–22, [149, 150]
586 Wilcoxon, F., *Some rapid approximate statistical procedures*, Stamford Res. Labs., Amer. Cyanamid Co., '49, [150]
587 Wilks, S. S., The likelihood ratio test of independence in contingency tables, *AMS* 6, '35, 190–96, [463]
588 Wilks, S. S., On the determination of sample sizes for setting tolerance limits, *AMS* 12, '41, 91–96, [254, 261, 262]
589 Wilks, S. S., Statistical prediction with special reference to the problem of tolerance limits, *AMS* 13, '42, 400–09, [275]
590 Wilks, S. S., *Mathematical statistics*, Princeton Univ. Press, '43, [64, 65]
591 Wilks, S. S., Order statistics, *BAMS* 54, '48, 6–50, [261, 262, 269]
592 Williams, C. A., Jr., On the choice of the number and width of classes for the chi-square test of goodness of fit, *JASA* 45, '50, 77–86, [442, 462]
593 Winsten, C. B., Inequalities in terms of mean range, *BA* 33, '43–'46, 283–95, [89, 98]
594 Wold, H., and Faxér, P., On the specification error in regression analyses, *AMS* 28, '57, 265–67, [115]
595 Wolfowitz, J., On the theory of runs with some application to quality control, *AMS* 14, '43, 280–88, [64, 67, 68]
596 Wolfowitz, J., Note on runs of consecutive elements, *AMS* 15, '44, 97–98, [75]
597 Wolfowitz, J., Asymptotic distribution of runs up and down, *AMS* 15, '44, 163–72, [67–69]
598 Wolfowitz, J., On sequential binomial estimation, *AMS* 17, '46, 489–92, [182, 410]
599 Wolfowitz, J., The efficiency of sequential estimates and Wald's equation for sequential processes, *AMS* 18, '47, 215–30, [182, 410]
600 Yates, F., Contingency tables involving small numbers and the χ^2 test, *JRSSB* 1, '34, 217–35, [460, 462]
601 Young, L. C., On randomness in ordered sequences, *AMS* 12, '41, 293–300, [71]
602 Zelen, M., Bounds on a distribution function that are functions of moments to order four, *Jour. of Res. of National Bur. of Stds.* 53, '54, 377–81, [91, 93, 94]

SUBJECT INDEX

This section contains a moderately detailed index of the many subjects that occur in the handbook. The SUBJECT INDEX, in combination with the TABLE OF CONTENTS and the AUTHOR INDEX, should furnish a reasonably complete coverage of the subject matter considered in the handbook.